By the Same Author

Nuclear Radiation Engineering—An Introduction

HEATING AND HUMIDIFYING LOAD ANALYSIS

F. W. HUTCHINSON

UNIVERSITY OF CALIFORNIA, BERKELEY

With

Thermal Tables and Numerical Examples

By

M. O. COTTER

ENGINEERING CONSULTANT

THE RONALD PRESS COMPANY · NEW YORK

Library of Congress Catalog Card Number: 62-9754

PRINTED IN THE UNITED STATES OF AMERICA

To
DOREMUS L. MILLS

PREFACE

The design of a comfortable indoor climate—whether for summer or for winter conditions—requires integration and synthesis of information and data from a great many different fields. Physiology and psychology contribute to the determination of an optimum inside thermal environment. Climatology, through statistical analysis, establishes the imposed outside design conditions. Architecture and structural engineering together establish the boundary conditions which are interposed between the indoor and outdoor environments. Mechanical engineering provides the scientific background needed for heat transfer and psychrometric evaluations. Both mechanical and electrical engineering—together with experience—are drawn on in selecting, coordinating, and controlling the components of a system. Thus many sciences and many arts are involved in the over-all problem of heating-system design.

This book is concerned primarily with the problems of accurately determining the design load necessary for maintaining a selected temperature and humidity within a structure. Design load is, in effect, the "prescription" which governs the size and the first cost of the heating system. Incorrect evaluation of load will inevitably lead to an ineffective or an uneconomical system. If the design load is too small, the system will be incapable of providing thermal comfort for the occupants; if it is too large, there will be a wasteful expenditure of capital.

The procedure followed here is to investigate the problem of load analysis from a rational and scientific point of view. In many actual cases a detailed rational solution is neither necessary nor justifiable, but in order to use approximate or empirical procedures properly, the professional engineer must know their limitations; such knowledge presupposes a thorough understanding of the more exact methods of analysis.

The book is divided into four logically consecutive parts. Part I investigates the physiological, psychological, and climatological influences which determine the *desired* inside environmental conditions and the *imposed* outside design conditions. These factors serve to define the boundaries within which the system must perform. If the problem is ill-defined, the solution is likely to be ineffective; hence, every care must be exercised in

v

the selection of design conditions. Further, the engineer must allow sufficient flexibility in the range of inside thermal conditions, particularly in residences, to accommodate the varying responses of individuals; a home heating system capable of providing optimum comfort for the statistically *average* man is not a satisfactory system unless it can also provide optimum comfort for the *particular* individuals (neurotic or hyperthyroid though they may be) who occupy the conditioned space.

Part II is primarily concerned with the effectiveness of the thermal barrier represented by the structure. In this connection the engineer has twin responsibilities. He must work with the architect in developing a structure which will have a reasonably high resistance to heat loss and to mass transmission. The more effective the structure is in these respects, the less will be the first and operating costs of any necessary remedial conditioning procedures. Also, he must determine the design value of the rate at which, for steady state, heat and vapor must be added (in winter) or removed (in summer). This latter requirement involves application of the steady-state heat-transfer relationships, the basic equations for mass transfer, and the empirical formulas which permit approximation to infiltration rates.

Part III is a treatment of several special design problems: Transmission load is evaluated in detail by means of room heat balances, which is a time-consuming method not often used in actual design, but extremely valuable as a means of checking the less complex design methods and of investigating the validity of various simplifying assumptions. A special form of the equivalent conductance method is used in load calculations for panel heating systems, and the design procedure is developed for sizing supplementary and local panel units. The thermal advantage (or disadvantage) of solar windows is rationally analyzed, and extensive winter solar data are exhibited for the design of any type of solar heating system. This part also establishes a procedure for evaluating humidifying load and for analyzing problems of vapor transmission.

Part IV presents the Schmidt and the Hölme methods for investigating transmission load under transient or periodic conditions. This information is helpful in estimating seasonal load, in designing controls, and in predicting performance of an intermittently operated heating system.

Necessarily, a large amount of material is covered in this detailed presentation of load analysis. Those aspects of the design problem which are more closely related to art than to science are covered in other books, including the *Guide* published by the American Society of Heating, Refrigerating and Air-Conditioning Engineers.

Although the arrangement of this book differs somewhat from that of other texts in the field, the subject matter with respect to load analysis is based on established thermal techniques. Standard procedures have been used throughout, and innovations are limited to those cases for which a new approach (as in the definition of "equivalent over-all coefficient") can justify itself in terms of increased design effectiveness. In this connection—as, for example, in discussing directional localized irradiation—material is sometimes included which has been revised and adapted, with permission, from *Refrigeration and Air Conditioning* and *Panel Heating and Cooling Analysis,* by B. F. Raber and the present writer.

F. W. HUTCHINSON

Berkeley, California
January, 1962

CONTENTS

PART I: Definition of a System

Part I

DEFINITION OF A SYSTEM

1

THE DEFINITION OF COMFORT:
THERMAL BASIS

An obvious need, before starting the design of a heating system, is to determine and specify exactly what it is intended to do. If the purpose of the system is to provide economical winter comfort, then some definition of the word "comfort" is needed, and it must be sufficiently general and sufficiently comprehensive to be applicable to all groups of average people. At the same time we are all aware, from personal experience, that the feeling of warmth varies among people and varies with the same person over a period of time. Since a heating system is a very personal thing, it must provide satisfaction to the people for whom it is intended, even if they happen to differ considerably from the statistical "average man." Thus a satisfactory definition of comfort must necessarily be flexible, and a system designed to meet the conditions of the definition must be capable of maintaining conditions over a range of thermal levels rather than at one fixed and arbitrarily selected condition.

The sensation of comfort is in part physiological (as determined by the feeling of warmth) and in part psychological (as reflected in such indefinable terms as "clammy," "stuffy," and similar expressions). An adequate definition of thermal comfort must include consideration of the following factors:

1. Air temperature.
2. Surround surface temperature.
3. Relative humidity.
4. Air movement.
5. Uniformity of heating effect.

A common but erroneous practice is to estimate the thermal criteria of comfort in terms of air temperature as the only variable. For small, well-insulated structures this is unlikely to lead to difficulty, but for many other cases serious error may result. The major advantage of establishing a comprehensive definition of comfort is that the one definition is then equally applicable to *all* types of heating systems. In many cases the designer will continue to use a simplified form of the general relationship (often the one based on air temperature alone), but he will do so with full knowledge of the particular circumstances that justify the simplification.

1–1. The Human Body as a Heat Engine. A curiously striking parallel exists between an internal combustion engine and the human body. Each receives stored chemical energy (as fuel in one case and as food in the other), each liberates the stored energy as heat, each transforms a portion of this energy for use as either internal or external work, and each dissipates waste heat to the surroundings. Further, the control procedures used with a heat engine or by the human body are in many respects similar.

Thus a typical internal-combustion engine receives fuel and delivers work and heat. Thermodynamic limitations make it impossible to convert all the energy of the fuel to shaft work; hence the residue of unconverted energy must be discharged as heat. For efficient operation the engine must not be too cold, since this would reduce its fuel economy. But neither must it be too hot, for this would constitute a hazard to continued operation. In order to assure operation at a reasonably constant temperature, modern engines are equipped with thermostatically controlled cooling systems that permit a flow of heat-carrying fluid from the engine to a cooling surface (often a so-called radiator). In some systems the flow is stopped when the engine drops below the desired operating temperature and starts only when there is need for dissipation of excess heat. In other systems flow occurs continuously, but regulation is achieved by opening or closing shutters to vary the effectiveness of the radiator.

By comparison the human body utilizes food as fuel and through the process of metabolism (equivalent to combustion) obtains thermal energy from the food. The energy is in part converted to internal work, that is, work done within the body in order to maintain the life processes. In addition, a person who is walking up or down hill, is lifting objects, or is similarly engaged will require expenditure of external work.

Similar to any other thermal engine the human body is not capable of transforming all the supplied thermal energy into work but must discharge the residue as waste heat. The amount of waste-heat production increases with the amount of external work which the person is doing, just as the amount of waste heat produced by a car increases with its speed or with the steepness of the grade up which it is traveling. But just as with the automobile engine, so too with a person must the operating temperature (in this case, 98.6 F) remain essentially constant if a condition of normality is to be maintained. Thus methods must be provided either by nature or by man to assure continuance of a body temperature of 98.6 F irrespective of variations in the rate at which work is being done.

The analogy between an internal combustion engine and the human body continues with the cooling system, though that of man is infinitely more complex and responsive than is the best of mechanical systems. Heat in the engine is produced within the cylinders and then carried by a working fluid to the radiator. Heat in man is produced in the inner organs and muscles and then carried by a working substance (blood) to the skin, which in turn plays the part of a radiator.

Just as a thermostat controls the flow of cooling water in accordance with the need for cooling effect, so too does the human nervous system provide thermostatic control of the flow of blood from the central organs to the outer body tissues. When external conditions are cold so that heat will be lost from the body at a rate exceeding that of its production, the blood vessels that flow to the outer tissues contract (vasoconstriction), increase the fluid resistance, and thereby divert more of the blood to the internal organs. When outside conditions are warm and it is difficult for the body to lose heat as rapidly as it is produced, the same blood vessels expand (vasodilation), thereby decreasing fluid resistance and allowing a greater flow of blood to the region adjacent to the body surface. In one respect the outer tissues of the human body act alternately (according to season or to load) as either a radiator or as an insulating layer. When "energized" by a flow of blood, the skin temperature increases and the rate of heat dissipation goes up; when "de-energized" by restriction of the blood flow, the outer tissue layer acts as a thermal barrier and prevents undue cooling of the body.

I–2. Body-Heat Production. As a mechanism for liberating energy and performing work, the human heat engine has a thermal efficiency of 20 per cent, which is surprisingly high when one considers the very small temperature range over which the body operates. With energy liberation occurring at a fixed temperature of approximately 98.6 F and with an average "receiver" temperature of 70 F, the ability of the body to do varying amounts of useful work and to dissipate waste heat effectively without permitting appreciable change in body temperature is a striking physiological achievement.

The average healthy adult, seated and at rest, must continuously perform internal work in order to maintain circulation, continue respiration, and carry on the many other energy-requiring internal operations and processes of the human body. Under such conditions the approximate energy requirement for carrying out these processes is a little more than 62,000 ft-lb/hr, or approximately 80 Btu/hr. But, with a thermal efficiency of 20 per cent, each Btu of useful (though internal) work must be accomplished by 4 Btu of waste heat. Further, since all the work is done in overcoming internal friction (for example, the process responsible for a pressure drop in the circulatory system or for the muscular and tissue friction from maintaining respiration), this quantity of energy must likewise be degraded to heat and will then be dissipated to the surroundings. Thus for a normal person, seated and at rest, a total heat-dissipation rate of approximately 400 Btu/hr must be maintained.

If external conditions are such as to prevent the loss of body heat at this rate, storage of waste heat in the body tissues will occur with a consequent rise in body temperature. Thus a 150-lb man (taking the specific heat of the body as 0.9 Btu/(lb)(°F)) would undergo a temperature rise of 1 F for each 135 Btu that entered storage; assuming (incorrectly) that the metabolic rate would remain constant even if no heat loss could occur for a full hour, the fever that would be induced in the man would be almost 3 F if for 1 hr he were prevented from losing waste heat. Obviously, therefore, it is highly important that effective means be provided for allowing the body to dispose of the heat energy that must be wasted in order to carry on the processes of living.

Metabolic rate varies widely with activity. As a person becomes more active, both the internal and external work requirements increase, the relationship between the two depending on the form of activity. If one man is sawing wood with a degree of exertion such that his total energy dissipation rate is 2000 Btu/hr, while another is walking fast with an equal dissipation rate, the problem of waste-heat disposal will not be the same for both men. A substantial fraction of the energy dissipated by the man sawing wood is transferred as shaft work to the saw and is later dissipated as heat from the saw blade or from the wood; this fraction constitutes an energy loss but not a heat loss from the man. The walker, on the other hand, does very little external work (providing his path is level) but performs a large amount of internal work, all of which must be reduced to heat and dissipated as a heat loss (assuming no storage) from the body. Thus the heating engineer is not so much concerned with the metabolic rate, the rate of total energy production, as he is with the sum of total internal work plus waste heat resulting from production of both internal and external work. This is demonstrated by the fact that the problem of establishing comfort in a ballroom is more difficult than that of establishing comfort in a warehouse, assuming that the steve-dores are lifting bags into a pile (thereby doing external work and storing energy, externally, in potential form) at a rate such that their total metabolism is equal to that of the dancers.

EXAMPLE 1–1. A 200-lb man climbs continuously for 2 hr to reach the top of a 3000-ft cliff. Assume that his increased metabolic rate is due entirely to work done in storing external potential energy and calculate: (a) the energy to external storage, Btu; (b) the man's metabolic rate, Btu/hr; (c) the rate at which body heat loss must occur if no energy is to go into internal storage.

Solution: (a) The energy that goes into external potential storage is equal to the man's weight times the vertical distance of travel:

$$wz = (200)(3000) = 600,000 \text{ ft-lb}$$

$$= \frac{600,000}{778} = 772 \text{ Btu}$$

(b) Assuming the body's thermal efficiency at the previously stated value of 20 per cent, the increased metabolic rate required to do 772 Btu of external work in 2 hr would be

$$\frac{772}{(0.20)(2)} = 1930 \text{ Btu/hr}$$

The total metabolic rate would then be the "at rest" value of 400 Btu/hr plus the increase of 1930 Btu/hr, or 2330 Btu/hr.

(c) Of the energy released during metabolism, all but that stored externally must be lost from the body as heat. Thus body heat loss will occur at a rate of

$$2330 - \frac{772}{2} = 1944 \text{ Btu/hr}$$

The maximum metabolic rate of an average person at work is roughly ten times greater than his rate when seated and at rest. When a person is actively at work, his skin temperature rises to a new equilibrium value; evaporative regulation may also assist in the more rapid dissipation of heat. But when one considers that the required rate of heat loss to prevent overheating must increase by as much as 1000 per cent, it is evident that a material readjustment will be needed in the thermal characteristics of the surround. This problem of adjusting a surround to meet wide variation in the activity of the occupants has not as yet received much attention in the technical literature, nor has much work been done on the task of assisting the designer in selecting optimum design inside-air temperature and wall surface temperature for a room in which the occupants are working at a relatively fixed rate.

For most design purposes, however, the customary procedure is to select inside conditions in which the average sedentary light worker, or the person seated and at rest, will normally experience comfort. Conforming to this practice, the treatment that follows will be restricted to the problem of establishing optimum comfort for such an individual. Thus the fundamental problem is to investigate the mechanisms of heat loss as they apply to a normal person, seated and at rest, and losing heat at a total rate of 400 Btu/hr.

I-3. Methods of Inducing Body-Heat Loss. The heat produced as a by-product of work is lost from the body in four ways. These are of far more than mere academic interest to the engineer because it is only by knowing the rates and mechanisms of body heat loss that he can formulate a comfort definition and thereby evaluate the effectiveness of the various methods of attaining comfortable warmth.

CONVECTION. The first way of inducing heat lost involves the "wiping" of heat from the body surface by passing air currents. The rate of loss depends on the exposed area, the condition of the surface, and the temperature difference between the skin surface and the ambient (surrounding) air. The more rapidly the air moves over the surface, the greater will be the rate of convective heat loss; this condition is familiar in the cooling effect of a breeze.

The influence on convection of skin condition is not subject to appreciable change, and such change as does occur is due to involuntary reactions such as the rising of hair follicles which accompanies the involuntary production of "goose pimples." This phenomenon is an emergency device by means of which nature arranges to trap a stagnant layer of air in the mass of rising hair and thereby to reduce heat loss and avoid overchilling.

The temperature difference from skin to air is subject to control by both nature and man. As indicated in Art. 1–1, the skin surface temperature varies (owing to vasoconstriction or to vasodilation) in accordance with the need for more or less cooling effect, whereas the control of ambient air temperature is the concern of the engineer and the major purpose of almost all types of heating systems (exceptions are true radiant systems such as electric spot heaters and the like). By increasing room air temperature the skin-to-air differential is reduced and the convective fraction of body heat loss decreases accordingly.

RADIATION. Whenever the average temperature of surfaces that surround a person is lower than the average exposed surface temperature of the occupant, he will undergo a net loss of energy by radiation. Radiant energy is not "heat" in the usual sense of the term, but upon absorption at a surface it becomes heat (strictly, internal energy), and hence in common practice the radiation is frequently referred to as radiant heat. Radiant loss is slightly influenced (something under 10 per cent) by the water vapor and carbon dioxide in the ambient (surrounding) atmosphere, but the loss of energy by radiation is independent of the temperature of the air through which it passes. The characteristics of radiant energy vary widely with the temperature of the surface from which it is emitted. Thus very-high-temperature radiant sources, such as the sun, emit energy that is largely transmitted through glass, whereas low-temperature sources, such as are found in ordinary heated rooms, emit energy that is almost wholly absorbed by glass. There is no net radiant loss from an occupant *through* a window, but if—as is usually the case in winter—the inside surface temperature of the window is lower than the temperature of other surfaces in the room, there will then be a net loss *to* the window.

EVAPORATION FROM LUNGS. The mucous membranes of the nose and throat and the surfaces of the human lungs are moist; hence as outside air enters through the nasal passages and moves down to the lungs, its humidity increases. The energy necessary to vaporize the moisture entering the air stream (approximately 1000 Btu are required to evaporate 1 lb of water under average atmospheric conditions) comes from the body tissue; hence a body heat loss of approximately 1000 Btu is experienced for each pound of water that leaves in the expired air. While the fraction of body heat loss that occurs by lung evaporation is by no means insignificant, it is nonetheless of very little interest to the heating engineer, since no means are available to him which will permit securing either an effective increase or an appreciable decrease in the loss by this mechanism.

EVAPORATION FROM SKIN. Skin evaporation occurs either as insensible perspiration or as sweat. The two fluids are different chemically, come from different physiological sources, and appear under different thermal circumstances. Sweat is a discharge from a special set of glands that serve an emergency function in bathing parts of the body area with moisture and thereby substantially increase the rate of body heat loss by evaporation. The sweat glands operate selectively, starting with the face and neck and then progressively including the remaining area of the body. In one sense the action of these glands is comparable, as an emergency measure, to the physical process of shivering; if conditions are extremely cold, nature uses shivering as a means of inducing involuntary exercise which increases metabolism and raises the rate of excess heat production. Similarly, if conditions are extremely hot, the sweat glands act as relief valves that accelerate body heat loss by evaporation. As far as the interests of the heating engineer are concerned, sweat gland activity is of no importance whatsoever, since these glands do not function until environmental conditions have become uncomfortably warm.

In contrast to sweat, insensible perspiration is experienced by the occupant of a comfortable room; hence this loss does have significance with respect to comfort heating. The loss associated with insensible perspiration is, however, practically constant for all comfort conditions; therefore this factor is valueless to the engineer as a control mechanism with which to adjust environmental conditions.

1–4. Rates of Body-Heat Loss. Dissipation of body heat occurs continuously by means of the mechanisms of evaporation, convection, and radiation. In the comfort range, the evaporative loss is almost entirely due to the latent heat of vaporization of insensible perspiration and is so nearly constant for all healthy, normal adults that it has been used by some investigators as an indirect means of calculating metabolic rate. For sedentary occupants with light clothing and in air at 74 F and 50 per cent relative humidity, evaporative losses amount to approximately 25 per cent of total heat losses, or 100 Btu/hr. This percentage of loss includes energy carried away in water vaporized from the lungs as well as losses due to insensible perspiration from the external surface of the body. Insensible perspiration occurs from all parts of the body surface but not at a uniform rate; more than 30 per cent of the total originates from the surfaces of the hands and feet, and yet these surfaces represent only about 12 per cent of total body area. Because the evaporative loss remains almost constant for all comfort conditions, this mechanism of heat loss need not be given further consideration; the entire thermal problem thus resolves itself into an investigation of the convection-radiation relationship and of the factors by means of which one or the other of these two basic heat-loss mechanisms can be increased or decreased in effectiveness.

An exact separation between radiation and convection losses is difficult to obtain, and the ratio will, of course, vary greatly as either the conditions of the environment or the activity of the subject vary. Dr. E. F. DuBois[1] has

[1] E. F. DuBois, *Lane Medical Lectures: The Mechanism of Heat Loss and Temperature Regulation*, Stanford University Press, 1937.

found experimentally that radiation, under ordinary atmospheric conditions, accounts for practically four times more body energy loss (240 Btu/hr) than does convection (60 Btu/hr). This ratio is based on still air conditions. The influence of air movement is to increase the convective fraction; therefore, in order to obtain a reasonably conservative ratio for practical purposes, this relationship should be altered to increase the influence of convection. For general comfort conditions it is recommended that a loss of 50 per cent by radiation and 25 per cent by convection be selected as a working relationship. Note that this selection raises the convection-radiation ratio from 1:4 to the higher value of 1:2. A further justification for selecting this ratio is that it corresponds with the value recommended by Bedford for a subject in a room with air and walls at 70 F.

A rough check on the accuracy of the above relationship can be obtained by resorting to theory for calculated values of the radiation and convection losses. The subject in Dr. DuBois' tests is reported as having a clothed surface area 16 per cent greater than body area. If the man is assumed to be of average build, the clothed area can be taken as 21.6 sq ft for calculating convective loss and 19.5 sq ft for calculating radiation loss. Dr. DuBois gives clothing surface temperature as 83 F in an environment at 74 F. On the assumption that the clothing has an emissivity of unity, the calculated loss from the clothed subject by radiation is (by Eq. 4–85)

$$q_r = 0.172 A_{b'} \left[\left(\frac{T_b}{100} \right)^4 - \left(\frac{T_w}{100} \right)^4 \right] \tag{1-1}$$

where $A_{b'}$ is the surface area of the clothed subject (for radiation) and T_b and T_w are the surface temperatures in degrees Fahrenheit absolute (°F + 460) of the clothed body and of the surround. Substituting to obtain a numerical solution gives

$$q_r = (0.172)(19.5) \left[\left(\frac{543}{100} \right)^4 - \left(\frac{534}{100} \right)^4 \right] = 195 \text{ Btu/hr}$$

which verifies the assumed 200 Btu/hr loss within 3 per cent.

The convective loss of body heat can be calculated from Newton's law of cooling (Eq. 4–42),

$$q_c = h A_b (t_b - t_a) = (h)(21.6)(83 - 74) = 194.4h \tag{1-2}$$

where A_b is the area of the clothed subject (for convection) and t_b and t_a are clothed body surface and ambient air temperatures, respectively; h is the film coefficient of heat transfer, Btu/(sq ft)(hr)(°F). Accurate selection of a value for the film coefficient provides considerable difficulty, but some help is available by considering that the value of h for convection changes from 0.4 to 0.7 to 1.1 for a flat surface in still air as it moves, respectively, from a position facing down, to a vertical position, to a position facing up. A large fraction of body surface area is normally in a position approaching the vertical, but folds and wrinkles in the clothing plus reduced convective losses from interferences (as in the spaces between the arms and the torso or on the inner surfaces of the legs) would be expected to reduce the average film coefficient somewhat below the value for a flat vertical surface. If these factors are assumed to reduce the value of h to a midvalue between 0.7 and 0.4 Btu/(sq ft)(hr)(°F), the calculated loss of body heat by convection would then be

$$q_c = (194.4)(0.55) = 106.9 \text{ Btu/hr}$$

Although this figure is 7 per cent higher than the value that is being checked, it does at least serve to verify qualitatively the reasonableness of the assumption and to provide further evidence in support of the 50 to 25 per cent radiation-convection ratio.

As a final check on the accuracy of the data which have been used for determining heat loss from a clothed figure, one can compare the rates of heat loss in Btu per hour per square foot of clothed surface. Dr. Bedford and associates of the London medical group frequently cite the 70 F estimated radiation and convection losses, based on the convection area, as 10 and 5 Btu/(hr)(sq ft), respectively. The 25 per cent convection-fraction standard gives $(0.25)(400)/21.6 = 4.63$, while the 50 per cent radiation-fraction standard gives twice that, or 9.26 Btu/(hr)(sq ft). These values are in reasonably close agreement with Bedford's.

I–5. The Comfort Equation. The discussion in Art. 1–4 has disclosed that of the methods which nature uses to dissipate excess body heat only two, convection and radiation, are available for use by the heating engineer to control body heat loss in a comfortable environment. Thus, since body surface temperature is fixed in terms of physiological factors, it would appear that the engineer is limited to control of room air temperature as a means of influencing convective loss and to control of average room surface temperature as a means of influencing radiant loss. Insofar as existing data go, it appears that comfort depends largely on the sum of convective and radiant losses (evaporative loss remaining constant) and that it makes little difference, within usual limits, whether the loss is largely by convection or largely by radiation.

From the heat-production, heat-loss, and surface-temperature relationships presented in Art. 1–4, it is possible to establish a functional relationship between the thermal comfort value of the temperature of still air within an occupied room and the corresponding surface temperature of a uniformly heated surround. Such an equation, established for an average sedentary adult, will then provide a first quantitative step toward specification of the design value of inside air temperature for a given structure situated in a particular geographical location.

In order, however, for a comfort equation to be of value in solving practical problems, a means must be found for expressing the integrated thermal effect of an actual non-uniformly heated room in terms of the surface temperature of an ideal uniformly heated surround. This can be accomplished by writing the comfort equation in terms of a *mean radiant temperature, mrt,* which by definition is the surface temperature of a large (to eliminate reflection characteristics) uniformly heated surround in which the occupant would experience a net radiant loss equal to that which occurs in the actual room. Thus the comfort equation will express a functional relationship between the ambient air temperature t_a and the mean radiant temperature *mrt* and will be applicable to any actual room for which the mean radiant temperature can be determined. (Numerical evaluation of the mean radiant temperature is a problem involving basic heat-transfer relationships; it will be covered in Chapter 7.)

In the analysis that follows, attention will be focused on a uniformly heated enclosure in which all the actual point-surface temperatures are equal in value to the mean radiant temperature. Such a room does not exist, since the uniform heating of floor, walls, and ceiling would be both costly and difficult. The concept of such a room does serve, however, as a simple and effective idealization for which a simple comfort equation can be written and as a comparison with which the performance of actual rooms can be expressed.

The problem of writing an acceptable comfort equation is therefore reduced to relating, for a condition of optimum comfort, the air temperature t_a and the mean radiant temperature *mrt*. When comfortable conditions exist the rate of body heat loss by radiation (expressed in Btu/(hr)(°F) difference between the clothed-body surface temperature and the mean radiant temperature) can be considered practically constant. Similarly, the rate of body-heat loss by convection (expressed in Btu/(hr)(°F) difference between the clothed-body surface temperature and the ambient air temperature) can be taken as constant. These rates, for the clothed subject at rest in a room with air and walls at 74 F, are (with values of transfer rate and clothing surface temperature from Art. 1–4)

By radiation, $$q_{r'} = \frac{200}{83 - 74} = 22.2 \text{ Btu/(hr)(°F)}$$

By convection, $$q_{c'} = \frac{100}{83 - 74} = 11.1 \text{ Btu/(hr)(°F)}$$

For optimum comfort the rate of body-heat loss must remain the same for all equilibrium air temperatures; therefore, when the air temperature is altered, the resulting change in convection loss must be exactly offset by an opposite change in the rate of radiant loss. The equation expressing this requirement is

$$11.1[(t_{b_1} - t_{a_1}) - (t_{b_2} - t_{a_2})] = 22.2[(t_{b_2} - mrt_2) - (t_{b_1} - mrt_1)]$$

$$(1\text{–}3a)$$

in which the subscripts b and a stand for body and ambient air and the secondary subscripts 1 and 2 identify temperatures as existing before or after the assumed change in ambient air temperature.

The above equation can be written

$$11.1\Delta(t_b - t_a) + 22.2\Delta(t_b - mrt) = 0 \qquad (1\text{–}3b)$$

where the delta in each term of Eq. 1–3b represents an algebraic quantity that is positive only when the change of temperature difference is an increase.

If the surface temperature of the body remained constant for all optimum comfort values of t_a and mrt, Eq. 1–3a would simplify to

$$11.1(t_{a_1} - t_{a_2}) = 22.2(mrt_2 - mrt_1)$$

or

$$\frac{\Delta t_a}{-\Delta mrt} = 2 \qquad (1\text{–}4)$$

thereby indicating that a 1 F increase in air temperature would be equivalent to a 0.5 F decrease in the mean radiant temperature. Actually, however, body surface temperature need not be the same for two different environments even though conditions of optimum comfort exist in both. Thus, in a room with air temperature of 65 F and a mean radiant temperature sufficiently high to maintain optimum comfort, the temperature of the clothed surface of an occupant may differ from that which would be found in a room with air at 75 F and mean radiant temperature sufficiently low to maintain optimum comfort. Note that in each of the above rooms, the total rate of heat loss from the occupant's surface is the same. Hence internal adjustments would have to occur in the circulatory system to keep the same rate of flow of heat from deep tissue to body surface at different temperatures.

Such limited experimental data as are available indicate that average body surface temperature can be expressed as a function of air and mean radiant temperatures by an equation of the form[2]

$$t_b = At_a + Bmrt + K \qquad (1\text{–}5)$$

in which A and B are experimental coefficients and K is a constant. Substitution of Eq. 1–5 into Eq. 1–3a leads to an equation of the form (refer to the derivation in Example 1–2)

$$\frac{\Delta t_a}{-\Delta mrt} = K_1 \qquad (1\text{–}6)$$

in which K_1 is a constant, the value of which is fixed as soon as A and B are assigned numerical values.

Unfortunately, existing data do not seem sufficiently consistent or well enough substantiated to permit evaluating K_1 in terms of the values of A and B which have at various times been suggested. Instead, a recommendation will be made for evaluation of K_1 from a consideration of such over-all experimental data on the $\Delta t_a/(-\Delta mrt)$ ratio as are available in the technical literature. The three most acceptable sources of information concerning

[2] Refer to Technical Advisory Committee reports in various volumes of *Transactions* of the ASHAE.

evaluation of this ratio appear to be the reports of Dr. Winslow and associates at the Pierce Laboratory at Yale University, the work of Dr. Bedford and associates in London, and the technical papers resulting from projects conducted for or by the American Society of Heating, Refrigerating and Air-Conditioning Engineers.

1–6. Recommended Constants for the Comfort Equation. Experimental work at the ASHRAE laboratory indicates that a change in *mrt* of 1 F requires an opposite change in *effective* air temperature (see Art. 1–10) of approximately 0.5 F. The term *effective* temperature includes the influence of humidity, but in the range of inside conditions usually found in a comfortably heated or cooled room, a 0.5 *effective* temperature change would represent a variation in dry-bulb temperature of 1.75 times that, or $(1.75)(0.5) = 0.9$ F. This result is in reasonably close agreement with Bedford's findings that a 1 F change in dry-bulb temperature requires an opposite change in the mean radiant temperature of approximately like amount. Further, this relationship is in agreement with Dr. Winslow's statement[3] that for a room in which the air velocity is low, "air and mean radiant temperatures exert approximately equal influence on comfort." On the basis of this evidence it is recommended that K_1 be taken equal to unity, thus establishing the comfort relationship (Eq. 1–6) in the form

$$\frac{\Delta t_a}{-\Delta mrt} = 1 \tag{1–7}$$

or

$$(t_{a_2} - t_{a_1}) + (mrt_2 - mrt_1) = 0$$

giving

$$(t_{a_2} + mrt_2) = t_{a_1} + mrt_1 = t_{a_x} + mrt_x \tag{1–8}$$

Thus when comfort conditions exist in a room in which all surfaces and room air are at the same temperature t_c, Eq. 1–8 shows that a 1 F, 2 F, or 3 F rise in air temperature above the value t_c would require, for equal comfort, that the mean radiant temperature drop 1 F, 2 F, or 3 F, respectively, below the t_c value. This is expressed in equation form as

$$t_a + mrt = 2t_c \tag{1–9}$$

If a room having air temperature and uniform surface temperature of 73.5 is taken as representative of optimum winter comfort (see Art. 1–10), Eq.1–9 becomes

$$t_a + mrt = 147 \tag{1–10}$$

This is the recommended form of the comfort equation relating the inside air temperature and the uniform inside surface temperature, although it is

[3] C. E. A. Winslow and L. P. Herrington, *Temperature and Human Life*, Princeton University Press, 1949.

equally applicable to a room in which there are many different surfaces at various surface temperatures. It is more commonly written as

$$t_a = 147 - mrt \qquad (1\text{--}11)$$

1–7. System Significance of the Comfort Equation. To show the applicability of the comfort equation to either convective or radiant types of heating systems, assume that t_c has the assigned value of 73.5 F. This would mean that comfort would be experienced in a room if the air temperature were 73.5 F and if, simultaneously, the mean radiant temperature were also 73.5 F (for relative humidity of 50 per cent and air motion of less than 50 fpm).

1. Consider a convector or a warm-air heating system installed in a house that has large window area and poor insulation. By calculation (see Example 5–1) it is found that at design load, the mean radiant temperature is 38 F lower than room air temperature. Assuming that the assigned t_c value of 73.5 F is correct, this room would feel uncomfortably cool if the convector (or warm-air) system were designed to maintain a 73.5 F air temperature. But since the air and surface temperatures are known to be 38 F apart, a comfortable room air temperature can be determined by adding one-half of the difference (or 19 F) to the t_c value, giving 92.5 F[4] as the optimum air temperature and 54.5 F as the consequent surface temperature. In this particular structure any air temperature greater than 92.5 F would be too warm and any value less than 92.5 F would be too cold.

2. Reversing the situation, consider that a ventilated room is to be panel-heated and that its thermal characteristics are found by calculation (see Example 8–11, part c) to be such that the average surface temperature will be 27 F above the air temperature. In this case the comfort equation would show 87 F as the optimum surface temperature and 60 F as the most comfortable room air temperature; values above 60 F would be uncomfortably warm, and vice versa. It is interesting to note that in both types of heating systems, the difference between air and surface temperatures increases as the load increases, and therefore the room air temperature is a maximum with maximum load for a convection system but is a minimum for maximum load with a radiant system.

1–8. Empirical Equations for Body Surface Temperatures. Returning now to Eqs. 1–5 and 1–6 calculations will show that an equation for body surface temperature consistent with the recommended value of K_1 would be obtained if A and B were taken as 0.21 and 0.54, respectively. Thus, if optimum comfort were found to exist in a room with t_a and mrt both at 70 F, and if t_a were lowered and mrt simultaneously raised through 10 F, there would be an increase in body surface temperature of $10(0.54 - 0.21) = 3.3$ F.

---

[4] Refer to the discussion of excessively high air temperature in the solution of Example 5–1.

The increase in convection loss for the new conditions within the room would then be

$$q_c = 11.1(10 + 3.3) = 148 \text{ Btu/hr}$$

and the reduction in radiant loss would be

$$q_r = 22.2(10 - 3.3) = 148 \text{ Btu/hr}$$

Therefore the total rate of body heat loss would therefore be unchanged.

On the basis of Bedford's finding that body surface temperature is 82.4 F in an environment with air and walls at 74 F, a value of K consistent with the values of A and B used above can be readily determined from

$$82.4 = (0.21)(74) + (0.54)(74) + K$$

giving $K = 26.9$. Thus an equation for body surface temperature consistent with the selected value of K_1 is

$$t_b = 0.21t_a + 0.54mrt + 26.9 \tag{1-12}$$

Eq. 1–7 should be used with caution because it was obtained by an indirect and theoretical procedure and is not directly supported by experimental evidence.

EXAMPLE 1–2. Verify the statement above that when the coefficients A and B in Eq. 1–5 have values of 0.21 and 0.54, respectively, the term K_1 of Eq. 1–6 will be equal to unity.

Solution: A generalized evaluation of the constant K_1 is obtained by substituting Eq. 1–6 into Eq. 1–3a to obtain

$$11.1[(At_{a_1} \times Bmrt_1 + K - t_{a_1}) - (At_{a_2} + Bmrt_2 + K - t_{a_2})]$$
$$= 22.2[(At_{a_2} + Bmrt_2 + K - mrt_2) - (At_{a_1} + Bmrt_1 + K - mrt_1)]$$

giving

$$11.1[(A - 1)(t_{a_1} - t_{a_2}) + B(mrt_1 - mrt_2)]$$
$$= 22.2[A(t_{a_2} - t_{a_1}) + (B - 1)(mrt_2 - mrt_1)]$$

or

$$[22.2A + 11.1(A - 1)](t_{a_2} - t_{a_1}) = -[22.2(B - 1) + 11.1B](mrt_2 - mrt_1)$$

giving

$$\frac{\Delta t_a}{-\Delta mrt} = \frac{33.3B - 22.2}{33.3A - 11.1} = K_1$$

By substituting the indicated numerical values of A and B,

$$K_1 = \frac{(33.3)(0.54) - 22.2}{(33.3)(0.21) - 11.1}$$

$$= \frac{-4.2}{-4.1} \approx 1$$

1–9. Influence of Humidity on Comfort. From the discussion in Art. 1–3 on the relative constancy of evaporative body heat losses, it may seem that humidity has little if any effect on comfort. There is not any theoretical justification for a contrary belief, but experimental work carried on many years ago by the American Society of Heating, Refrigerating, and Air-Conditioning Engineers (ASHRAE) led to a correlation of dry-bulb temperature with relative humidity (for equal feeling of warmth) which indicates that humidity is markedly influential in determining a condition of thermal comfort[5]. Many indications have appeared in the literature that the ASHRAE

TABLE 1–1*
Conditions for Which 98 Per Cent of Subjects
Are Thermally Comfortable

Dry-Bulb Temperature, F	Relative Humidity, %
68	100
70	76
72	55
74	35

* Compiled from data in Bibliography, item 1.

results unduly emphasize the humidity effect, but until further research is carried out, it is very probable that these data will continue to be widely used.

The ASHRAE data for winter thermal comfort show the range of combined temperature-humidity conditions for which the majority (over 50 per cent) of subjects tested felt neither too hot nor too cold. The correlations are based on air movement corresponding to that usually found in a closed space (15 to 25 fpm) and were established for a room in which all interior surfaces are assumed to be at air temperature. The temperature-humidity relationship for which 98 per cent of the subjects expressed a feeling of thermal comfort are given in Table 1–1. Conditions for which 85 per cent of the subjects expressed a feeling of thermal comfort are listed in Table 1–2.

The locus of states for which the same feeling of warmth exists is defined as the *effective temperature*, the numerical value of which is fixed by a condition of saturation. Thus the optimum winter relationship given in Table 1–1 corresponds to a fixed value of the effective temperature of 68 F, since the feeling of warmth associated with saturated air at 68 F is said to be the same as that for the other states listed in the same table. From Table 1–2 the range of effective temperatures in which the majority of occupants experience thermal comfort during the heating season is from 65 F to 70 F. (In summer

[5] Since *comfort* is a psychophysiological term, it is indicative of a state that can be influenced by many factors other than those responsible for degree of warmth; for this reason it is advantageous to express the factors that influence warmth in terms of the special term *thermal comfort*.

the ASHRAE data indicate a higher effective temperature range due to physiological adjustments associated with seasonal acclimatization.)

If the data from Tables 1–1 and 1–2 were plotted on a psychrometric chart, it would be found that the states corresponding to a particular value of effective temperature would lie very nearly along a line of constant specific volume. This circumstance is interesting (and helpful in finding states of equal effective temperatures on the psychrometric chart), but it is not subject to theoretical explanation because constancy of specific volume is determined from thermodynamic considerations, whereas constancy of effective temperature is determined empirically.

TABLE 1–2*

Conditions for Which 85 Per Cent of Subjects Are Thermally Comfortable

15 Per Cent Too Cool		15 Per Cent Too Warm	
Dry-Bulb Temperature, F	Relative Humidity, %	Dry-Bulb Temperature, F	Relative Humidity, %
65	100	70	100
66	90	72	80
68	55	75	50
70	35	76	45
		77	35

* Compiled from data in Bibliography, item 1.

1–10. Range of Comfort Temperatures. The thermal comfort zone established by the states of Table 1–2 determines the region of inside states within which the designer must work. In practice, however, there is very slight possibility of using relative humidities in excess of 50 per cent during the heating season. Hence the corresponding minimum acceptable comfort temperature[6] (by interpolation of states from the "cool" data of Table 1–2) would be 68.5 F; the corresponding maximum permissible comfort temperature would be 75 F and the optimum value would be (by interpolation from Table 1–1) 72.5 F. For structures in which there is not a positive means of humidification, the indoor relative humidity may be substantially less than 50 per cent, in which case the selected comfort temperature should, of course, be raised accordingly. Relative humidities less than 30 per cent are undesirable in that drying of the mucous membranes of the nose and throat then occurs, with a possible increased hazard of respiratory infection. Thus the range of inside air states for conditions of optimum thermal comfort in winter (by interpolation from Table 1–1) is between comfort temperatures of 72.5 F at 50 per cent relative humidity and 74.5 F at 30 per cent relative humidity. The range in which 50 per cent or more of the occupants would be comfortable

[6] The term *comfort temperature* as used here is the t_c value of Eq. 1–9. This value is numerically equal to the inside-air temperature only if the mean radiant temperature is equal to the room air temperature.

is from 68.5 F at 50 per cent relative humidity to 77.5 F at 30 per cent relative humidity.

The 72.5 F to 74.5 F range of optimum comfort temperatures will probably appear much too small to many engineers who have been using higher design values of inside air temperature. It must be remembered, however, that this defined range is for an "ideal" room in which *all surfaces* are at the same temperature as the room air. For general design purposes the author recommends use of 73.5 F based on 50 per cent relative humidity, as a conservative value of t_c for optimum inside design state. The actual design value of inside air temperature for a comfort temperature of t_c may be either greater or less than t_c, the actual value being determined by the thermal characteristics of the structure (see Art. 5–6) and by the comfort equation, Eq. 1–9.

I–11. Range of Room Air Temperatures. Although the comfort equation does not impose any limit on a maximum or minimum air temperature corresponding to a given value of the comfort temperature, the fact remains that both physiological and economic considerations do impose such limits.

PHYSIOLOGICAL LIMITATIONS ON AIR TEMPERATURES. To use an extreme example, the occupant of a room with walls, floor, and ceiling made entirely of double glass would experience an optimum feeling of warmth (equivalent to a comfort temperature of 73.5 F at 40 per cent relative humidity) if the room air temperature were maintained at 93.5 F with outside air temperature of −30 F. Even though such an occupant would be thermally comfortable (neither too hot nor too cold), it is nonetheless evident that he would not accept such an environment as meeting his over-all comfort requirements, since the effect of 93.5 F air on the respiratory passages would be an unpleasant one. At the other extreme, conditions corresponding to a 73.5 F comfort temperature would exist in a room if all surfaces were heated to 97 F and the air temperature were held at 50 F. Here again, however, the occupant would merely have to sit on a 50 F chair to persuade himself that the environment, though thermally comfortable, was not an acceptable one.

ECONOMIC LIMITATIONS ON AIR TEMPERATURE. Any structure so poorly insulated as to require an inside air temperature higher than 75 F or 76 F would have such a high rate of heat loss that its operating cost would be prohibitive. To avoid large fuel bills, adequate insulation must be provided; when this is done, it will be found that the maximum room air temperature will always be in the range from 72 F to 76 F.

At the other extreme, no commercially practicable method of heating has yet been developed which will permit raising the mean radiant temperature more than a few degrees above room air temperature (the only possible exception would be that of a space with extremely high, hence uneconomical, rate of mechanical ventilation). Even if this difference could be made to go as high as 10 F, the resultant depression of room air temperature below comfort temperature would be only 5 F. Hence it is safe to say that under any but the most unique conditions the minimum attainable comfort value of room air temperature will be approximately 68 F.

1-12. Shock and Acclimatization. The physiological experience defined as thermal shock occurs whenever a person passes from one thermal atmosphere to a markedly different one. For the conditions of summer air conditioning, we are all familiar with the common sensation of coldness on entering a conditioned space and we know from experience that this initial reaction disappears after we have remained within this space for an appreciable length of time. Shock is a transitory phenomenon that indicates sudden need for adjustment in the circulatory system to permit the body to reach a thermal balance with the new environment. The period required for complete adjustment varies with individuals, but it is almost always less than 3 hr.

The ASHRAE data[7] on thermal comfort, and the 73.5 F and 50 per cent relative humidity optimum design state which has been selected therefrom, are based on the assumption that shock conditions do not exist in the structure for which the heating system is to be designed. This assumption is a conservative one, since the effect of shock would be to reduce the optimum air temperature. For spaces in which the density of continued occupancy is low and for which the transient rate is high, it may be permissible to reduce the thermostat setting to counteract shock effects, but in terms of design the engineer should always select design inside-air temperature for steady occupancy conditions.

Acclimatization is a bodily adjustment provided by nature for the purpose of reducing the physiological strain resulting from prolonged exposure to outside conditions that are thermally extreme. Acclimatization is a seasonal effect which may require minor upward adjustment of the room air temperature, at fixed load, during the early part of the season and minor downward adjustment during the later part of the season. Aside from changes in optimum comfort temperature with season, acclimatization is also effective in altering the optimum value geographically as a function of changes in the mean outside-air temperature with climate. To correct for this effect, it is suggested that the design value of the comfort air temperature be raised 1 F for each 5 deg decrease in northern latitude from 40 deg.

Shock and acclimatization always operate to make a change of conditions seem more severe; because of them, cold outside air seems colder and warm outside air warmer. In this respect it is somewhat paradoxical that the one defense mechanism which nature provides for man as partial protection against extremes of climate is a pronounced obstacle in the path of the heating and air-conditioning engineer whose object is also to provide protection from the same extremes. If it were not for the protection afforded by

---

[7] Bibliography, item 1.

acclimatization, the discomfort caused by summer heat would be greater, but the shock attendant upon the use of summer air conditioning would not be so great. The same can be said of extreme winter conditions and the heating systems that alleviate them, except that, for winter, occupants somewhat reduce the severity of shock effects by use of protective outdoor clothing.

I–13. Influence of Age and Sex on Comfort Temperature. Extensive statistical data are not available on the effect of either age or sex on optimum comfort temperature. General experience and some small-group tests, however, show that the influence of sex is not more than 2 F (women preferring warmer conditions than men), and the influence of age is of the same order of magnitude (younger people preferring cooler conditions). Thus no consideration need be given by the designer to either age or sex except in cases where the great majority of the occupants are either very young or extremely old. From the above discussion it would follow that optimum comfort temperature in grammar schools should be less than in homes; this is true but is rarely the actual case, since the thermal desire of the adult teacher (with lower metabolism) usually takes precedence over that of the children (with higher metabolic ratio).

I–14. Thermal Uniformity. The conditions defining thermal comfort as so far discussed, are for a system (consisting of occupant and room) in which the air temperature, humidity, air motion, and radiant transfer have fixed and uniform values throughout all parts of the enclosure. Departures from this prescribed condition of uniformity may be such that the average values remain unchanged although thermal comfort may not exist at all points within the enclosure. To use an extreme example, consider that though a man is comfortably warm when submerged in a tub of 100 F water, he would no longer be comfortable if half of the tub were filled with 150 F water and the other half with 50 F water; the average temperature, however, would be the same in both cases.

On a lesser scale the situation described above is one which exists in a heated space when the distribution of heat sources (such as radiators, convectors, panels, or warm air inlets) is not carefully planned or when rapid infiltration of outside air occurs locally (as from an open window). Such a situation leads to thermal drafts. A draft is defined literally as a current of air, but in the comfort sense it is arbitrarily defined as any thermal non-uniformity of an environment sufficient to cause an average subject to experience a 10 per cent change, either general or local, in the feeling of warmth. Thus thermal drafts can be due to any of three causes:

1. Local variations in air temperature.
2. Local variations in air movement.
3. Local variations in radiant transfer.

Irrespective of which of these three factors is responsible, the effect will in each case be undue heating or chilling either of the occupant as a whole or of some localized part of his body.

CONVECTIVE DRAFTS. Convective drafts result from local changes in air temperature or air movement, or both. Houghten and co-workers carried on an extensive experimental investigation of such drafts some years ago. The Houghten studies[8] were limited to healthy adult occupants of a room maintained at a temperature of 70 F with 50 per cent relative humidity. Draft effects were studied with respect to local variations of thermal effect at the subject's ankle and neck, it being assumed that any environmental change so inoffensive as not to be objectionably evidenced on the ankle or neck would not be of sufficient importance to warrant consideration.

Results of the Houghten tests showed that the neck is very much more sensitive to thermal changes than is the ankle. In order to cause a feeling of ankle draft, the local velocity of air at room temperature had to be raised to a value greater than 165 fpm (as compared with the 20 fpm that corresponds to air movement in an average room), whereas for a neck draft the required local velocity change was only 60 fpm. Drafts produced by changes in air temperature (without velocity difference) required a 4 F dry-bulb temperature reduction for the neck and an 8 F dry-bulb temperature reduction for the ankle. Draft conditions for combinations of changes in temperature and air motion can be estimated from the above data by interpolation.

RADIANT DRAFTS. Thermal non-uniformity due to radiation is more difficult to recognize and to correct than that due to convection. Man is "submerged" in a sea of air, and hence to avoid convective drafts, it is merely necessary to provide adequate and uniform mixing and to prevent local changes in air movement. With radiation, however, non-uniformity is the rule rather than the exception; radiant energy does not surround the occupant but bombards him directionally. A fireplace warms only that part of the occupant which "sees" the fire; similarly, a radiant heating panel warms only the fraction of body surface which is directly exposed to it. Fortunately for the designer, the actual radiant effect associated with heating panels is relatively slight. Panels are large in area and operate at temperatures that are quite low (usually less than 120 F); direct irradiation of the occupant is therefore based on such a small surface-to-surface temperature difference (of the order of 30 F) that it is usually below the threshold of recognition.

Drafts due to local cooling are much more uncomfortable than those due to local heating. Experimental data on heating drafts are not yet available, but common experience tells us that occasional "breaths" of warmer air are pleasant, rather than otherwise, in contrast to the decided discomfort associated with a draft of cool air. Similarly, moderate radiant drafts are pleasant as long as their effect is one of local heating; however, radiant cooling (such

[8] Bibliography, item 1.

as occurs when one sits close to a large single-pane window) is decidedly uncomfortable. The only corrections for radiant-cooling drafts are to place a compensating heated surface near the cold surface or to raise the air temperature locally and thereby compensate for the radiant-cooling draft with a corresponding convective-warming draft. Where the arrangement of the room will permit, a screen of any thermally opaque material can be used to cut off radiation between an occupant and the offending surface.

I–15. Conclusion. Analysis of the physiological factors that affect and determine the feeling of thermal comfort shows that the problem of comfort heating is not one of supplying heat to the occupant but rather of maintaining the environment in which the occupant is located at a thermal level such that he will not lose heat at a rate greater than that at which his body is producing it. The body, like all other heat engines, always requires cooling rather than heating, but the occupied room may require heating in order to prevent overcooling of the occupant. This fact is of great importance, since it means that the heating system serves to heat the house and not the people who are within it; as a corollary, the energy requirements of the heating system are fixed by the thermal characteristic of the structure and not by any heat requirements of the occupants. The thermal comfort requirements of the occupants determine and define the thermal environment that must be maintained within the structure, but the structure itself determines the size, capacity, and required performance of the heating system.

PROBLEMS

1–1. People acclimatized to the tropics do less external work, but do it at greater thermal efficiency, than those in colder climates. If the thermal efficiency of an Indonesian is 23 per cent, estimate his rate of heat loss when seated and at rest.

1–2. A warehouseman is lifting 60-lb packing cases and stacking them on a shelf 4 ft above the floor. His work rate averages 70 packages per hour. (a) Calculate the thermal equivalent of the external work rate. (b) Calculate the workman's required rate of heat loss to maintain thermal equilibrium. (c) If environmental conditions are such that he can lose only 400 Btu/hr, calculate his body temperature at the end of 1 hr of work, assuming his weight as 140 lb and his specific heat as 0.9 Btu/(lb)(°F).

1–3. Two workmen in a cold-storage plant (room temperature of 10 F) are piling crates at equal work rates. . Sweat-gland activity for each man is such that face and neck moisture appears at a rate of 0.8 lb/hr and at a temperature of 85 F. One man "mops his brow," whereas the other allows face and neck moisture to evaporate. Calculate the rate of body heat loss due to sweat-gland activity for each of the men.

1–4. Calculate the ratio of heat loss by insensible perspiration from unit area of foot to unit area of shoulder for an average man.

1–5. According to the comfort equation, occupants of a room with air and walls at 73.5 F would experience the same feeling of warmth as occupants of a room with air at 63.5 F and walls at 83.5 F or as occupants of a room with air at 83.5 F and walls at 63.5 F. Investigate the clothed surface-temperature differences among occupants of these three rooms.

1-6. In terms of the results of Example 1–5 discuss the effect of increased *mrt* for fixed value of t_c, on the human circulatory system.

1-7. Establish Eq. 1–5 in explicit form based on arbitrary selection of the coefficient A as unity.

1-8. For a room having air temperature of 63.5 F and mean radiant temperature of 83.5 F, compare the value of clothed surface temperature obtained from Eq. 1–12 with that given by the equation derived in problem 1–7.

1-9. A heating system operates in such a way that the mean radiant temperature is 86 F when optimum thermal comfort is established in an environment having 35 per cent relative humidity. Determine the corresponding room air temperature.

1-10. For the conditions of problem 1–9, at what air temperature would it be expected that 15 per cent of the occupants would be (a) too warm (b) too cool?

2

THE DEFINITION OF COMFORT:
QUALITY BASIS

In addition to meeting the requirements of thermal comfort, the heating and air-conditioning engineer has the responsibility of establishing environmental conditions that will utilize subjective factors to improve the comfort of the occupants. He is also responsible for providing a supply of outside ventilation air sufficient to replenish the oxygen consumed in respiration and to dilute to below the acceptable concentration any unpleasant or unhealthful contaminants that may be introduced into the space by the occupants. The two basic purposes of ventilation in conjunction with heating are to supply oxygen and to remove odor. Many other purposes have been suggested and some of them explored, but there is not now any dependable evidence to show that these other reasons, such as ozonation and ionization, are of general significance.

2–1. "Freshness" Versus Air Temperature. For many years attempts have been made to isolate that special quality of outdoor air which many people refer to as "fresh," but such attempts have not been successful. Present opinion is that the quality called "fresh" is subjective and largely of psychological origin. One established influence on the feeling of freshness, however, is temperature. Given a choice between warmer and cooler air in thermal environments of equal warmth, statistical studies have shown that the average person prefers the lower temperature.

Provided comfortable warmth is maintained, cooler air has an invigorating and stimulating effect which seems to originate in its cooling effect on the respiratory passages. This effect is of great practical significance and requires particular consideration in the case of structures that have extreme exposure or which are poorly insulated. Thus, in a poorly insulated structure where the required optimum inside-air temperature is above 75 F (as calculated from the comfort equation, Eq. 1–9), the feeling of warmth of the occupants would be identical with that experienced in a well-insulated structure with an optimum air temperature of close to 73 F; although the feeling of warmth would be the same in these two cases, the sensation of comfort would be greater in the room with the lower temperature. Warmer temperatures lead to a feeling of drowsiness, development of muscular lassitude, and the indefinite sensation vaguely described as "stuffy."

Thus, from the standpoint of providing comfort over and above that which comes from warmth, it is desirable either to correct the structure thermally or to adjust the distribution and design of heating elements to permit operation with an optimum inside air temperature not greatly in excess of 73 F. The former correction can be achieved by use of insulation or of double-glass panes for oversize windows; the latter, by designing and distributing the heating elements so that there will be provision for a sufficiently large fraction of energy input by radiation to offset the "cold-wall" effect.

2-2. Oxygen Requirement. As do all other machines that convert chemical energy into mechanical work, the human body requires an adequate supply of oxygen to sustain the process of combustion (in this case, metabolism), and it dissipates carbon dioxide as "exhaust gas." The first requirement of ventilation is to supply the requisite oxygen and dispose of the exhaled carbon dioxide. Fortunately this requirement is very simply met, so the influence of oxygen supply as a criterion of ventilation design is extremely slight.

Under normal comfort conditions the average individual consumes approximately 2 cu ft of oxygen per hour. In the same interval he produces approximately 0.6 cu ft of carbon dioxide (CO_2). Thus a definite relationship exists between the concentrations of oxygen and carbon dioxide in the air of an occupied enclosure; the rise in concentration of CO_2 is therefore an index of oxygen consumption. Because of this relationship it was thought for many years that carbon dioxide was harmful and should never be allowed to reach a concentration in room air greater than 2 per cent. Actually, the CO_2 concentration in the *true* atmosphere in which man lives, that in the lungs, is close to 6 per cent and must be maintained near this concentration for physiological reasons. Dill[1] has pointed out that one of the most undesirable attributes of intemperate deep-breathing exercises is that the carbon dioxide concentration in the lungs can be reduced so far below normal that dizziness and other severe physiological consequences may result. In any concentration likely to occur in an occupied enclosure, carbon dioxide is, in itself, physiologically unimportant; the only deleterious effect of a high CO_2 concentration is that it serves to indicate an oxygen shortage.

Experiment has shown that when the CO_2 concentration in an occupied space exceeds 2 per cent, the partial pressure of oxygen will have been reduced to a value such that breathing will be more difficult; the respiratory rate will then increase. When the concentration reaches 6 per cent, extreme discomfort is likely, but not until the concentration is 10 per cent will loss of consciousness occur. Noting that the carbon dioxide concentration in

---

[1] David Dill, *Life, Heat, and Altitude*, Harvard University Press, 1938.

outside air is approximately three parts in 10,000, the time X in hours during which occupants could remain in an enclosure with *no* fresh air whatsoever can be readily calculated as a function of the available enclosure space Y, in cubic feet per occupant. Thus the concentration at time X will be the value for outside air (3/10,000, or 0.03 per cent) plus the percentage of carbon dioxide introduced from respiration (0.6 cu ft/hr)(X hrs)(100%)/(Y cu ft/occupant), or $60X/Y$. In equation form,

$$\text{Per cent } CO_2 \text{ (by volume) after } X \text{ hr} = 0.03 + 60\,\frac{X}{Y} \qquad (2\text{--}1)$$

Table 2–1, based on Eq. 2–1, presents time intervals prior to observation of oxygen deficiency in a sealed space.

TABLE 2–I

Oxygen Deficiency as a Function of Time for Occupancy
of a Space with Zero Ventilation

	Time in Hours Before Evidence of Oxygen Deficiency Air Space per Occupant, cu ft				
	100	200	300	400	500
Difficult breathing (2% CO_2 by volume)	3.3	6.6	9.9	13.1	16.4
Extreme discomfort (6% CO_2 by volume)	10.0	19.9	29.9	39.8	49.8
Loss of consciousness (10% CO_2 by volume)	16.6	33.2	49.9	66.5	83.1

In actual practice, the available air space per occupant is rarely less than 180 cu ft. For such a density of occupancy, Eq. 2–1 (or interpolation in Table 2–1) will show that rapid breathing would first be noticed (2 per cent CO_2) after 6 hr; marked discomfort would not occur until 18 hr; loss of consciousness would not occur until more than a full day (30 hr).

The danger of a health hazard existing in any ventilated room, owing to inadequate oxygen supply, is seen, then, to be extremely remote. This fact is even more clearly recognized when one realizes that a single occupant could be sealed in an airtight box 10 ft by 10 ft by 10 ft for a week before loss of consciousness would be expected from oxygen deficiency. Note that the above examples are based on considerations of oxygen alone; other factors could lead to serious physiological disorders in a much shorter time than the examples would seem to indicate.

This same problem can be approached from a different point of view by assuming that it is desired to supply only sufficient outside air to an occupied enclosure to prevent the carbon dioxide concentration from exceeding 2 per cent. In order for equilibrium to exist, the volume of carbon dioxide introduced into the room in the incoming ventilation air plus the volume produced by the occupant must be equal to the volume of carbon dioxide leaving the room in the discharged air during the same time interval. By taking 1 hr as the time interval, the above balance gives

$$\text{Volume in} + \text{volume produced} = \text{volume discharged}$$

or

$$0.0003 \text{ cu ft/hr} + (0.60)(N) = 0.02 \text{ cu ft/hr} \qquad (2\text{--}2)$$

where N is the number of occupants and the "volume in" (0.0003) is the required minimum ventilation rate, expressed in cu ft/hr of outside air intake per occupant. Solving this equation gives

$$\text{Volume in} = 30.4 \text{ cu ft/hr/occupant}$$

Infiltration due to wind and to atmospheric pressure differences can be depended on in all but literally sealed spaces to provide at least one-half air change per hour, and since the minimum air space per occupant, even in very crowded conditions, is over 100 cu ft, it follows that infiltration air will always provide almost twice as much oxygen as that needed to prevent evidence of discomfort. Further, the requirement of outside air as a diluent for prevention of odor in an occupied space (refer to Art. 2–3) is more than ten times that needed for oxygen supply; it follows, therefore, that no possible oxygen deficiency can exist in a normally occupied space that is free from objectionable body odor.

In spite of the above statements, cases frequently occur where death results from inadequate ventilation. Invariably, however, it will be found that the oxygen deficiency resulted not from normal processes of respiration but from other oxygen-consuming processes such as that of combustion. A tightly sealed, unventilated room is a very undesirable place to use a fireplace or a stove, because, entirely aside from the possible hazard of carbon monoxide poisoning, there will be the very definite hazard of asphyxiation. Other instances of health hazard through oxygen deficiency have been associated with spaces containing some chemical materials (such, for example, as certain paints) that combine with oxygen and discharge carbon dioxide in much the same manner as human respiration.

Summarizing, special provision of ventilation to care for oxygen supply is unnecessary in all but very unusual cases. In any average structure, even if well built and weatherstripped, normal infiltration will supply far more air than is needed to avoid discomfort or hazard to health because of oxygen deficiency. In any room, irrespective of size, ventilation for this purpose will be adequate if outside air enters at a rate of $\frac{1}{2}$ cfm per occupant.

2–3. Odor Removal. Odor control is essentially a problem of diluting the odor-producing agents released by occupants of an enclosed space. Since odor is a sensation resulting from exposure of the olfactory bulb to contaminated air, the degree of dilution required is dependent on the concentration corresponding to the threshold at which the sensation of odor first appears. The threshold concentration varies somewhat with different individuals, but average values have been well established. Odor intensity varies as an inverse function of humidity.

The air quantities needed for dilution obviously depend on the rate at which odoriferous material is added to the room air. For the usual type of ventilation problem the principal sources of air contamination are body odors resulting from breathing, insensible perspiration, and the products of organic decomposition. Contamination of the air occurs either directly from the bodies of the occupants or from their clothes. The seriousness of the odor problem varies with the personal cleanliness, occupation, and degree of exertion of the occupants, but the basic requirement of ventilation air for odor dilution exists and is of real significance even though the occupants of the space under consideration are sedentary and given to the practice of a high degree of personal cleanliness.

The effective rate of air contamination is now known to be a function of the air space available per occupant. Many of the products causing odor are self-oxidizing and disappear spontaneously when the time interval and the mixing volume are sufficient; thus body odor disappears from a closed room within a short time after the occupants leave. Because of self-oxidation the required ventilation rate decreases as the air space per occupant is increased. Thus in a room that is sufficiently large, the rate of oxidation may be equal to or greater than the rate of discharge of odor-producing contaminants, and the threshold concentration will then not be reached even though no ventilation air is provided. This factor is the one that makes high ceilings desirable in rooms which are to be crowded, since by providing a large air space per occupant, the problem of odor prevention is materially simplified. Conversely, the ventilation requirement for odor control becomes particularly severe as the density of occupancy increases.

In contrast to the condition described above, odors resulting from tobacco smoke are largely non-oxidizing; hence they remain for very long intervals of time after the room becomes unoccupied. The only satisfactory means of controlling such odors is by masking them with a stronger but more pleasing odor or by providing sufficient ventilation air to "sweep" the smoke from the occupied space at a rate that will prevent a disagreeable concentration. The latter method is the one most widely used. Since the smoke problem solution is one of discharge rather than dilution, it follows that ventilation of a smoking room is most easily accomplished if the ceiling is low and the air space per occupant is at a minimum. Recent experimental work by Yaglou[2] has shown that maintenance of the odor level at a value acceptable to nonsmokers in a room where some of the occupants are smoking will require supplementary outside air at a rate of not less than 25 cfm per smoker.

Fig. 2–1 gives the minimum outdoor air requirements for control of body

[2] C. P. Yaglou, "Ventilation Requirements for Cigarette Smoke," *ASHRAE Trans.* Vol. 61, 1955, p. 25.

odor as reported by the Harvard School of Public Health.[3] Differences in requirements because of age and activity result primarily from differences in metabolism, whereas differences in terms of socioeconomic class result primarily from variations in the standard of personal hygiene.

Control of odor in occupied spaces is a health as well as a comfort necessity. Even in rooms where the occupants are unaware of odor, the psychological and physiological effects persist and are evident later in symptomatic loss of appetite and other signs of decreased health, energy, or working effectiveness. The sensation of odor is controlled by the response

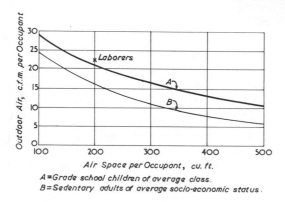

Fig. 2–1. Outside air ventilation requirements for odor control. A: Grade school children of average socioeconomic class. B: Sedentary adults of average socioeconomic status.

of the olfactory bulb; as time of exposure increases, olfactory fatigue occurs, and the threshold of odor detection is raised to a higher concentration. For this reason occupants of a poorly ventilated space can be unaware of an extremely high odor concentration that would be very disagreeable to someone entering from the outside. But as already mentioned, subconscious effects on appetite and general physiological condition make contaminated air undesirable even if the occupants do not find it unpleasant.

2–4. Odor Masking. Lacking adequate ventilation, a number of methods have been suggested for avoiding disagreeable odor. Most of them depend on masking the undesired odor by providing a greater concentration of some other material that does not have an objectionable smell. Another class of additive materials operates by hastening oxidation of the objectionable body odors, while a third type of additive seemingly irritates or "paralyzes" the olfactory bulb, thereby lessening its degree of sensitivity.

Ozone has been proposed as a means of reducing body odor, but opinion is by no means unanimous as to its effective value. The known physiological effects of ozone are predominantly harmful, and concentrations as small as 1 part of ozone in 10 million parts of air may be definitely injurious

[3] C. P. Yaglou, E. C. Riley, and D. J. Coggins, "Ventilation requirements," *ASHRAE Trans.* Vol. 42, 1936, p. 133.

to respiratory membranes; for comfort heating and cooling systems, the ASHRAE recommends limiting the ozone concentration to a maximum of 5 parts per 100 million.

2–5. Ionization.   The search for a clue concerning the intangible quality of outside air, which is commonly called "freshness," was directed for a time to the subject of ions. A collection of substantial mass of data indicated that the types of ions and the degree of concentration might correlate directly with the sensation of "freshness." Although nothing conclusive has as yet developed, the subject is of interest to heating engineers not only because of its potentialities but also because data conclusively show that—whether intended to do so or not—modern air-conditioning and heating equipment does alter the ion concentration of the air that passes through it.

Ions are small positive- or negative-charged particulate groups that are always present in air. They are of two different types: Small ions are clusters of molecules surrounding a charged center, held in position by electrical force; large ions consist of small ion clusters surrounding condensation nuclei. Ions are produced by radioactive elements in the soil, by cosmic rays, and possibly by solar radiation; they can be produced artificially by electricity.

Investigation of small ions has shown that increased concentrations usually coexist with atmospheric conditions that correspond to the average person's subjective concept of "fresh" air. Thus small-ion concentration decreases from day to night, from summer to winter, and from clear day to cloudy day; most people would agree that in each of these comparative cases, the expectation of a feeling of outdoor "freshness" would be greater for the first of each pair of conditions. The small-ion concentration has also been shown to decrease markedly in occupied rooms but to increase again as soon as the occupants depart. The extent of occupancy effect is evident from the fact that a ventilation rate of approximately 160 cfm per occupant would be required to maintain an indoor small-ion concentration equal to that which exists in outside air; this ventilation rate is roughly six times greater than that needed under the most extreme conditions for odor control.

Large ions, irrespective of charge, seemingly have no physiological effect. Small, negatively charged ions predispose toward a relaxed condition and induce an increase in mental activity. When more conclusive data are available, it may be that artificial ionization with ions of this type can be used advantageously in offices, classrooms, and other group areas to establish conditions particularly conducive to thinking processes. Small positive ions, in contrast with small negative ones, tend to increase metabolism but to slow up mental activity, induce headaches, and possibly lead to irritation of the nasal passages. The effect on mental effort of small positive ions is so great that after brief exposure to moderate concentrations, it is said that a well-educated person will lose (during the interval of exposure) the ability to add a simple column of figures.

The entire matter of ionization and its possible influence on comfort is still in a very indefinite stage of investigation and of understanding. At present there is no proven reason why the heating engineer should take ionization into account when designing a heating system. However, since experiment has conclusively shown that the passage of air through ducts, overheated surfaces, and humidifying equipment does alter the degree of ionization, it follows that the engineer may need to consider it. He may be expected to either control the ionizing effect of the equipment which he uses or compensate for it by use of artificial ionization.

2–6. Fluctuating Conditions. It is interesting and instructive to note that some investigators commend modern heating systems for one characteristic which engineers have long considered an undesirable one. Irrespective of the heating method employed, most systems make use of some form of control mechanism that involves intermittency of operation. Thus, to maintain a room at a design inside-air temperature of 72 F usually requires acceptance of plus and minus tolerances (often 1 deg or less) within which the control system will operate. Designers of control equipment have made great effort to reduce these tolerances to a minimum and thereby to approach what they considered the ideal case of a heating system that would maintain fixed room conditions.

There is now some evidence to suggest that minor fluctuations in a heating system are desirable. Obviously the degree of "swing" must be so small that the room air temperature will not depart from the comfort range, but within this range it appears that periodic variation has a stimulating effect on the occupant and increases his psychological sensation of comfort as distinguished from a neutral comfort state in which he has no positive response and is neither actively comfortable nor actively uncomfortable.

The evidence on this subject is still fragmentary and is certainly insufficient to justify effort on the engineer's part to provide thermal variation. The subject is primarily of interest in that it implies the desirability of the minor changes in both temperature and air movement which necessarily occur in almost all systems and which it is not within the power of the designer or the control system to eradicate. A further practical point in connection with fluctuation of temperature is that its possible psychological desirability suggests that the added cost of high-precision controls which minimize fluctuation be not only uneconomical but also unjustified if they cause reduction rather than improvement in the resultant sensation of comfort.

2–7. Air Contamination. In the average occupied space the principal sources of contamination due to occupancy are discharges from the human body. During a sneeze, for example, there is an intense discharge of droplets which may provide transportation for enough organisms to constitute a health hazard throughout a very large air volume. The larger droplets leaving the mouth during a sneeze are discharged at velocities in excess of

100 mph. For droplets of moderate size this velocity provides sufficient kinetic energy to assure transportation across a room of average size. It has been established experimentally that a person sneezing unguardedly out of an open window on a still day could expose a passerby on the sidewalk *across* the street from the window.

The smaller droplets discharged during a sneeze leave the mouth at high velocity, but because of their large surface-volume ratio, they are rapidly slowed down as a result of drag effects. Such droplets will not travel long distances, but the gain due to shorter travel is largely offset by the fact that small droplets will remain in suspension for a longer time interval and hence may actually provide a more extensive hazard to exposure than do the large ones.

Floor drafts are one of the most serious causes of air contamination in that they greatly increase the time of suspension of small, contaminating particulate matter. The physical reason for this can be readily understood: Assume that an occupant sneezes and that contaminating material is spread uniformly through the room with a concentration of 100 droplets per cubic foot of air space. At any time subsequent to that at which uniformity existed, the concentration would be less near the ceiling and greater near the floor, since the particles would slowly settle, owing to the action of gravity. If now a floor draft acts to sweep 1 cu ft of air from near the floor and transfer it to the breathing level, it is evident that this volume of air will transport upward a greater number of particles than will be brought down by the replacing unit volume that comes from the breathing level. Thus the effect of turbulence due to floor drafts is to carry suspended matter upward against the action of gravity. For a given amount of turbulence, there will be a given distribution of concentrations from floor to ceiling, the gradient of concentrations increasing as turbulence decreases and the time for settlement of contaminating particles increasing as turbulence increases.

Floor drafts are thus very serious offenders against both health and comfort. They are responsible for local cooling of one of the most sensitive and exposed parts of the body, the ankle; they build up the dust concentration in room air (hence establish an added cleaning problem) and prolong suspension of airborne contaminants.

2–8. Aerosols. The problem of air contamination due to occupancy (autocontamination) can be solved, in decreasing order of effectiveness, by prevention, removal, or neutralization. The first method is applicable to contaminants that are of non-human origin, but with respect to contamination of air by sneezes and coughs, nothing can be done toward prevention other than to depend on the care and thoughtfulness of the occupants. Removal is largely a matter of adequate ventilation either to sweep the contaminated air from the occupied space (often using local exhaust outlets) or to dilute it greatly by general ventilation.

In densely occupied spaces or in spaces (such as hospitals) where the hazard of contamination is particularly great, neutralization is the most effective method of solving the autocontamination problem. Within the last decade great progress has been made in the development of mists carrying germicides, insecticides, and deodorants. Mists of this type, known as aerosols, consist of suspensions of droplets of some inert fluid to which is added an active ingredient. The effectiveness of such a suspension depends on the surface area of the droplets, the uniformity of distribution throughout the room of this area of the droplets, and the rate at which evaporation of the active ingredient takes place. In the first requisite, surface area, the problem of forming an aerosol is similar to that of achieving humidification; in both cases the fluid in question must be broken up into very small droplets in order to provide the largest possible ratio of surface area to volume. In the second requisite, rate of evaporation, aerosols and humidifiers differ entirely, since with an aerosol the object is to delay evaporation, whereas with a humidifier the intent is to accelerate it.

An effective aerosol is therefore one that exists as very small droplets, which rapidly attains uniform concentration throughout the treated space, and which has a sufficiently low vapor pressure to assure maintenance of the suspension for an adequate time; the time can be increased by maintaining a high (60 per cent or greater) relative humidity in the room which is to be treated. Many types of aerosols are commercially available, the active ingredient in each varying with its purpose. Although regular use of aerosols as part of the function of heating and ventilating systems has been recommended by some authorities, it is suggested that (for the present) heating engineers should secure medical advice before making provision for aerosol distribution in such systems.

PROBLEMS

2–1. An underground air-raid shelter 30 ft by 40 ft has a 7-ft ceiling and provides standing room for 400 occupants. In the event that the ventilation system failed, how long would it be before the occupants would experience difficulty in breathing?

2–2. For the shelter of problem 2–1, (a) calculate the temperature in the shelter after 40-min occupancy, assuming that heat loss to the walls, floor, and ceiling is negligible and that there is no ventilation. Hint: Take the specific volume of the air as 13 cu ft/lb and its specific heat as 0.24 Btu/(lb)(°F). (b) Calculate the shelter temperature after 5-min occupancy.

2–3. During a robbery four employees of a bank are locked in the airtight 15-ft by 10-ft by 8-ft vault. (a) How many hours do rescuers have in which to open the vault before the captives lose consciousness? (b) How many hours would pass before oxygen deficiency became noticeable?

2–4. What ventilation rate would be required for the vault of problem 2–3, to assure an adequate oxygen supply for an indefinite period of time?

2-5. Discarded home refrigerators that cannot be opened from the inside are a recognized hazard to small children. If a child were accidentally locked in a 12-cu ft airtight refrigerator, how long would it be before loss of consciousness would occur?

2-6. Ventilation by infiltration into a tightly built prefabricated house amounts to only 200 cfh. If there are four occupants and if an unvented gas stove burns methane (CH_4) at the rate of 3 cfh, determine whether or not there would be a problem of oxygen deficiency. (Hint: One volume of methane combines with two volumes of oxygen to yield products of combustion of one volume of carbon dioxide and two volumes of water vapor.)

2-7. For the same conditions of occupancy and the same ventilation rate given in problem 2-7, is odor more likely to be noticed in a given room at 70 F in winter or in summer?

2-8. A grade school auditorium affords 200 cu ft of air space per occupant and provides mechanical ventilation at a rate just sufficient to prevent noticeable odor. Fan speed is adjustable so that the ventilation rate (in cfm) can be varied according to need. Determine the required, or permitted, percentage change in ventilation rate when (a) the auditorium is occupied by parents, (b) the auditorium is used for a noon-hour meeting of a labor union.

2-9. If the auditorium of problem 2-8 were occupied by half as many grade school children as it could seat, what percentage reduction in design ventilation rate would be permissible?

2-10. For equal conditions of personal cleanliness, would a sedentary child require more ventilation air for control of odor than would a sedentary adult? Explain in terms of a major physiological difference between a child and an adult.

3

SELECTION OF OUTSIDE DESIGN TEMPERATURE

Sun, wind, and outside air temperature are the three major factors that determine the transmission heat losses from a given structure when it is maintained at a selected inside comfort temperature. Sunshine, or appreciable sky radiation, cannot be depended on during the coldest days of the heating season; hence these occasional heat gains are not considered in the selection of a design value of the outside air temperature. Wind is the major factor in designing the resistance to heat loss through the air film at the outside surface of the structure. The importance of outside surface resistance, however, is integrally related to the over-all heat-transmission characteristics of the particular structure; hence wind effect is properly considered (Art. 5–3, page 169) in connection with evaluation of the over-all, inside air to outside air, thermal resistance of each transmitting section of the building.

3–1. Basic Functional Relationship Involving Outside Design Air Temperature. For a given system the maximum transmission load will be related to the insulating characteristics of the structure and to design values of the inside and outside air temperatures. The functional relationship, which shows that q_d is some function ϕ of K, t_{id}, and t_{od}, would be of the form

$$q_d = \phi(K, t_{id}, t_{od}) \tag{3-1}$$

where q_d = maximum allocated capacity, Btu/hr, of the heating system for the purpose of meeting losses by transmission when outside temperature is t_{od}. (Additional design capacity must be available for simultaneously meeting heat losses due to infiltration or to mechanical ventilation.)

t_{id} = design value of the inside air temperature.

t_{od} = design value of the outside air temperature.

K = a thermal *constant* of the structure which, under design conditions, defines its over-all transmission losses in Btu/(hr) (deg air-to-air temperature difference).

The value of K in Eq. 3–1 will depend on the size of the building, the design wind velocity, and the thermal resistance of the various types of structural sections (such as windows, exterior walls, roofs, and floors) through which heat losses by transmission are occurring. Explicit evaluation of K can be carried out by usual engineering procedures (see Art. 5–2), but the method of doing so is not of significance for purposes of the present discussion.

In evaluating K as a constant of the structure, the assumption is implicitly made that the transmission of heat from inside air to inside surface of the structure is at a rate equal to that from outside surface to outside air. This necessarily means that the structure is considered to be at thermal equilibrium and hence is neither receiving heat to storage nor liberating heat from storage. Such a condition would be true for any structure, whether of heavy or of light construction, if the outside temperature t_o did not change with time. In this case the ϕ function of Eq. 3–1 would be equal to the product of K and the inside-to-outside air temperature difference, and Eq. 3–1 would then take the explicit steady-state form

$$q = K(t_{id} - t_o) \qquad (3\text{--}2)$$

where t_o is the *constant* outside temperature and q is the *constant* transmission load which is then also equal to q_d.

3–2. Definition of Outside Design Temperature in Terms of Steady State. For any variation of t_o as a function of time, there will necessarily be a flow of heat to or from storage; hence Eq. 3–2 will no longer be exactly applicable. The exact equation would take the functional form

$$q_d = K(t_{id} - t_o) \pm \phi'\left(\frac{\Delta S}{\Delta \theta} \frac{\Delta t_o}{\Delta \theta}\right) \qquad (3\text{--}3)$$

where $\quad \Delta\theta =$ increment of time, hr.

$\Delta S =$ increment of heat to or from storage in time $\Delta\theta$, Btu.

$\Delta t_o =$ increment ($\pm$) of outside temperature, °F.

$\Delta S/\Delta\theta =$ average rate of flow of energy to or from storage during time $\Delta\theta$, Btu/hr.

$\Delta t_o/\Delta\theta =$ average rate of change of outside temperature during time $\Delta\theta$, °F/hr.

$t_o =$ actual outside air temperature at time of load, q_d, °F.

A quantitative analysis of the thermal storage characteristics of a structure properly comes under the discussions of periodic and transient heat flow (Chapters 11 and 12), but for present purposes a qualitative interpretation will be helpful. For a homogeneous structure, or for a homogeneous transmitting section (as one solid exterior wall) of a heterogeneous structure, the storage increment can be evaluated as

$$\Delta S = (\rho c A x)(\Delta t_m) \quad \text{Btu} \qquad (3\text{--}4)$$

where $\quad \rho =$ density of the homogeneous transmitting section, lb/cu ft.

$A =$ transmitting area, sq ft.

$x =$ wall thickness, ft.

$c =$ specific heat of the homogeneous transmitting section, Btu/(lb)(°F).

Δt_m = mean temperature change of the wall during the time interval $\Delta\theta$, °F.

ρc = thermal capacity per unit volume, (often referred to as volumetric specific heat), Btu/(cu ft)(°F).

ρcx = thermal capacity (per unit area), Btu/(sq ft)(°F).

ρcxA = total thermal capacity, Btu/°F.

The first parenthetical term on the right of Eq. 3–4 is defined as the total thermal capacity of the transmitting section and is equal to the number of Btu that enter or leave storage as the mean temperature is raised or lowered by 1 F.

In general, a massive structure is likely also to be "thermally heavy" and a light-weight structure (such as a residence of frame construction) to be "thermally light," but this need not always be the case. Thus one must note that the value of *thermal capacity*, ρcx, is directly proportional to three separate factors: density, specific heat, and wall thickness. For walls of equal thickness the controlling value would be the thermal capacity per unit volume (volumetric specific heat), ρc, and this can vary by a relatively small amount even for materials of very different density. A concrete wall, for example, with a density of 140 lb/cu ft would be almost four times heavier than an equally thick wall of softwood with a density of 37.2 lb/cu ft. The specific heat of the concrete, however, is 0.215 Btu/(lb)(°F), whereas that of the softwood is more than twice as great at 0.47 Btu/(lb)(°F). Thus the volumetric thermal capacity of the concrete wall would be $\rho c = (140)(0.215) = 30$ Btu/(cu ft)(°F), whereas that of the wood wall would be $(37.2)(0.47) = 17.5$ Btu/(cu ft)(°F); the "thermal weight" of the concrete wall is thus less than twice that of the wood wall of equal thickness even though its actual weight is almost four times greater. As an extreme example, lead has a density (710 lb/cu ft) which is close to 20 times that of softwood, but its thermal capacity per unit volume (21.7 Btu/(cu ft)(°F) is only 24 per cent greater than that of softwood.

Referring again to Eq. 3–4, the ΔS term is seen to be a function of mean temperature change, Δt_m, as well as of thermal capacity. For fixed inside air temperature, Δt_m would vary as a function of the outside temperature, but it would also be subject to influence by both the thermal capacity (for a thermally heavy structure the change in t_m would occur more slowly, owing to a given change in t_o) and the rate of change, $\Delta t_o/\Delta\theta$, in outside temperature. Thus, in functional form, Eq. 3–4 becomes

$$\Delta S = \left\{(\rho Axc)f'\left[(\rho Axc),\, t_o,\, \frac{\Delta t_o}{\Delta\theta}\right]\right\}\Delta\theta \qquad (3\text{–}5)$$

$$= f''\left[(\rho Axc),\, t_o,\, \frac{\Delta t_o}{\Delta\theta},\, \Delta\theta\right] \qquad (3\text{–}6)$$

and, substituting back into Eq. 3–3,

$$q_d = K(t_{id} - t_o) \pm \phi''\left[(\rho cAx),\, t_o,\, \frac{\Delta t_o}{\Delta \theta},\, \Delta \theta\right] \qquad (3–7)$$

The basic problem in the selection of a design value of the outside air temperature t_{od} is thus to evaluate or estimate the influence of each term in the ϕ function of Eq. 3–7 on the equivalent steady-state rate of transmission loss. Thus, for any structure under any operating conditions, a defining equation for outside design temperature is

$$q_d = K(t_{id} - t_{od})$$
$$= K(t_{id} - t_o) \pm \phi''\left[(\rho cAx),\, t_o,\, \frac{\Delta t_o}{\Delta \theta},\, \Delta \theta\right] \qquad (3–8)$$

Eq. 3–8 states that if the design value of maximum transmission loss, q_d, occurs under transient outside conditions when actual outside air temperature is t_o and outside rate of change of outside temperature is $\Delta t_o/\Delta\theta$, then the corresponding selected design value of outside air temperature, t_{od}, is that value at which (for steady state) the calculated transmission load would be q_d.

The selection of t_{od} will therefore be influenced by climatological data for both t_o and rate of change of t_o and by engineering data on the thermal capacity and thermal resistance of the structure. In a broad sense t_{od} is more correctly an "answer factor" rather than a true temperature, for it is a number that serves to adjust the steady-state transmission equation to provide a transmission loss that is applicable under transient conditions. This being so, it is evident that the selection of t_{od} is a problem that must be carefully investigated in terms of both structure and climate. Various compilations of climatological data are available to assist the designer in estimating frequencies of given low outside temperature, but the use of such tables must be in combination with experience, judgment, and technical understanding of the behavior of a structure under transient conditions. In the subsequent articles the problem of selection will be presented in qualitative terms leading to generalizations for various types of structures when subjected to certain broad classifications of climatological exposure. For a given structure, of sufficient size to justify the analysis, a quantitative evaluation can be obtained by using the methods presented in Chapters 11 and 12.

3–3. Structures of Low Thermal Capacity. For a very light structure, such as an all-glass hothouse, the thermal capacity would be so low that the heat flow to or from storage in the glass, ΔS, would be negligible (as compared with the heat transmitted) even when the outside air-temperature gradient, $\Delta t_o/\Delta\theta$, was very great. In this case the corrective term of Eq. 3–7 would drop out, and the actual air temperature t_o at time of design load q_d would be the design outside-air temperature t_{od}, and Eq. 3–7 would become

$$q_d = K(t_{id} - t_{od}) \qquad (3–9)$$

Thus, for a thermally very light structure, the maximum transmission load would be determined by the actual minimum outside temperature at which the system would be expected to maintain t_{id}; maximum transmission load would occur at the time of minimum outside temperature even though the duration of the minimum t_o might be very short.

In selecting t_{od} for such a structure, interest would center on the minimum temperature to be expected during a given time period and not on the minimum average daily temperature to be expected in such a period. Selection of the period during which the probability would be in favor of having t_o remain above t_{od} would then be a matter of judgment based on the degree of necessity of preventing t_i from dropping below t_{id}. Recommendations for selection of t_{od} will be given in Art. 3–8.

3–4. Structures of High Thermal Capacity; Small Diurnal Change in Outside Air Temperature.   In order for the correction term of Eq. 3–7 to approach zero for a thermally heavy structure, it would be necessary for the outside air-temperature gradient, $\Delta t_o / \Delta \theta$, to be very small. This means that in a locality where in cold weather there is very little periodic diurnal change in t_o, Eq. 3–7 would revert to the form of Eq. 3–2 (not to Eq. 3–9) if the seasonal transient $\Delta t_o / \Delta \theta$ gradient were also small. If, further, the slow decrease of t_o were to continue to a seasonal minimum, it would then permit selection of that minimum as t_{od}, and Eq. 3–9, with t_{od} in place of the t_o of Eq. 3–2, would be applicable. In this case the design value of outside air temperature for a heavy structure would equal that for a light structure and would be taken as equal to that minimum value of t_o (seasonal or otherwise) at and above which t_i could be maintained at or above t_{id}.

For a thermally heavy structure in a locality where diurnal periodic change in t_o is very small but where seasonal transient change t_o as given by the $\Delta t / \Delta \theta$ gradient is large, the instantaneous steady-state transmission load calculable from Eq. 3–2 would exceed the actual load during periods of decrease in t_o and would be less than the actual load during increase in t_o. It can be stated as a corollary that the actual transmission load would lag in time behind the calculated steady-state load (Eq. 3–2) based on the instantaneous t_o. This means that when t_o reached a minimum and then started to rise sharply, the effect would be to reduce the delayed actual load so that it would never reach a maximum value equal to the load calculated on the basis of minimum t_o. In such a case the selected design value t_{od}, would be higher than the seasonal minimum t_o; the magnitude of the difference would increase as the thermal capacity of the structure increased and also as the $\Delta t / \Delta \theta$ gradient increased.

3–5. Structures of High Thermal Capacity; Large Diurnal Change in Outside Air Temperature.   Neglecting seasonal climatological changes and hourly weather changes, the normal periodic diurnal change of outside air temperature can be approximated as a single sinusoidal function. On this basis the corresponding transmission load will also vary sinusoidally, but the maximum load during the 24 hr will be less than the value that would be obtained by calculation from Eq. 3–2, with t_o taken as the minimum diurnal temperature. The magnitude of the difference will be found to increase with increasing thermal "heaviness" of the structure and with increasing differences between minimum and maximum diurnal outside air temperature; it will decrease as K increases. A number of theoretical and experimental methods have been used in seeking an effective means of selecting the outside design temperature so that the calculated maximum load (using Eq. 3–9) will be in agreement with the actual maximum.

One such method, recently proposed by Ghai and Sundaram,[1] is based on theory, but has been shown to provide t_{od} values that give transmission loads which agree closely with those determined by experimental means. The Ghai and Sundaram results are limited to an enclosure of uniform and homogeneous construction but can, if necessary, be corrected for heterogeneity. The method is to seek explicit evaluation of the functional relationship

$$t_{od} = \propto \left(t_{min}, t_{mean}, \rho c, \frac{k}{x} \right) \tag{3–10}$$

where t_{min} = minimum daily temperature during periodic diurnal sinusoidal temperature change, °F.

   t_{mean} — mean daily temperature during periodic diurnal sinusoidal temperature change, °F.

   k = thermal conductivity of a homogeneous transmitting section, Btu/(hr)(sq ft)(°F/ft).

   x = thickness of the transmitting section, ft.

Since the $\Delta t / \Delta \theta$ gradients are fixed in terms of the assumed sinusoidal temperature variation and since k/x is a function of the value of K reduced to unit area of transmitting section, it follows that Eq. 3–10 is a special form of Eq. 3–7.

The Ghai and Sundaram equation (derived in the Appendix of their paper) as proposed for heating is

$$\frac{t_{min} - t_{od}}{t_{od} - t_{mean}} = 0.0007 (\rho c x)^2 \left[1 + 2 \left(\frac{x}{k} \right)^{3/2} \right] \tag{3–11}$$

To show the significance of the equation, the authors use it in the following example to calculate t_{od} and the corresponding maximum heat gain for a concrete and for a wooden structure.

EXAMPLE 3–1. All transmitting surface of a particular structure consists of 18 in. thick concrete with K' (K per unit area) of 0.42 Btu/(hr)(sq ft)(°F). The volumetric specific heat of the concrete is 30 Btu/(ft³)(°F), and its thermal

[1] M. L. Ghai and R. Sundaram, "Selection of Outside Design Temperature for Heat Load Estimation," *ASHAE Trans.*, Vol. 61, 1955, pp. 169–188.

conductivity is 1.0 Btu/(hr)(sq ft)(°F/ft). For a locality where sinusoidal daily temperature variation is from a minimum of -15 F to a mean of 0 F, determine (a) the design value of outside air temperature if inside air temperature is 75 F; (b) the maximum transmission load [q_d', Btu/(hr)(sq ft)] that occurs during the 24-hr period.

Solution: The thermal capacity of this structure is

$$\rho c x = 30\,\frac{18}{12} = 45 \text{ Btu/(sq ft)(°F)}$$

and the x/k term is

$$\frac{x}{k} = \frac{18/12}{1} = 1.5$$

Substituting in Eq. 3–11,

$$\frac{-15 - t_{od}}{t_{od} - 0} = 0.0007(45)^2[1 + 2(1.5)^{3/2}] = 6.64$$

$$t_{od} = -1.96 = -2 \text{ F}$$

Maximum heat transfer is then

$$q_d' = K'(t_{id} - t_{od}) = 0.42(75 + 2) = 32.3 \text{ Btu/(hr)(sq ft)}$$

Note that the influence of diurnal temperature variation has been to bring the design value of t_{od} up from t_{min} by $86\frac{1}{2}$ per cent of the difference between t_{mean} and t_{min}. In this case it is evident that the *mean* daily temperature is far more important than the *minimum* daily temperature in selection of t_{od}. If it is assumed that the day used in this example is the coldest day of the year and if it were to be used as a basis of design, then it would follow that the erroneous selection of q_d based on t_{min} would have given a transmission load of

$$q_d = 0.42(75 + 15) = 37.8 \text{ Btu/(hr)(sq ft)}$$

which is [(37.8 − 32.3)/32.3]100, or 17 per cent greater than the actual value.

EXAMPLE 3–2. For the same inside and outside conditions given in Example 3–1, consider a structure having the same K' value as before but consisting of a homogeneous wooden wall 1.26 in. thick. The volumetric specific heat of the wood is 17.5 Btu/(cu ft)(°F), and its thermal conductivity is 0.07 Btu/(hr)(sq ft) (°F/ft). Determine (a) the design outside air temperature and (b) the maximum transmission load [q_d', Btu/(hr)(sq ft)] that occurs daily.

Solution: The thermal capacity of this structure is

$$\rho c x = 17.5\,\frac{1.26}{12} = 1.84$$

and the x/k term is

$$\frac{x}{k} = \frac{1.26/12}{0.07} = 1.5$$

Substituting in Eq. 3–11,

$$\frac{-15 - t_{od}}{t_{od} - 0} = 0.0007(1.84)^2[1 + 2(1.5)^{3/2}] = 0.011$$

$$t_{od} = -14.8 \text{ F}$$

Maximum heat transfer is then

$$q_d' = K'(t_{id} - t_{od}) = 0.42(75 + 14.8) = 37.7 \text{ Btu/(hr)(sq ft)}$$

In this case the influence of diurnal temperature variation is practically negligible and the true value of the outside design temperature is almost entirely determined by the minimum daily outside temperature. Thus, for a thermally "light" structure, the minimum rather than mean temperature is controlling.

Comparison of the results of Examples 3–1 and 3–2 brings out the highly significant fact that two structures in the same climatological location and having thermal barriers of identical steady-state effectiveness $(K_1 = K_2)$ may have maximum heat loads that differ markedly. This means that the structure with lower thermal capacity would have to have a substantially larger heating plant to maintain equal comfort. It does not necessarily mean that the structure with the larger plant would also have the higher heating costs, since this structure will respond to the daily maximum air temperature just as readily as it does to the daily minimum. Thus analysis would be necessary to establish relative operating costs as a function of average hourly load over the 24-hr period.

3–6. The Influence of Discontinuous Heating. The discussion in preceding articles has been based on the assumption that the inside design temperature t_{id} is held constant. When this is not the case, as in many office buildings and residences, the lowered night value of the inside temperature can be shown to afford a saving in seasonal operating cost. (Refer to Chapter 12 for a detailed technical analysis of intermittent heating.) With respect to the selection of design outside temperature, however, great care must be exercised in attempting to reflect the reduced night loads in an increased value of t_{od}.

Since minimum daily outside-air temperature usually occurs during the night hours, it follows that with intermittent heating, the maximum rate of transmission loss can be substantially less than that which would occur with continuous heating. But when the heating system is turned on in order to reheat the structure to t_{id}, the system will operate at maximum capacity, since in addition to meeting the actual transmission losses, it must put heat into structural storage at a rate sufficient to raise the inside air temperature to the design value by the time normal occupancy occurs (8 A.M. or earlier). Thus the longer the shutdown period, the shorter will be the time available to restore the inside temperature to its design value, and in consequence the greater will be the required design value of rate of transmission loss q_d. If data from a thermal analysis of the particular structure is lacking, it is recommended that the value of t_{od} be selected on the basis of continuous heating.

3–7. Statistical Analysis of Actual Outside-Air Temperatures. Preceding articles have shown that the design for winter outside temperature should be selected at a value, dependent on the thermal capacity of the structure, that lies in the range between minimum and mean temperatures for the day selected as representative of design conditions. If the structure has high thermal capacity and high-to-moderate resistance (or both) to heat loss, the value of t_{od} should be taken at or close to the mean temperature on the coldest day for which the inside temperature is to be maintained at its design value. If the structure has low thermal capacity and moderate-to-low resistance to heat loss (or both), the value of t_{od} should be taken at or close to the minimum temperature on the same day.

The climatological problem of selection is thus one of choosing the day, or the statistically probable day, that is to be used as a criterion of design. Many methods of selection have been and are being used, but the final decision must in every case depend on the judgment of the designer. If the design day were chosen as that one on which the lowest temperature ever recorded in the particular locality occurred, it would be evident that there would be a very unlikely chance that the heating system would ever fail. Conversely, the premium paid for almost 100 per cent guarantee of design performance would be substantially out of proportion to the risk, and the excess heating capacity would have practically a zero usage factor.

As the selected minimum temperature, or minimum average daily temperature, rises above the lowest recorded value, the probability of t_i falling below t_{id} increases. The fundamental problem is one of analyzing the danger (as in a hospital) or the discomfort (as in a residence) of a t_i less than t_{id} and of then estimating the permitted frequency with which this can be allowed to occur. To assist in doing this, Table 3–1 presents an assortment of climatological data for over 200 cities in the United States.

MINIMUM TEMPERATURES; MICROCLIMATOLOGICAL VERSUS MACROCLIMATOLOGICAL VALUES. The second column of Table 3–1 gives the average annual minimum temperature recorded over a period of years, usually more than 60, for which weather data are available. Since this average is based on minimum temperature for both warm and cold years, it would be expected that on a probability basis, the minimum daily temperature would be below this value once every two years. Further, during unusually cold years the value of the minimum daily outdoor temperature might frequently drop below the stated value and, thermally far worse, might remain below that value for a number of successive days. Although useful as an indication of average coldest weather, the average annual minimum temperature does not provide sufficient statistical assurance to safely permit its use for design purposes if other supporting data are lacking.

Another significant weakness of an averaged minimum temperature is that it strongly reflects microclimatological as contrasted with macroclimatological conditions. In San Francisco, for example, a diurnal minimum temperature as recorded in Golden Gate Park has been observed as 50 F when the temperature near city center was 70 F. Microclimatological differences

TABLE 3–I*
Winter Design Outside-Air Temperature, °F

Station	Avg. Annual Min. Temp.	Design Temp. in Common Use	Probability Exists of Lower Daily Avg. Air Temp. Once in:					Design Temp. on TAC† 97½ Per Cent Basis
			40 yr	20 yr	13 yr	10 yr	5 yr	
Alabama								
Anniston	—	5	5	9	12	14	18	—
Birmingham	12	10	6	10	12	14	18	21
Mobile	22	15	17	20	22	24	27	30
Montgomery	18	10	11	15	18	19	23	—
Arizona								
Flagstaff	−15	−10	−12	−7	−4	−2	3	—
Kingman	—	—	—	—	—	—	—	22
Phoenix	26	25	33	35	36	37	39	31
Tucson	—	25	—	—	—	—	—	30
Winslow	−1	10	—	—	—	—	—	6
Yuma	27	30	34	36	38	39	41	—
Arkansas								
Fort Smith	6	10	4	7	9	11	14	—
Little Rock	10	5	6	10	12	13	16	21
California								
Bakersfield	25[a]	25	—	—	—	—	—	33
Burbank	—	—	—	—	—	—	—	35
Daggett	—	—	—	—	—	—	—	27
Eureka	29	30	28	30	32	33	35	—
Fresno	26	25	29	31	32	32	34	32
Los Angeles	37	35	37	39	41	41	44	—
Oakland	—	30	—	—	—	—	—	36
Redding	—	—	—	—	—	—	—	32
Sacramento	28	30	27	29	30	31	33	—
San Diego	37	35	41	42	43	44	46	43
San Franscisco	37	35	34	36	37	38	40	—
San Jose	—	25	—	—	—	—	—	—
Williams	—	—	—	—	—	—	—	29
Colorado								
Denver	−11	−10	−20	−15	−12	−10	−5	0
Grand Junction	−2	−15	−11	−6	−3	−1	4	—
Pueblo	—	−20	−24	−18	−14	−12	−5	2
Connecticut								
Hartford	—	0	−7	−4	−2	0	3	4
New Haven	−1	0	−5	−2	0	1	5	11
District of Columbia								
Washington	−1	0	5	8	10	11	14	14
Florida								
Apalachicola	—	25	—	—	—	—	—	—
Jacksonville	29	25	24	27	28	30	33	31
Key West	—	45	50	52	53	54	56	—
Miami	38	35	—	—	—	—	—	45

* Compiled, by selection, from data in *ASHRAE Trans.*, Vol. 63, 1957, pp. 117–119; and *ASHRAE Guide*, 1960, pp. 162–165.

† Technical Advisory Committee of the *ASHRAE*.

[a] Temperatures identified by superscript "a" are based on data from airport weather stations; all other temperatures are based on data from city weather stations.

TABLE 3–I (continued)

Station	Avg. Annual Min. Temp.	Design Temp. in Common Use	Probability Exists of Lower Daily Avg. Air Temp. Once in:					Design Temp. on TAC† 97½ Per Cent Basis
			40 yr	20 yr	13 yr	10 yr	5 yr	
Pensacola	23	20	19	22	24	25	29	—
Tampa	32	30	32	35	36	38	41	—
Titusville	—	—	—	—	—	—	—	38
Georgia								
Atlanta	12[a]	10	5	9	11	13	17	22
Augusta	—	10	15	18	20	21	25	—
Macon	—	15	14	18	20	21	24	—
Savannah	22	20	19	22	24	25	28	29
Idaho								
Boise	−1[a]	−10	−20	−14	−10	−7	0	5
Burley	—	—	—	—	—	—	—	2
Idaho Falls	—	—	—	—	—	—	—	−7
Lewiston	1	5	−24	−16	−12	−8	0	—
Pocatello	−12	−5	−27	−20	−17	−14	−7	6
Illinois								
Cairo	—	0	−8	−3	0	2	7	—
Chicago	−8	−10	−17	−13	−11	−9	−5	−3
Moline	—	−10	—	—	—	—	—	−6
Peoria	−8[a]	−10	−20	−15	−13	−11	−6	−6
Springfield	−7	−10	—	—	—	—	—	−2
Indiana								
Evansville	1	—	−12	−7	−4	−2	3	—
Fort Wayne	—	−10	−13	−9	−7	−5	−2	—
Helmer	—	—	—	—	—	—	—	−1
Indianapolis	−6	−10	−14	−10	−8	−6	−1	2
Terre Haute	−5	—	−12	−8	−6	−4	0	—
Iowa								
Charles City	−22	—	−28	−24	−21	−20	−16	—
Davenport	−13	−15	−18	−14	−12	−10	−5	—
Des Moines	—	−15	−19	−15	−13	−12	−8	−8
Dubuque	−17	−20	−22	−18	−15	−14	−9	—
Keokuk	−12	—	−21	−16	−13	−11	−6	—
Sioux City	−20	−20	−22	−18	−16	−15	−11	—
Kansas								
Concordia	−13	−10	−17	−13	−11	−9	−5	—
Dodge City	−10	−10	−16	−11	−9	−7	−2	—
Topeka	—	−10	−15	−11	−8	−7	−2	—
Wichita	−4	−10	−13	−9	−6	−4	0	6
Kentucky								
Louisville	−5	0	−9	−5	−2	0	4	9
Louisiana								
New Orleans	26	20	21	24	26	27	30	36
Shreveport	16[a]	20	8	12	14	16	20	27
Maine								
Eastport	−15	−10	−14	−11	−9	−8	−5	—
Portland	−6	−5	−15	−11	−9	−7	−3	—
Maryland								
Baltimore	8	0	3	6	8	9	13	13
Massachusetts								
Boston	−3	0	−6	−2	0	1	4	8
Nantucket	—	0	—	—	—	—	—	—

TABLE 3–I (continued)

Station	Avg. Annual Min. Temp.	Design Temp. in Common Use	Probability Exists of Lower Daily Avg. Air Temp. Once in:					Design Temp. on TAC† 97½ Per Cent Basis
			40 yr	20 yr	13 yr	10 yr	5 yr	
Michigan								
Alpena	−12	−10	−16	−12	−10	−8	−5	—
Detroit	−11	−10	−10	−6	−4	−3	1	4
Escanaba	—	−15	−25	−21	−18	−17	−12	—
Grand Rapids	—	−10	−9	−6	−4	−2	1	—
Lansing	—	−10	−14	−10	−8	−7	−3	—
Marquette	−13	−10	−22	−18	−16	−14	−10	—
Sault St. Marie	−22	−20	−24	−21	−19	−17	−14	—
Minnesota								
Duluth	−28	−25	−32	−29	−27	−25	−22	—
Minneapolis	−23	−20	−28	−25	−23	−21	−18	—
St. Paul	−25	−20	−28	−25	−23	−21	−18	−15
Mississippi								
Meridian	15	10	8	12	14	16	20	—
Vicksburg	18	10	9	13	15	17	21	—
Missouri								
Columbia	—	−10	−16	−11	−9	−7	−2	—
Kansas City	−6	−10	−15	−11	−8	−6	−2	2
St. Louis	−2	0	−12	−8	−5	−3	1	3
Springfield	−5[a]	—	−12	−8	−5	−4	1	8
Montana								
Billings	−30[a]	−25	−42	−35	−31	−28	−21	−17
Butte	—	−20	—	—	—	—	—	−18
Havre	−36	−30	−49	−43	−39	−36	−29	—
Helena	−24	−20	−53	−44	−39	−36	−27	—
Kalispell	−17	−20	−43	−35	−31	−27	−19	—
Miles City	−30	−35	−44	−38	−35	−32	−26	−18
Nebraska								
Lincoln	−13	−10	−22	−18	−15	−14	−9	−2
North Platte	−17	−20	−21	−17	−15	−13	−9	−9
Omaha	−14	−10	−24	−19	−17	−15	−10	−8
Valentine	−22	−25	−27	−23	−21	−19	−15	—
Nevada								
Elko	—	—	—	—	—	—	—	−4
Las Vegas	16[a]	—	—	—	—	—	—	23
Reno	—	−5	−4	0	3	5	9	7
Winnemucca	−10	−15	−17	−12	−9	−6	0	—
New Hampshire								
Concord	−15	−15	−17	−13	−11	−9	−5	—
New Jersey								
Atlantic City	6	5	3	6	8	9	12	—
Camden	—	0	—	—	—	—	—	12
Newark	—	0	—	—	—	—	—	10
Sandy Hook	—	0	—	—	—	—	—	—
Trenton	2	0	−4	0	2	3	7	—
New Mexico								
Albuquerque	—	0	3	6	8	10	14	16
El Morro	−19[a]	—	—	—	—	—	—	−6
Rodeo	—	—	—	—	—	—	—	25
Roswell	—	−10	−4	1	4	6	11	—
Tucumcari	—	—	—	—	—	—	—	13

TABLE 3–I (continued)

Station	Avg. Annual Min. Temp.	Design Temp. in Common Use	Probability Exists of Lower Daily Avg. Air Temp. Once in:					Design Temp. on TAC† 97½ Per Cent Basis
			40 yr	20 yr	13 yr	10 yr	5 yr	
New York								
Albany	−11	−10	−16	−12	−9	−8	−4	0
Binghamton	−11	−10	−12	−9	−7	−5	−2	—
Buffalo	−4	−5	−11	−7	−5	−4	0	3
Canton	−26	−25	−28	−25	−22	−21	−17	—
Elmira	—	—	—	—	—	—	—	5
Ithaca	−10	−15	−9	−6	−4	−3	0	—
New York	−3	0	1	3	5	6	9	—
Oswego	−9	−10	−12	−9	−7	−5	−1	—
Rochester	−4	−5	−9	−6	−4	−3	1	4
Syracuse	—	−10	−16	−12	−10	−8	−4	−1
North Carolina								
Asheville	6	0	−2	2	5	6	11	—
Charlotte	12	10	9	12	14	16	19	22
Greensboro	—	10	—	—	—	—	—	17
Raleigh	13	10	9	12	14	15	18	20
Wilmington	18	15	16	19	20	22	25	—
North Dakota								
Bismarck	−31	−30	−38	−34	−31	−29	−24	−24
Devils Lake	−33	−30	−37	−34	−32	−30	−27	—
Dickinson	—	—	—	—	—	—	—	−20
Fargo	—	−25	—	—	—	—	—	−25
Pembina	—	—	—	—	—	—	—	−30
Williston	—	−35	−44	−38	−35	−33	−27	
Ohio								
Akron	—	−5	—	—	—	—	—	9
Cincinnati	−2	0	−9	−5	−3	−1	3	7
Cleveland	−2	0	−11	−7	−5	−3	1	6
Columbus	−3[a]	−10	−9	−5	−3	−2	2	4
Dayton	—	0	−10	−6	−4	−2	2	—
Sandusky	—	0	−10	−6	−4	−2	2	—
Toledo	−5	−10	−11	−7	−5	−4	0	4
Oklahoma								
Ardmore	—	—	—	—	—	—	—	18
Oklahoma City	2	0	−9	−4	−1	1	6	14
Tulsa	—	0	—	—	—	—	—	13
Waynoka	—	—	—	—	—	—	—	10
Oregon								
Arlington	—	—	—	—	—	—	—	7
Baker	−17	−5	−24	−17	−14	−11	−5	3
Eugene	—	15	—	—	—	—	—	23
Medford	—	5	—	—	—	—	—	23
Portland	18	10	1	7	10	12	18	22
Roseburg	19	10	14	17	19	20	24	—
Pennsylvania								
Curwensville	—	—	—	—	—	—	—	0
Erie	−3	−5	−9	−5	−3	−2	2	6
Harrisburg	3	0	0	2	4	5	8	7
Philadelphia	6	0	1	4	6	7	11	—
Pittsburgh	−2	0	−9	−6	−3	−2	2	6
Reading	—	0	−2	1	3	4	8	9

TABLE 3–1 (continued)

| Station | Avg. Annual Min. Temp. | Design Temp. in Common Use | Probability Exists of Lower Daily Avg. Air Temp. Once in: | | | | | Design Temp. on TAC† 97½ Per Cent Basis |
			40 yr	20 yr	13 yr	10 yr	5 yr	
Scranton	—	−5	−8	−4	−2	−1	3	—
Sunbury	—	—	—	—	—	—	—	7
Rhode Island								
Block Island	—	0	3	5	7	8	10	—
Providence	1	0	−4	−1	1	2	5	—
South Carolina								
Charleston	22	15	17	20	22	23	27	26
Columbia	19	10	14	17	19	20	24	—
Greenville	—	10	—	—	—	—	—	—
South Dakota								
Huron	−26	−20	−27	−23	−21	−20	−17	—
Rapid City	−21	−20	−28	−24	−22	−20	−16	—
Tennessee								
Chattanooga	9	10	0	5	8	10	14	19
Knoxville	2	0	−3	2	5	7	12	—
Memphis	9	0	0	4	6	8	13	19
Nashville	5	0	−4	0	3	5	10	14
Texas								
Abilene	—	−5	0	5	7	9	14	20
Amarillo	0	−10	−10	−5	−2	0	5	11
Austin	—	20	—	—	—	—	—	—
Brownsville	29	30	—	—	—	—	—	—
Corpus Christi	—	20	16	20	23	24	29	—
Dallas	13	0	1	6	8	10	15	23
Del Rio	—	15	—	—	—	—	—	—
El Paso	16	10	15	18	20	21	25	26
Fort Worth	12	10	0	5	8	10	15	—
Galveston	—	20	16	20	23	24	29	—
Houston	22	20	13	17	19	21	25	33
Palestine	—	15	4	8	11	13	18	—
Port Arthur	—	20	—	—	—	—	—	—
San Antonio	21	20	12	16	19	20	25	32
Waco	—	—	—	—	—	—	—	26
Wink	—	—	—	—	—	—	—	23
Utah								
Milford	—	—	—	—	—	—	—	−2
Modena	−15	−15	—	—	—	—	—	—
Salt Lake City	−2	−10	−8	−3	−1	1	6	7
Vermont								
Burlington	−17	−10	−23	−19	−17	−15	−11	—
Virginia								
Cape Henry	—	10	13	16	17	18	21	—
Lynchburg	8	5	7	10	11	12	15	—
Norfolk	15	15	11	14	15	17	20	—
Richmond	10	15	6	9	11	12	16	15
Roanoke	—	—	—	—	—	—	—	21
Washington								
Ellensburg	—	—	—	—	—	—	—	1
North Head	24	20	—	—	—	—	—	—
Seattle	20	15	9	13	15	17	21	24
Spokane	−5	−15	−28	−20	−16	−13	−5	4

TABLE 3–I (continued)

Station	Avg. Annual Min. Temp.	Design Temp. in Common Use	Probability Exists of Lower Daily Avg. Air Temp. Once in:					Design Temp. on TAC† 97½ Per Cent Basis
			40 yr	20 yr	13 yr	10 yr	5 yr	
Tacoma	—	15	9	13	15	16	20	—
Tatoosh Island	—	15	12	16	18	20	25	—
Yakima	—	−5	—	—	—	—	—	—
West Virginia								
Elkins	−8	−10	−10	−7	−4	−3	1	—
Parkersburg	−1	−10	−7	−3	−1	1	5	—
Wisconsin								
Green Bay	−18	−20	−27	−23	−20	−18	−14	—
La Crosse	−21	−25	−27	−23	−20	−19	−14	−17
Madison	—	−15	−25	−21	−19	−17	−13	−8
Milwaukee	−12	−15	−24	−20	−17	−15	−10	−6
Wyoming								
Cheyenne	−18	−15	−26	−22	−19	−17	−12	−3
Lander	−12	−18	−39	−33	−30	−27	−21	—
Rock Springs	—	—	—	—	—	—	—	−7

of the same order of magnitude have been observed in many other cities. In Toronto the suburban minimum is often 15 F less than the urban minimum, and in Washington, D.C., a difference of 12 F is not uncommon. As a general approximation it is recommended that when minimum temperatures are used for design, the values obtained from airport records be applied to suburban locations but that 10 F be added to these values for structures near city centers. Similarly, when minimums are based on readings from city weather offices, they should be reduced by 10 F for suburban locations. Note, however, that this recommendation applies only to *minimum* temperatures as the microclimatological differences between urban and suburban daily mean temperatures are so much less (often of the order of 2 F) that they can be neglected. As stated in a footnote to Table 3–1, all second-column temperatures are based on city weather station data except where superscript "a" denotes use of data from an airport station.

DESIGN TEMPERATURES IN COMMON USE. The statistical analysis of climatological data and the probability basis of design temperature selection are both developments that have gained significant attention within the last decade. Prior to that time, design outside temperature was usually selected on an arbitrary basis and was often taken as from 10 F to 15 F above the lowest temperature ever recorded at a particular locality. The third column of Table 3–1 gives commonly used design temperatures as reported by engineers in various cities; these values are for urban structures. Comparison of the second and third columns will show that design temperatures in common use usually do not differ greatly from the average annual minimum temperature and in most (but not all) cases they are from 2 F to 5 F below the average annual minimum. In order to interpret the commonly used design temperatures in terms of design values of average daily temperature, it is first necessary to make a probability analysis of average daily temperatures; this is done in the next discussion.

PROBABILITY ANALYSIS OF AVERAGE DAILY TEMPERATURES. The fourth through eighth columns of Table 3–1 present the results of a statistical analysis carried out by Thom.[2] The analysis is based on use of a frequency curve derived from statistical distribution theory and using the minimum annual average daily temperatures for each city (mainly from downtown weather stations) over a 30-yr period ending in 1950. Thus column 4 gives minimum average daily temperatures which, on a probability basis, would be exceeded daily for a period of 40 yr. Statistically, one would therefore expect that use of the fourth column temperatures as the outside design temperature for a thermally heavy structure would mean that the heating system would fail to maintain t_i at the design value t_{id} once in 40 yr.

In order to relate a probability-selected design value of daily average temperatures with the design temperature in common use, Thom investigated various probabilities and selected that for a period of 13 yr as the most acceptable. This means that when the temperature given in the sixth column is subtracted from that in the third column and the difference is averaged for all cities in the table, the average will be found to be practically zero. Since the 13-yr probability temperature is based on a statistical analysis of weather data, whereas the commonly used design temperature is of uncertain and arbitrary origin, it follows that the 13-yr probability temperatures are the more likely to be correct in design cases where the outside design temperature is to be selected in terms of daily mean rather than minimum temperature. This would be the case for structures having a large thermal capacity. For buildings of very low thermal capacity the preferred design temperature would be the lower of the two temperatures in columns 3 and 6.

A comparison of temperatures based on 5-, 10-, 13-, 20-, and 40-yr probabilities (the fourth through eighth columns of Table 3–1) shows that the variation in temperature between a 5-yr probability and a 40-yr probability is very small for warm localities (5 F for Fresno, California, and 6 F for Key West, Florida) but large for cold localities (15 F for Keokuk, Iowa, and 26 F for Helena, Montana). This difference is not surprising and is consistent with the corresponding range of transmission loads. Thus, using the design temperature for a 13-yr probability and taking t_{id} as 70 F, the transmission load at Helena, Montana, would be almost three times, $(70 + 39)/(70 - 32)$, that at Fresno, California, whereas the difference in 5- and 40-yr probability temperatures at Helena as compared with those at Fresno is approximately five (26/5) times greater. This shows that the

[2] H. C. S. Thom, "Revised Winter Outside Design Temperatures," *ASHRAE Trans.*, Vol. 63, 1957, pp. 111–128.

percentage change in load due to a change in the selected probability temperature is nearly the same magnitude for the two locations.

The availability of temperatures for five different probabilities affords the designer a range sufficient to provide the needed flexibility in selecting a design temperature. If the 13-yr probability is taken as average, then a 10-yr or even a 5-yr value may be used in cases where the thermal characteristics and the transient performance of a heavy structure are well defined. For an ill-defined structure, or for one that is of thermally light construction, the designer may prefer to be more conservative and may select a temperature based on a 20-yr or even a 40-yr probability.

The probability values as determined for average daily temperatures do not necessarily apply to annual minimum temperatures, since the minimums may not occur on the same day as the lowest averages. Brisken investigated four cases (New York, N.Y., for 1950 and 1952; Charleston, South Carolina, for 1948; and Madison, Wisconsin, for 1951) and found that in these instances, the lowest daily average temperature and the lowest hourly temperature did occur on the same day. If this were regularly the case, it would follow that the five probabilities given for average daily temperature would be expected to apply closely to probabilities for lowest annual hourly temperature.

Similarly, Everetts[3] made a spot check on eight cities and found a close correlation between the probabilities of Table 3–1 and the percentage of January hours (times 10) that the hourly temperature was at or below the corresponding daily average temperature. For example, the 5-yr probability (20 per cent) for Atlanta, Georgia, shows a minimum daily average temperature of 17 F; in Atlanta during January approximately 2 per cent (20/10) of the hours show temperatures equal to or lower than 17 F. Everetts emphasizes that the spot checks which he made are not sufficient to permit generalization, but they do seem to be indicative of a trend. If the experimental data on January hourly temperature are lacking, it is recommended that the relationship indicated by Everetts' check be used as a basis of estimate.

DESIGN TEMPERATURES RECOMMENDED BY ASHRAE TECHNICAL ADVISORY COMMITTEE. The last column of Table 3–1 presents outside design temperatures, based almost entirely on data from airport weather stations, compiled from hourly temperature records for the months of December, January, February, and March. The basic data have been processed according to a recommendation of the ASHRAE Technical Advisory Committee (TAC) on weather conditions. The TAC recommendation is that design for outside winter temperature be selected at that value of outside temperature which is equaled or exceeded during $97\frac{1}{2}$ per cent of the total hours in the four-month period from December through March. Processing of data according to the TAC recommendation has not yet been completed for all the cities listed in Table 3–1; hence numerous gaps appear in the last column.

[3] Refer to discussion of the Thom paper on page 125 of the *ASHRAE Trans.*, Vol. 63, 1957.

There are 2904 hr in the four months used in the TAC formula; hence the actual outside temperature would, statistically, be expected to fall below the design value for some 72 hr during this four-month period. If these hours occurred as scattered minimums of diurnal temperature, there would be little hazard of failure of the heating system to maintain the design inside-air temperature t_{id}, but if a large fraction of the 72 hr were to occur as a cold period of extended duration, it is evident that a heating system sized according to the TAC recommendation would be inadequate.

Comparison of design temperature on the TAC hourly basis with those on the average daily probability basis (columns 4 through 8) shows that the TAC values are higher than the 5-yr probability values for 95 per cent (110 out of 116 cities) of the cities for which TAC design values are available. Of the six cities for which the TAC value was lower, four (Fresno, San Diego, Jacksonville, Phoenix) have 5-yr probability temperatures that are above freezing. In general the TAC values are from 2 F to 10 F higher than the 5-yr probability temperatures and are usually from 4 F to 22 F higher than the corresponding value of the design temperatures in common use (an exception is Winslow, Arizona, where the TAC value is 4 F *lower* than the commonly used design value).

From the above discussion it would appear that the TAC $97\frac{1}{2}$ per cent hourly recommendation results in a design temperature substantially higher (hence less conservative) than that which would be obtained from the probability basis or from design temperatures in common use. In order to provide closer agreement among the various bases for selection of design outside temperature, it would be helpful if columns in Table 3–1 could be provided for temperatures that are equaled or exceeded during 99 per cent and $99\frac{1}{2}$ per cent, respectively, of the hours during the period selected. Such data are not available but can be approximated from the column for $97\frac{1}{2}$ per cent. The recommended approximation is based on a paper by Thomas[4] in which he establishes values of design temperature for 15 Canadian cities on a $97\frac{1}{2}$ per cent and a 99 per cent basis. The Thomas results are for percentages of hours during one month, January, in contrast to the TAC use of four months, but a reasonable correlation can be expected. For cities having design temperatures on the $97\frac{1}{2}$ per cent basis which range from +11 F (Vancouver, B.C.) to −56 F (Dawson, Y.T.) the temperature reduction due to selection of a 99 per cent basis (below that for $97\frac{1}{2}$ per cent) varies from 1 F to 6 F (3 F for Vancouver and 6 F for Dawson), with an average of 3.6 F. Thomas states that for a $99\frac{1}{2}$ per cent basis, a further reduction of approximately 3 F could be expected. If one assumes applicability of the same criterion to cities in the United States, a reduction by 7 F in the TAC $97\frac{1}{2}$ per cent basis temperature, given in the last column of Table 3–1, should provide a new set of temperatures that would approximate those corresponding to a $99\frac{1}{2}$ per cent

[4] M. K. Thomas, "A Method for Determining Winter Design Temperatures," *ASHRAE Trans.*, Vol. 61, 1955, pp. 387–396.

basis. That is, subtracting 7 F from the last-column temperatures would give values that could be expected to be equaled or exceeded for all but 15 hr during the period from December 1 through March 31 of an average year.

In summary the TAC $97\frac{1}{2}$ per cent basis for design temperature averages 11 F warmer than the corresponding design temperature in common use. On a statistical basis the TAC value would probably lead to effective sizing of a heating system for an office building or for any other structure having a large thermal capacity; for such a structure, thermal storage would serve to provide sufficient time lag in load so that inside design temperature could be maintained even during moderately extensive periods (as up to 12 hr) in which the outside temperature remained below the design value. For a structure having low thermal capacity, the TAC $97\frac{1}{2}$ per cent basis would lead to underheating for some 70 hr during the winter months. If the low temperatures could be expected during the night hours and if occupancy conditions permitted a nighttime temperature setback, no disadvantage would occur, but if need existed for 24-hr maintenance of the inside design temperature, considerable discomfort could be expected. Thus, for structures of low thermal capacity, it is recommended that the TAC design temperature be reduced by 7 F.

3–8. Summary of Recommendations for Selection of Design Outside Temperature for Evaluation of Transmission Load. The purpose of selecting a design outside temperature for evaluation of transmission loads is to permit determination of the maximum transmission load that must be carried by the heating system. This load, plus that due to ventilation (see Art. 3–9), will determine the maximum sensible heat load on the system and will therefore fix the size of the heating plant. The basic significance of design outside temperature, therefore, is its relationship to first cost, rather than operating cost, of the heating system. Selection of an unduly conservative value of t_{od} will result in increased first cost and a resultant oversized plant. Depending on the method of control, such an overly large heating plant may also increase seasonal operating cost, since it will operate at a very low load factor and may in consequence have a low thermal efficiency.

In usual engineering practice, maximum transmission load is calculated from the steady-state equation (Eq. 3–9) even though transient and periodic variation in outside temperature makes it highly improbable that steady-state conditions actually exist at the time of maximum load. When the structure possesses very little thermal capacity, its approach to steady state is quite close, and in this case the design outside temperature should be the actual minimum t_o at which the inside t_{id} is to be maintained. The recommended t_{od} for thermally light structures (such as frame houses) is the 13-yr probability temperature given in the sixth column of Table 3–1 or the design temperature in common use (third column), whichever is the smaller.

For structures having high thermal capacity, the recommended design outside temperature is the 20-yr probability value (given in the fifth column) for very cold climates (below zero) or the 10-yr probability value for warm climates (above 32 F). For a structure of high thermal capacity in which t_{id} need not be maintained between midnight and 5 A.M., the designer may prefer to use either the TAC $97\frac{1}{2}$ per cent basis temperature or, more conservatively, the TAC values reduced by 7 F to approximate a $99\frac{1}{2}$ per cent basis.

The above recommendations are necessarily rather general. In every case the decision with respect to selection must be made by the designer and tempered with judgment plus local experience. For large structures in which the first cost of the heating system is a major item, the designer may prefer to base his selection of design outside temperature on a transient analysis of the particular structure rather than on the pseudo–steady-state procedure.

3–9. Selection of Design Outside Temperature for Evaluation of Ventilation Load.

Outside air is continuously introduced into all structures, owing either to infiltration or to mechanical ventilation. From a mass balance on the enclosure it is evident that room air must exit from the structure at a weight rate equal to that at which outside air is introduced. Thus the energy needed to raise the temperature of ventilation air from the actual outside value to the design inside-air temperature will constitute a sensible heat load on the heating system which will superimpose on the transmission load. Unlike the transmission load, however, the ventilation load will be directly and instantly related to the actual outside air temperature. This will be true regardless of whether the structure is large or small, regardless of whether its thermal capacity is high or low.

The importance of design outside-air temperature for use in evaluating ventilation heat loss depends on the ratio of sensible ventilation load to transmission load. When this ratio is small, the significance of the ventilation fraction is slight and the need for precision is not great. For structures with a high ventilation rate, the opposite situation holds and the selection of an accurate t_{od} for ventilation will be of more thermal importance than accurate selection of a t_{od} for transmission.

Further, the thermal capacity of the structure influences the rate at which inside air temperature will change if the heating-plant capacity is incapable of handling the instantaneous ventilation load. Thus a sudden drop in outside air temperature would mean that entering colder outside air would mix with room air (except where separate facilities, such as mechanical ventilation, provide for tempering the outside air) and tend to reduce room air temperature. If the structure has high thermal resistance and large thermal capacity, the inside surfaces would be at approximately the design inside-air temperature, and since inside air temperature tends to fall below t_{id}, there will be a sustained reverse heat flow from walls back into room air; this "thermal flywheel" effect would delay the drop in t_i. For a structure of low thermal resistance and small thermal capacity, the reverse flow would not start until after marked depression of t_i, and it would then be of short duration. Thus, although neither thermal resistance nor thermal capacity of the structure affects the value of instantaneous ventilation load, each of these structural characteristics influences the extent to which such load affects t_{id} and the rate at which the t_i changes.

Opinion differs on selection of t_{od} for ventilation load, but the value should approximate the instantaneous minimum outside temperature that is likely to occur during a period in which transmission load is at its maximum. This would mean that t_{od} for ventilation load would approximate t_{od} for transmission load in localities where diurnal change is small and where seasonal gradient is low. In localities where the difference between daily minimum and daily mean temperature is large, the minimum value should be used in calculating ventilation load. As a general recommendation, t_{od} for ventilation can be conservatively taken as the lower of the temperatures in the second and third columns of Table 3–1. For structures of large thermal capacity, the ventilation t_{od} can safely be raised to a value halfway between the t_{od} for transmission load and the lower of the temperatures in the second and third columns.

PROBLEMS

3–1. An 18-in. concrete wall is at a uniform temperature of 0 F. If one surface of the wall is raised to 75 F, while the other surface remains at 0 F, determine (a) the rate of steady-state heat transmission, per unit area, for the new condition and (b) the quantity of heat that would go into storage in unit area of the wall during the transient interval. [$\rho = 140$ lb/cu ft; $k = 1$ Btu/(hr)(sq ft)(°F/ft); $c = 0.215$ Btu/(lb)(°F).]

3–2. Calculate, by the Ghai and Sundaram method, the design outside-air temperature for a 6 in. thick concrete wall (all other conditions being the same as in Example 3–1) and compare the results with those of Example 3–1.

3–3. Repeat problem 3–2 for a 36 in. concrete wall and compare the results with those from Example 3–1 and problem 3–2.

3–4. In terms of operating performance, would you expect the heating system in the structure with 6 in. walls (problem 3–2) to have a greater or lesser thermal efficiency than in the structure with 36 in. walls (problem 3–3)?

3–5. Select an design outside-air temperature for calculating transmission load of an uninsulated Quonset hut located in the city of Little Rock, Arkansas.

3–6. If the Quonset hut of problem 3–5 were located on the outskirts of the city, what value of t_{od} should then be used in calculating transmission losses?

3–7. An uninsulated, thermally "light" structure is to be mechanically ventilated with untempered outside air. It is located near the civic center of Fort Smith, Arkansas. Select the design outside-air temperature for (a) evaluation of transmission load, (b) evaluation of ventilation load.

3–8. A heavy monumental-type structure is to be erected in Eureka, California. (a) Select an design outside-air temperature for calculating transmission load. (b) Repeat for an identical structure located in Flagstaff, Arizona.

Part II

EVALUATION OF LOAD

4

FUNDAMENTALS OF HEAT
TRANSMISSION

The two major interests of the heating engineer in thermal energy are with respect to its storage and to its transfer. By definition, heat is a form of energy in *transition* (another form being shaft work); hence, in the thermodynamic sense, heat is *not* energy in storage. This means, in effect, that a hot object does not possess heat (it does, however, possess stored internal energy), but since the person who touches it will be burned by the energy that leaves as heat, it follows that the distinction between heat and internal energy is usually of only academic importance. Following common usage, the phrase "heat in storage" will be used in subsequent discussions in place of the more exact statement "internal energy in storage."

The relatively huge amounts of energy with which the heating engineer deals are often not recognized as such. For example, to heat 1 gal of water (8.345 lb) from 32 F to the boiling point (212 F) requires 8.345(212 − 32), or 1502 Btu, which is equal to (778)(1502) or 1,168,556 ft-lb. This much energy would suffice to raise a 10-ton weight to a height of (1,168,556)/(10)(2000), or 58 ft above the ground. The hourly heat loss from a residence of moderate size (say, 100,000 Btu) would be sufficient to raise that residence (if it is assumed to weigh 100 tons) approximately 400 ft straight up in the air. Fortunately there is no likelihood that the heat supplied to make up residential losses will exert itself to elevate the residence, but the example is offered as a means of emphasizing the order of magnitude of the energy quantities with which the heating engineer ordinarily deals.

4–1. Thermal Units. Since 778 ft-lb equal 1 Btu, and since 550 ft-lb/sec are defined as 1 hp, it is evident that the usual unit of heat loss, Btu/hr, is equivalent to 1/2545 hp. That is, if the heat loss from a structure is known to be 2545 Btu/hr, this could with equal accuracy be expressed as 1 hp, and the loss through unit area of wall or window could be expressed in fractional horsepower. In some European countries heat losses are actually expressed as either horsepower or as watts, but convention in the United States is to restrict the use of such power units to electrical or to mechanical or to electrical systems. Note, however, that the difference among electrical, mechanical, and thermal units is merely a matter of definition and that *any* unit for energy rate can be correctly used in place of Btu per hour.

SPECIFIC HEAT. The quantity of heat that enters storage in unit weight of any non-expanding substance as it undergoes 1 F temperature rise is defined as the *specific heat c* (strictly, the specific heat at constant volume) of that substance. The reciprocal of specific heat is therefore equal to the temperature rise of 1 lb of material as a consequence of the addition of 1 Btu of energy as heat. It is interesting to note that 1 lb of lead gains more than 30 F through addition of 1 Btu, whereas the temperature gain of a pound of water is only 1 F for the same heat addition. This brings out the point that temperature is not a trustworthy indication of heat in storage; it is instead indicative of the *intensity* of the internal energy contained within the hot object.

VOLUMETRIC SPECIFIC HEAT. Specific heat alone is not an adequate criterion of heat-carrying capacity because it is expressed on a weight basis and hence gives no indication of the quantity of heat that can be contained within structural sections of the same size (as two walls of equal thickness). For this purpose the *volumetric specific heat* is often used. This term (previously defined in Art. 3–2) is numerically equal to the product of the specific heat multiplied by the density ρ of the material in pounds per cubic foot. The resultant property, ρ_c, is thus equal to the number of Btu needed to raise 1 cu ft of material through a 1 F temperature rise.

The great practical importance of volumetric specific heat appears both in selection of a working substance (such as hot water, steam, or warm air) and in determination of the heat-up characteristics of a particular structure. To use an extreme example, consider two otherwise identical thin-walled warehouses that contain the same total volume of stored material, one warehouse containing material having a volumetric specific heat four times as great as that stored in the other. Under this circumstance the amount of heat that would have to go into storage to raise the temperature in one warehouse would be four times greater than that needed to achieve an equal temperature rise in the other.

From another standpoint, consider two warehouses that have the same kind and amount of material in storage but which have very thick walls and are made from materials having greatly different volumetric specific heats. For the same reasons as in the preceding example, the time required to raise the temperature in one (all other conditions being the same) would be much greater than for the other, since a much larger quantity of heat would have to go into storage in the walls of the structure with the higher volumetric specific heat in order to raise them to the new temperature level. The entire wall would not, of course, be raised to the inside air temperature, but the mean wall temperature would increase as the inside air temperature increased. Thus volumetric specific heat is one of the most important properties for use in determining the ease with which the temperature within a structure can be either varied or (for variable outside temperature) held constant. Volumetric specific heat has no influence on operation at design conditions because the system is then in equilibrium and heat is flowing through the walls under steady-state conditions; hence it is not going either into or out of storage in the structure. For any type of transient operation, however, whether due to heat-up, variable load, or change in strength of internal sources, the performance analysis will be greatly influenced by the volumetric specific heat.

4–2. The Basic Storage Equation.   The fundamental equation applicable to heat storage is

$$Q_{in} = wc(t_h - t_c) \tag{4-1}$$

where $\quad Q_{in}$ = heat entering storage, °F.

$\qquad\qquad w$ = weight of homogeneous material, lb.

$\qquad\qquad c$ = specific heat, Btu/(lb)(°F).

$\qquad t_h - t_c$ = mean change in temperature, °F.

Eq. 4–1 gives no information concerning the *rate* of heat transfer or the time required to achieve the stated temperature rise.

The term Q of Eq. 4–1 reappears frequently in performance analyses because it represents a shifting of energy with changing load. This can be visualized by analogy with a hydraulic system: Consider a bucket in which a hole has been drilled in or near the bottom. When the level of water in the bucket is low, the rate of leakage will be low; as the level in the bucket is increased, the hydrostatic head will increase and flow will occur at an ever greater rate. For such a system it is evident that the rate of leakage (at fixed level) will determine the rate at which water must be supplied, but the diameter of the bucket will determine how much water must be added or removed in order to bring about a change in level. In such a bucket there would be a given quantity of water in storage within the bucket, and irrespective of the rate of loss (that is, of the size of hole through which leakage is occurring), the quantity in storage would be constant as long as the level did not change.

The above example is analogous to the problem of heating a house. In the latter case, however, the thermal "level" drops outside rather than rising inside, and as it drops, the quantity of heat contained within the structure of the house (stored there) decreases. Thus, for fixed inside-air temperature, the *rate* of heat input from the heating system will increase with decreasing temperature, but the *quantity* of heat in storage will decrease. This effect is helpful because it means that a sudden or sharp increase in load will not have to be carried entirely by the heating system but will be partially met by a discharge of heat from storage in the walls and furnishings of the structure. The contrary condition occurs when the load decreases: Demand on the heating system to maintain *rate* of loss goes down, but during the transient interval the output of the heating system will not decrease proportionately because it will have to supply energy for storage in the structure. Curiously, therefore, the reservoir of heat energy stored in the structure is greatest at a time of minimum heating load.

4–3. Availability of Thermal Energy. All objects at a temperature greater than absolute zero (-460 F) possess some heat, but the usefulness or availability of that energy depends on the temperature of the object. All thermal processes (by the second law of thermodynamics) occur in a direction of decreasing temperature, and the rate at which the process proceeds increases with the temperature difference. Thus a small amount of energy at a high temperature is far more useful to the engineer than a much larger quantity at a lower temperature level. If a pound of coal were to undergo oxidation at room temperature, the products would be of no value to the heating engineer, whereas when such oxidation occurs at furnace temperature, the products of combustion provide energy that is *available* for heating air or water or for producing steam. The availability concept can be readily visualized in terms of another hydraulic analogy: A small quantity of water deposited by rainfall on a mountain top possesses a high degree of availability based on its elevation (as evidenced by the use of hydroelectric plants), whereas a very large body of water in the sea cannot, without expenditure of pump work, be effectively made use of. In the hydraulic case all spontaneous processes occur from high elevation to low elevation; in the thermal case all spontaneous processes occur from high "thermal elevation" to lower thermal elevation. Temperature can thus be said to be indicative of "thermal elevation."

4–4. The Three Mechanisms of Heat Transmission. The mechanisms of heat transmission have their counterparts in various other fields of engineering. Continuing with the hydraulic analogy, the identifying characteristics of each of the three mechanisms can be readily visualized. Thus, if a fire were to occur in one part of a building and a group of men and a hydrant were available in another part of the building, the men could set about putting the fire out by any of three methods:

1. By obtaining a group of buckets, taking up fixed positions in a line between the hydrant and the fire, and passing buckets of water from hand to hand. In this method the *men* remain in given positions, but the *water* is moved from one man to another until it is finally discharged onto the fire. This method of transporting water corresponds very closely with *conduction* as a means of transporting heat. In conduction, heat flows through a solid from hot side to cold by (in effect) being "passed" from molecule to molecule, the individual molecules retaining fixed positions just as do the men on the fire line. The heat is passed from the high-temperature source (the thermal "hydrant") to the low-temperature receiver. The important point about conduction is that there is no movement of mass; the energy flows, but the

molecules of copper, or iron, or wood through which it flows remain fixed just as do the men and just as would a conduit through which any real fluid could be transported.

2. Instead of taking up fixed positions, the fire-fighting men could increase their speed and effectiveness by forming a continuous moving chain, each man keeping one bucket and carrying water from the hydrant to the fire. This system is analogous to heat transfer by *convection*, since in convection the energy is literally carried by individual molecules of air, of water, or of some other fluid; the transfer of mass is accompanied by a transfer of heat. Thus, air passing through a convector picks up its molecular load of heat, carries it across the room, and gives it up in passing over the colder exterior room surfaces; the "unloaded" or cooler air molecule now returns, through the action of thermal air currents, to pick up another load of energy and to repeat the cycle. Of interest in terms of convective transfer are the speed and the load-carrying capacity of the molecules. In fire fighting, the rate at which water is delivered to the fire will depend on both the size of the bucket that a man can carry and on how fast he can move with it. In convection, heat transfer will depend on the quantity of heat that a molecule can carry and on the velocity with which the molecule moves.

3. If the first two methods of fire fighting are not successful, it is probable that the fire department will arrive, connect a hose and nozzle to the hydrant, and transfer the water directly to the fire, without benefit of either bucket or of man. This process is analogous to the third mechanism of heat transfer, which is *radiation*. Like a stream of water passing through the air, thermal radiation streams from the source and goes to the receiver without need of any molecular assistance. Radiation is energy, not matter, and can travel just as easily (in fact more easily) through a vacuum as it can through air or through any other medium. The quantity and force of energy in a radiant stream depends on the thermal "pressure" at the source, just as the quantity and force of a stream of water depends on the pressure at the hydrant. Radiation travels at the speed of light, 186,000 mps, but like light it is subject to the severe disadvantage of traveling always in a straight line. Thus radiation from a point source can never surround an occupant (in the way that warm air surrounds him) but will instead impinge on only those surfaces of the occupant that are in the direct path of the radiant stream.

Each of the three above-described mechanisms of heat transfer plays a part in the performance of every heating system. The relative importance of the mechanisms will vary with the type of system, but there is no method of heating which does not involve all three methods of transfer to some extent. The transfer of energy from a hot body to a cold body can occur by any one of the mechanisms of conduction, convection, and radiation. Even though the three phenomena are strikingly different, facility in computation is best realized by expressing the transfer coefficients for radiation and convection in a form suitable for insertion in the fundamental conduction equation.

There is need for some such unified procedure, since most practical problems involve transfer by at least two mechanisms.

A general classification of heat-transfer problems can be established with respect to time as a variable. The first group is that in which conditions do not change with time; problems of this type occur in systems that are in equilibrium and are generally referred to as *steady-state heat-transfer systems*. A second group is that in which the heat-transfer rate varies with time from an original boundary value toward some new boundary value. Problems of this type frequently occur in both heating and air-conditioning design; typical examples are an insulated hot water pipe during the interval between starting the heating system and reaching equilibrium, or the problem of establishing heating and cooling curves for an intermittently heated structure. Such problems come under the heading of *transient heat flow* and require a more complex treatment than that needed for steady-state problems. The third group, *periodic heat transfer*, covers the type of problem resulting from the load variation due to diurnal changes in the outside temperature or wind velocity. A satisfactory method of analysis for such cases is needed to determine the maximum heating load on a structure and the time at which it will occur.

This chapter takes up the problems that come under the first group in the above classification. Steady-state equations are presented and methods developed for expressing all three mechanisms of heat transfer in terms of the basic conduction equation. Problems of transient and periodic heat transfer are discussed in Chapters 11 and 12.

4–5. Conduction. The mechanism of heat transfer by conduction has already been defined as limited to transfer from molecule to molecule where no displacement of the molecules takes place. In heating practice, conduction occurs through walls, floor, and ceiling of any structure, and through the metal walls of transfer surfaces such as heat exchangers. An equation for determining rate of conductive heat transfer can be established by analogy with a fluid flow system, as given in the subsequent paragraph.

Common experience tells us that the rate of fluid flow through a given pipe increases with the cross-sectional area of the pipe, increases with the difference in elevation of the two ends, and decreases as the length of pipe becomes greater. For a given fluid flow it follows that

$$\text{Flow rate} = \phi\left[\frac{A}{x}\,(z_2 - z_1)\right]$$

where A = cross-section area, sq ft.
x = length of pipe, ft.
$z_2 - z_1$ = difference in elevation, ft.

If the above functional relationship were to be generalized to permit its application to more than one fluid, it would have to include one additional term that could take account of the viscous characteristic of the fluid; thus, all other conditions being the same, alcohol would flow through a pipe at a much greater flow rate than would molasses. The revised form of the equation would be

$$\text{Flow rate} = \phi \left[\frac{Ak}{x} (z_2 - z_1) \right]$$

where the new term k is a fluid property that increases as the viscosity of the fluid decreases.

An equation for the conductive transfer of heat is identical in form to the above flow equation but differs in that the k term now refers to a property of the material through which the heat is flowing rather than to a property of the fluid itself. For conduction through a plane wall under equilibrium (*steady state*) conditions (no change of flow rate with time), the conduction equation is

$$q = \frac{kA}{x} (t_h - t_c) \tag{4–2}$$

which in differential form becomes the basic Fourier equation,

$$\frac{dQ}{d\theta} = q = -kA \frac{dt}{dx} \tag{4–3}$$

where $dQ =$ quantity of heat transferred, Btu, during the time interval $d\theta$.
      $d\theta =$ time interval, hr.
      $q =$ instantaneous rate of heat transfer, Btu/hr.
      $k =$ thermal conductivity, Btu/(hr)(sq ft)(°F/ft), usually a function of temperature.
      $A =$ area normal to the path, sq ft; depending on the type of system, the area may be a function of path length.
      $dt =$ change in temperature along path length dx, °F.
      $x =$ length of path, ft.
      $t_h =$ temperature of the hot surface, °F.
      $t_c =$ temperature of the cold surface, °F.

The minus sign on the right-hand side of Eq. 4–3 indicates that the temperature is decreasing in the direction in which the heat is flowing (increase in x is associated with decrease in t).

EXAMPLE 4–1. A granite wall under conditions of steady-state heat loss is found to have inside and outside surface temperatures of 68 F and 18 F, respectively, at a time when the rate of heat transmission is measured at 39 Btu/(hr)(sq ft). Thermal conductivity of the granite is 1.17 Btu/(hr)(sq ft)(°F/ft). Determine the wall thickness.

Solution: Utilizing Eq. 4–2,

$$q = 39 = \frac{(1.17)(1)}{x} (68 - 18) = \frac{58.5}{x}$$

giving

$$x = 1.5 \text{ ft}, \quad \text{or 18 in.}$$

THERMAL CONDUCTIVITY. Referring to Eq. 4–2, if heat transfer were to occur unidirectionally through 2 sides of a 1-ft cube of material which was perfectly insulated on the other four sides, the terms A and x would both be numerically equal to unity. If the temperatures of the two remaining opposite faces of the cube were maintained 1 F apart, the term $(t_h - t_c)$ would likewise be unity, and the equation would reduce to the form $q = k$. This shows that the term k, defined as thermal conductivity, is numerically equal to the quantity of heat that would be transferred by conduction in 1 hr through a 1-ft insulated cube if opposite faces were kept at a temperature difference of 1 deg. In symbol form,

$$k = \text{Btu}/(\text{hr})(\text{sq ft})(°\text{F/ft})$$

The dimensions of k are sometimes given as $\text{Btu}/(\text{hr})(\text{ft})(°\text{F})$; this form is dimensionally correct but has the disadvantage of obscuring the physical picture of k as heat transfer per unit time per unit area per unit temperature gradient. As a matter of convenience the units of k are sometimes changed to permit expression of the gradient in $°\text{F/in.}$ instead of $°\text{F/ft}$, since for most of the cases that occur in heating, the length of path (such as through a floor) is a matter of inches rather than feet. To distinguish between these two values of the thermal conductivity, the latter, expressed in inches, will always be identified by use of a prime, k'. When this value of conductivity is used in the conduction equation, it is evident that the length x must be expressed in inches rather than feet.

Variation in thermal conductivity among different materials is very great. Hence it is vitally important that the engineer check the value of k for a particular material rather than estimate it. To show how important such variation can be, an otherwise ridiculous example is presented in Example 4–2.

EXAMPLE 4–2. Assume that a certain Maharajah has generous supplies of silver and asks that his palace walls be made of this metal but that they be sufficiently thick to reduce heat losses to an amount equal to that which would occur if the walls were made of 6 in. of cork. How thick would the thermally equivalent walls have to be?

Solution: The thermal conductivity of granulated cork is approximately (accurately at 32 F) 0.0208 $\text{Btu}/(\text{hr})(\text{sq ft})(°\text{F/ft})$, whereas the value of k for silver (at 64 F) is 243.0 $\text{Btu}/(\text{hr})(\text{sq ft})(°\text{F/ft})$. Neglecting the changes of k with temperature, the silver conducts heat almost 12,000 times more rapidly than does cork; hence the necessary wall thickness of the Maharajah's sterling palace would be in excess of 1 mile. Although ridiculous in itself, the example emphasizes that literally enormous errors can be made if thermal conductivities are incorrectly determined or estimated.

Table 4–1 gives representative values of the thermal conductivity for a few typical substances. In the temperature range (0 F to 70 F) that is important in heating-system design, the variation of thermal conductivity as a function of temperature can usually be neglected; when this is not the case, the variation of k with t can be taken into account either by expressing k as a function of t in Eq. 4–3 or (where the functional relationship is linear) using in Eq. 4–2 the arithmetical average of the k values at t_h and t_c.

TABLE 4–I
Selected Values* of k, Btu/(hr)(sq ft)(°F/ft)

Water, as steam at 212 F	0.0126
Air, dry, at 1 atm, and 64 F	0.0147
Cork, granulated, grains $\frac{1}{32}$ to $\frac{1}{8}$ in., density 10.05 lb/cu ft, dry, at 32 F	0.0208
Glass wool, fibers 0.0003 to 0.0006 in. in diam., density 1.5 lb/cu ft	0.0225
Cork, ground and made into board with asphalt binder, at 32 F	0.0292
Magnesia, 85%, and asbestos, density 13.5, 50 F to 1100 F, average	0.0475
Wood, yellow pine, 16% moisture, across grain	0.0831
Hydrogen, dry at 1 atm, and at 64 F	0.1050
Plaster, gypsum	0.275
Water, at 64 F, liquid	0.336
Brick, common	0.416
Glass, ordinary window, soda base	0.433
Concrete, solid, with ordinary stone aggregate, average	1.00
Granite, average	1.17
Aluminum, at 64 F	83.0
Copper, at 64 F	225.0
Silver, at 64 F	243.0

* Various sources.

EXAMPLE 4–3. The thermal conductivity of pulverized cork ($\rho = 10$ lb/cu ft) varies from 0.021 Btu/(hr)(sq ft)(°F/ft) at 32 F to 0.026 Btu/(hr)(sq ft)(°F/ft) at 100 F. Assuming that k varies linearly with t, (a) establish the equation relating k and t for pulverized cork and (b) check the applicability of an arithmetical average of $k_{32\ F}$ and $k_{212\ F}$ for use in Eq. 4–2 when $t_h = 212$ F and $t_c = 32$ F.

Solution: (a) An equation expressing linear variation between k and t would be of the form

$$k = k_0(1 + at)$$

where k_0 is the thermal conductivity at any arbitrarily selected reference temperature, usually 0 F. Then, substituting the known data for pulverized cork at the two temperatures,

$$0.021 = k_0(1 + 32a)$$

and

$$0.026 = k_0(1 + 100a)$$

Solving each of the above equations for k_0 and equating the result gives

$$\frac{0.021}{1 + 32a} = \frac{0.026}{1 + 100a}$$

for which a is equal to 0.00394; hence

$$k_0 = \frac{0.026}{1 + 0.394} = 0.01865 \doteq 0.019$$

The equation for thermal conductivity for pulverized cork is therefore

$$k = 0.019(1 + 0.0039t)$$

(b) Substituting the linear k versus t equation into Eq. 4–3,

$$q = -[k_0(1 + at)](A)\frac{dt}{dx}$$

giving

$$\frac{q}{A}\int_0^x dx = -k_0\int_{t_h}^{t_c}(1 + at)dt$$

which integrates to

$$\frac{q}{A}x = +k_0\left[(t_h - t_c) + \frac{a}{2}(t_h^2 - t_c^2)\right]$$

$$= k_0\left[1 + (a)\frac{t_h + t_c}{2}\right](t_h - t_c)$$

where k_0 times the bracketed term is equal to the arithmetical average of k_{t_h} and k_{t_c}.

CONDUCTANCE AND RESISTANCE. A difficulty in application of Eq. 4–2 arises when the wall through which heat is flowing is not homogeneous. Thus, hollow tile or concrete with large rocks in it will not have a uniform conductivity. To overcome this difficulty and for convenience in many other applications (as for lath and plaster, or wood framing), it is frequently desirable to group the k and x terms and define k/x as the thermal conductance C for the material, or group of materials, in question. The units of conductance are Btu per unit time per unit area per unit temperature difference; thus

$$C = \frac{k}{x} \quad \text{Btu/(hr)(sq ft)(°F)}$$

For a uniform material, such as Norway pine, the thermal conductivity is used in calculating conductive transfer, whereas for a non-uniform material, such as a cored concrete block, the conductance is used. Thus Eq. 4–2 takes the alternative form

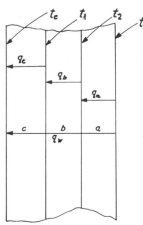

$$q = \frac{kA}{x}(t_h - t_c) = CA(t_h - t_c) \quad (4\text{–}4)$$

The reciprocal of conductance, $1/C$ or x/k, is defined as thermal resistance r. The resistance concept is useful in providing a close parallel between heat flow and flow of electricity. In an electric circuit, doubling the resistance at fixed voltage will halve the current, whereas in a thermal circuit, doubling the resistance at fixed temperature difference will halve the rate of heat transfer. Written in terms of thermal resistance, Eq. 4–2 generalizes to the form

Fig. 4–1. Heat transfer through series system.

$$q = \frac{kA}{x}(t_h - t_c) = CA(t_h - t_c) = \frac{A}{r}(t_h - t_c)$$

$$(4\text{–}5)$$

SERIES TRANSFER. If heat transfer by conduction occurs at steady state through a plane wall made up of a number of different homogeneous sections that are in direct contact with one another and in series (see Fig. 4–1), the transfer rates for each of the sections (from Eq. 4–5) would be

$$q_a = \frac{k_a A_a}{x_a} (t_h - t_2) = C_a A_a (t_h - t_2)$$

$$q_b = \frac{k_b A_b}{x_b} (t_2 - t_1) = C_b A_b (t_2 - t_1)$$

$$q_c = \frac{k_c A_c}{x_c} (t_1 - t_c) = C_c A_c (t_1 - t_c)$$

But the three values of q obtained from the above equations must be the same, since otherwise heat would be entering or leaving storage in the wall, and hence the assumed condition of steady state could not exist.

However, no one of the above equations can be solved directly because each includes at least one unknown interface temperature. What is needed is a single equation giving the rate of heat transfer in terms of the surface-to-surface temperature difference, $t_h - t_c$, and a surface-to-surface conductance, C_w. Assuming the existence of such an equation, it is then possible to write

$$q_w = C_w A (t_h - t_c) \tag{4–6}$$

But

$$q_w = q_a = q_b = q_c \tag{4–7}$$

so

$$C_w A (t_h - t_c) = C_a A (t_h - t_2) \tag{4–8}$$

$$C_w A (t_h - t_c) = C_b A (t_2 - t_1) \tag{4–9}$$

$$C_w A (t_h - t_c) = C_c A (t_1 - t_c) \tag{4–10}$$

Solving Eqs. 4–8, 4–9, and 4–10 for the unknown temperature difference in the right-hand side of each gives

$$t_h - t_2 = \frac{C_w}{C_a} (t_h - t_c) \tag{4–11}$$

$$t_2 - t_1 = \frac{C_w}{C_b} (t_h - t_c) \tag{4–12}$$

$$t_1 - t_c = \frac{C_w}{C_c} (t_h - t_c) \tag{4–13}$$

Adding these three equations eliminates the unknown interface temperatures t_2 and t_1 and gives

$$t_h - t_c = \left(\frac{C_w}{C_a} + \frac{C_w}{C_b} + \frac{C_w}{C_c} \right) (t_h - t_c)$$

or

$$1 = C_w \left(\frac{1}{C_a} + \frac{1}{C_b} + \frac{1}{C_c} \right)$$

from which

$$C_w = \frac{1}{(1/C_a) + (1/C_b) + (1/C_c)} \qquad (4\text{--}14)$$

or

$$C_w = \frac{1}{r_a + r_b + r_c} = \frac{1}{r_w} \qquad (4\text{--}15)$$

where r_w = the surface-to-surface thermal resistance.
= the sum of the individual resistances in series.
= $1/C_w$.

By analogy with Eqs. 4–14 and 4–15, the values of C_w and r_w can be readily obtained for a plane wall made up of any number of sections in series.

Substituting for C_w in Eq. 4–6 gives the general equation for series conduction through a plane wall:

$$q_w = \frac{1}{(1/C_a) + (1/C_b) + (1/C_c) + \cdots + (1/C_n)} A(t_h - t_c) \qquad (4\text{--}16)$$

$$= C_w A(t_h - t_c) = \frac{1}{r_w} A(t_h - t_c) \qquad (4\text{--}17)$$

EXAMPLE 4–4. A 6-in. wall is made of a lightweight aggregate concrete having density of 120 lb/cu ft and thermal conductivity of 5.2 Btu/(hr)(sq ft)(°F/ft). (a) Determine the outside surface temperature if the inside surface temperature is 70 F when the rate of heat loss is 312 Btu/(hr)(sq ft). (b) A second wall is identical in construction to the first but is insulated on the inside with a material having a k of 0.25 Btu/(hr)(sq ft)(°F/ft). With inside surface temperature at 70 F, this wall has an outside surface temperature of 5 F when the rate of heat loss is 140 Btu/(hr)(sq ft). Calculate the thickness of the insulating layer.

Solution: (a) By Eq. 4–2,

$$q = \frac{kA}{x} (t_h - t_c) = 312 = \frac{5.2}{0.5} (70 - t_c)$$

giving

$$t_c = 40 \text{ F}$$

(b) By Eq. 4–16, with x_i as the thickness of insulation,

$$q_w = \frac{1}{(1/C_i) + (1/C_c)} A(t_h - t_c) = 140 = \frac{1}{(x_i/0.25) + (0.5/5.2)} (70 - 5)$$

giving

$$x_i = 0.092 \text{ ft,} \quad \text{or 1.1 in.}$$

CONDUCTION THROUGH NON-PLANE WALLS. The discussion thus far has been concerned with heat transfer through plane walls in which the cross-section normal to flow, A, does not change. When heat flows through a non-plane wall, such as through a pipe, the cross-sectional area will vary as a function of path length. For bare pipes and tubes the value of A will increase with increasing diameter, but for average diameters and wall thicknesses the influence of changing area is usually so small that it can be neglected or can be taken into account by using the arithmetical average of inside and outside area. The arithmetical average is accurate to better than 96 per cent for any case in which the outside diameter is less than twice as great as the inside diameter; thus it is valid for all usual bare piping except capillary tubes.

TABLE 4–2

Natural Logarithm of Ratios for Use in
Calculating Logarithmic Mean Average*

A_2/A_1	$\log_e (A_2/A_1)$
1.25†	0.22314
1.50†	0.40547
1.75†	0.55962
2.00†	0.69315
2.50	0.91629
3.00	1.09861
3.50	1.25276
4.00	1.38629
4.50	1.50408
5.00	1.60944
5.50	1.70475
6.00	1.79176
6.50	1.87180
7.00	1.94591
7.50	2.01490
8.00	2.07944
8.50	2.14007
9.00	2.19722
9.50	2.25129
10.00	2.30259

* Although values indicated are in terms of area, it is evident that tabular values can be used for obtaining the logarithmic mean average of any property, such as temperature difference, radius, and diameter.

† For ratio values less than 2, the maximum error due to use of the arithmetical average in place of the logarithmic mean average is less than 4 per cent.

When insulation is added to a pipe or tube, the outside diameter of the insulation may be substantially greater than twice the inside diameter, and in this case the arithmetical average cannot be used with accuracy. The mean area, A_m, for use in such cases can be shown to be a logarithmic average of the inside and outside values:

$$\text{Logarithmic mean area} = \frac{(A_o - A_i)}{\log_e (A_o/A_i)} \qquad (4\text{–}18)$$

Table 4–2 gives values of $\log_e (A_o/A_i)$ as a function of the simple ratio of areas. This table can, of course, be used to find the value of the log of any ratio, whether it be area, diameter, temperature difference or any other property for which a logarithmic average is to be evaluated. In using the equation for logarithmic average, note that the numerator is the difference of areas, in contrast to the sum of areas that would be used in calculating an arithmetical average.

For systems in which the area varies as the square of the path length (as in radial heat transfer out through a sphere), the mean area can be shown to be equal to the square root of the product of the larger and smaller area:

$$A_m = (A_1 A_2)^{1/2} \qquad (4\text{--}19)$$

For series systems in which the area varies among the different sections through which conduction is occurring (as with an insulated pipe), Eqs. 4–16 and 4–17 become

$$q_w = \frac{1}{(1/C_a A_a) + (1/C_b A_b) + (1/C_c A_c) + \cdots + (1/C_n A_n)} (t_h - t_c) \qquad (4\text{--}20)$$

$$= \frac{1}{(1/C_a') + (1/C_b') + (1/C_c') + \cdots + (1/C_n')} (t_h - t_c) \qquad (4\text{--}21)$$

$$= C_w'(t_h - t_c) \qquad (4\text{--}22)$$

$$= \frac{1}{(1/r_a') + (1/r_b') + (1/r_c') + \cdots + (1/r_n')} (t_h - t_c) \qquad (4\text{--}23)$$

$$= \frac{1}{r_w'} (t_h - t_c) \qquad (4\text{--}24)$$

where $A_a, A_b, A_c \cdots A_n$ = mean areas normal to heat transfer of each of the sections in series.

$C_a', C_b', C_c' \cdots C_n'$ = conductances, including area, of each section in series, Btu/(hr)(°F).

$r_a', r_b', r_c' \cdots r_n'$ = resistances, including area, of each section in series.

C_w' = surface-to-surface conductances for the series system, including area, Btu/(hr)(°F).

r_w' = surface-to-surface resistance for the series system, including area.

EXAMPLE 4–5. A nominal $1\frac{1}{2}$-in. steel pipe (k = 26 Btu/(hr)(sq ft)(°F/ft)) has outside diameter of 1.900 in. and inside diameter of 1.500 in. The pipe is insulated with a 2 in. thick homogeneous layer of 85 per cent magnesium and asbestos. Steam at 350 F flows within the pipe. Assuming that the inside surface temperature is very close to 350 F, calculate the rate of heat loss from 100 ft of pipe if the outside surface temperature of the insulation is 68 F.

Solution: The ratio of outside to inside diameters of the steel pipe is less than 2, and therefore the arithmetical average surface area can be used; thus

$$A_{m(\text{pipe})} = A_{mp} = \frac{(100)(\pi)(1.9 + 1.5)}{(2)(12)} = 44.5 \text{ sq ft}$$

The ratio of diameters for the insulation is $(1.9 + 4)/(1.9)$, or 3.1, so it is necessary to use the logarithmic mean area; thus

$$A_{m(\text{ins})} = A_{mi} = (100)(\pi) \frac{5.9 - 1.9}{12 \log_e (5.9/1.9)} = 92.7 \text{ sq ft}$$

From Table 4–1 the value of k for the insulator is 0.0475 Btu/(hr)(sq ft)(°F/ft). Then

$$C'_{\text{pipe}} = C'_p = \frac{k_p A_{mp}}{x_p} = \frac{(26)(44.5)}{(1.9 - 1.5)/(2)(12)} = 69{,}300 \text{ Btu/(hr)(°F)}$$

$$C'_{\text{ins}} = C'_i = \frac{k_i A_{mi}}{x_i} = \frac{(0.0475)(92.7)}{(2/12)} = 26.4 \text{ Btu/(hr)(°F)}$$

Then, by Eq. 4–21,

$$q = \frac{1}{(1/69{,}300) + (1/26.4)} (350 - 68) = \frac{282}{0.000014 + 0.0379}$$

$$= \frac{282}{0.0379} = 7440 \text{ Btu/hr}$$

In this case the resistance of the pipe wall, r'_p, is so small in comparison with that of the insulation that it has no appreciable effect on the rate of heat transfer.

INTERFACE TEMPERATURES. The need for a surface-to-surface conductance, C_w, arose from lack of data on, or adequate means of determining, the interface temperatures in a series system. Since C_w is known, however, it is now possible to calculate interface temperatures. Referring again to the system of Fig. 4–1 and equating the rate of heat transfer through section a with that for the wall as a whole,

$$C_w A(t_h - t_c) = C_a A(t_h - t_2)$$

giving

$$\frac{t_h - t_2}{t_h - t_c} = \frac{C_w}{C_a} = \frac{1/r_w}{1/r_a} = \frac{r_a}{r_w} \tag{4-25}$$

which shows that the ratio of temperature drop through any two parts of a plane-wall series system is equal to the ratio of thermal resistances through the same sections. For a non-plane series system the same ratio applies except that C' and r' replace C and r; generalizing Eq. 4–25 for a non-plane system and for temperature t_x at any plane x,

$$\frac{t_h - t_x}{t_h - t_c} = \frac{C'_w}{C'_x} = \frac{1/r'_w}{1/r'_x} = \frac{r'_x}{r'_w} \tag{4-26}$$

where r'_x is the thermal resistance, including areas, from the warmer surface of any series transmitting system to any intermediate plane x which is normal to the direction of heat flow.

Solving Eq. 4–26 for the unknown temperature t_x,

$$t_x = t_h - \frac{r'_x}{r'_w} (t_h - t_c) \tag{4-27}$$

$$= t_h - r'_x C'_w (t_h - t_c) \tag{4-28}$$

An alternative form of Eq. 4–28 is

$$t_x = t_c + (r'_w - r'_x)C'_w(t_h - t_c)$$
$$= t_c + r'_{xx}C'_w(t_h - t_c) \qquad (4\text{–}29)$$

where r'_{xx} is the thermal resistance, including areas, from any intermediate plane x (normal to the direction of heat flow) of a series system to the colder surface.

EXAMPLE 4–6. Determine the temperature at the interface between the concrete and the insulation for the wall of Example 4–4b.

Solution: Using data from the solution of Example 4–4b, the conductance of the insulation is

$$C_i = \frac{k_i}{x_i} = \frac{0.25}{0.092} = 2.72 \text{ Btu/(hr)(sq ft)(°F)}$$

and the conductance of the concrete is

$$C_g = \frac{k_g}{x_g} = \frac{5.2}{0.5} = 10.4 \text{ Btu/(hr)(sq ft)(°F)}$$

The surface-to-surface conductance of the wall (by Eq. 4–15) is therefore

$$C_w = \frac{1}{(1/C_i) + (1/C_g)} = \frac{1}{(1/2.72) + (1/10.4)} = \frac{1}{0.464} = 2.16$$

The interface temperature is obtained by substitution into Eq. 4–28 (noting that this solution is for a plane wall),

$$t_{\text{interface}} = t_h - r_i C_w(t_h - t_c)$$
$$= 70 - \frac{1}{2.72}(2.16)(70 - 5)$$
$$= 70 - 51.6 = 18.4 \text{ F}$$

Thus the temperature drop through the 1.1 in. of insulation is 51.6 F, whereas the drop through the 6 in. of concrete is only 18.4 F.

EXAMPLE 4–7. A plane furnace roof consists of an outside layer of structural brick having thermal resistance of 10 and an inside layer of refractory brick with equal resistance. Inside and outside surface temperatures are 2100 F and 100 F. A proposal is made to add sufficient insulation on top of the structural brick to halve the transmission loss. Assuming that inside and outside surface temperatures remain the same, determine: (a) the required resistance of the insulating layer; (b) the effect of the insulation on the maximum temperature to which the structural brick is subject.

Solution: (a) The surface-to-surface resistance of the roof is originally 10 plus 10, or 20. In order to halve the transmission loss, assuming the same surface temperatures, the resistance would have to be doubled. Required thermal resistance of the insulating layer is therefore 20. (b) Under the original condition the maximum temperature to which the structural brick would be subjected would be the interface temperature between refractory and structural brick.

Since resistances of refractory and of structural brick layers are equal, it follows (from Eq. 4–25) that the interface temperature would be halfway between 2100 F and 100 F, or 1100 F. Addition of the insulator would change the situation so that the interface temperature (by Eq. 4–25) would be

$$\frac{2100 - t_x}{2100 - 100} = \frac{10}{10 + 10 + 20} = 0.25$$

giving (Eq. 4–28)

$$t_x = 2100 - 10\frac{1}{10 + 10 + 20}(2100 - 100)$$

$$= 2100 - (10)(0.025)(2000)$$

$$= 2100 - 500 = 1600 \text{ F}$$

The effect of adding insulation would therefore be to increase the maximum temperature to which the structural brick is subjected from 1100 F to 1600 F. Assuming that the roof was originally designed to assure a safe temperature of the structural brick, it would appear that addition of the insulation would increase the temperature of the structural brick by an amount such that failure might occur.

If a perfect ($k = 0$) insulator were used, the structural brick temperature would equal the temperature of the gases within the furnace; it is evident, therefore, that in cases where excess temperature may lead to structural damage, it is important to limit the resistance of any applied insulation to an acceptable value.

CONDUCTION THROUGH COMPLEX SHAPES. The procedures so far developed have been for paths of conductive heat transfer in which the area normal to the direction of heat flow varies as some simple mathematical function of the path length. For walls, concentric cylinders, and concentric spheres, the constant temperature (isothermal) surfaces are all parallel to one another. For more complex shapes, however, evaluation of area as a function of path becomes very difficult, and in many cases an analytical solution of the problem will be either mathematically difficult or impossible. In such cases numerical methods have been developed which provide approximate solutions, the degree of approximation increasing as the number of steps is increased. Such solutions are simple, convenient, and often rapid.

Typical examples of shapes that lead to two-dimensional conduction and that are readily solved by numerical procedures are:

1. Steady-state heat transfer through an irregularly shaped conduit (Fig. 4–2) for which inside and outside surfaces are at uniform temperature.
2. Steady-state heat loss from a steam pipe centered in a square box (Fig. 4–3) containing insulation.
3. Steady-state transfer from a steampipe which, owing to proximity to a wall, had to be insulated off center (Fig. 4–4).
4. Steady-state conduction through the corner of a thick-walled structure.

In each of these cases, and in any other two-dimensional system, the steady-state temperature distribution throughout the transfer material and the rate of heat transfer by conduction can be obtained numerically by the relaxation procedure.

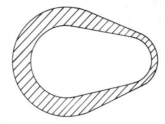

Fig. 4–2

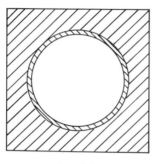

Fig. 4–3

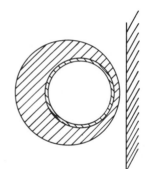

Fig. 4–4

Fig. 4–2. Conduit affording two-dimensional non-radial heat transfer by conduction.

Fig. 4–3. Boxed conduit affording non-radial heat transfer by conduction.

Fig. 4–4. Off-centered insulation affording non-radial heat transfer.

THE RELAXATION METHOD FOR TWO DIMENSIONS. For convenience in deriving the equations for the relaxation method, consider a simple (but impracticable) two-dimensional system consisting of a slab (Fig. 4–5) which is perfectly insulated on the front and rear faces and has each of its four edges A, B, C, and D with different uniform surface temperatures t_A, t_B, t_C, t_D. The temperature distribution through such a slab would be difficult to obtain by analytical means, and lacking such knowledge, the rate of heat transfer through the slab could not be evaluated.

In order to apply the relaxation method to such a slab, a series of yz planes (1, 2, 3, 4, 5) is established, each pair being Δx distance apart; a similar series of xz planes is established (a, b, c, d, e) with separating distance of Δy. Although not necessary, it is usually convenient to establish a square network, thus having $\Delta x = \Delta y$. The accuracy of the result of the analysis will increase as the value of Δx decreases, but the time required for the analysis also increases with decreasing Δx; a compromise between time and accuracy must therefore be made.

Referring to the cross-hatched element of slab having dimensions Δx, Δy, z for steady state, the rate of heat flow in must equal the rate of heat flow

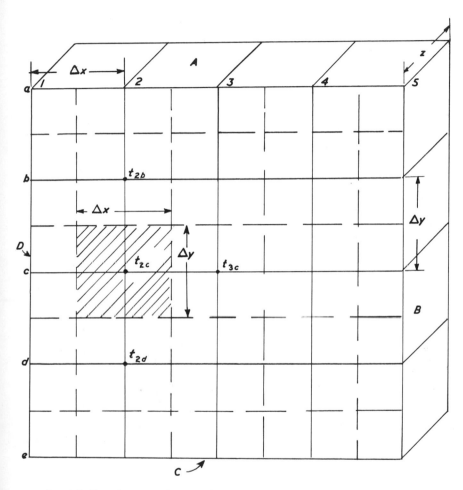

Fig. 4–5. Two-dimensional system for analysis of conduction by relaxation method.

out. But the midelement temperature t_{2c} is not known; hence initially it is not possible to state in what direction heat is crossing each of the four edges of the element. The basis of the relaxation method is to assume existence of an imaginary heat sink of strength S_{2c} Btu/hr at the element center, the point of intersection 2c of the xz plane c and yz plane 2, and to equate the sink strength to the sum of the rate of heat transfer in through each of the four edges. In equation form,

$$S_{2c} = \begin{pmatrix} \text{rate of heat gain by conduction through left plus top plus right} \\ \text{plus bottom edges} \end{pmatrix}$$

$$= \frac{kz\,\Delta y}{\Delta x}(t_{1c} - t_{2c}) + \frac{kz\,\Delta x}{\Delta y}(t_{2b} - t_{2c})$$

$$+ \frac{kz\,\Delta y}{\Delta x}(t_{3c} - t_{2c}) + \frac{kz\,\Delta x}{\Delta y}(t_{2d} - t_{2c})$$

Factoring out kz and recalling that Δx is constructed equal to Δy,

$$\frac{S_{2c}}{kz} = R_{2c}^* = t_{1c} + t_{2b} + t_{3c} + t_{2d} - 4t_{2c} \qquad (4\text{--}30)$$

where S_{2c} = strength of heat sink at point $2c$, Btu/hr.
  z = thickness of slab, ft.
  R^* = residual = $S_{2c}/kz = \phi(S_{2c})$.

When steady state exists, the value of the sink S_{2c} must be zero; hence the left side of Eq. 4–30 must be zero. The problem, therefore, is to establish a temperature network across the slab such that the value of S/kz at each intersection of xz and yz planes will be zero.

A first step in applying the relaxation procedure is to guess the temperature at each of the intersections in the network. If the guesses happen to be correct, equations similar in form to Eq. 4–30 would verify the distribution by giving a *residual* (S/kz or R^*) of zero for each point in the network. If, as is most likely, the guesses are not correct, the residuals will not be zero. A next step would be to adjust the assumed temperatures in such a manner as to cause the residuals to approach zero. Step-by-step adjustment, each step utilizing the largest residual, will alter the assumed temperature distribution, causing it to approach the steady-state temperature distribution. In applying the relaxation procedure, it is interesting to note that the correct solution will be obtained regardless of how erroneous the original guesses may have been; the number of steps required, however, will increase as the accuracy of the estimated distribution decreases. The method of adjusting residuals can be most simply described by giving an example.

EXAMPLE 4–8. For the slab of Fig. 4–5 assume that the left, top, right, and bottom edges are, respectively, at uniform surface temperature of 120 F, 100 F, 80 F, 60 F. For steady state determine the temperature distribution throughout the slab and the rate of heat transfer by conduction that is occurring through it.

Solution: Fig. 4–6a shows the slab with given edge conditions and with estimated temperature distribution. Based on this initial condition the residuals are

$$R_{2b}^* = t_{1b} + t_{2a} + t_{3b} + t_{2c} - 4t_{2b}$$
$$= 120 + 100 + 95 + 105 - 4(110) = -20 \tag{4–31}$$

$$R_{3b}^* = t_{2b} + t_{3a} + t_{4b} + t_{3c} - 4t_{3b}$$
$$= 110 + 100 + 90 + 90 - 4(95) = +10 \tag{4–32}$$

$$R_{4b}^* = t_{3b} + t_{4a} + t_{5b} + t_{4c} - 4t_{4b}$$
$$= 95 + 100 + 80 + 85 - 4(90) = 0 \tag{4–33}$$

$$R_{2c}^* = t_{1c} + t_{2b} + t_{3c} + t_{2d} - 4t_{2c}$$
$$= 120 + 110 + 90 + 95 - 4(105) = -5 \tag{4–34}$$

$$R_{3c}^* = t_{2c} + t_{3b} + t_{4c} + t_{3d} - 4t_{3c}$$
$$= 105 + 95 + 85 + 80 - 4(90) = +5 \tag{4–35}$$

$$R_{4c}^* = t_{3c} + t_{4b} + t_{5c} + t_{4d} - 4t_{4c}$$
$$= 90 + 90 + 80 + 75 - 4(85) = -5 \tag{4–36}$$

$$R_{2d}^* = t_{1d} + t_{2c} + t_{3d} + t_{2e} - 4t_{2d}$$
$$= 120 + 105 + 80 + 60 - 4(95) = -15 \tag{4–37}$$

$$R_{3d}^* = t_{2d} + t_{3c} + t_{4d} + t_{5e} - 4t_{3d}$$
$$= 95 + 90 + 75 + 60 - 4(80) = 0 \tag{4–38}$$

$$R_{4d}^* = t_{3d} + t_{4c} + t_{5d} + t_{4e} - 4t_{4d}$$
$$= 80 + 85 + 80 + 60 - 4(75) = +5 \tag{4–39}$$

Table 4–3 gives the step-by-step method of adjusting residuals. Based on the assumed initial temperature distribution, the largest residual is −20 at point 2b. Thus, in step 1, the temperature t_{2b} is reduced by 5 F, thereby increasing the residual R_{2c}^* (from Eq. 4–31) by four times this amount, or +20. Another effect of decreasing t_{2b} by 5 F is to decrease the residual at points 3b and 2c (by Eqs. 4–32 and 4–34) by 5. The revised values are carried into the second step, and the t and R^* for the point having the largest residual 4c is also carried down. In step 2, R_{2d}^* is reduced to +1 by subtracting 4 F from t_{2d}; the effect is to alter R_{2c}^* and R_{3d}^* by −4. In step 3 the largest residual is R_{2c}^*, so this value is reduced and the process continued as before. After the tenth adjustment, the maximum residual is ±1, indicating that the temperatures given in step 11 are within a fraction of a degree of the steady-state values; Fig. 4–6b shows the steady-state temperature distribution (from step 11).

The rate of heat flow into the slab (noting again that Δx is equal to Δy and using temperatures from Fig. 4–6b) is the sum of the rates of heat flow into the individual elements around the edge. Starting from the lower left-hand corner of Fig. 4–6b,

$$q_{in} = k(z\,\Delta x)\frac{[(t_{1d} - t_{2d}) + (t_{1c} - t_{2c}) + (t_{1b} - t_{2b}) + (t_{3a} - t_{3b}) + (t_{4a} - t_{4b}) + (t_{5d} - t_{4d})]}{\Delta x}$$

$$= k(z\,\Delta x)$$
$$\times \frac{[(120 - 90) + (120 - 101) + (120 - 104) + (100 - 96) + (100 - 90) + (80 - 76)]}{\Delta x}$$

$$= 83kz$$

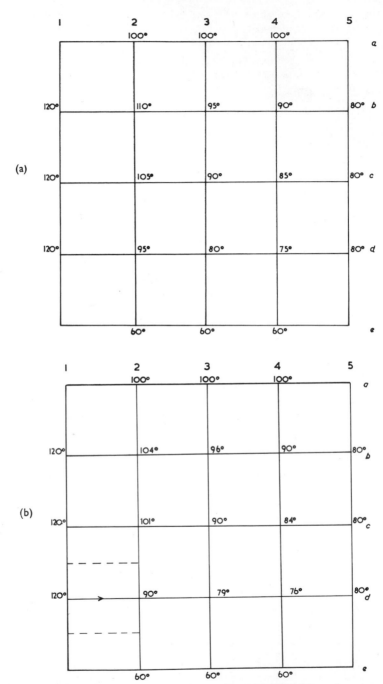

Fig. 4–6. (a) Assumed temperature distribution (Example 4–8); (b) steady-state temperature distribution (Example 4–8).

TABLE 4–3

Detailed Solution of Example 4-8

Point Step	2b t	2b R*	3b t	3b R*	4b t	4b R*	2c t	2c R*	3c t	3c R*	4c t	4c R*	2d t	2d R*	3d t	3d R*	4d t	4d R*
1	110 / −5	−20 / +20	95	+10 / −5	90	0	105	−5 / −5	90	+5	85	−5	95	−15	80	0	75	+5
2	105	0		+5				−10 / −4					95 / −4	−15 / +16		0 / −4		
3		0 / −3					105 / −3	−14 / +12		+5 / −3			91	+1 / −3		−4		
4		−3				0 / −1	102	−2		+2 / −1	85 / −1	−5 / +4		−2		−4 / −1		
5			95 / +1	+5 / −4		−1				+1 / −1	84	−1		−2 / −1	80 / −1	−5 / +4		+5 / −1
6		−3 / +1	96	+1		−1 / +1				0 / +1				−3	79	−1		+4
7		−2				0				+1		−1 / +1				−1 / +1	75 / +1	+4 / −4
8								−2 / −1				0	91 / −1	−3 / +4		0 / −1	76	0
9		−2 / −1					102 / −1	−3 / +4		+1 / −1			90	+1		−1		0 / −1
10	105 / −1	−3 / +4		+1 / −1			101	+1 / −1		0								−1
11	104	+1	96	0	90	0	101	0	90	0	84	0	90	+1	79	−1	76	−1

Note: For each step, the residual in italics is the one which is adjusted.

If the solution is actually valid for steady-state conditions, the rate of heat flow in must equal that out. Then from Fig. 4–6b,

$$q_{out} = k(z\,\Delta x)$$
$$\times \frac{[(t_{2b} - t_{2a}) + (t_{4b} - t_{5b}) + (t_{4c} - t_{5c}) + (t_{4d} - t_{4e}) + (t_{3d} - t_{3e}) + (t_{2d} - t_{2e})]}{\Delta x}$$
$$= k(z\,\Delta x)$$
$$\times \frac{[(104 - 100) + (90 - 80) + (84 - 80) + (76 - 60) + (79 - 60) + (90 - 60)]}{\Delta x}$$
$$= 83kz$$

The relaxation method can be effectively used to obtain a generalized solution to a problem that is of very considerable importance in the calculation of heating load for thick-walled structures. Usual steady-state calculations for heat transmission through walls are based on the assumption that

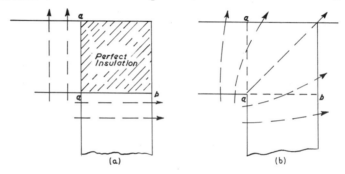

Fig. 4–7. (a) Insulated corner; (b) uninsulated corner.

the heat flow is in a direction normal to the wall. This method would be applicable (referring to Fig. 4–7a) if the corner were constructed of a perfect insulant, but in usual practice the corner is made of the same material as the wall; hence it is responsible for an increased heat loss due to "leakage" of heat through the wall ends aa and ab of Fig. 4–7b. The important practical questions involved are two: (1) How far back from the inside corner (the distance being expressed in wall thicknesses) is the influence of two-dimensional heat transfer through the corner experienced? (2) How can the increased transmission loss through a wall due to corner effect be expressed as a function of wall thickness? Example 4–9 provides answers to both these questions.

EXAMPLE 4–9. A wall of thickness L (ft) is assumed to have uniform inside surface temperature t_1 and uniform outside surface temperature t_2. Determine: (a) the distance back from the inside corner of the wall, expressed as a multiple of wall thickness, at which the influence of two-dimensional heat flow is experienced; (b) the increased steady-state transmission loss through a wall due to a corner (and expressed as a function of wall thickness).

Solution: (a) The desired generalized results are independent of both the actual wall thickness and the surface temperatures. Thus it is permissible to assign, for convenience, a wall thickness and surface temperatures. Refer to Fig. 4–8a; assume a wall thickness of 1 ft and inside and outside surface temperatures of, respectively, 100 F and 0 F. At that distance from the inside corner at which the two-dimensional effect is not experienced, the midplane temperature of the

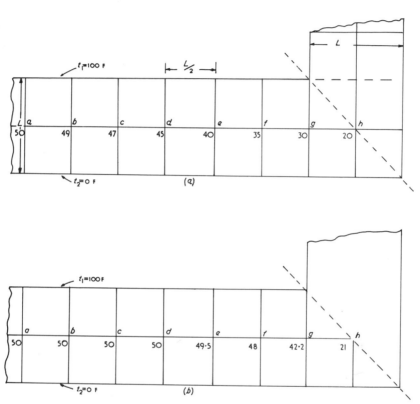

Fig. 4–8. Coarse grid (Example 4–9): (a) Assumed temperature distribution; (b) steady-state temperature distribution.

wall will be (assuming that k does not vary appreciably with t) halfway between inside and outside surface temperatures, or 50 F.

If the relaxation method is to provide an answer to the first question (distance back from inside corner at which corner effect is experienced), it would be conservative to overestimate the effect in the initial guess at temperature distribution. Then, in Fig. 4–8a, it is assumed that corner effect is experienced to a distance of three wall thicknesses back from the inside of the corner. On the basis of this assumption, temperatures at the midplane of the wall are assumed to decrease (Fig. 4–8a) as the corner is approached; the values selected for midplane temperatures are guesses based on judgment. Beyond three wall thicknesses, the heat flow is unidirectional, so midplane temperature is 50 F.

TABLE 4-4

Detailed Solution of Example 4-9

Point	a		b		c		d		e		f		g		h	
Step	t	R^*	t	R^*	t	R^*	t	R^*	t	R^*	t	R^*	t	R^*	t	R^*
1	50	−1	49	+1	47	+6	45	+7	40	+20	35	+30 / +8	30 / +8	+35 / −32	20	−20 / +16
2									40 / +7	+20 / +9	35 / +9	+38 / −36	38	+3 / +9		−4
3									47	+29 / −28	44	+2 / +7		+12		
4			+1	+2	47 / +2	+6 / +3	45 / +3	+7 / +7 ; +14 / −12	47	+1 / +3		+9				
5				+3	49	+9	48	+2		+4	44 / +3	+9 / +3 ; +12 / −12	38 / +3	+12 / −12		−4 / +6
6									47 / +1	+4 / +3	47	0	41	0 / +3		+2
7					47 / +2	+9 / −8			47 / +1	+7		0		+3		
8					49	+1	48 / +1	+4 / +1 ; +5 / −4	48	+7 / −4		0 / +1				
9						+1 / +1	48 / +1	+5 / −4		+3 / +1		+1				

10		−1 +2		+2		+1 +1		+4 −4		+1 +1
								0		+2
11		+1	49 +1	+2 +1	49	+1 +1	48 +1		+2 +1	
			50			49		+3 −4		+41 +1
12			−1 +1	+3 −4	49 +1	+2	49	0 +1	−1	42
			0		50			+1		
13				−1 +1		+2 +1	49 +1	+1	+3 +1	0 +1
						0	50		48	+1
14				0		+3 −4		+1 +1	+47 +1	+1
									+2 +1	48
15						−1		+2 −2	+3	−1 +0.5
16								0	49 +0.5	−0.5 +0.25
17						−1 +0.5		49.5	48	+7 −1
18						−0.5		0	−0.5 +0.25	42 +0.25
19	50 +1	50	0	50	−0.5	49.5	0	48	−0.25	42.25 0

Note: For each step, the residual in italics is the one which is adjusted.

For the midplane points of Fig. 4–8 from a through h, the residuals, based on the assumed point temperatures of Fig. 4–8a, are

$$R_a^* = t_a + t_1 + t_b + t_2 - 4t_a = 50 + 100 + 49 + 0 - 4(50) = -1$$
$$R_b^* = t_a + t_c + t_1 + t_2 - 4t_b = 50 + 47 + 100 + 0 - 4(49) = +1$$
$$R_c^* = t_b + t_d + t_1 + t_2 - 4t_c = 49 + 45 + 100 + 0 - 4(47) = +6$$
$$R_d^* = t_c + t_e + t_1 + t_2 - 4t_d = 47 + 40 + 100 + 0 - 4(45) = +7$$
$$R_e^* = t_d + t_f + t_1 + t_2 - 4t_e = 45 + 35 + 100 + 0 - 4(40) = +20$$
$$R_f^* = t_e + t_g + t_1 + t_2 - 4t_f = 40 + 30 + 100 + 0 - 4(35) = +30$$
$$R_g^* = t_f + t_h + t_1 + t_2 - 4t_g = 35 + 20 + 100 + 0 - 4(30) = +35$$
$$R_h^* = 2t_g + 2t_2 - 4t_h = 2(30) + 0 - 4(20) = -20$$

Table 4–4 gives the step-by-step adjustment of temperature leading to the steady-state distribution, as given, with an accuracy within better than 1 F, at the end of step 18. The point temperatures corresponding to steady-state conditions are shown on Fig. 4–8b. From the results it is evident that the two-dimensional influence of the corner is experienced only within one and a half wall thicknesses back from the inside of the corner. Thus, for walls of average thickness, corner effect can be considered negligible.

(b) For thick walls (as in monumental structures) the increased heat transfer due to corner effect can be accurately evaluated by using the results of part (a) as the basis of a relaxation analysis using a finer network. Thus Fig. 4–9a shows an assumed temperature distribution in a wall section one and a half wall thicknesses back from the inside corner. Applying the relaxation method to this case gives a steady-state temperature distribution as shown in Fig. 4–9b. From the temperature distribution of Fig. 4–9b, the rate of conductive heat flow through unit height of wall (when wall thickness is L) is

$$q = \frac{kA}{L/4} \sum \Delta t = k \frac{L/4}{L/4} \sum \Delta t$$

$$= k \sum \Delta t$$

$$= k\left(\frac{25}{2} + 24.9 + 24.8 + 24.2 + 23.8 + 22.5 + 19.8 + 15.7 + 10.4 + 5.2\right)$$

$$= 183.8k$$

If there were no corner effect, the rate of conductive heat flow through the wall would be determined by the steady-state unidirectional gradient of $(25 - 0)$, or 25 F; hence the rate would be

$$q = k\left[\frac{25}{2} + 5(25) + \frac{25}{2}\right] = 150k$$

From the results of Example 4–9 it follows that the corner effect leads to an increased transmission loss of $(183.8 - 150)/150$, or 22.5 per cent, through the wall sections which extend one and a half wall thicknesses back from the inside of the corner; the effect is experienced in a total wall length equal to three wall thicknesses. Thus, to correct unidirectional transmission losses for corner effect, the actual inside length of wall should be increased by two-thirds: accurately $(22.5)(3)/100$, or 0.675 of the wall thickness for each corner.

For walls of average thickness in rooms of average size the corner effect is therefore negligible, but in a small corner room of a structure having thick

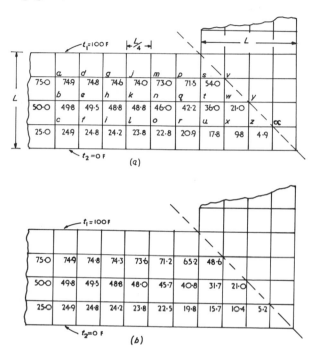

Fig. 4–9. Fine grid (Example 4–9): (a) Estimated temperature distribution; (b) calculated temperature distribution.

walls the effect would be appreciable. Thus in a 10 ft by 10 ft corner office in a structure with walls 2 ft thick, the increased transmission load would amount to $[(0.675)(2)/(10 + 10)]100$, or 6.75 per cent.

(*Note:* The above analysis is based on assumed uniformity of the inside and outside surface temperatures of the wall. A more precise method would be to assume constancy of inside and outside air temperatures and then to take into account the convective and radiant transfer from the wall surfaces. This corrected method is discussed in Art. 4–8, page 156, but its influence on the practical results arrived at in this article is negligible.)

CONDUCTION FOR BURIED PIPES AND PLATES. Steady-state conduction for pipes or horizontal flat surfaces buried in the earth involves two-dimensional heat transfer from the heated surface to the surface of the earth. If the submergence ratio (pipe diameter or plate width divided by depth of installation) is small, the effect of the air film at the earth's surface can be neglected, and the temperature distribution through the earth can then be obtained by the relaxation procedure described above. Heat transfer from such surfaces can also be calculated analytically by using equations developed by A. L. London and given by McAdams.[1]

For a buried horizontal pipe, the transfer rate is given by

$$q = 2\pi L k \frac{1}{\log_e (4z/D)} (t_h - t_c) \qquad (4\text{--}40)$$

where L = length of pipe, ft.
   k = thermal conductivity of the earth, Btu/(hr)(sq ft)(°F/ft).
   z = depth of installation, measured from earth's surface to the axis of the pipe, ft.
   D = pipe diameter, ft.
   t_h = pipe surface temperature (approximately equal to the temperature of the fluid within the pipe), °F.
   t_c = surface temperature of the earth, °F.

For a heated flat plate the equation is

$$q = 2\pi D_1 k \frac{1}{\log_e (2\pi z/D_2)} (t_h - t_c) \qquad (4\text{--}41)$$

where D_1 = length of longer side of the plate, ft.
   D_2 = length of smaller side of the plate, ft.

and other symbols are the same as for Eq. 4–40. Eq. 4–41 is limited to cases for which D_1 is large with respect to D_2 and z is large as compared with $2D_2$.

EXAMPLE 4–10. A 6-in. outside diameter steam pipe is buried 4 ft below the surface of earth, which has a thermal conductivity of 1.5 Btu/(hr)(sq ft)(°F/ft). The steam within the pipe is at 250 F, and the surface temperature of the earth is 60 F. (a) Calculate the steady-state rate of heat loss per lineal foot, assuming that outside surface temperature of the pipe is at 250 F. (b) If an identical pipe were in air and insulated with 85 per cent magnesia, $k = 0.0475$ Btu/(hr)(sq ft) (°F/ft), what would be the required thickness of insulation in order for the rate of heat loss to be the same as for the buried pipe (outside surface temperature of the insulation is 60 F)?

Solution: (a) By Eq. 4–40,

$$q = (2)(3.1416)(1)(1.5)\left[1/\log_e \frac{(4)(4)}{0.5} \right](250 - 60)$$

$$= 517 \text{ Btu/(hr)(ft)}$$

[1] Bibliography, item 3.

(b) Neglecting the temperature drop through the pipe wall, the conduction rate through the insulation would be

$$q = \frac{kA_m}{x}(t_h - t_c)$$

$$= \frac{2k}{D_o - D_i}\frac{\pi}{2}(D_o + D_i)(t_h - t_c)$$

$$517 = \frac{(2)(0.0475)}{D_o - 0.5}\frac{\pi}{2}(D_o + 0.5)(250 - 60)$$

$$= \frac{28.3(D_o + 0.5)}{D_o - 0.5}$$

giving

$$D_o = 0.558 \text{ ft,} \quad \text{or } 6.7 \text{ in.}$$

Thus $(6.7 - 6.0)/2$, or $\frac{1}{3}$ in., of 85 per cent magnesia insulation would be equivalent to a 4 ft depth of installation in soil of the stated conductivity. It is evident, therefore, that buried heating pipes require insulation unless the soil is very dry and of low conductivity.

EXAMPLE 4–11. All other conditions being the same, repeat the calculation of Example 4–10 for installation in dry sand; $k = 0.19$ Btu/(hr)(sq ft)(°F/ft).

Solution: (a) The heat loss from the buried pipe would be

$$q = \frac{k_{\text{sand}}}{k_{\text{soil}}}(517) = \frac{0.19}{1.5}\,517 = 65.5 \text{ Btu/(hr)(ft)}$$

(b) The equation for the insulated pipe would be (by analogy with the solution in Example 4–10)

$$65.5 = \frac{28.3(D_o + 0.5)}{D_o - 0.5}$$

giving

$$D_o = 1.26 \text{ ft,} \quad \text{or } 15.1 \text{ in.}$$

Thus $(15.1 - 6.0)/2$, or 4.5 in., of 85 per cent magnesia insulation would be required. This shows that insulation would not be needed if the earth in which the pipe was embedded had a low thermal conductivity. The range of k values for earth is from 0.19 for dry sand to 0.30 for coarse gravelly dry soil to 0.739 Btu/(hr) (sq ft)(°F/ft) for dry clay. When moisture is likely to be present, the conductivity can be expected to increase markedly, and in such cases insulation of the buried pipe will be a thermal necessity.

4–6. Convection.   Whenever heat transfer occurs between a surface and a fluid or within the body of the fluid, there will necessarily be a temperature gradient and therefore a point-to-point variation in the density of the fluid. Since the molecules of a gas or a liquid are free to move with respect to one another, it follows that the colder and more dense molecules will be displaced downward, while the warmer and less dense molecules move upward. Thus movement, whether initially present or not, will always occur when a gas or a liquid receives or rejects heat. The process of heat transfer by convection is defined as conduction between molecules that are moving with respect to one another. It follows, therefore, that the rate of convective transfer would be expected to vary as some function of the thermal conductivity of the fluid and of the temperature and velocity patterns within the fluid. Thus knowledge of flow as well as thermal conditions is essential to analysis of convective transfer.

Rational evaluation of convective heat transfer is complicated by the fact that two, and sometimes three, separate and distinct regions of flow exist

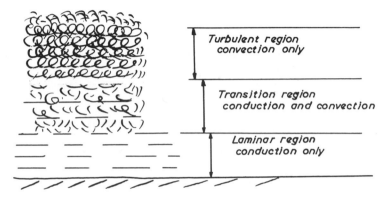

Fig. 4–10. Heat transfer from a fluid to a solid.

between the surface to or from which heat is flowing and the main body of the passing fluid stream (Fig. 4–10). The fluid in a very thin molecular layer immediately next to the surface is stationary, and from this layer the velocity increases almost as a straight-line function out through a sublayer in which there is laminar or streamline flow. In this region, heat transfer is entirely by the mechanism of conduction and could be evaluated by Eq. 4–2 if data were available on the thickness of the layer and the temperature difference across it. Such data are not directly available and cannot be easily obtained.

Beyond the region of laminar flow is a transition layer of variable thickness across which there is a temperature drop and through which heat is transferred partly by conduction and partly by the convection resulting from eddy currents. In this region the relative importance of the factors influencing heat transfer becomes increasingly difficult to evaluate. The transition layer is of greatest importance when flow occurs with a high degree of turbulence; as turbulence decreases and the main body of the fluid approaches streamline flow, the transition region tends to disappear.

The third convection mechanism is represented by conditions in the core of a turbulent stream. Heat entering or leaving the core must cause an increase or a drop in its temperature, but eddy-current activity is so great in this region that no appreciable temperature gradient exists, and heat transfer occurs almost entirely as a result of mechanical mixing. Core conditions can be roughly visualized by considering that in a heated room, the temperature in a horizontal plane does not appreciably vary until the walls are closely approached. The entire temperature drop from room air temperature to inside surface temperature of an exterior wall occurs within the thin laminar and transition layers adjacent to the wall surface.

The rate of heat transfer by convection is given by Newton's law of cooling, which serves to define a film coefficient of convective heat transfer, h_c. Newton's equation possesses the additional advantage of resembling the basic conduction equation

$$q = h_c A(t_f - t_s) = \frac{A(t_f - t_s)}{r_f} = C_f'(t_f - t_s)$$

$$= \frac{t_f - t_s}{r_f'} \tag{4–42}$$

where
h_c = film coefficient of convective heat transfer, Btu/(hr)(sq ft)(°F).

A = the area of the boundary surface across which the heat is being transferred.

t_f = the temperature of the core or main stream of passing fluid.

t_s = the temperature of the surface to which heat is flowing.

r_f = film resistance to heat transfer.

C_f' and r_f' = respectively, the conductance and thermal resistance of the film, including area, through which heat is flowing.

The accurate evaluation of h_c depends on establishing a functional relationship among all those properties or characteristics of the particular system which affect either the temperature gradient or the velocity gradient. Hydrodynamically, the velocity gradient for an isothermal (no heat transfer) system would be a function of the length and smoothness of the bounding surface, the mean velocity, and the density and viscosity of the fluid. Thermally, the effect of heat transfer would influence the velocity pattern as some function of the temperature, surface-to-fluid temperature difference, specific heat, thermal conductivity, and coefficient of thermal expansion of the fluid. Thus, in the general case, the film coefficient h_c must be evaluated from a functional relationship of the form

$$h_c = \phi(D, s, V \text{ (or } V'), \rho, \mu \text{ (or } \mu'), t_f, \Delta t_f, c_p, k, \beta)$$

where D = a characteristic dimension, ft, such as the diameter of a pipe
or the length of a flat plate.

s = a roughness coefficient, usually taken as the ratio of thickness
of surface protuberances.

V = mean velocity of the fluid, fps   (in many cases it is more
convenient to express velocity as V', ft/hr).

ρ = fluid density, lb/cu ft.

μ = absolute viscosity, lb/(sec)(ft). Note that the most common
units of viscosity, centipoises, can be converted to units of
lb/(sec)(ft) when multiplied by 0.000672   (in many cases it is
more convenient to express viscosity as μ', in units of lb/
(hr)(ft)).

t_f = temperature of the main body of the fluid.

Δt_f = temperature change across the film to or from the surface and
the main body of fluid, °F.

c_p = specific heat of the fluid (at constant pressure), Btu/(lb)(°F).

k = thermal conductivity of the fluid, Btu/(hr)(sq ft)(°F/ft).

β = coefficient of thermal expansion   (for a perfect gas β is equal
to $1/T$, where T is in degrees Fahrenheit absolute (°F plus 460)).

The explicit forms of the above relationship are usually very complex.
Thus it is necessary to investigate the types of flow patterns that are likely
to occur and then to attempt to establish an explicit form of the equation
for each flow type. When heat transfer occurs to or from a fluid which is
otherwise at rest, the resultant motion of the fluid is due entirely to the
relative changes of density (associated with the temperature gradient) and
is known as *free convection*. When a pump or fan is responsible for maintaining flow past a transfer surface, the heat transfer is said to be due to
forced convection and may then occur under conditions of either laminar
(streamline) or turbulent flow.

FLUID FLOW PARAMETERS. When the velocity of the fluid with respect
to the transfer surface is established by mechanical means, as by a pump or
fan, the fluid will have a characteristic velocity V, which can be readily
established from the equation of continuity

$$V = \frac{W \bar{V}}{A}$$

where V = mean fluid velocity, fps.

W = flow rate, lb/sec.

$\bar{V}$ = specific volume of the fluid, cu ft/lb.

A = cross-sectional area, sq ft.

As this fluid flows past any surface, whether through a pipe or over an imposed
obstacle, there will be at the surface a retarding force, per unit surface area,

due to viscous drag, which will be determined by the equation

$$\text{Viscous drag} = \frac{\mu V}{D} \qquad (4\text{–}43a)$$

The influence of the drag force is to reduce the velocity (hence the momentum) of the fluid; the decrease in momentum, per unit area of resisting surface, will be

$$\text{Momentum decrease} = \rho V^2 \qquad (4\text{–}43b)$$

But if the two systems that are being compared are geometrically similar, the ratio of unit area of retarding surface to unit area of cross-section through which flow is occurring will be a constant; hence the representative dimension D of Eq. 4–43a can refer either to surface area or to cross-sectional area. In order for similar flow patterns to exist, it is necessary that geometrical similarity exist and that the ratio of the momentum decrease to drag force remain constant. This ratio, defined as the Reynolds number N_{Re}, is

$$N_{\text{Re}} = \frac{\rho V^2}{\mu V/D} = \frac{DV\rho}{\mu} \qquad (4\text{–}44)$$

$$= \frac{(\text{ft})(\text{fps})(\text{lb/cu ft})}{(\text{lb})/(\text{sec})(\text{ft})} = \frac{(\text{cu ft})(\text{lb})(\text{sec})}{(\text{cu ft})(\text{lb})(\text{sec})}$$

or

$$N_{\text{Re}} = \frac{DV'\rho}{\mu'}$$

where N_{Re} = Reynolds number, a dimensionless parameter applicable to any flow condition (streamline or turbulent) in which there is a characteristic mean fluid velocity V.

In the case of free convection, the effect of buoyancy becomes significant; hence the coefficient of thermal expansion, β, would be expected to attain importance and so also would the acceleration due to gravity g. In order to relate the free convective condition to the forced convective condition, it is necessary to establish an *equivalent* free convective velocity for use in Reynolds number. This is done by noting that the effect of buoyant force is to do work on the fluid in an amount equal to force times distance or $[(\rho\beta\,\Delta t)/2]L = (\rho\beta\,\Delta tL)/2$. By equating this work to the external kinetic energy, $\rho V^2/2g$, an equivalent characteristic velocity for free convection can be established as

$$V = (g\beta\,\Delta tL)^{1/2} \qquad (4\text{–}45)$$

When this equivalent velocity, with x in place of L, is substituted into the Reynolds number, a new dimensionless parameter, the Grashof number, N_{Gr}, is obtained:

$$N_{\text{Gr}} = \frac{x^3\rho^2\beta g(\Delta t)}{\mu^2}$$

$$= \frac{(\text{cu ft})(\text{lb/cu ft})^2(1/°\text{F})(\text{ft/sec}^2)(°\text{F})}{[(\text{lb})/(\text{sec})(\text{ft})]^2} \qquad (4\text{–}46)$$

with x as a characteristic dimension.

Thus, in summary, N_{Re} is the characteristic dimensionless parameter applicable to systems in which the flow is streamline or turbulent (but at a velocity below the velocity of sound), whereas N_{Gr} is the corresponding dimensionless parameter that is applicable to systems in which free convection prevails.

THERMAL PARAMETERS. In order to relate the temperature and velocity patterns in a convective flow system and to establish a basis of similarity among such systems, the boundary temperatures must be similar and the temperature fields must possess similarity. The velocity field is largely determined by the viscous properties of the fluid as identified in the ratio of viscosity to density, μ/ρ, whereas the temperature field is associated with the ratio of thermal conductivity k (indicative of ability to transfer heat) and the product ρc_p, which is indicative of the heat-storage capacity of the fluid. The μ/ρ ratio is often designated *kinematic viscosity*, ν, and the $k/\rho c_p$ ratio is called thermal diffusivity, α. A convenient dimensionless thermal parameter, the Prandtl number N_{Pr}, is thus obtained in the form

$$N_{\text{Pr}} = \frac{\mu'/\rho}{k/\rho c_p} = \frac{c_p \mu'}{k} \qquad (4\text{-}47)$$

noting that μ' is in units of (lb)/(ft)(hr) because k is expressed in terms of hours.

A second dimensionless thermal parameter is obtained by taking the ratio of the actual convective transfer (per unit time per unit surface area) to the pure conduction (per unit time per unit surface area) that would occur if the same temperature difference existed and if the fluid were at rest. The new group is known as the Nusselt number N_{Nu}, and is

$$N_{\text{Nu}} = \frac{h_c}{k/D} = \frac{h_c D}{k} \qquad (4\text{-}48)$$

FREE CONVECTION FOR UNHEATED VERTICAL WALLS. Effective correlations of large amounts of free convection data for many types of systems have been accomplished by logarithmic plottings of the Nusselt number versus the product of the Grashof and Prandtl numbers. The equation of such curves is in the form

$$N_{\text{Nu}} = a[(\text{Gr})(\text{Pr})]^m \qquad (4\text{-}49)$$

where a and m are constants over limited sections of the curves. The correlations for various fluids in free convection past vertical planes or large-diameter vertical cylinders indicate that three regions exist in each of which the characteristic flow pattern is well established. For values of the N_{Nu} less than 6.0, the rate of convective heat transfer is so low that no characteristic velocity applies. This region is of very little concern to the heating engineer, however, since values of N_{Nu} as low as this are not likely to occur in problems that will commonly be of concern to him. Thus, noting that an average convective film coefficient over an inside vertical wall surface might be of the order of 0.4 Btu/(hr)(sq ft)(°F) and that the value of the thermal conductivity of air (Table 4–1) at 64 F is 0.0147 Btu/(hr)(sq ft)(°F/ft), it follows that N_{Nu} for this case would be $h_c D/k = (0.4)(D)/(0.0147)$, or approximately $27D$. The influence of wall height is not experienced over a distance appreciably greater than 2 ft, so it follows that for any wall of average height, the minimum expected Nusselt number would be some ten times greater than the maximum value (6.0) which determines the upper limit of very low velocity flow.

Laminar Flow Range for Unheated Walls. In the streamline flow region, the value of N_{Nu} is between 6.0 and 100, and it is near the upper end of this region that most problems involving free convection from warm room air to the cold inside surface of exterior walls occur. The general equation (for various fluids) recommended by McAdams[2] for this streamline region is

$$N_{Nu} = 0.59[(N_{Gr})(N_{Pr})]^{0.25} \qquad (4\text{–}50)$$

For air, the product of the Grashof and Prandtl numbers can be written as

$$(Gr)(Pr) = \frac{D^3 \rho^2 g' \beta \, \Delta t_f}{(\mu')^2} \frac{c_p \mu'}{k}$$

$$= \frac{\rho^2 g' \beta c_p}{\mu' k} D^3 \, \Delta t_f \qquad (4\text{–}51)$$

where g' is in units of ft/hr² and the first term contains only physical properties. For air at 32 F the first parenthesis is numerically equal to $(2.21)(10)^6$, whereas at an air temperature of 100 F, it decreases to $(1.21)(10)^6$. Then, taking this term as $(2.0)(10)^6$ at average room temperature, Eq. 4–50 becomes

$$\frac{h_c D}{k} = 0.59[(2)(10)^6 (D^3 \, \Delta t_f)]^{0.25}$$

$$h_c = (0.59)(0.0147)(37.6)\left(\frac{\Delta t_f}{D}\right)^{0.25} \qquad (4\text{–}52)$$

$$= 0.326\left(\frac{\Delta t_f}{D}\right)^{0.25}$$

Noting that wall height above 24 in. has no effect on convection, the above equation simplifies further (based on $D = 2$ ft) to

$$h_c = 0.274(\Delta t_f)^{0.25} \qquad (4\text{–}53)$$

When the film coefficient is calculated for short vertical sections (as for baseboard heating panels), the height D should be accounted for; hence Eq. 4–52 should be used.

[2] Bibliography, item 3.

Turbulent Flow Range for Unheated Walls. The general equation, which McAdams recommends for the turbulent region (N_{Nu} between 100 and 1000), is

$$N_{Nu} = 0.13[(Gr)(Pr)]^{1/3} \tag{4-54}$$

which for air at room temperature (by analogy with Eq. 4–52) reduces to

$$\frac{h_c D}{k} = 0.13[(2)(10)^6(D^3 \, \Delta t_f)]^{1/3}$$

giving

$$h_c = (0.13)(0.0147)(126)(\Delta t_f)^{1/3}$$

$$= 0.241(\Delta t_f)^{1/3} \tag{4-55}$$

The above equations are for free convection over unheated walls under winter conditions.

Eqs. 4–53 and 4–55 are also applicable, without significant error, to all the gases that normally constitute products of combustion. (In the unusual case of unburned hydrogen the equation would not apply because hydrogen has a thermal conductivity which is almost ten times higher than that of air.)

EXAMPLE 4–12. Under design load conditions the inside surface temperature of an exterior wall of an enclosure is 3 F lower than room air temperature. Calculate the rate of heat transfer based on: (a) the assumption that laminar flow exists in the inside film; (b) the assumption that turbulent flow exists in the inside film.

Solution: (a) For laminar flow by Eqs. 4–42 and 4–53,

$$q = h_c A(t_f - t_s) = 0.274(3)^{1.25}A = 1.083A \quad \text{Btu/hr}$$

(b) For turbulent flow by Eqs. 4–42 and 4–55,

$$q = h_c A(t_f - t_s) \doteq 0.241(3)^{1.3}A = 1.041A \quad \text{Btu/hr}$$

Thus, at small values of the film-temperature difference (such as would exist in well-insulated structures), the difference in heat loss between laminar and turbulent flow in the inside film is very small. In this case the percentage of decrease for turbulent flow is [(0.361 − 0.347)/0.361]100, or less than 4 per cent.

Note, however, that the value of N_{Nu} for this case is

$$N_{Nu} = \frac{h_c D}{k} = \frac{(0.35)(2)}{0.0147} = 47.6$$

so the actual film condition (since N_{Nu} is between 6.0 and 100) is one of laminar flow.

EXAMPLE 4–13. Repeat Example 4–12 for a single-pane window under load conditions such that the temperature drop across the inside film is 50 F. Compare the results of Examples 4–12 and 4–13.

Solution: (a) For laminar flow,

$$q = 0.274(50)^{1.25}A = 36.40A \quad \text{Btu/hr}$$

(b) For turbulent flow,

$$q = 0.241(50)^{1.3}A = 44.40A \quad \text{Btu/hr}$$

Thus, even at the largest temperature difference likely to occur in heating system design, the difference in values of the laminar and turbulent film coefficients for walls will be of the order of 0.16 Btu/(hr)(sq ft)(°F). At large temperature differences, however, the percentage difference increases (in this case [(0.888 − 0.728)/0.888]100, or 18 per cent in contrast with the 4 per cent of the preceding example).

For the case of this example the value of the Nusselt number would be

$$N_{\text{Nu}} = \frac{hD}{k} = \frac{(0.80)(2)}{0.0147} = 109$$

which indicates that the flow is turbulent rather than streamline. Thus, for the case of the preceding example, the flow would be laminar with $h_c = 0.361$, whereas for the large film-temperature drop of this example, turbulent flow would exist and the convective film coefficient would be 0.888 Btu/(hr)(sq ft)(°F), showing an increase of [(0.888 − 0.361)/0.361]100, or 146 per cent.

The critical temperature difference for separating laminar and turbulent flow can be readily established. Thus, for laminar flow,

$$h_{c_{\text{max}}} = \frac{k}{D} N_{\text{Nu}} = \frac{0.0147}{2} 100 = 0.735$$

and

$$\Delta t_{f_{\text{max}}} = \left(\frac{h_c}{0.274}\right)^4 = \left(\frac{0.735}{0.274}\right)^4 = 52 \text{ F}$$

For turbulent flow,

$$h_{c_{\text{min}}} = \frac{0.0147}{2} 100 = 0.735$$

and

$$\Delta t_{f_{\text{min}}} = \left(\frac{0.735}{0.241}\right)^3 = 28.4 \text{ F}$$

The flow pattern is indeterminate in the region for Δt_f greater than 28.4 F and less than 52 F; 40 F can therefore be taken as an average dividing value. Thus, in cases where the temperature drop through the inside film is great, accurate design will require use of a calculated h_c rather than use of a so-called standard value (see Art. 5–3).

FREE CONVECTION TO UNHEATED FLOORS AND CEILINGS. For unheated ceilings (equivalent to cooled horizontal planes facing downward), Fishenden and Saunders[3] have given specific correlations.

Laminar Flow Range for Unheated Ceilings (N_{Nu} between 10 and 40).

$$N_{\text{Nu}} = 0.54[(\text{Gr})(\text{Pr})]^{0.25} \qquad (4\text{–}56)$$

which for air at room temperature reduces to (by the same substitutions used in obtaining Eq. 4–53)

$$h_c = 0.251(\Delta t_f)^{0.25} \qquad (4\text{–}57)$$

[3] M. Fishenden and O. A. Saunders, *An Introduction to Heat Transfer*, Oxford University Press, 1950.

In order for Eq. 4–56 to be applicable, N_{Nu} would have to exceed 10; so,

$$h_{c_{\min}} = \frac{k}{D} N_{\mathrm{Nu}} = \frac{0.0147}{2} 10 = 0.073$$

and the minimum value of Δt_f would be

$$\Delta t_{f_{\min}} = \left(\frac{h_c}{0.25}\right)^4 = \left(\frac{0.073}{0.251}\right)^4 \doteq 0 \text{ F}$$

Likewise, the maximum applicable value of h_c would be

$$h_{c_{\max}} = \left(\frac{0.0147}{2}\right) 40 = 0.294$$

and the corresponding maximum value of Δt_f would be

$$\Delta t_{f_{\max}} = \left(\frac{0.294}{0.251}\right)^4 = 1.9 \text{ F}$$

Thus it is evident that for unheated ceilings, the free convective flow pattern will be turbulent rather than laminar in all cases except those in which the ceiling is very effectively insulated.

Turbulent Flow Range for Unheated Ceilings (N_{Nu} greater than 40).

$$N_{\mathrm{Nu}} = 0.14[(\mathrm{Gr})(\mathrm{Pr})]^{1/3} \qquad (4\text{–}58)$$

which for air at room temperature reduces to

$$h_c = 0.259(\Delta t_f)^{1/3} \qquad (4\text{–}59)$$

This equation will be applicable in all cases where the temperature drop from room air to ceiling exceeds 2 F.

For unheated floors (equivalent to cooled horizontal planes facing upward) the recommended equations are also given by Fishenden and Saunders.

Laminar Flow Range for Unheated Floors (N_{Nu} between 10 and 126).

$$N_{\mathrm{Nu}} = 0.27[(\mathrm{Gr})(\mathrm{Pr})]^{0.25} \qquad (4\text{–}60)$$

which for air at room temperature reduces to

$$h_c = 0.126(\Delta t_f)^{0.25} \qquad (4\text{–}61)$$

The range of N_{Nu} for laminar flow over an unheated floor is so great that Eq. 4–61 is applicable for h_c up to

$$h_{c_{\max}} = \frac{h}{D} N_{\mathrm{Nu}} = \frac{0.0147}{2} 126 = 0.926$$

and the corresponding maximum value of Δt_f is

$$\Delta t_{f_{\max}} = \left(\frac{0.926}{0.126}\right)^4 = 2880 \text{ F}$$

Thus the laminar flow equation will always apply to unheated floors.

FREE CONVECTION IN VERTICAL AIR SPACES. The convective conductance of an air space is defined by the equation

$$q_c = a_c A(t_h - t_c) = a_c A(\Delta t_a) \tag{4-62}$$

where $q_c =$ the heat transfer by convection and conduction (but not including radiation) from surface to surface of the air space, Btu/hr.

$a_c =$ conductance of the air space for heat transfer by convection, Btu/(hr)(sq ft)(°F).

$A =$ area of one of two vertical and parallel bounding planes, sq ft.

$t_h =$ surface temperature on the warmer side.

$t_c =$ surface temperature on the cooler side.

$\Delta t_a =$ temperature difference across the air space.

For an air space of width x ft, a special Nusselt number is defined by the equation

$$N_{\mathrm{Nu}} = \frac{a_c x}{k}$$

and a corresponding special Grashof number is defined by

$$N_{\mathrm{Gr}} = \frac{x^3 \rho^2 g \beta \; \Delta t_a}{\mu^2} \tag{4-63}$$

Effective correlation of experimental data is obtained from the relationship

$$N_{\mathrm{Nu}} = y \left(\frac{25x}{L} \right)^{1/9} (N_{\mathrm{Gr}} N_{\mathrm{Pr}})^z \tag{4-64}$$

where L is the height of the air space and the parameter $(25x/L)^{1/9}$ is no longer important after L/x exceeds 25; the coefficient y and the exponent z have values that depend on the range of N_{Nu}. When applied to air at room temperature, this equation becomes (by the same substitutions used in establishing Eq. 4–52)

$$N_{\mathrm{Nu}} = y \left(\frac{25x}{L} \right)^{1/9} [(2)(10)^6 (x^3 \; \Delta t_a)]^z \tag{4-65}$$

For the range of $x^3 \; \Delta t_a$ between 0.0005 and 0.5, the values of y and z are, respectively, 0.15 and 0.25; hence the equation takes the form

$$N_{\mathrm{Nu}} = 5.64 \left(\frac{25x}{L} \right)^{1/9} (x^3 \; \Delta t_a)^{0.25} \tag{4-65a}$$

Further, the minimum L/x for an air space in a vertical wall would rarely be less than 25; hence, for walls, the L/x parameter can be dropped, giving

$$N_{\mathrm{Nu}} = 5.64 (x^3 \; \Delta t_a)^{0.25}$$

giving

$$a_c = 5.64 \frac{k}{x} (x^3 \; \Delta t_a)^{0.25} = 0.083 \left(\frac{\Delta t_a}{x} \right)^{0.25} \tag{4-66}$$

The minimum value of $x^3 \Delta t_a$ is so small (0.0005), even with Δt_a of 0.5 F, that the corresponding air space would have to be less than

$$x_{min} = \left(\frac{0.0005}{0.5}\right)^{1/3} = 0.1 \text{ ft}, \quad \text{or} \quad 1.2 \text{ in.}$$

For air spaces of average size (say, 4 in.) with surface-to-surface temperature drops of the order of 10 F, the value of $x^3 \Delta t_a$ would be $(4/12)^3(10)$, or 0.47.

For values of $x^3 \Delta t_a$ greater than 0.5, the constants y and z are 0.05 and 0.333, and Eq. 4–65 becomes (with L/x taken as greater than 25)

$$N_{Nu} = 6.3(x^3 \Delta t_a)^{1/3} \tag{4–67}$$

giving

$$a_c = 0.093(\Delta t_a)^{1/3} \tag{4–68}$$

which shows that the air space has now become so wide that the effect of width no longer influences convective transfer.

EXAMPLE 4–14. A 4-in. air space separates parallel vertical walls. Known surface-to-surface temperature difference is 70 F. Calculate the rate of convective transfer per unit area per unit time.

Solution: The value of $x^3 \Delta t_a$ for this case is $(4/12)^3(70)$, or 2.59; hence Eq. 4–68 applies rather than Eq. 4–66. Then

$$a_c = 0.093(\Delta t_a)^{1/3} = 0.093(70)^{1/3} = 0.385 \text{ Btu/(hr)(sq ft)(°F)}$$

EXAMPLE 4–15. Calculate the conductance of the air space of Example 4–12 by considering it to consist only of two surface films in series.

Solution: In this case

$$a_c = \frac{1}{(1/h_c) + (1/h_c)}$$

where h_c would be calculable from Eq. 4–55 with a temperature difference equal to one-half that of the air space. Thus

$$h_c = 0.241\left(\frac{70}{2}\right)^{1/3} = 0.787$$

and

$$a_c = \frac{1}{(1/0.787) + (1/0.787)} = \frac{1}{2.54} = 0.393$$

which agrees very closely (within 2 per cent) with the answer obtained by the method of Example 4–14 for the same air space.

FREE CONVECTION DOWNWARD THROUGH HORIZONTAL AIR SPACES. For convective transfer out through air spaces located in the floor, available data are not so consistent as for vertical air spaces. As an approximation, which is in agreement with many of the experimental data, it is recommended that the conductance calculated by Eq. 4–66 for a vertical air space be increased by 40 per cent for use with a narrow ($x^3 \Delta t_a < 0.5$) horizontal space and that the conductance from Eq. 4–68 for a vertical space be increased by 20 per cent for use with a large ($x^3 \, \Delta t_a > 0.5$) horizontal air space. Thus

$$a_c = 0.117 \left(\frac{\Delta t_a}{x}\right)^{0.25} \tag{4–69}$$

when $x^3 \, \Delta t_a$ is less than 0.5; alternatively,

$$a_c = 0.112 (\Delta t)^{1/3} \tag{4–70}$$

when $x^3 \, \Delta t_a$ is greater than 0.5.

FREE CONVECTION UPWARD THROUGH HORIZONTAL AIR SPACES. For this case a correlation is obtained in the same form as Eq. 4–65 but without x/L as a parameter. For values of $x^3 \, \Delta t_a$ between 0.0036 and 0.11, the values of y and z are 0.21 and 0.25; the equation then becomes

$$N_{\mathrm{Nu}} = 7.88 (x^3 \, \Delta t_a)^{0.25}$$

giving

$$a_c = 7.88 \, \frac{k}{x} \, (x^3 \, \Delta t_a)^{0.25} - 0.128 \left(\frac{\Delta t_a}{x}\right)^{0.25} \tag{4–71}$$

For $x^3 \, \Delta t_a$ greater than 0.11, the constants y and z are 0.075 and $\frac{1}{3}$; the equation then becomes

$$N_{\mathrm{Nu}} = 9.45 (x^3 \, \Delta t_a)^{1/3}$$

giving

$$a_c = 0.140 (\Delta t_a)^{1/3} \tag{4–72}$$

LIMITATIONS OF FREE CONVECTION COEFFICIENTS FOR AIR. Eqs. 4–49 to 4–72 and their complements, for free convection, all require knowledge of the temperature drop across the air film or the air space as a condition for evaluating h_c or a_c. But the fraction of total temperature drop that occurs across any one part of a series thermal system is determined by the ratio of the resistance of that part to the resistance of the whole system. Thus, in cases where h_c is not known, Δt_f will likewise be unknown. One method of solving for h_c in such a situation would be by trial and error. Assume a value of Δt_f, calculate the corresponding h_c, then use the calculated h_c to calculate (in terms of other resistances in the system) a revised Δt_f, and use this value to obtain a second approximation for the true value of h_c; when the calculated Δt_f gives the calculated h_c (and vice versa), a solution will have been attained.

Another complicating factor is that heat transfer by radiation will always be occurring simultaneously across an air film; hence it will alter Δt_f from the value that it would have if convection occurred alone. For this reason the over-all problem of evaluating h_c in terms of Δt_f can best be postponed until after radiation has been discussed; in a subsequent article (Art. 4–8, page 150), therefore, relationships will be established for evaluating the temperature drop across the film as a function of the parallel transfer of heat by convection and radiation.

FORCED CONVECTION INSIDE TUBES AND DUCTS. For flow occurring in a tube or duct with Reynolds number greater than 10,000 and with ratio of length to diameter greater than 20, turbulence can be considered to be fully developed, and the equation for the film coefficient is

$$N_{\mathrm{Nu}} = 0.023 N_{\mathrm{Re}}^{0.8} N_{\mathrm{Pr}}^{0.4} \qquad (4\text{--}73)$$

where all the fluid properties are evaluated at the average (bulk) temperature of the fluid. The equation is valid for gases or liquids, either heating or cooling, provided the range of Prandtl number is between 0.7 and 120 (most fluids except oils have Prandtl numbers in this range).

Air in Turbulent Flow. Eq. 4–73 as applied to air over the range from 32 F to 200 F would use average values of viscosity of 0.0455 lb/(hr)(ft), of density of 0.072 lb/(cu ft), of thermal conductivity of 0.0147 lb/(hr)(sq ft)(°F/ ft), and an average specific heat of 0.240 Btu/(lb)(°F). The Prandtl number would be taken as 0.70. By making these substitutions,

$$h_c = 0.023 \, \frac{k}{D} \left(\frac{DV'\rho}{\mu'} \right)^{0.8} (N_{\mathrm{Pr}})^{0.4}$$

$$= \frac{0.297 \, V^{0.8}}{D^{0.2}} \qquad (4\text{--}74)$$

where h_c = film coefficient for convective transfer, Btu/(hr)(sq ft)(°F).
     D = tube or duct diameter, ft.
     V = fluid velocity, fps.

EXAMPLE 4–16. Air at a mean temperature of 95 F is flowing at 10 fps through a 1-ft diameter duct. Determine the film coefficient for convective heat transfer.

Solution: The viscosity of 95 F air is 0.0455 lb/(hr)(ft), and the density is 0.072 lb/cu ft, so the Reynolds number can be calculated as

$$N_{\mathrm{Re}} = \frac{DV'\rho}{\mu'} = \frac{(1)(10 \times 3600)(0.072)}{0.0455} = 57{,}000$$

(Note that the velocity must be in units of feet per hour, V', since the viscosity is in hourly time units.) The flow is therefore in the region of fully developed turbulence, and the film coefficient can be evaluated by Eq. 4–74 as

$$h_c = \frac{0.297(V)^{0.8}}{D^{0.2}}$$

$$= \frac{0.297(10)^{0.8}}{(1)^{0.2}} = 1.88 \; \text{Btu/(hr)(sq ft)(°F)}$$

(Note that Eq. 4–74 is not dimensionless and that the stated units of velocity are feet per second.)

Water in Turbulent Flow. For water in turbulent flow in the temperature range from 40 F to boiling, McAdams[4] has suggested use of averaged properties to reduce Eq. 4–73 to the simplified form of

$$h_c = \frac{150(1 + 0.011t)(V)^{0.8}}{d^{0.2}} \qquad (4\text{--}75)$$

where
$\quad t =$ average (bulk) temperature of the water, °F.
$\quad V =$ fluid velocity, fps.
$\quad d =$ inside pipe or tube diameter, in.

EXAMPLE 4–17. Water at a mean temperature of 100 F is flowing within a 1-ft inside diameter pipe at a velocity 10 fps. Calculate the film coefficient for convective heat transfer and compare it with the value for air (Example 4–16) flowing in the same size pipe at the same temperature and the same velocity.

Solution: The Reynolds number for this flow system [based on density of 62.0 lb/cu ft at 100 F and viscosity of 1.66 (lb)/(hr)(ft) at 100 F] is

$$N_{\text{Re}} = \frac{DV'\rho}{\mu'} = \frac{(1)(10 \times 3600)(62.0)}{1.66}$$

$$= 1,345,000$$

By Eq. 4–75,

$$h_c = \frac{150[1 + (0.011)(t)](V)^{0.8}}{d^{0.2}}$$

$$= \frac{150[1 + (0.011)(100)](10)^{0.8}}{(12)^{0.2}}$$

$$= 681$$

The value of h_c for water, 681, is 360 times greater than for air (Example 4–16) flowing at the same velocity through a pipe of the same diameter.

Streamline and Transition Flow. In the field of comfort heating, the engineer rarely has occasion to work with high-viscosity fluids other than fuel oils. Heat-transfer problems relating to air almost always involve either free convection (as over a wall) or forced convection (in a tube or duct or exchanger) under conditions of turbulent flow. Likewise, heat-transfer problems associated with water, the other major working fluid, are usually for flow in or over a tube under conditions of turbulent forced convection. In those unusual circumstances where a design involves forced convection in the streamline or transition region, reference should be made to one of the standard texts on heat transmission.

FORCED CONVECTION OUTSIDE AND NORMAL TO TUBES OR DUCTS. A general correlation for gases and liquids flowing in forced convection normal to single tubes or ducts has been obtained in a form similar to that of Eq. 4–73

[4] Bibliography, item 3.

but with a different coefficient and different exponents. For Reynolds number in the range from 0.1 to 50, the recommended equation is

$$N_{\text{Nu}} = 0.91(N_{\text{Re}})^{0.385}(N_{\text{Pr}})^{0.31} \qquad (4\text{--}76a)$$

whereas for the N_{Re} range from 50 to 10,000, the recommended equation is

$$N_{\text{Nu}} = 0.6(N_{\text{Re}})^{0.5}(N_{\text{Pr}})^{0.31} \qquad (4\text{--}76b)$$

where $N_{\text{Nu}} = hD_o/h_f$, based on outside diameter of the pipe and on conductivity measured at the temperature of the film.

$N_{\text{Re}} = D_o V\rho/\mu$, based on the outside diameter of the pipe, D_o, the velocity through the minimum cross-section V, and the viscosity at film temperature.

$N_{\text{Pr}} = c_p\mu'/k$, based on values of all three fluid properties at film temperature.

Simplified Equation for Air. For air at a film temperature of 200 F, a simplified approximate equation for forced convection outside and normal to a tube or duct takes the form (for N_{Re} between 1000 and 50,000)

$$h_c = \frac{0.665 V^{0.6}}{D_o^{0.4}} \qquad (4\text{--}77)$$

where V = fluid velocity through minimum cross-section, fps.
D_o = outside diameter.

EXAMPLE 4–18. Air at 200 F and a velocity of 10 fps flows outside and normal to a 12-in. outside-diameter pipe. Calculate the film coefficient and compare it (Example 4–16) with that for air flow at the same velocity within the same pipe.

Solution: Air at 200 F has a density and viscosity of 0.0603 lb/cu ft and 0.0519 lb/(ft)(hr), respectively. The Reynolds number is therefore

$$N_{\text{Re}} = \frac{D(3600V)\rho}{\mu'} = \frac{(1)(3600)(10)(0.0603)}{0.0519}$$

$$= 41,700$$

so Eq. 4–77 is applicable. Thus

$$h_c = \frac{0.665(10)^{0.6}}{(1)^{0.4}} = 2.64 \text{ Btu/(hr)(sq ft)(°F)}$$

This value of h_c is 2.64/1.88, or 40 per cent, greater (Example 4–16) than for air flowing within the same pipe at the same velocity.

Simplified Equation for Water. For water at a film temperature of 200 F, the values of ρ, k, μ', and N_{Pr} are, respectively, 60.1 lb/cu ft, 0.406 Btu/(hr)(sq ft)(°F/ft), 0.738 lb/(hr)(ft), and 1.83. The Reynolds number is therefore

$$N_{\text{Re}} = \frac{DV'\rho}{\mu'} = \frac{DV'(60.1)}{0.738}$$

$$= 81.5DV'$$

In order for a simplified equation to reflect the conditions of Eq. 4–76a (for which $N_{\text{Re}_{\max}}$ is 50), it would be a requirement that

$$(D_oV')_{\max} = \frac{50}{81.5} = 0.614$$

which is an impractically small value. To meet the conditions of Eq. 4–76b, however, the $(D_oV')_{\max}$ would increase to

$$(D_oV')_{\max} = \frac{10,000}{81.5} = 123$$

This limiting value of $(D_oV')_{\max}$ for which data have been effectively correlated is very low when applied to most relatively non-viscous fluids and is lower than the usual operating range for water. Lacking better data, however, it is suggested that Eq. 4–76b be used with water as the fluid for higher values of N_{Re}. Then, to obtain the simplified equation, substitute into Eq. 4–76b the given properties of water at a film temperature of 200 F

$$
\begin{aligned}
h_c &= 0.6 \frac{k}{D_o}\left(\frac{D_oV'\rho}{\mu'}\right)^{0.5}(N_{\text{Pr}})^{0.31} \\
&= (0.6)(0.406)\left[\frac{(3600)(60.1)}{0.738}\right]^{0.5}(1.83)^{0.31}\left(\frac{V}{D_o}\right)^{0.5} \\
&= (0.6)(0.406)(541)(1.205)\left(\frac{V}{D}\right)^{0.5} \qquad (4\text{–}78) \\
&= 159\left(\frac{V}{D}\right)^{0.5}
\end{aligned}
$$

where V is in units of feet per second.

EXAMPLE 4–19. Water at 200 F and a velocity of 1 fps is flowing outside and normal to a 4-in. outside-diameter pipe. Calculate the film coefficient.

Solution: The Reynolds number is

$$N_{\text{Re}} = \frac{D_oV'\rho}{\mu'} = \frac{(4/12)(1)(3600)(60.1)}{(0.738)} = 97,600$$

and the approximate film coefficient is, by Eq. 4–78,

$$h_c = 159\left[\frac{1}{4/12}\right]^{0.5} = 175 \text{ Btu/(hr)(sq ft)(°F)}$$

SPECIAL CASES (1. Non-circular Ducts; 2. Logarithmic Mean Temperature Difference). In applying to actual design problems the previously developed equations for film coefficients, two special situations deserve consideration. The first is that of developing a method for using the circular tube or duct equations for evaluation of film coefficients with respect to (either inside or outside) square, rectangular, or other conduits of non-circular cross-section. The second is to establish a mean temperature difference for use in those cases where the fluid is heated or cooled through a substantial temperature difference.

Non-circular Tubes or Ducts. Equations that include diameters as a variable can be used for conduits of non-circular cross-section by utilizing an equivalent diameter equal to four times the actual cross-sectional area divided by the perimeter. In the case of flow through annular spaces, as between concentric tubes, the equivalent diameter is equal to four times the cross-sectional area divided by that perimeter for which the film coefficient is to be evaluated. Thus, for concentric tubes, the equivalent diameter D_{ei} for heat transfer through the film adjacent to the inner tube is

$$D_{ei} = \frac{4[(\pi D_o^2/4) - (\pi D_i^2/4)]}{\pi D_i} = \frac{D_o^2 - D_i^2}{D_i} \qquad (4\text{--}79a)$$

whereas for heat transfer through the film adjacent to the outer tube, the equivalent diameter is

$$D_{eo} = \frac{D_o^2 - D_i^2}{D_o} \qquad (4\text{--}79b)$$

EXAMPLE 4–20. Determine the relative values of inside film coefficients for three ducts of equal area through which air is passing at the same velocity; one duct is circular, another is square, and the third is rectangular with a width-to-depth ratio of 6. Compare the results.

Solution: The film coefficient for turbulent flow of air within a duct varies as a function (Eq. 4–74) of the reciprocal of the diameter to the 0.2 power. If the diameter of the circular duct is taken as unity, the length of side of the square duct is

$$L = \left(\frac{\pi D^2}{4}\right)^{0.5} = \left(\frac{\pi}{4}\right)^{0.5} = 0.886$$

and its equivalent diameter is

$$D_e = \frac{4\pi/4}{(4)(0.886)} = 0.908$$

The film coefficient for the square duct is therefore

$$h_{c(sq)} = 100\left(\frac{1}{0.908}\right)^{0.2} = 104.4 \text{ per cent}$$

of h_c for a circular duct.

The width W of the rectangular duct is

$$(W)\frac{W}{6} = \frac{\pi(1)^2}{4}$$

or

$$W = (1.5\pi)^{0.5} = 2.17 \text{ ft}$$

so its equivalent diameter is

$$D_e = \frac{4\pi/4}{(2.333)(2.17)} = 0.621$$

The film coefficient for the rectangular duct is therefore

$$h_{c(\text{rect})} = 100 \left(\frac{1}{0.621} \right)^{0.2} = 110 \text{ per cent}$$

of h_c for a circular duct.

Thus the rate of heat loss from non-circular ducts of equal area increases at a rate more rapid than the increase in perimeter. For the circular duct, the inside film conductance (area included) is

$$C'_{(\text{circ})} = \pi(1)(h_c) = \pi h_c$$

For the square duct,

$$C'_{i(\text{sq})} = (4)(0.886)(1.04)h_c = 3.685 h_c$$

or 117 per cent of that for the circular.

For the rectangular duct,

$$C'_{i(\text{rect})} = (2.333)(2.17)(1.10)h_c = 5.57 h_c$$

or 177 per cent of that for the circular.

Logarithmic Mean Temperature Difference.   One of the most common types of heat-transfer problem is that in which heat flows from a hot fluid to a cold fluid through an intervening solid surface. The usual type of heat exchanger, for example, permits flow of the hot and cold fluids on opposite sides of the transfer surface, the heat flow then occurring by convection from the warm fluid to the surface, by conduction through the metallic wall, and by convection from the cool side of the wall to the colder fluid. With common shell-and-tube exchangers the hot fluid enters at one end of the exchanger and undergoes a loss of temperature as it travels the length of the unit. Similarly, the cool fluid enters at one end (the same end as the hot fluid for *parallel* flow, the opposite end for *counterflow*) and undergoes a temperature rise as it passes through the unit. In condensers or evaporators the temperature of one of the fluids does not change, whereas for an exchanger in which one fluid is condensing while the other evaporates, there is no temperature change of either fluid and hence no change in the temperature difference between them.

Along any small finite length of a heat exchanger the temperature difference between hot and cold fluid is practically constant; hence the rate of heat transfer at that small section can be readily evaluated. The over-all heat transfer is the summation of heat transferred at each of the small lengths. In order to avoid the difficulty of summing up transfer rates over small lengths, it is necessary to establish a mean value of the fluid-to-fluid temperature difference. It can be readily shown that the correct value of such a mean temperature difference for either a parallel flow or counterflow exchanger or for a condenser or evaporator is the logarithmic mean of the temperature differences at entrance and at exit. Thus

$$(t_h - t_c)_m = \frac{(t_{h_1} - t_{c_1}) - (t_{h_2} - t_{c_2})}{\log_e \dfrac{t_{h_1} - t_{c_1}}{t_{h_2} - t_{c_2}}} \qquad (4\text{--}80)$$

where $(t_h - t_c)_m$ = logarithmic mean fluid-to-fluid temperature difference.

$t_{h_1} - t_{c_1}$ = temperature difference between the hot and cold fluids at that end of the exchanger where the temperature difference is greatest.

$t_{h_2} - t_{c_2}$ = temperature difference between the hot and cold fluids at that end of the exchanger where the temperature difference is least.

$\log_e$ = natural (Naperian) logarithm.

EXAMPLE 4–21. Hot and cold fluids enter a parallel-flow heat exchanger at respective temperatures of 500 F and 80 F. They leave at 210 F and 190 F. Determine the percentage error that would result if the arithmetical mean temperature difference were used in place of the logarithmic mean temperature difference.

Solution: The arithmetic mean temperature difference is

$$\left[\frac{(500 - 80) + (210 - 190)}{2} \right] = 220 \text{ F}$$

The logarithmic mean temperature difference, by Eq. 4–80, is

$$\frac{(500 - 80) - (210 - 190)}{\log_e [(500 - 80)/(210 - 190)]} = \frac{400}{3.0445} = 131.4 \text{ F}$$

The error due to incorrect use of the arithmetic average temperature difference would then be

$$\left[\frac{(220 - 131.4)}{131.4} \right] 100 = 67.4 \text{ per cent}$$

The result shows the great importance of correct and accurate evaluation of the mean temperature difference in all problems involving heat transfer between heating or cooling fluids.

Convective Film Coefficient for Outside Surfaces of Walls. The film coefficient for convective transfer from an outside wall surface is usually of the order of 4 or 5 Btu/(hr)(sq ft)(°F); hence the convective film resistance (0.25 or 0.2) is such a small fraction of the total wall resistance that the temperature drop across the outside film is very small. This means that Δt_f varies over such a small range that it need not be considered as a determining factor in evaluation of the outside film coefficient. Thus h_c is evaluable as a function of two factors only: (1) roughness of the surface, (2) design value of the wind velocity. The values of h_c given by the equations which follow are based on data from the ASHRAE Guide,[5] but are lower by 0.7 Btu/(hr)(sq ft)(°F) than the ASHRAE Guide values for film conductance. This is because the Guide values include the effect of radiation, whereas the following equations are for convective transfer only.

$$h_c = 0.7 + 0.28V'' \qquad (4\text{–}81)$$

[5] Bibliography, item 1.

for very smooth surfaces such as glass.

$$h_c = 0.9 + 0.3V'' \tag{4-82}$$

for smooth surfaces such as planed wood and plaster.

$$h_c = 1.3 + 0.4V'' \tag{4-83}$$

for moderately rough surfaces such as finished concrete and smooth brick.

$$h_c = 1.4 + 0.5V'' \tag{4-84}$$

for rough surfaces such as stucco and rough brick.

In Eqs. 4–81 through 4–84, V'' is the wind velocity over the surface, expressed in miles per hour.

Examination of the above equations shows that convection across the outside film increases with roughness; this is due largely to the greater effective transfer area of the more irregular surfaces. The use of Eqs. 4–81 through 4–84, in combination with the parallel transfer coefficient for radiation, is discussed in Art. 4–8a.

4–7. Radiation.   Radiant transfer—whether in a structure heated with a convector, baseboard, radiator, or warm-air heating system—accounts for a substantial, though varying, fraction of the total loss of heat from a room to its interior exposed surfaces. This fact is not commonly recognized by the heating engineer even though he does use inside film coefficients that do include a factor to take account of the radiation loss. The net radiant transfer between any two surfaces depends on their respective temperatures, areas, surface characteristics (as smooth or rough, glossy or dull), distance apart, and angle with respect to one another. The last four of the above factors are commonly grouped in a coefficient, F_{ae}, which is dependent on both the geometry of the system and the characteristics of the two surfaces. The fundamental equation for radiant exchange between surfaces separated by a non-absorbing medium is the Stefan-Boltzmann law:

$$q = 0.1713 A F_{ae} \left[\left(\frac{T_h}{100} \right)^4 - \left(\frac{T_c}{100} \right)^4 \right] \tag{4-85}$$

where A = the area of one of the surfaces between which radiant energy is flowing.

F_{ae} = a term dependent on the relative geometrical position of one body with respect to the other and the emissivity characteristics of the two surfaces.

T_h and T_c = the temperatures in degrees Fahrenheit absolute of the hot and cold surfaces.

q = the net rate of heat transfer, Btu/hr.

The principal disadvantage of the above equation is the difficulty of evaluating the term F_{ae}. In many cases (but this is not always possible) this term can be broken down into a product of two factors, $(F_a)(F_e)$, where the first, F_a, is called the *shape factor* and is fixed entirely by the geometry of the system; the second, F_c, depends on the surface characteristics and is called the *emissivity factor*. In cases where highly reflective surfaces are used for inside surfaces of all or part of an enclosure, the problems involved in evaluating F_{ae} become much greater than those usually associated with radiant exchange within a room in which all surfaces are essentially non-reflecting. The present article deals primarily with development of the basic radiation equations and discussion of their application to non-reflective systems; their application to enclosures that constitute reflective systems is developed in Chapter 8.

EQUATIONS FOR DIRECT (NON-REFLECTED) RADIANT TRANSFER. The equations for evaluating the radiant-energy contribution to transmission load in a heating system are modified forms of the basic rational equations for radiant exchange. In order to visualize the boundary conditions beyond which the modified equations cannot be accurately applied, it is necessary first to establish the precise rational equations and then to show, step by step, the limitations applied to these precise equations in reducing them to the less general but greatly simplified forms used in practice. The ability to design or analyze a typical heating system may be somewhat independent of a complete understanding of the basic rational equations. The background acquired from such a comprehension, however, will permit use of the simplified equations with greater confidence; it will provide facility, not otherwise obtainable, in extending these equations to unusual conditions, in interpreting results, and in estimating the probable inaccuracy resulting from a given assumption.

The total energy emitted by a small finite area of a perfectly radiating, *black-body* surface is given by

$$q' = \sigma T_1^4 \, \Delta A_1 \qquad (4\text{--}86)$$

where $q' =$ radiant energy emitted (the prime indicating that it is from a small finite area), Btu/hr.

$\sigma =$ an experimentally determined constant (Stefan-Boltzmann constant) having the value $0.1713(10)^{-8}$.

$T_1 =$ temperature of the surface expressed in degrees Fahrenheit absolute, °F $+$ 460.

$\Delta A_1 =$ small finite area of radiating surface, sq ft.

The product σT_1^4 is defined as the *emissive power* of a perfect radiator.

In practice, no surface is available that emits as much energy as a perfect radiator, but many actual surfaces emit energy at a rate that is a constant fraction of the energy emitted by a black body at the same temperature. If this fraction has a fixed value independent of temperature and of the wavelength of emitted energy, the emitting surface is said to be a *gray* body, and its total energy emission is expressed as

$$q' = \sigma e_1 T_1^4 \, \Delta A_1 \qquad (4\text{--}87)$$

where $e_1 = $ *emissivity*, or the ratio of emissive power, of actual surface ΔA_1 to that of a black body at the same temperature. (Typical values of e are given in Table 4–5.)

Intensity and Normal Intensity. Eq. 4–87 gives the energy leaving ΔA_1 in all directions; that is, through a hemispherical solid angle of 2π

TABLE 4–5
Emissivities of Typical Materials*

Highly polished copper plate	0.02–0.03
Highly polished iron plate	0.05–0.06
Aluminum-surfaced roofing	0.21
Aluminum paint	0.3–0.5
Building brick	0.45
Bronze radiator paint	0.51
Clean, smooth, sheet iron	0.55–0.60
Concrete tile	0.63
Sheet steel with oxide layer	0.80
White enamel fused on iron	0.90
Oak, planed	0.90
Plaster, rough lime	0.91
Red brick, rough	0.93
Marble, polished	0.93
Smooth glass	0.94
Oil paints, all colors	0.92–0.96
Water	0.95–0.96
Lampblack	0.96–0.98

* In temperature range from 30 F to 110 F; various sources.

steradians. The fraction of energy emitted from ΔA_1 through a small solid angle $\Delta\omega$ in a direction normal to ΔA_1 is, then,

$$q'' = i_n \, \Delta A_1 \, \Delta\omega \qquad (4\text{–}88a)$$

where $q'' = $ radiant energy emitted by ΔA_1 through $\Delta\omega$ (the double prime indicating that both area and angle are very small), Btu/hr.

$i_n = $ the *normal intensity* equal to the quantity of energy emitted by a perfectly diffusing surface per unit area through unit solid angle in a direction normal to the surface.

When the solid angle $\Delta\omega$ is in a direction making an angle ϕ_1 with the normal to ΔA_1 (Fig. 4–11), the energy emitted through $\Delta\omega$ is

$$q'' = i \, \Delta A_1 \, \Delta\omega \qquad (4\text{–}88b)$$

where i, the *intensity*, is the quantity of energy emitted per unit area of diffusing surface through unit solid angle at angle ϕ to the surface normal. But since Lambert's law states that the intensity varies as the cosine of angle ϕ,

$$i = i_n \cos\phi \qquad (4\text{–}89)$$

Substituting for i in Eq. 4–88b,

$$q'' = i_n \cos\phi \, \Delta A_1 \, \Delta\omega \qquad (4\text{–}90)$$

Solution of Eq. 4–90 requires the evaluation of i_n. Refer to Fig. 4–12 and note that

$$\Delta\omega = \frac{\Delta S}{r^2} = \frac{(p\,\Delta\beta)(r\,\Delta\phi)}{r^2} = \frac{(r\sin\phi\,\Delta\beta)(r\,\Delta\phi)}{r^2}$$

$$= \sin\phi\,\Delta\phi\,\Delta\beta$$

Substituting in Eq. 4–90,

$$q'' = i_n \sin\phi \cos\phi\,\Delta\phi\,\Delta\beta\,\Delta A_1 \qquad (4\text{--}91)$$

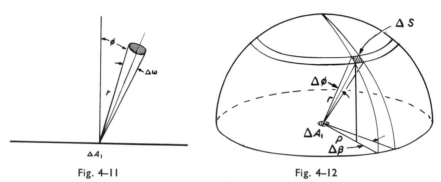

Fig. 4–11   Fig. 4–12

Fig. 4–11. Geometry of solid-angle emission.

Fig. 4–12. Geometrical data for evaluation of normal intensity.

As angle ϕ varies from zero to 90 F and as angle β sweeps through an entire circle, Eq. 4–91 integrates to give the total energy emitted by ΔA_1, in all directions, as

$$q' = i_n \pi\,\Delta A_1$$

from which the normal intensity is evaluable as

$$i_n = \frac{q'}{\pi\,\Delta A_1} \qquad (4\text{--}92)$$

From Eq. 4–87, $q'/\Delta A_1 = \sigma e_1 T_1^4$, and so, by substitution in Eq. 4–92,

$$i_n = \frac{\sigma e_1 T_1^4}{\pi} \qquad (4\text{--}93)$$

and substituting in Eq. 4–90,

$$q'' = \sigma e_1 T_1^4\,\Delta A_1 \cos\phi_1 \left(\frac{\Delta\omega}{\pi}\right) \qquad (4\text{--}94)$$

Since $\cos\phi_1\,\Delta A_1$ is the projected area of the emitting surface on a plane normal to the direction of radiation, Eq. 4–94 shows that the quantity of energy leaving unit projected area through unit solid angle is independent of the angle ϕ and has the constant value $(\sigma e_1 T_1^4)/\pi$, equal to the normal intensity i_n.

Shape Factors. The energy emitted by ΔA_1 in the direction of any infinitesimal area ΔA_2 (Fig. 4–13) is given by Eq. 4–94 when $\Delta \omega$ has a value equal to the solid angle subtended by ΔA_2, or

$$\Delta \omega = \frac{\cos \phi_2 \, \Delta A_2}{r^2} \tag{4–95}$$

where $\phi_2 =$ angle between r and a normal to ΔA_2.
$\cos \phi_2 \, \Delta A_2 =$ projected area of ΔA_2 on a plane normal to r.
$r =$ distance from ΔA_1 to ΔA_2.

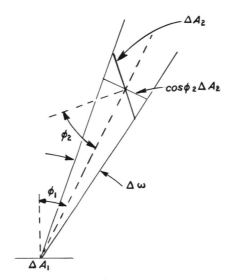

Fig. 4–13. Geometrical data for small-surface shape-factor determination.

Substituting the above value of $\Delta \omega$ into Eq. 4–94 yields

$$q'' = \frac{(\sigma e_1 T_1^4 \, \Delta A_1)(\cos \phi_1 \cos \phi_2 \, \Delta A_2)}{\pi r^2} \tag{4–96}$$

The first term of Eq. 4–96 is identical with the right side of Eq. 4–87 and equals total energy emitted by ΔA_1; the second term of this equation must therefore represent the fraction of energy leaving ΔA_1 which travels in the direction of ΔA_2. This term depends only on the size and geometrical arrangement of surfaces ΔA_1 and ΔA_2 and is defined as the *shape factor* F, or *seeing factor*, of area ΔA_2 with respect to energy leaving ΔA_1; thus

$$F_{\Delta A_2 \Delta A_1} = \frac{\cos \phi_1 \cos \phi_2 \, \Delta A_2}{\pi r^2} = \frac{1}{\Delta A_1} \frac{\cos \phi_1 \cos \phi_2 \, \Delta A_1 \, \Delta A_2}{\pi r^2} \tag{4–97}$$

where the subscripts to the shape factor identify the areas with respect to which it is evaluated; the first subscript is for the receiving area and the second for the emitting area. Thus $F_{A_x A_y}$ would be the shape factor of A_x with respect to area A_y and would be equal to the fraction of energy striking A_x from A_y of that initially emitted by A_y.

The Reciprocity Theorem. If Eq. 4–96 were written to express the energy leaving ΔA_2 in the direction of ΔA_1, the shape factor of ΔA_1 with respect to energy leaving ΔA_2 would be

$$F_{\Delta A_1 \Delta A_2} = \frac{1}{\Delta A_2} \frac{\cos \phi_1 \cos \phi_2 \, \Delta A_1 \, \Delta A_2}{\pi r^2} \qquad (4\text{–}98)$$

Eqs. 4–97 and 4–98 show that

$$F_{\Delta A_2 \Delta A_1} \Delta A_1 = F_{\Delta A_1 \Delta A_2} \Delta A_2 \qquad (4\text{–}99)$$

This relationship is known as the *reciprocity theorem*; it is useful in reducing the computations necessary to evaluate shape factors of a system. When ΔA_1 is completely enclosed by other surfaces, the sum of the shape factors of enclosing surfaces with respect to energy leaving ΔA_1 must be equal to unity.

The Simple (Non-reflective) Radiation Equation. Continuing with the development of an equation to evaluate direct transfer of radiation from one surface to another, and using the shape factor concept as a means of simplification, substituting from Eq. 4–97 into Eq. 4–96 gives

$$q'' = \sigma e_1 T_1^4 \, \Delta A_1 F_{\Delta A_2 \Delta A_1} \qquad (4\text{–}100)$$

as the rate at which energy emitted by ΔA_1 strikes ΔA_2 directly.

By analogy the energy emitted by ΔA_1 in the direction of the finite area A_2 is

$$q' = \sigma e_1 T_1^4 \, \Delta A_1 F_{A_2 \Delta A_1} \qquad (4\text{–}101)$$

whereas the energy emitted by finite area A_1 in the direction of A_2 is

$$q = \sigma e_1 T_1^4 A_1 F_{A_2 A_1} \qquad (4\text{–}102)$$

where

$$F_{A_2 A_1} = \frac{1}{A_1} \sum_{A_1} \sum_{A_2} \frac{\cos \phi_1 \cos \phi_2 \, \Delta A_1 \, \Delta A_2}{\pi r^2} \qquad (4\text{–}103)$$

Eq. 4–102 is the simple (non-reflective) radiation equation from which, for any case, the energy emitted by one surface in the direction of another surface can be calculated. This equation is sometimes written in the form

$$q = E_1 A_1 F_{A_2 A_1} \qquad (4\text{–}104)$$

where $E = \sigma e_1 T_1^4$ and is defined as the emissive power of the surface expressed in Btu per unit time per unit area.

Net Radiant Transfer Between Surfaces. By Kirchhoff's law the absorptivity (the fraction of incident radiant energy that is absorbed) of a surface is numerically equal to the emissivity. Then, since Eq. 4–104 gives the energy incident on A_2 from emitting surface A_1, it follows that the energy absorbed by A_2 of that emitted by A_1 is

$$q_{1-2} = e_2(\sigma e_1 F_{A_2 A_1} A_1 T_1^4) \tag{4–105}$$

and, by analogy, the energy absorbed by A_1 of that emitted by A_2 is

$$q_{2-1} = e_1(\sigma e_2 F_{A_1 A_2} A_2 T_2^4) \tag{4–106}$$

The net transfer of heat by radiation between surfaces A_1 and A_2 is therefore

$$q = \sigma e_1 e_2 (F_{A_2 A_1} A_1 T_1^4 - F_{A_1 A_2} A_2 T_2^4) \tag{4–107}$$

But by the reciprocity theorem (Eq. 4–99),

$$F_{A_2 A_1} A_1 = F_{A_1 A_2} A_2 \tag{4–108}$$

so it follows that the net transfer from A_1 to A_2 is

$$q = \sigma e_1 e_2 F_{A_2 A_1} A_1 (T_1^4 - T_2^4) \tag{4–109}$$

or, alternatively,

$$q = \sigma e_1 e_2 F_{A_1 A_2} A_2 (T_1^4 - T_2^4) \tag{4–110}$$

Substituting $(0.1713)(10)^{-8}$ for σ and generalizing by substituting F_e in place of $e_1 e_2$ (the latter product having limited the derived equations to surfaces small in area with respect to their distances apart) give an explicit equation for radiant transfer in the same form as Eq. 4–85:

$$q = 0.1713 F_e F_{A_2 A_1} A_1 \left[\left(\frac{T_1}{100} \right)^4 - \left(\frac{T_2}{100} \right)^4 \right] \tag{4–111}$$

For convenience and to facilitate their use, Eqs. 4–85 and 4–111 can be written in the form

$$q = F_e F_{A_2 A_1} h_r A_1 (t_1 - t_2) = F_{ae} h_r A(t_1 - t_2) = h_r' A(t_1 - t_2) \tag{4–112}$$

where h_r, the equivalent film coefficient for radiant transfer, is defined by the equation

$$h_r = \frac{0.1713[(T_1/100)^4 - (T_2/100)^4]}{t_1 - t_2} = h_r'/F_{ae} \tag{4–113}$$

Values of h_r are given graphically in Fig. 4–14. The term h_r' is the corrected equivalent film coefficient for radiant transfer and is equal to $F_{ae} h_r$.

EVALUATION OF F_{ae} FOR SIMPLE GEOMETRICAL SYSTEMS. In a relatively small number of actual systems it is possible to establish a simple expression for the combined $F_e F_{A_2 A_1}$, or F_{ae}, term in Eq. 4–112. The most important of such systems are discussed in the subsequent paragraphs.

Gray Object in Black Surround. Any object having emissivity e_1 and temperature T_1, when completely surrounded by a thermally black ($e_2 = 1$)

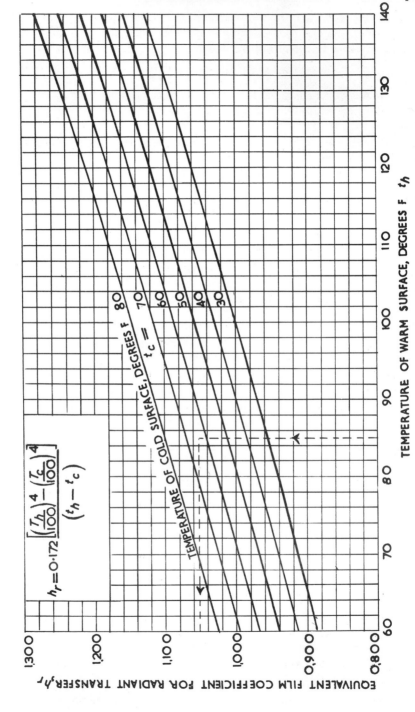

Fig. 4-14. Graphical evaluation of equivalent film coefficient, h_r, for radiant transfer.

surface at T_2, necessarily emits all its radiant energy in the direction of the surround; hence $F_{A_2A_1}$ is unity. Further, all energy received by the surround of a black object is absorbed by it, whereas of the energy received from the surround by the gray object, only a fraction equal to its emissivity e_1 (since absorptivity is equal to emissivity) is absorbed. The F_e term is therefore equal to e_1; hence

$$F_{ae} = (F_e)(F_{A_2A_1}) = (e_1)(1) = e_1$$

For this system,

$$F_{ae} = e_1$$

and $\hspace{10cm}$ (4–114)

$$A = A_1$$

Small Gray Object in Large Gray Surround. This case is similar to the preceding one except that the surround is not black. The object must therefore be so small with respect to the surround that it intercepts only a negligible fraction of *reflected* energy. This means that $F_{A_1A_2}$ must be very small, but since, by the reciprocity theorem, $F_{A_1A_2}$ is equal to $F_{A_2A_1}A_1/A_2$ (and $F_{A_2A_1}$ is known to be unity), the requirement reduces to the condition that the ratio of areas of object to enclosure, A_1/A_2, be small. For this system,

$$F_{ae} = e_1$$

and $\hspace{10cm}$ (4–115)

$$A = A_1$$

Gray Object in Small Surround. This case is the converse of the preceding one in that the enclosed object must now be so large that $F_{A_1A_2}$ is practically equal to $F_{A_2A_1}$ (unity) and hence must receive almost all the energy reflected from A_2. The emissivity factor can be shown to be

$$F_e = \frac{e_1e_2}{e_1 + e_2 - e_1e_2}$$

Hence, for this system,

$$F_{ae} = \frac{e_1e_2}{e_1 + e_2 - e_1e_2}$$

and $\hspace{10cm}$ (4–116)

$$A = A_1$$

Infinite Parallel Planes. This case is approximated by parallel planes that are large in both width and length as compared with the separating distance. Emissivities are e_1 and e_2, temperatures T_1 and T_2, and the areas and shape factors are equal. The emissivity factor is equal to that for the preceding case (of which this case is a limit); hence

$$F_{ae} = \frac{e_1e_2}{e_1 + e_2 - e_1e_2}$$

and $\hspace{10cm}$ (4–117)

$$A = A_1$$

Gray Concentric Cylinders. The inner cylinder has an emissivity of e_1, a temperature T_1, and all energy leaving this cylinder strikes (but is not totally absorbed by) the outer cylinder. Thus $F_{A_2 A_1}$ is unity, and it can be shown that

$$F_{ae} = \frac{e_1 e_2}{e_2 + e_1 (1 - e_2)(r_1/r_2)}$$

and   (4–118)

$$A = A_1$$

This case represents an intermediate condition between the second and third cases. As the ratio of radii, r_1/r_2, becomes smaller, the F_{ae} term of Eq. 4–118 approaches

$$F_{ae} \doteq \frac{e_1 e_2}{e_2 + 0} = e_1$$

which is the value established for the second case (Eq. 4–115). As r_1/r_2 increases toward a maximum (for concentric cylinders) of unity,

$$F_{ae} \doteq \frac{e_1 e_2}{e_2 + e_1 (1 - e_2)} = \frac{e_1 e_2}{e_1 + e_2 - e_1 e_2}$$

which is the value given for the third case in Eq. 4–116. Thus the F_{ae} values of the second, third, and fifth cases afford a range over which estimate can be made for slightly different systems.

Gray Plane Surfaces Small Compared with the Separating Distance. This case corresponds to the geometrical arrangement of Fig. 4–13. The solution is given by Eq. 4–109, noting that the shape factor is explicitly evaluated in Eq. 4–98. Thus, for use in Eq. 4–112,

$$F_e = e_1 e_2$$

$$F_{\Delta A_2 \, \Delta A_1} = \frac{1}{\Delta A_1} \frac{\cos \phi_1 \cos \phi_2 \, \Delta A_1 \, \Delta A_2}{\pi r^2}$$ (4–119)

and $$A = \Delta A_1$$

An approximate method of solving Eq. 4–119, which is sufficiently accurate for many practical problems, can be obtained by noting that the equation can be written in the form

$$F_{\Delta A_2 \, \Delta A_1} = \frac{\cos \phi_1}{\pi} \cos \phi_2 \frac{\Delta A_2}{r^2} = K_1 K_2 \frac{\Delta A_2}{r^2}$$ (4–120)

where the subscripts 1 and 2 refer to source and receiver; the angles ϕ are measured between the normal to each infinitesimal area and the line of length r which connects the areas (see Fig. 4–13); the coefficients K_1 and K_2 have values as determined by the first and second parentheses of the right side of the full equation.

Eq. 4–120 applies exactly to very small finite areas. As the areas become larger, the length r and the angles ϕ_1 and ϕ_2 vary from point to point across the two surfaces. If, however, the two finite areas are small with respect to the separating distance, then variations in ϕ_1, ϕ_2, and r will be negligible, and the shape factor of one finite area with respect to the other will be the same as the shape factor of any point on one with respect to any point (or, more correctly, any infinitesimal area) on the other. When this is true, the shape factor of A_2 with respect to energy received from A_1 is exactly equal to

$$F_{A_2 A_1} = K_1 K_2 \frac{A_2}{r^2} \qquad (4\text{–}121)$$

Values of the coefficients K_1 and K_2 are given in tabular form, as functions of the angle ϕ, in Table 4–6.

TABLE 4–6
Radiation Coefficients as Functions of Angle of Incidence

ϕ	K_1	K_2	ϕ	K_1	K_2
0	0.3182	1.0000	50	0.2046	0.6428
5	0.3170	0.9962	55	0.1824	0.5736
10	0.3133	0.9848	60	0.1590	0.5000
15	0.3071	0.9659	65	0.1345	0.4226
20	0.2990	0.9397	70	0.1089	0.3420
25	0.2883	0.9063	75	0.0822	0.2588
30	0.2755	0.8660	80	0.0552	0.1736
35	0.2606	0.8192	85	0.0277	0.0872
40	0.2438	0.7660	90	0.0000	0.0000
45	0.2250	0.7071			

To solve Eq. 4–120 for a given problem, the receiver area, distance from receiver to source, and the two angles ϕ_1 and ϕ_2 must be known. In Table 4–6, then, the value of K_1 is read for ϕ_1 and the value of K_2 for ϕ_2; substitution of these values in Eq. 4–120 gives the required shape factor. Note that the area of the source is not needed in evaluation of the shape factor, although some idea of size of source is necessary in order to determine whether this approximate method is applicable to a given problem. If the source area is too great, it can be divided into parts, and the approximate method can be applied separately to each component system. The over-all shape factor would then be the average of the component system factors, provided the source has been divided into equal-area sections; if it has not, the over-all shape factor will be the weighted average of shape factors for the various sections. The source area must, of course, be known before calculation of energy transfer from source to receiver is possible.

For the special cases of areas that are in parallel or normal planes, further simplification of the approximate method is possible. For areas in parallel planes the angles ϕ_1 and ϕ_2 must be equal; hence a single coefficient K_{12} can be determined and set up in tabular form as a function of ϕ_1. Similarly, for areas in normal planes, the sum of angles ϕ_1 and ϕ_2 must be 90 deg, and a single coefficient K'_{12} can be set up as a function of ϕ_1. Table 4–7 gives values of both K_{12} and K'_{12}. Values of coefficients from this table are for use in the two following equations.

Areas in parallel planes, A_1 and A_2 small with respect to separating distance r:

$$F_{A_2 A_1} = \frac{K_{12} A_2}{r^2} \tag{4–122}$$

TABLE 4–7
Radiation Coefficients as Functions of Angle of Incidence

ϕ_1	K_{12}	K'_{12}	ϕ_1	K_{12}	K'_{12}
0	0.3182	0.0000	50	0.1395	0.1568
5	0.3170	0.0276	55	0.1047	0.1495
10	0.3080	0.0545	60	0.0795	0.1375
15	0.2960	0.0797	65	0.0570	0.1220
20	0.2810	0.1020	70	0.0372	0.1020
25	0.2610	0.1220	75	0.0213	0.0797
30	0.2380	0.1375	80	0.0096	0.0545
35	0.2140	0.1495	85	0.0024	0.0276
40	0.1865	0.1568	90	0.0000	0.0000
45	0.1590	0.1590			

Areas in normal planes, A_1 and A_2 small with respect to separating distance r:

$$F_{A_2 A_1} = \frac{K'_{12} A_2}{r^2} \tag{4–123}$$

Note that the distance r in Eqs. 4–122 and 4–123 is the actual separating distance between A_1 and A_2 and not a projected distance; similarly the angles ϕ_1 and ϕ_2 are absolute and cannot be measured in a vertical or a horizontal projection. Eqs. 4–122 and 4–123 should be used only where accuracy is not important or where speed of calculation is essential. In all other problems the exact shape factors for the same conditions covered by these equations can be obtained by the methods given in this article on page 121.

EXAMPLE 4–22. A 4-sq ft circular glass window is located in a sloping skylight and is 30 feet distant from a 3-sq ft plane shield (bronze radiator painted) in front of a wall radiator. The normal to the 180 F shield makes an angle of 25 deg with a line connecting the two plane areas, whereas the normal to the 40 F window makes an angle of 10 deg with the same line. (a) Calculate the shape factor of the window with respect to energy emitted by the shield. (b) Determine the net transfer rate from shield to window. (c) Evaluate the equivalent film coefficient for radiant transfer h_r for this system. (d) Evaluate the corrected equivalent film coefficient h'_r for radiant transfer.

Solution: (a) From Table 4–6 at ϕ_1 of 25 deg and ϕ_2 of 10 deg, read K_1 of 0.2883 and K_2 of 0.9848. Then, by Eq. 4–121,

$$F_{A_2A_1} = K_1K_2\frac{A_2}{r^2} = (0.2883)(0.9848)\frac{4}{(30)^2} = 0.00126$$

which shows that only 0.126 per cent of the energy emitted by the shield is directed toward the window.

(b) The emissivities e_1 and e_2 of shield and window are (from Table 4–5) 0.51 and 0.94, respectively. The transfer rate, by Eq. 4–109, is

$$q = \sigma e_1 e_2 F_{A_2A_1} A_1 (T_1^4 - T_2^4)$$
$$= (0.1713)(0.51)(0.94)(0.00126)(3)\left[\left(\frac{460 + 180}{100}\right)^4 - \left(\frac{460 + 40}{100}\right)^4\right]$$
$$= 0.33 \text{ Btu/hr}$$

(c) The equivalent film coefficient for radiant transfer, by Eq. 4–113, is

$$h_r = \frac{0.1713\left[\left(\frac{T_1}{100}\right)^4 - \left(\frac{T_2}{100}\right)^4\right]}{t_1 - t_2}$$

$$= \frac{0.1713\left[\left(\frac{460 + 180}{100}\right)^4 - \left(\frac{460 + 40}{100}\right)^4\right]}{180 - 40}$$

$$= 1.505 \text{ Btu/(hr)(sq ft)(°F)}$$

(d) The corrected equivalent film coefficient is

$$h_r' = F_{ae}h_r = F_e F_a h_r = (0.51)(0.94)(0.00126)(1.505)$$
$$= 0.00091 \text{ Btu/(hr)(sq ft)(°F)}$$

EVALUATION OF SHAPE FACTORS FOR LARGE PLANE RECTANGULAR SURFACES. Shape factors of large surfaces with respect to one another are needed when setting up the heat-balance equations on individual surfaces of an enclosure. For an ordinary room, which is a parallelepiped, two basic shape-factor solutions will suffice for any pair of areas. These are: (1) for two rectangular surfaces in parallel planes; (2) for rectangular surfaces in normal planes.

Parallel Planes. Even for such a simple problem as that represented by two rectangles of equal size in parallel planes and directly opposed to one another (as a floor and ceiling, or opposite walls), the analytical solution of Eq. 4–97 does not lend itself to rapid solution. The general solution is of the form

$$F = \phi(D, W, L) \qquad (4\text{–}124)$$

where D and W are the dimensions of the rectangles, L is the distance between them, and ϕ indicates the existence of a functional relationship.

Fig. 4–15 gives a simple graphical solution of Eq. 4–124 from which the shape factor can be obtained directly in terms of two dimensionless parameters. Entering the lower scale at the correct ratio of length to separating

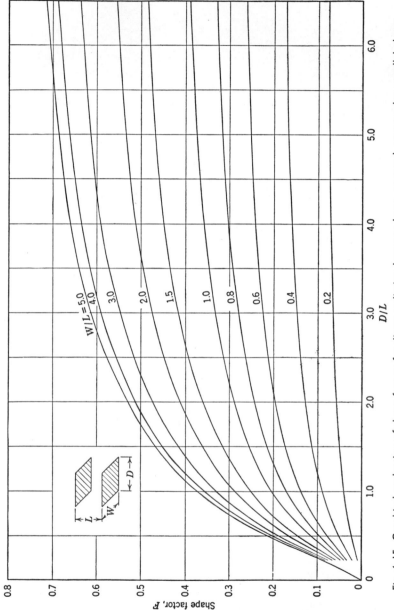

Fig. 4–15. Graphical evaluation of shape factors for direct radiation between large, opposed, rectangular, parallel planes.

distance (see pilot sketch on the figure), rise to intersection with the curve for ratio of width to separating distance; then move horizontally to the left to read from the vertical scale the numerical value of the shape factor. By simple arithmetic, the data obtainable from Fig. 4–15 can be readily extended to determine the shape factor of a rectangle of any size and shape with respect to a rectangle of any other size and shape, provided only the two rectangles are in parallel planes and are so oriented that their sides are respectively parallel. In practice, this extension permits determination of the shape factor of a wall or wall section with respect to a window in the opposite side of the room, or it permits evaluating the shape factor of the floor with respect to a heating panel which occupies only a fraction of the ceiling area. To demonstrate the procedure, consider a few examples.

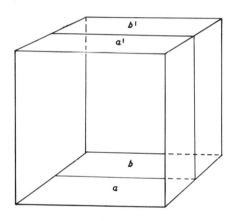

Fig. 4–16

CASE 1. Referring to Fig. 4–16, the shape factor of area $A_{b'}$ is wanted with respect to area A_a in the opposite plane. By examination of the figure,

$$F_{b'a}A_a = F_{(a'b')(ab)}A_{ab} - F_{a'a}A_a - F_{b'b}A_b - F_{a'b}A_b$$

But by the reciprocity theorem (Eq. 4–99),

$$F_{a'b}A_b = F_{ba'}A_{a'}$$

By observation,

$$F_{ba'}A_{a'} = F_{b'a}A_a$$

and so, by substitution,

$$F_{b'a}A_a = F_{(a'b')(ab)}A_{ab} - F_{a'a}A_a - F_{b'b}A_b - F_{b'a}A_a$$

giving

$$F_{b'a} = \frac{1}{2A_a}\left[F_{(a'b')(ab)}A_{ab} - F_{a'a}A_a - F_{b'b}A_b\right] \qquad (4\text{–}125)$$

where all three shape factors on the right side of the equation can be directly obtained from the fundamental parallel-plane solution of Fig. 4–15. (Note that this is true for the condition that $A_a = A_{a'}$, but it does not require that $A_a = A_b$.)

CASE 2. Refer to Fig. 4–17 and determine the shape factor of $A_{d'}$ with respect to A_a. By examination of the figure (and considering the total areas of the two planes to be $A_{w'}$ and A_w),

$$F_{w'w}A_w - (F_{a'a} + F_{b'a} + F_{c'a})A_a - (F_{a'b} + F_{b'b} + F_{d'b})A_b$$
$$- (F_{a'c} + F_{c'c} + F_{d'c})A_c - (F_{b'd} + F_{c'd} + F_{d'd})A_d$$
$$= F_{d'a}A_a + F_{c'b}A_b + F_{b'c}A_c + F_{a'd}A_d$$
$$= 2F_{d'a}A_a + 2F_{c'b}A_b = 2(F_{d'a}A_a + F_{c'b}A_b) \qquad (4\text{–}126)$$

The two terms on the right side of the above equation are of the same form; thus in order to solve for $F_{d'a}$, means must be found of expressing $F_{c'b}$ in terms of $F_{d'a}$.

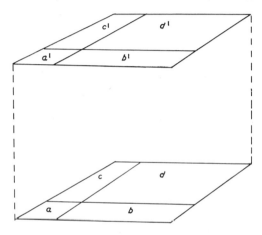

Fig. 4–17

Yamauti[6] has developed a special form of the reciprocity theorem applicable to this case; his method leads to the simple relationship

$$F_{d'a}A_a = F_{c'b}A_b \qquad (4\text{–}127)$$

Now substituting for $F_{c'b}A_b$ in Eq. 4–126 and solving for the unknown shape factor gives

$$F_{d'a} = \frac{\begin{array}{c} F_{w'w}A_w - (F_{a'a} + F_{b'a} + F_{c'a})A_a - (F_{a'b} + F_{b'b} + F_{d'b})A_b \\ - (F_{a'c} + F_{c'c} + F_{d'c})A_c - (F_{b'd} + F_{c'd} + F_{d'd})A_d \end{array}}{4A_a}$$

$$(4\text{–}128)$$

where all shape factors on the right side of the equation can be obtained either directly from Fig. 4–15 or indirectly by means of Eq. 4–125.

CASE 3. The case to be considered now is of great practical importance, since it develops an equation used in obtaining the shape factor of one wall with respect to a window in the opposite wall. Refer to Fig. 4–18; determine the shape

[6] *Research Bulletin 250*, Electrotechnical Laboratory, Tokyo, 1929.

factor of the inside partition of total area $A_{w'}$ with respect to the glass area A_g of a window in the opposite wall. By inspection of the figure,

$$F_{w'g} = \frac{\begin{aligned}F_{w'w}A_w &- [F_{(a'd'f')(adf)} + F_{(b'c'g'e'h'i')(adf)}]A_{adf} \\ &- [F_{(c'e'i')(cei)} + F_{(a'b'd'g'f'h')(cei)}]A_{cei} \\ &- [F_{b'b} + F_{a'b} + F_{c'b} + F_{(g'h')b} + F_{(d'f')b} + F_{(e'i')b}]A_b \\ &- [F_{h'h} + F_{f'h} + F_{i'h} + F_{(b'g')h} + F_{(a'd')h} + F_{(c'e')h}]A_h\end{aligned}}{A_g}$$

(4–129)

where all shape factors on the right side of the equation can be obtained either directly from Fig. 4–15 or indirectly by means of Eqs. 4–125 and 4–128.

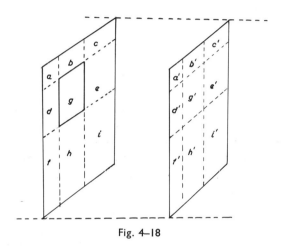

Fig. 4–18

The expression for $F_{w'g}$ can be written in many ways, some simpler in form than Eq. 4–129, others more complex. The particular form given here was selected primarily because of its simplicity in statement and because the logic in arrangement of its terms is readily visualized.

CASE 4. The last case is represented by the problem of determining the shape factor of a window in one wall with respect to a window in the opposite wall, the two windows not being opposite each other. A solution can be obtained by projecting one window on the opposite wall, then enclosing the actual and projected windows (a' and i' of Fig. 4–19) inside a large rectangle which can be broken into the component rectangle a', b', c', d', e', f', g', h', i', as shown. The problem is then reduced to determining the shape factor of a' in one wall with respect to i in the opposite wall. By examination of the figure (taking $A_w = A_{abcdefghi}$),

$$F_{a'i} = \frac{\begin{aligned}F_{w'w}A_w &- [F_{(a'b'c'd'e'f')(abcdef)} + F_{(g'h'i')(abcdef)}]A_{abcdef} \\ &- [F_{(g'h')(gh)} + F_{(a'b'd'e')(gh)} + F_{(c'f')(gh)}]A_{gh} \\ &- [F_{i'i} + F_{(c'f')i} + F_{(g'h')i} + F_{(b'e')i} + F_{(d'e')i} - F_{e'i}]A_i\end{aligned}}{A_i}$$

(4–130)

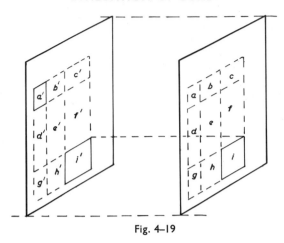

Fig. 4–19

where all shape factors on the right side of the equation can be obtained either directly from Fig. 4–15 or indirectly by means of Eqs. 4–125 and 4–128.

The four cases discussed above include all the more common types of problems encountered in precise heating-load analysis or in design of panel heating. Thus from the graphical solution of Fig. 4–15 and the four standard equations, 4–125, 4–128, 4–129, and 4–130, shape factors can be found for a system consisting of rectangles of any size and shape, provided they are in parallel planes and are oriented so that their sides are parallel.

Normal Planes. Fig. 4–20 presents a graphical solution for shape factors of a system consisting of two rectangles in planes normal to each other and having a common side, like ceiling-wall, floor-wall, or wall-wall combinations. For this problem, again, the graphical solution gives the shape factor of one rectangle with respect to the other in terms of two dimensionless parameters. Entering the lower scale of the figure at the correct value of the ratio of unique to common side of the rectangle for which the shape factor is to be obtained, rise to the intersection with the curve for ratio of unique to common side of the other rectangle; then move horizontally left to read on the vertical scale the shape factor of the first rectangle with respect to the second. Unlike Fig. 4–15, this graph gives different shape factors for the two rectangles (depending on which is considered the source) except in the special case in which they are both the same size. The shape factor for one having been determined, that for the other, if needed, can be determined from the figure or can be calculated from the reciprocity theorem. By the same methods as were used for extending the data of Fig. 4–15, the data of Fig. 4–20 can be extended to permit simple arithmetical determination of the shape factor of any two rectangles of whatever sizes and shapes, provided only they are in perpendicular planes and are oriented so that one pair of sides of one rectangle is parallel to a pair of sides of the other.

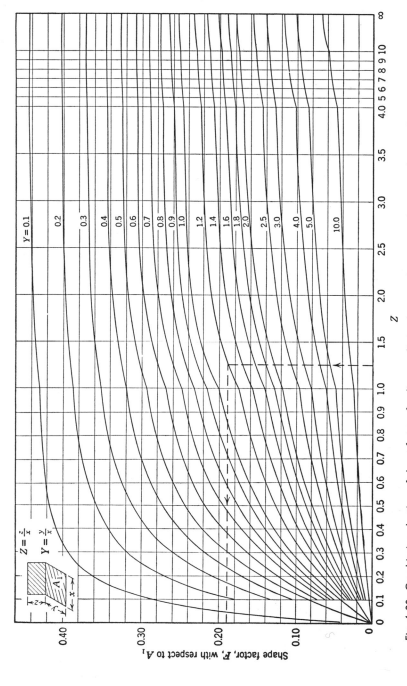

Fig. 4–20. Graphical evaluation of shape factors for direct radiation between large, normal, rectangular, parallel planes having one common edge.

CASE 1. Refer to Fig. 4–21; the shape factor of area A_d with respect to A_a is to be obtained. By examination of the figure,

$$F_{da} = \frac{F_{(cd)(ab)}A_{ab} - F_{(cd)b}A_b - F_{ca}A_a}{A_a}$$

But

$$F_{ca}A_a = F_{c(ab)}A_{ab} - F_{cb}A_b$$

and so

$$F_{da} = \frac{F_{(cd)(ab)}A_{ab} - F_{(cd)b}A_b - F_{c(ab)}A_{ab} + F_{cb}A_b}{A_a} \qquad (4\text{–}131)$$

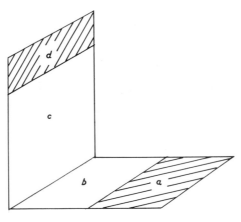

Fig. 4–21

where all shape factors on the right side of the equation can be obtained directly from Fig. 4–20.

CASE 2. Refer to Fig. 4–22; the shape factor of area A_d with respect to area A_a is to be obtained. By examination of the figure,

$$F_{da} = \frac{F_{(cd)(ab)}A_{ab} - F_{ca}A_a - F_{db}A_b - F_{cb}A_b}{A_a} \qquad (4\text{–}132)$$

The term F_{cb} on the right side of the above equation is exactly the same in form as the unknown term F_{da}; hence, before solving Eq. 4–132, some relationship must be found between these terms. By the same method used in establishing Eq. 4–127, it can be shown that

$$F_{da}A_a = F_{cb}A_b \qquad (4\text{–}133a),$$

But F_{da} and F_{ad} are related by the reciprocity theorem, as are F_{cb} and F_{bc}; then, necessarily,

$$F_{ad}A_d = F_{bc}A_c \qquad (4\text{–}133b)$$

The proof of the above special relationship can be readily extended to show that the same equations are true if areas a, b, c, and d are separated from one another as shown in Fig. 4–23.

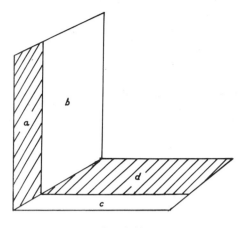

Fig. 4–22

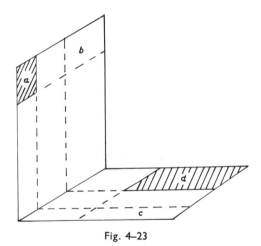

Fig. 4–23

Returning now to Eq. 4–132 and substituting for $F_{cb}A_b$ give

$$F_{da} = \frac{F_{(cd)(ab)}A_{ab} - F_{ca}A_a - F_{db}A_b}{2A_a} \tag{4–134}$$

where all shape factors on the right side can be obtained from Fig. 4–20.

CASE 3. The last special case is the perfectly general one of any two rectangles in planes perpendicular to each other and oriented so that the four pairs of sides run in the directions of the three major axes. Referring to Fig. 4–24, consider any rectangle f, the shape factor of which is desired with respect to any other rectangle a, properly oriented. As a first step, draw lines enclosing the two rectangles in a system as shown; then divide this system into the elements a, b, c, d, e, f. By examination of Fig. 4–24,

$$F_{fa} = \frac{[F_{(cdef)(ab)} - F_{(cd)(ab)} - F_{(ce)(ab)} + F_{c(ab)}]A_{ab}}{A_a} \qquad (4\text{–}135)$$

where all shape factors on the right-hand side can be obtained directly from Fig. 4–20 or indirectly from this figure by means of Eq. 4–134.

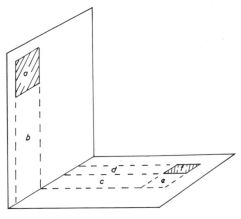

Fig. 4–24

The special reciprocal relationship developed for areas such as shown in Fig. 4–23 plus the two equations for cases 2 and 3 (Eqs. 4–134 and 4–135), together with Fig. 4–20, will provide all the information needed in computing the shape factors of rectangular surfaces located in walls normal to each other.

EVALUATION OF SHAPE FACTORS FOR AN INFINITESIMAL PLANE SURFACE WITH RESPECT TO A LARGE RECTANGULAR PLANE SURFACE. The methods developed in the preceding section can be followed in solving many of the shape-factor problems that occur in heating design, but other problems will be found that require determination of the shape factor of a rectangular surface with respect to a non-rectangular plane surface. The problems represented by circular windows and oval-shaped heating panels are examples. Further, the point-to-point shape-factor variation over room surfaces must sometimes be checked in order to test the accuracy of the assumption that the temperature across a given surface is uniform. Problems of either of the above types can be readily solved in terms of point shape factors or, more specifically, the shape factor of a large plane surface with respect to an infinitesimal area which is in a plane either normal or parallel to the large surface.

Once a method is available for determining shape factors with respect to an infinitesimal area, the analysis can then be readily extended to larger plane

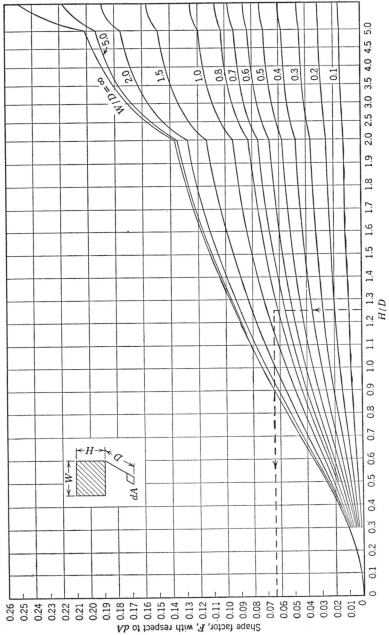

Fig. 4–25. Graphical evaluation of shape factors for direct radiation between a small area and a large, normal, rectangular plane.

areas of any size and shape, since the shape factor with respect to the larger area will be the average of point shape factors for points equidistantly located over the surface of the large area. The accuracy of the resultant shape factor will obviously depend on the number of point values taken in its determination. Thus the method of infinitesimal areas should give a general solution of which the finite area shape factors in Figs. 4–15 and 4–20 are but special cases.

Infinitesimal Area in a Plane Normal to and Passing Through One Side of a Large Rectangular Area and on a Normal Line Through a Corner of the Large Rectangle. This solution gives the shape factor of a rectangular area with respect to a point located in a plane normal to and passing through one side of the rectangular area, the point being on a normal drawn through one corner of the rectangle. Fig. 4–25 provides a graphical solution for this system in terms of the two dimensionless parameters H/D and W/D, where H and W are the dimensions of the large rectangle measured, respectively, in directions normal and parallel to the plane of the infinitesimal area. D is the distance of the infinitesimal area from the corner of the large rectangle. Entering the base scale at H/D, rise to the intersection with the curve for W/D and then move left to read the shape factor from the vertical scale; note that the ratios H/D and W/D are *not* interchangeable. Extension of the data from Fig. 4–25 to cases in which the infinitesimal area is not located on a normal through one corner of the rectangle can be readily accomplished:

CASE 1. Consider the system shown in Fig. 4–26a in which an infinitesimal area at P is in a plane normal to the large rectangle but is not located on a normal

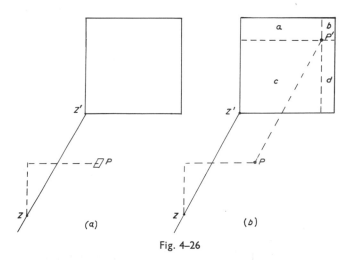

Fig. 4–26

(such as zz') through a corner of the rectangle. Fig. 4–26b shows the method of solution; through P draw a line normal to the large surface and piercing it at point P'. Through P' draw lines parallel to the sides of the rectangle and dividing

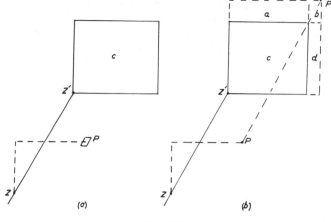

Fig. 4–27

it into areas a, b, c, and d, each of which meets the conditions of Fig. 4–25. The shape factor of the large rectangle with respect to point P is, then,

$$F_{wp} = \tfrac{1}{2}(F_{ap} + F_{bp} + F_{cp} + F_{dp}) \qquad (4\text{–}136)$$

where the shape factor F_{wp} is for energy leaving both top and bottom surfaces of P but is based on the area of one side only. If the two sides were at different temperatures, the F_{wp} given here could not be used, but separate shape factors for each side would then be necessary; these would be

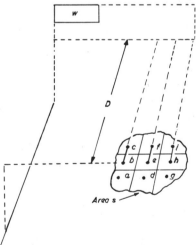

$$F_{wp_{bot}} = F_{cp} + F_{dp}$$
$$\text{and} \quad F_{wp_{top}} = F_{ap} + F_{bp} \qquad (4\text{–}137)$$

All shape factors on the right of Eqs. 4–136 and 4–137 can be read from Fig. 4–25.

Refer to Fig. 4–27a and determine the shape factor of the finite area c with respect to the infinitesimal perpendicular area at P. The system can be converted to one which meets the conditions of Fig. 4–25 by the construction shown in Fig. 4–27b. By examination of this figure,

$$F_{cp} = F_{(abcd)p} - F_{(ab)p} - F_{(bd)p} + F_{bp}$$
$$(4\text{–}138)$$

where all shape factors on the right are obtainable directly from Fig. 4–25.

Fig. 4–28

CASE 2. Consider the extension of the point method to determination of the shape factor of rectangle w (Fig. 4–28) with respect to the irregularly shaped surface s, which lies in a plane normal to the plane of w. As shown in Fig. 4–28, the surface s is divided into small areas of approximately equal size, the number of areas being so selected that the variation of shape factor from point to point within any one area will be negligible. This construction reduces the problem to determining the shape factor of w with respect to each of the points a, b, c, d, e, f, g, h, and i and then averaging these point shape factors to obtain the shape factor of w with respect to the surface s. For the case shown, the shape factors of w with respect to a and b and c differ only through variation of the separating distance D; similarly, the factors in respective groups d, e, f, and g, h, i differ only through variation in D. The shape factor of w with respect to the irregularly shaped (but *plane*) surface s is, then,

$$F_{ws} = \frac{F_{wa} + F_{wb} + F_{wc} + F_{wd} + F_{we} + F_{wf} + F_{wg} + F_{wh} + F_{wi}}{9} \quad (4\text{–}139)$$

where each of the individual factors on the right can be evaluated by the method of Eq. 4–138. Note in particular that the over-all shape factor for cases involving extension of point factors is the average and not the sum of the shape factors with respect to the individual points.

If carried to the extreme, Eq. 4–139 would have an infinite number of terms and would give the exact integrated shape factor of w with respect to s. In most practical problems, however, the point factor can be considered approximately constant over reasonably large areas (like a wall section 2 ft by 2 ft, or even larger), so that the number of terms needed in this equation will not be excessive. Division of surface s into elements of equal area is not necessary, but if different-sized areas are selected, a weighted average of point shape factors must be used to obtain the final result rather than (as in Eq. 4–139) a simple arithmetical average.

Infinitesimal Area in a Plane Parallel to a Large Rectangular Area and on a Normal Line Through a Corner of the Large Rectangle. This solution gives the shape factor of a rectangular area with respect to a point located in a plane parallel to the rectangular area, the point being on a normal line drawn through one corner of the rectangle. Fig. 4–29 presents a graphical solution of this problem in terms of the same two dimensionless parameters as were used in Fig. 4–25. The principal difference in the application of Figs. 4–25 and 4–29 is that care must be exercised with Fig. 4–25 to be certain that all factors obtained from the graph are for the same surface (as top or bottom) of the infinitesimal area, whereas no such caution is required with Fig. 4–29, since all shape factors are necessarily for the same side of the surface.

The methods of extending Fig. 4–29 to systems other than the particular one for which it is constructed do not involve any procedures different from those already developed; hence examples will not be given. From an examination of the procedures followed with Fig. 4–28, analogous methods can be found for extending the graphical solution of Fig. 4–29 to permit finding the shape factor of any rectangular area with respect to any plane

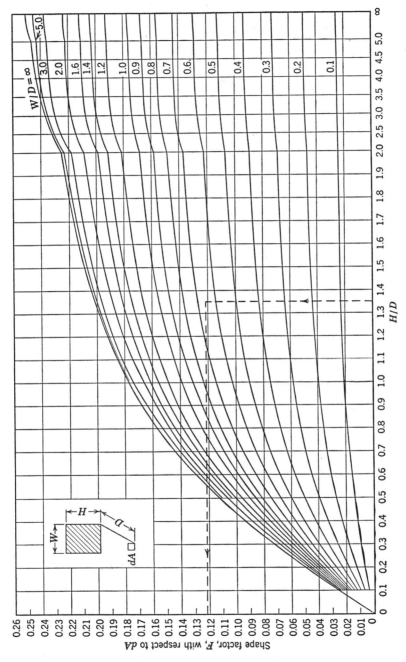

Fig. 4–29. Graphical evaluation of shape factors for direct radiation between a small area and a large, parallel, rectangular plane.

surface, irrespective of size and shape, that is in a plane parallel to that of the rectangle.

EVALUATION OF SHAPE FACTORS FOR A PLANE AREA WITH RESPECT TO A SPHERE. One widely used experimental method of evaluating the radiant exchange in an occupied space is by means of a blackened sphere. Readings of temperature within such a sphere (or of heat loss from it, if it is designed with a self-contained energy source) have frequently been regarded as indicative of the mean radiant temperature of the enclosure. Investigation of the validity of such an interpretation requires determination of the extent to which the radiant exchange between sphere and enclosure approximates that between the enclosure and an occupant.

Evaluation of the shape factor of a plane surface with respect to an infinitesimal sphere is somewhat simplified in that the projected area of the sphere is the same regardless of the direction from which it is viewed, so that it is unnecessary to make any specification as to the plane of the surface; one solution is valid for all possible orientations of the surface with respect to the sphere. Fig. 4–30 gives the shape factor of a plane rectangular area with respect to an infinitesimal sphere located on a normal through one corner of the rectangle; the two parameters are dimensionless ratios, as shown in the pilot diagram on the figure. Data from the graphical solution can be extended, of course, to rectangles that do not meet the conditions of Fig. 4–30 by the methods described in connection with Fig. 4–25.

In applying the reciprocity theorem to a system which includes either a sphere or an occupant, the flat-surface visualization of hemispherical radiation no longer holds, and hence the shape factor with respect to the spherical area is only one-half its value with respect to the projected area. However, the 50 per cent reduction in shape factor is exactly offset by the 100 per cent increase in area, and so the mathematical statement of the reciprocity is unchanged:

$$F_{es}A_s = F_{se}A_e \qquad (4\text{–}140)$$

where subscripts e and s represent enclosure and sphere (or subject), respectively. Since the total energy leaving the sphere must be received by the enclosure, the sum of the shape factors of the sections of the enclosure with respect to the sphere must be unity, and hence the sum of products of shape factors of the sphere with respect to parts of the enclosure by surface areas of those parts must be equal to the area of the sphere:

$$\sum F_{sx}A_x = \sum F_{xs}A_s = A_s \sum F_{xs} = A_s \qquad (4\text{–}141)$$

where subscript x denotes any particular surface that constitutes part of the enclosure. The same equation can be used for determining the equivalent surface area, for radiant exchange, of an occupant in a given room.

EVALUATION OF SHAPE FACTORS OF STANDING HUMAN SUBJECTS WITH RESPECT TO PLANE AREAS. The mean radiant temperature as used in the comfort equation (Eq. 1–10) is a term representing one of the environmental factors which serve to establish conditions of comfort. Therefore this temperature should be evaluated with respect to the occupant and for a position which most closely parallels the normal occupancy condition found within the room. The distributing units of any type of heating system should be so located that the variation in mean radiant temperature with respect to the occupant does not vary greatly as the occupant moves around the room. To meet this condition, a shape-factor analysis with respect to the occupants is required; hence data are needed on the shape factor of the human body with respect to either finite or infinitesimal areas.

The non-mathematical shape of the human body introduces a complication into the boundary conditions of the shape factor expression (Eq. 4–97) that makes an analytical solution practically impossible. Fortunately, however, experimental techniques are available that permit laboratory determination of shape factors for irregular and non-planar surfaces by means of a mechanical integrator. Based on results of a cooperative research project conducted at the University of California, in conjunction with the American Society of Heating, Refrigerating and Air-Conditioning Engineers, experimental data are available[7] for shape factors of an average male subject (5 ft 10 in. tall and weighing 165 lb) in the standing position with respect to an infinitesimal area located on the ceiling or floor or walls. These data can be used in practice to check on the mean radiant temperature as experienced by the occupant and to assist in locating the heating units so as to provide uniformity of heating effect.

Subject Standing; Area in Ceiling. Experimentally determined shape factors of a standing subject with respect to a point located on an 8-ft, 10-ft, or 12-ft ceiling are given in Figs. 4–31, 4–32, and 4–33, respectively. Each of these graphs can be visualized as a plan view of the room with the occupant standing at the center of coordinates and facing in the positive direction along the Y-axis. The scales marked on X- and Y-axes permit super-position on the graph of a tracing of the ceiling, with respect to which the occupant's shape factor is desired. Curved lines on the graphs are isoshape factor lines that give values of the point shape factors at locations throughout the ceiling plane.

The shape factor of the occupant with respect to any section of the ceiling can be obtained by superimposing the section on the graph in its correct position with respect to the occupant, dividing the section into equal areas sufficiently small (usually 2 ft by 2 ft) so that the shape factor of each area

[7] B. F. Raber and F. W. Hutchinson, "Optimum Surface Distribution in Panel Heating and Cooling Systems," ASHVE *Trans.*, Vol. 50 1944; and F. W. Hutchinson and M. Baker, "Optimum Panel Surface Distribution Determined from Human Shape Factors," ASHVE *Trans.* Vol. 57, 1951.

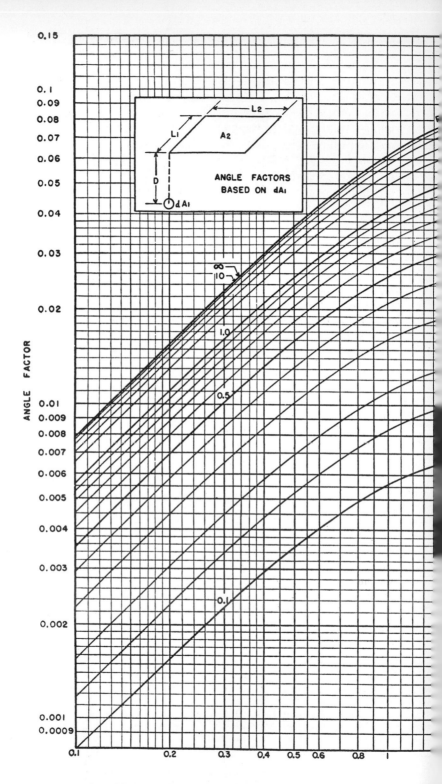

Fig. 4–30. Graphical evaluation of shape factor for direct

138

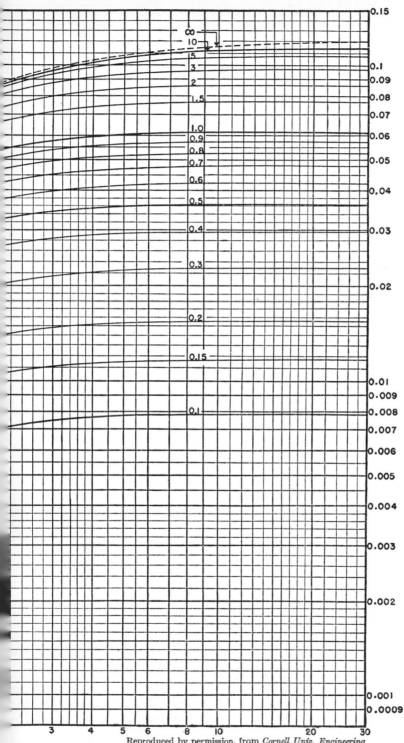

Reproduced by permission, from *Cornell Univ. Engineering Experiment Station Bulletin* 32, August, 1943, by C. O. Mackey, L. T. Wright, R. E. Clark, and N. R. Gay.

radiation between a large, rectangular plane area and a sphere.

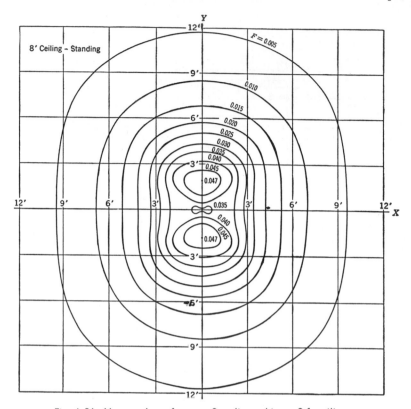

Fig. 4–31. Human shape factors: Standing subject; 8-ft ceiling.

will be substantially constant, and then interpolating between isoshape factor lines to obtain the point shape factor at the center of each small area; these point factors are then averaged to obtain the shape factor of the occupant with respect to the total area. A simple procedure is to sketch the ceiling on tracing paper to the same scale as that on the coordinate axes of the graphs, and then superimpose the tracing on the graph and read directly the necessary point shape factors. By moving the tracing with respect to the center of coordinates, a new set of point shape factors can be obtained corresponding to those that would apply if the subject had moved. Thus the three graphical solutions of Figs. 4–31, 4–32, and 4–33 can be used to obtain either the shape factors of a fixed subject with respect to different points or the shape-factor variation of a moving subject with respect to a fixed point. Problems of the first type occur in determining the mean radiant temperature; problems of the second occur in connection with investigations of the effectiveness of distribution of heating units.

For all three ceiling heights the graphs show that as the occupant walks out from under a point on the ceiling directly overhead, his shape factor

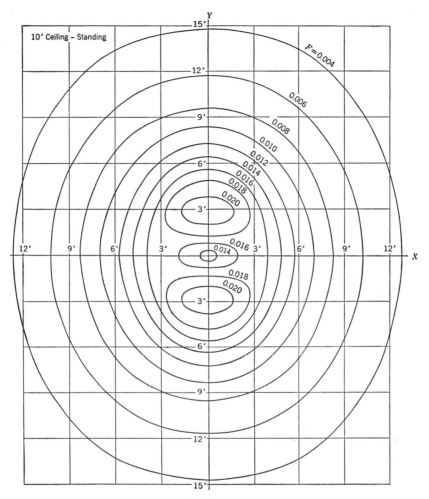

Fig. 4–32. Human shape factors: Standing subject; 10-ft ceiling.

with respect to that point first progressively increases for a distance which is greater for higher ceilings and then continuously decreases toward zero at distance of infinity. At first glance this fact seems somewhat strange because it indicates that less energy is received from a small heating panel by a subject standing directly under it than by a subject standing out some distance from a line drawn normal to it. Brief consideration will indicate, however, that the effective receiving area of the body is very small when the occupant is standing directly under the panel element (the element then *sees* only the head and shoulders of the subject). But as the subject starts to move out from under the element, the receiving area at first increases rapidly and then more slowly approaches the maximum value that would occur when

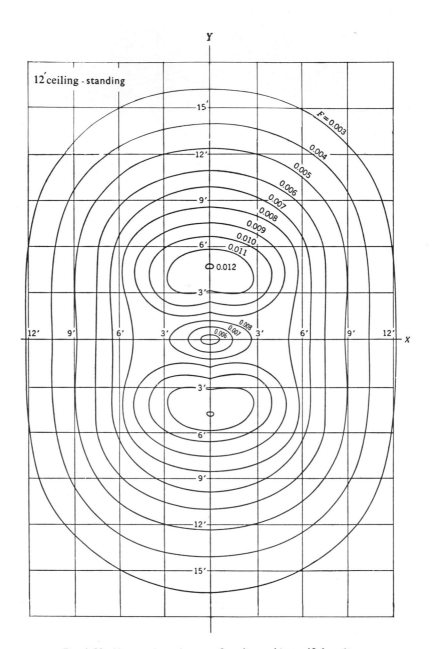

Fig. 4–33. Human shape factors: Standing subject; 12-ft ceiling.

the subject had moved an infinite distance out from under the element. (At that time a line drawn from element to subject would be horizontal and the visible area of the body would then be the full silhouette represented by the outline of a vertical cross-section through the subject.) The initial rapid increase in area more than offsets the effect of greater distance from the element and sharper angle of intersection of the radiation, but as the rate of area increase becomes less, these two factors increase in influence and a reduction in shape factor with distance then sets in.

EXAMPLE 4–23. A man is standing in a room having 8 ft ceiling height. On the ceiling is a 1000-watt diffuse radiating source that is located 3 ft ahead of him and 2 ft to the right of the direction in which he is facing. At what rate, Btu/hr, is he irradiated by this source?

Solution: Fig. 4–31 is applicable to an 8-ft ceiling. From the center of coordinates move up 3 ft in the Y-direction and to the right 2 ft in the X-direction, where the shape factor is read as 0.035. This means that 3.5 per cent of the energy from the source travels in the direction of the man. Irradiation rate is therefore 0.035×1000, or 35 watts/hr, which corresponds to $35 \times 3.413 = 119.5$ Btu/hr.

Subject Standing; Area in Wall. Shape factors for both full-face and full-profile subjects with respect to non-normal areas as X are presented in Tables 4–8 and 4–9. If the subject is oblique with respect to X, the correct shape factor can be estimated by interpolation between the data from the two tables, though such added refinement will usually be unnecessary. From the data in Tables 4–8 and 4–9, the shape factors can be obtained for a standing subject with respect to any number of points on a vertical wall of any size. If the points are selected at the center of equal areas, the over-all shape factor of subject with respect to wall will then be equal to the arithmetical average of the point shape factors.

Subject Standing; Area in Floor. Fig. 4–34 presents experimental data for shape factors of a standing subject with respect to a point on the floor. As for Figs. 4–31, 4–32, and 4–33, the visualization is of a subject standing at the center of coordinates and facing in the positive direction of the Y-axis. Although values of the shape factor shown on the figure are specifically determined for point sources, they are nonetheless applicable to any finite area of floor over which the average shape factor approaches with adequate engineering accuracy the value of the shape factor at the center of that area. To determine the shape factor of occupant with respect to any large area (such as a floor panel), the panel can be sketched on Fig. 4–34 in its proper position with respect to the occupant and the over-all shape factor then determined as the average (not the sum) of shape factors of selected unit areas of the large panel.

EVALUATION OF SHAPE FACTORS OF SEATED HUMAN SUBJECTS WITH RESPECT TO PLANE AREAS. For general heating design an analysis based

TABLE 4–8*

Shape Factors of Subject in Full Face with Respect to Element of Wall Area

L = length of normal from wall to feet of subject.
H = height of element of wall area.
D = horizontal distance of element of wall area to right or left of normal
from wall to feet of subject.

L	D, ft	H, ft 0	2	4	6	8	10	12
	2	0.108	0.211.	0.230	0.094	0.020	0.005	0.002
	4	0.068	0.133	0.145	0.060	0.012	0.003	0.001
2 ft	6	0.048	0.094	0.103	0.042	0.009	0.002	0.001
	8	0.037	0.072	0.079	0.034	0.007	0.002	0.001
	10	0.030	0.058	0.064	0.026	0.006	0.002	0.001
	12	0.025	0.049	0.054	0.022	0.005	0.001	0.001
	2	0.064	0.098	0.101	0.064	0.029	0.013	0.006
	4	0.050	0.077	0.080	0.051	0.023	0.010	0.005
4 ft	6	0.039	0.061	0.063	0.040	0.018	0.008	0.004
	8	0.032	0.049	0.051	0.033	0.014	0.006	0.003
	10	0.026	0.041	0.042	0.027	0.012	0.005	0.002
	12	0.022	0.034	0.036	0.023	0.010	0.004	0.002
	2	0.038	0.048	0.049	0.040	0.025	0.014	0.008
	4	0.034	0.042	0.042	0.035	0.022	0.012	0.007
6 ft	6	0.029	0.036	0.036	0.030	0.019	0.010	0.006
	8	0.024	0.031	0.030	0.026	0.016	0.009	0.005
	10	0.021	0.026	0.026	0.022	0.014	0.007	0.004
	12	0.018	0.023	0.023	0.019	0.012	0.007	0.004
	2	0.024	0.026	0.025	0.025	0.019	0.013	0.009
	4	0.022	0.024	0.023	0.023	0.018	0.012	0.008
8 ft	6	0.019	0.021	0.021	0.021	0.016	0.011	0.007
	8	0.017	0.019	0.018	0.018	0.014	0.010	0.006
	10	0.015	0.017	0.016	0.016	0.012	0.009	0.006
	12	0.014	0.015	0.014	0.014	0.011	0.008	0.005
	2	0.016	0.016	0.015	0.017	0.014	0.011	0.008
	4	0.015	0.015	0.014	0.016	0.014	0.011	0.007
10 ft	6	0.014	0.014	0.013	0.014	0.013	0.010	0.007
	8	0.013	0.013	0.012	0.013	0.012	0.009	0.006
	10	0.012	0.011	0.011	0.012	0.010	0.008	0.006
	12	0.011	0.010	0.010	0.011	0.009	0.007	0.005
	2	0.011	0.011	0.011	0.012	0.011	0.009	0.007
	4	0.011	0.011	0.011	0.012	0.011	0.009	0.007
12 ft	6	0.010	0.010	0.010	0.011	0.010	0.008	0.007
	8	0.010	0.010	0.010	0.010	0.010	0.008	0.006
	10	0.009	0.009	0.009	0.009	0.009	0.007	0.006
	12	0.008	0.008	0.008	0.009	0.008	0.007	0.005

* Reproduced with permission from Raber and Hutchinson, "Optimum Surface Distribution in Panel Heating and Cooling Systems," ASHVE *Trans.* Vol. 50, 1944.

TABLE 4–9*

Shape Factors of Subject in Profile with Respect to Element of Wall Area

L = length of normal from wall to feet of subject.

H = height of element of wall area.

D = horizontal distance of element of wall area to right or left of normal from wall to feet of subject.

L	D, ft	H, ft						
		0	2	4	6	8	10	12
2 ft	2	0.061	0.139	0.144	0.059	0.013	0.004	0.002
	4	0.039	0.088	0.091	0.037	0.008	0.002	0.001
	6	0.027	0.062	0.065	0.026	0.006	0.002	0.001
	8	0.021	0.049	0.050	0.020	0.004	0.001	0.001
	10	0.017	0.039	0.040	0.016	0.004	0.001	0.001
	12	0.014	0.032	0.034	0.014	0.003	0.001	0.0004
4 ft	2	0.033	0.051	0.053	0.035	0.018	0.008	0.003
	4	0.026	0.041	0.042	0.028	0.014	0.006	0.003
	6	0.020	0.032	0.033	0.022	0.011	0.005	0.002
	8	0.016	0.026	0.026	0.018	0.009	0.004	0.002
	10	0.014	0.021	0.022	0.015	0.007	0.003	0.001
	12	0.012	0.018	0.019	0.013	0.006	0.003	0.001
6 ft	2	0.020	0.025	0.026	0.022	0.016	0.009	0.005
	4	0.018	0.022	0.022	0.019	0.014	0.008	0.004
	6	0.015	0.019	0.019	0.016	0.012	0.006	0.004
	8	0.013	0.016	0.016	0.014	0.010	0.005	0.003
	10	0.011	0.014	0.014	0.012	0.009	0.005	0.003
	12	0.010	0.012	0.012	0.010	0.007	0.004	0.002
8 ft	2	0.013	0.014	0.014	0.014	0.012	0.008	0.005
	4	0.012	0.013	0.013	0.012	0.011	0.007	0.005
	6	0.011	0.012	0.011	0.011	0.010	0.006	0.004
	8	0.010	0.010	0.010	0.010	0.009	0.006	0.004
	10	0.009	0.009	0.009	0.009	0.008	0.005	0.003
	12	0.008	0.008	0.008	0.008	0.007	0.004	0.003
10 ft	2	0.009	0.010	0.010	0.011	0.009	0.006	0.004
	4	0.008	0.010	0.009	0.010	0.008	0.006	0.004
	6	0.008	0.009	0.008	0.009	0.008	0.006	0.004
	8	0.007	0.008	0.008	0.008	0.007	0.005	0.004
	10	0.006	0.007	0.007	0.008	0.006	0.005	0.003
	12	0.006	0.007	0.006	0.007	0.006	0.004	0.003
12 ft	2	0.006	0.006	0.006	0.007	0.006	0.005	0.004
	4	0.006	0.006	0.006	0.006	0.006	0.005	0.004
	6	0.006	0.006	0.006	0.006	0.006	0.005	0.003
	8	0.005	0.005	0.005	0.006	0.005	0.004	0.003
	10	0.005	0.005	0.005	0.005	0.005	0.004	0.003
	12	0.005	0.005	0.004	0.005	0.005	0.004	0.003

* Reproduced, with permission, from Raber and Hutchinson, "Optimum Surface Distribution in Panel Heating and Cooling Systems," ASHVE *Trans.* Vol. 50, 1944.

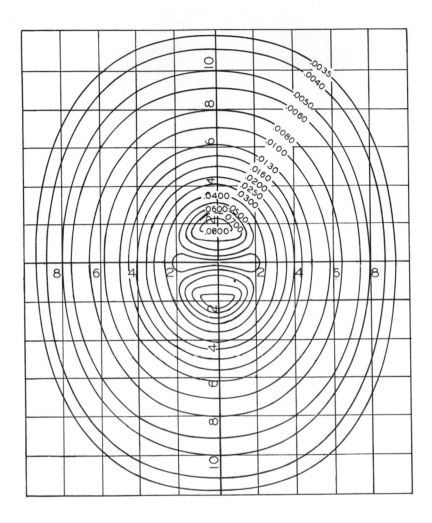

Fig. 4–34. Human shape factors with respect to area in floor.

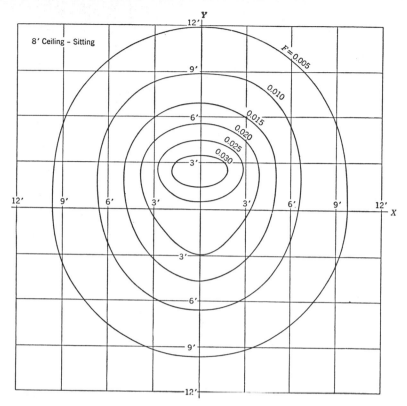

Fig. 4–35. Human shape factors: Seated subject; 8-ft ceiling.

on a standing subject will suffice. In some special cases, however, (as in the design of local heating panels), data on the seated subject are useful. Such experimental data have been obtained for areas located in the ceiling, and when needed for walls or floors, approximate shape-factor values can be obtained by approximation from the experimental data for a standing subject.

Subject Sitting; Area in Ceiling. Experimental data for a seated subject are given in Figs. 4–35, 4–36, and 4–37. Since the method of showing the data is the same as that already described for the standing subject, no additional discussion is necessary. Further uses of shape factors for the seated occupant are no different from those for the standing, and so this subject also need not be discussed.

4–8. Combined Mechanisms of Heat Transfer. Previous sections have considered the separate effects of heat transfer through solids, across fluid films, between separated surfaces, and across air spaces. In most problems that occur in practice, many of or all these types of heat transfer occur simultaneously. Considering transfer through the exposed wall of a

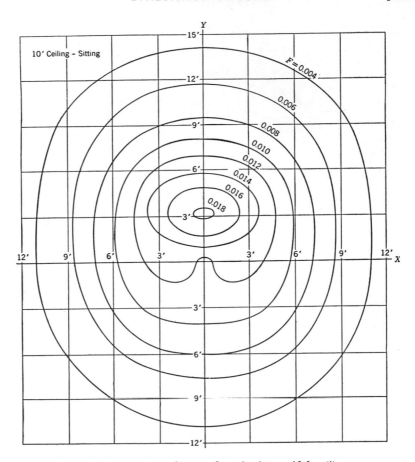

Fig. 4–36. Human shape factors: Seated subject; 10-ft ceiling.

room (refer to Fig. 4–38), for example, the following conditions will apply:

1. Transfer by convection, q_{ci}, from the room air to the inside surface of the exposed wall.
2. Transfer by radiation, q_{ri}, from the interior surfaces of the room to the inside surface of the exposed wall.
3. Transfer by conduction, q_{w_1}, through the one or more layers of solid material that may precede an air space (such as the air space, equal in width to the framing members, of an uninsulated frame house).
4. Transfer from the inner to the outer surface of the air space by convection, q_{ca}.
5. Transfer from the inner to the outer surface of the air space by radiation, q_{ra}.

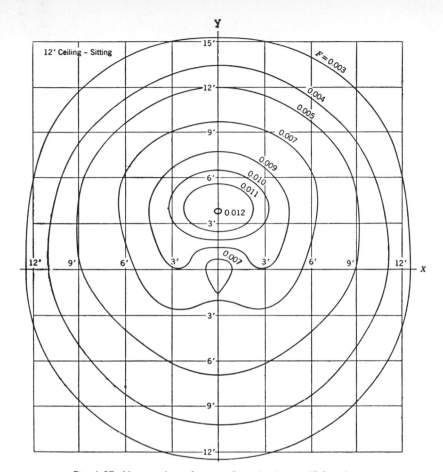

Fig. 4–37. Human shape factors: Seated subject; 12-ft ceiling.

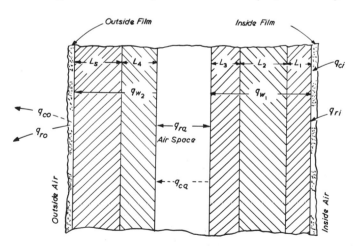

Fig. 4–38. Combined mechanisms of heat transfer.

6. Transfer by conduction, q_{w_2}, through the one or more adjacent solid sections of wall that are outside of the air space (such as siding plus sheathing in frame construction).
7. Transfer by convection, q_{co}, from the exterior surface to outside air.
8. Transfer by radiation, q_{ro}, from the exterior surface to outside air.

Since the designer is primarily interested in the rate of heat transfer from inside air to outside air, it is evident that he would prefer to develop a means of obtaining this rate directly rather than having to investigate in detail each of the above eight conditions. Further, a preferred equation would be one expressing heat transfer in terms of the inside-to-outside air-to-air temperature difference.

Convection and Radiation in Parallel. Examining the eight mechanisms of heat loss which are listed above, it is evident that the first two (for the inside film) occur in parallel, the two for the air space (4 and 5) occur in parallel, and the last two (for the outside film) occur in parallel. In each of these cases the effect of both convection and radiation is additive and can usually be expressed in a single combined coefficient,

$$h = h_c + h_r' \qquad (4\text{-}142a)$$

or

$$a = a_c + h_r' \qquad (4\text{-}142b)$$

where h = combined equivalent film coefficient for parallel heat transfer by convection and radiation across an air film, Btu/(hr)(sq ft)(°F).
a = combined conductance of an air space, Btu/(hr)(sq ft)(°F).
h_c = film coefficient for convective transfer.
h_r' = corrected equivalent film coefficient for radiant transfer.

The number of series steps in the transfer of heat from room air to outside air therefore reduces to five:

1. Transfer across the inside film as determined by the combined film coefficient $h_i = h_{ci} + h_{ri}'$.
2. Transfer through the series of adjacent wall sections as given (by Eq. 4–15) in terms of the surface-to-surface conductance of these sections, C_{w_1}
3. Transfer across the air space as determined by the combined conductance $a = a_c + a_r$.
4. Transfer through the series of adjacent wall sections, C_{w_2}, (given by Eq. 4–15) which are on the outer side of the air space.
5. Transfer across the outside film as given by the combined film coefficient $h_o = h_{co} + h_{ro}'$.

THE OVER-ALL COEFFICIENT OF HEAT TRANSFER. For steady-state conditions the rates of heat transfer in all five of the above steps must be the same;

hence each Btu of heat that leaves the room air passes through a group of five thermal resistances which are arranged in series. The over-all rate of heat transfer will equal the transfer rate across any one resistance; hence in terms of inside and outside air temperatures, an over-all equation can be written (by analogy with Eqs. 4–15 and 4–16) as

$$q = \left[\frac{1}{r_i + r_{w_1} + r_a + r_{w_2} + r_o} \right] A(t_i - t_o) \qquad (4\text{–}143)$$

or

$$q = \frac{1}{\dfrac{1}{h_{ci} + h'_{ri}} + \dfrac{1}{C_{w_1}} + \dfrac{1}{a} + \dfrac{1}{C_{w_2}} + \dfrac{1}{h_{co} + h'_{ro}}} A(t_i - t_o) \qquad (4\text{–}144)$$

where r_i = resistance of the inside film to parallel transfer of heat by convection and radiation, where: $r_i = 1/h_i = 1/(h_{ci} + h'_{ri})$, and h_{ci} and h'_{ri} are respectively the convective and radiant fractions of heat transfer across the inside film.

r_{w_1} = resistance of the inner section of wall through which heat transfer is occurring by conduction only: $r_{w_1} = 1/C_{w_1}$, where C_{w_1} is calculated as in Eqs. 4–14 or 4–15.

r_a = resistance of the air space, $1/(a_c + a_r)$.

r_{w_2} = resistance of the outer section of wall through which heat transfer is occurring by conduction only.

r_o = resistance of the outside film to parallel transfer of heat by convection and radiation, where: $r_o = 1/h_o = 1/(h_{co} + h'_{ro})$ and h_{co} and h'_{ro} are respectively the convective and radiant fractions of heat transfer across the outside film.

Eqs. 4–143 and 4–144 can be rewritten in the form

$$q = \frac{A(t_i - t_o)}{R} = UA(t_i - t_o) \qquad (4\text{–}145)$$

where R = sum of thermal resistances of all series elements of the system.
U = over-all (air-to-air) coefficient of heat transfer, Btu/(hr)(sq ft)(°F).

For walls that are either more or less complex than the one described above, Eq. 4–145 is applicable, but the value of R is then taken as the sum of all series resistances of the actual wall. Thus, for any transfer problem in which steady state is assumed to apply (and this is true of most load calculations that occur in design of heating systems), the problem of evaluating the over-all coefficient of heat transfer is no more complex than the simple addition of a series of individual resistances, each of which is calculable from the combined film coefficient, or the thermal conductivity and thickness, or the conductance of the section in question. Numerical evaluation of R for various types of typical building construction is described in Chapter 5.

SURFACE TEMPERATURE EVALUATION. Once the air-to-air thermal resistance has been determined, it becomes a simple matter to calculate the temperature of the inside or outside surface of a structural section. By analogy with Eq. 4–25,

$$\frac{t_i - t_{si}}{t_i - t_o} = \frac{r_i}{R} \tag{4-146}$$

giving

$$t_{si} = t_i - \frac{r_i}{R}(t_i - t_o) = t_i - r_i U(t_i - t_o) \tag{4-147}$$

Likewise,

$$\frac{t_i - t_{so}}{t_i - t_o} = \frac{R - r_o}{R}$$

giving

$$t_{so} = t_i - \frac{R - r_o}{R}(t_i - t_o) = t_i - (R - r_o)U(t_i - t_o) \tag{4-148}$$

or

$$t_{so} = t_o + r_o U(t_i - t_o) \tag{4-149}$$

where t_i = inside air temperature.

t_{si} = inside surface temperature.

t_{so} = outside surface temperature.

t_o = outside air temperature.

r_i = combined (convection and radiation) coefficient for inside film.

r_o = combined (convection and radiation) coefficient for outside film.

R = air-to-air thermal resistance.

U = over-all (air-to-air) coefficient of heat transfer.

EXAMPLE 4–24. A single-glass window has an over-all (air-to-air) coefficient of heat transfer of 1.13 Btu/(hr)(sq ft)(°F) when the value of the combined inside film coefficient is 1.65 Btu/(hr)(sq ft)(°F). Calculate the inside surface temperature of the window when outside air is at 0 F and room temperature is 72 F.

Solution: By Eq. 4–147,

$$t_{si} = 72 - \frac{1}{1.65}(1.13)(72 - 0) = 72 - 49.3 = 22.7 \text{ F}$$

The resistances of actual single-glass windows correspond closely to the values used in this example. It is evident, therefore, that in cold weather such windows represent significant low temperature receivers to which the occupants will lose body heat by radiation.

A graphical method of determining surface or interface temperatures is shown in Fig. 4–39. An insulated pipe is subject to a flow of heat from the surrounding atmosphere through an outside air film, through the insulation (wall section *a*), the pipe wall (section *b*), and the inside fluid film to the main body of fluid passing through the pipe at temperature t_i. A longitudinal cross-section of the pipe and insulation is drawn to scale (left side of Fig. 4–39) then an arbitrary scale of temperature is set up on a vertical line SS to the right of this cross-section. Moving to the right from SS a distance $1/h_oA_o$ gives the equivalent thickness in feet of an air film of unit conductance and establishes line 2—2, which represents the outside surface of the insulation. Continuing to the right a distance $x_a/k_aA_{m_a}$ sets up a section equivalent to the actual insulation, but of unit conductance, and serves also to establish the location of the interface, line 3—3, between the insulation and the pipe wall. In the same way the width of an equivalent pipe wall of unit conductance $x_b/k_bA_{m_b}$ is laid off, establishing line 4—4; to the right of this is set off the equivalent inside film of width $1/h_iA_i$.

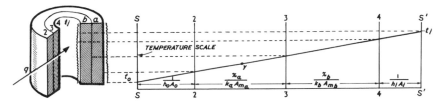

Fig. 4–39. Graphical determination of intermediate temperatures.

The resultant equivalent wall of width $S'S'$ (including both surface films) is of unit resistance throughout and must therefore have a straight and continuous temperature gradient. From the temperature scale establish the point t_o on line SS and t_i on $S'S'$, where t_o and t_i are the fluid temperatures outside and inside, respectively, of the pipe. A straight line connecting these two points is the temperature gradient through the equivalent wall. From the intersection of this line with surfaces 2—2 and 4—4 and with the interface 3—3, the temperatures on these lines can be readily determined by direct reading from the temperature scale. The points can then be transposed back to the cross-section to permit interpretation of the steepness of the temperature gradient through the different wall sections. However, the true gradient through the scale drawing of the pipe cannot yet be drawn, since the area is variable, and this gradient between surfaces or interfaces is therefore curved; thus the point y, located midway between lines 2—2 and 3—3 of the equivalent wall, does not correspond to a point midway through the insulation but rather to that point in the insulation at which the resistance is one-half of the total value for the insulating layer. By breaking down the insulation into sections each having a separate value of A_m, as many points on the temperature gradient can be found as may be desired; usually, however, a determination of surface and interface temperatures will alone provide all information needed in the solution of practical problems.

For plane walls the difficulty of variable resistance does not occur (except when the thermal conductivity varies appreciably with temperature), and immediate determination of the temperature at any point in the wall is therefore directly possible by the graphical method. Surface and interface temperatures are fixed as on the scale drawing in Fig. 4–39, but it is now possible to connect such points by means of straight lines, thereby fixing the true gradient and permitting the determination of any desired point temperature by direct transposition of the gradient intersection to the temperature scale. If the temperature at but one point in a wall is required, calculation by Eq. 4–26 usually gives the most rapid and direct solution, but if the complete temperature gradient across a wall consisting of more than one homogeneous section is needed, the graphical method is more direct and less time consuming.

CONTROLLING RESISTANCES. The importance of accurate evaluation of any particular conductance for a parallel or series heat-transfer system varies greatly among systems and depends in every case on that section of the thermal path for which the thermal resistance is greatest. If conductive heat transfer were being evaluated from end to end of an insulated metal rod, the importance of exact determination of the thermal conductivity of the metal would be paramount because, all other conditions being the same, the rate of heat transfer would vary directly with the thermal conductivity. Thus, for a single-path system of this kind, copper with a thermal conductivity of approximately 240 Btu/(hr)(sq ft)(°F/ft), as compared with iron with a k value of approximately 24 Btu/(hr)(sq ft)(°F/ft), would provide a heat-transfer rate ten times greater than would iron.

In practical application, however, the thermal difference between copper and iron, or between any other metals or transfer surfaces, is usually very much less than the difference in conductivities would indicate because the major or controlling thermal resistance is usually in one of or both the fluid films rather than in the wall of the transfer surface. Consider a heat exchanger with hot air on one side and cold air on the other. Heat must flow through the air film on the hot side, through the metal wall, and through the cold-side air film; the convective film coefficients will depend on the air velocities (as well as on diameter of tubes, direction of flow, and other factors), but will usually be of the order of 100 Btu/(hr)(sq ft)(°F). The conductance of the solid barrier, taking a thickness of 0.01 ft, would be approximately 24/0.01 = 2400 for iron or 240/0.01 = 24,000 for copper. Thus the resistance of each film will be from 24 to 240 times greater than the wall resistance, and it is evident that a large difference in the thermal conductivity will affect the over-all coefficient of the system by only a very small amount.

As an opposite case, consider the heavily insulated wall of a cold-storage warehouse; the resistance of the insulating material is likely to represent such a large fraction of the over-all resistance that little consideration need be given to accurate evaluation of either the outside air conductance or the conductance of non-insulating structural materials of the wall itself.

THE HEAT BALANCE. In order for steady state to exist, the rate of heat reception at any surface or at any plane in a solid must be equal to the rate of heat loss. This concept permits setting up a heat balance and thereby determining the state at such a surface or plane. As a simple example consider a refractory material (such as a brick) located inside a furnace in full view of the walls and ceiling and surrounded by high-temperature but non-luminous products of combustion. The brick will reach a steady-state condition at which its rate of convective heat gain from the surrounding gases plus its radiant gain from the luminous flame will be exactly equal to its rate of radiant heat loss to the lower temperature walls of the furnace space. Thus the temperature of the brick at steady state will necessarily be between the temperature of the gases and that of the furnace walls.

An opposite situation occurs when an object is cooled by being placed in a refrigerator or a cold storage room. Since heat gain is occurring through the room walls, the inside surface of the walls will necessarily be at a temperature greater than that of the inside air; thus the object in the space will reach steady state at a temperature between air and inside surface values. If the material in cold storage is highly temperature-sensitive, consideration must then be given to this radiant-heating effect, as it may be responsible for raising the steady-state object temperature by enough to cause either product damage or spoilage.

In the fields of heating and air conditioning the effects noted above occur in similar manner but to lesser degree. In a heated structure the average inside surface temperature will be less than the inside air temperature (see Example 4–24); hence a heat balance on the occupant will show that body heat loss is occurring at a rate greater than that which would be due to air temperature alone. In a cooled room, average inside surface temperature will exceed room air temperature; hence the rate of body heat loss will be less than that due to air temperature alone.

EXAMPLE 4–25. Produce gardeners frequently complain that the outer leaves of heads of lettuce sometimes freeze on nights when the air temperature is greater than 32 F. Investigate, qualitatively, the possibility of such an occurrence.

Solution: Neglect conduction along the leaves and consider that the equivalent temperature of the clear night sky is (as experiment has shown) approximately equal to minus 60 F. Assume that there is little breeze and that the film coefficient for convection between surrounding air and the leaves is of the order of 1 Btu/(hr)(sq ft)(°F). Now assume 32 F as the leaf temperature and calculate the corresponding equilibrium temperature of the night air. Note that for equilibrium the rate of heat loss by radiation to the clear sky will be equal to the rate of heat gain by convection from the surrounding air. (For further simplification set up the heat balance on a leaf that is on top of the head and which therefore "sees" *only* the sky.) Then, writing the heat-balance equation,

$$h_c(t_a - t_1) = h_r F_{ae}(t_1 - t_s) = h'_r(t_1 - t_s)$$

where t_a, t_1, and t_s are, respectively, the temperatures of air, leaf, and sky. But h_r can be evaluated by use of Eq. 4–113:

$$h_r = \frac{0.172[(492/100)^4 - (400/100)^4]}{32 + 60} = 0.62$$

Then, substituting into the heat balance equation,

$$(1)(t_a - 32) = (0.62)(32 + 60)$$

giving

$$t_a = 89 \text{ F}$$

Thus on a clear night the radiant loss to the night sky is so great that freezing may occur at relatively high air temperatures, *provided* the air movement is sufficiently restricted to minimize convection.

EXAMPLE 4–26. For the conditions of Example 4–25 assume that there is sufficient wind to provide a film coefficient of approximately 10 Btu/(hr)(sq ft)(°F), corresponding to a wind velocity of approximately 20 mph. Determine the air temperature for which equilibrium leaf temperature would be 32 F.

Solution: Writing a heat balance as in the preceding example,

$$(10)(t_a - 32) = (0.62)(32 + 60)$$

giving

$$t_a = 37.7 \text{ F}$$

This result (compared with that of Example 4–25) shows why air movement provides a warming effect on sky-exposed inanimate objects during clear nights.

THE RELAXATION METHOD WITH FILM CORRECTION. In Art. 4–5, in the discussion on conductive heat transfer, the relaxation procedure for determination of temperature distribution in a complex solid was developed for

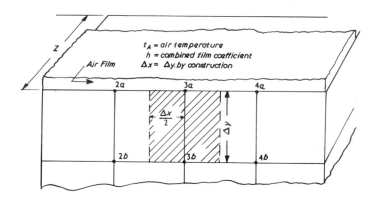

Fig. 4–40. Geometry for film coefficient inclusion in relaxation analysis.

the case of conduction only. It is now possible to extend this procedure to include series transfer through the surface film (by convection, radiation, or a combination thereof). Fig. 4–40 shows a detail of Fig. 4–5 with added film and with constant air temperature t_a. For this case the surface temperature will no longer be constant; hence a method must be established for independent evaluation of t_{2a}, t_{3a}, t_{4a}, ... This can be done by setting up a heat balance on the surface for a distance $\Delta x/2$ on either side of the point (as $3a$) for which the surface temperature is to be determined. Thus

$$h(z\,\Delta x)(t_A - t_{3a}) = \frac{k}{\Delta x}\,(z\,\Delta x)(t_{3a} - t_{3b})$$

giving

$$t_{3a} = \frac{(h\,\Delta x/k)t_A + t_{3b}}{1 + (h\,\Delta x/k)}$$

For a given system the parenthetical term is a constant; hence

$$t_{3a} = \frac{Bt_A + t_{3b}}{1 + B} \tag{4–150}$$

where

$$B = \frac{h\,\Delta x}{k} \tag{4–151}$$

By analogy with Eq. 4–31, the residual R_{3b}^* becomes

$$R_{3b}^* = t_{2b} + t_{3a} + t_{4b} + t_{3c} - 4t_{3b}$$

$$= t_{2b} + \frac{Bt_A + t_{3b}}{1 + B} + t_{4b} + t_{3c} - 4t_{3b} \tag{4–152}$$

$$= t_{2b} + t_{4b} + t_{3c} + \frac{Bt_A}{1 + B} - \left(4 - \frac{1}{1 + B}\right)t_{3b}$$

where $Bt_A/(1 + B)$ is a constant.

Similar equations can be written (see Fig. 4–5) to progress clockwise around the slab for R_{4b}^*, R_{4c}^*, R_{4d}^*, R_{3d}^*, R_{2d}^*, R_{2c}^*, R_{2b}^*, and R_{3c}^*. The procedure for evaluation of the temperature gradient is the same as that followed in Example 4–8 except that the residuals listed above are now calculated by equations in the form of Eq. 4–152 and additional surface temperature residuals are calculated by equations in the form of Eq. 4–150. Note that inclusion of the air film reduces the generality of the solution since the magnitudes of h, k, and Δx now influence the equilibrium temperature distribution.

PROBLEMS

4–1. Calculate the energy release, Btu/hr, within a room in which the lighting load consists of six 150-w lamps, and a $\frac{1}{2}$-hp power grinder is in operation. (Note that 1 Btu = 0.293 whr.)

4–2. Compare the heat output of a 100-w lamp with that of a sedentary adult.

4–3. Under conditions of maximum exertion, metabolic rate may reach 4000 Btu/hr. Assuming 20 per cent thermal efficiency, calculate the horsepower that is developed under such conditions.

4–4. Estimate the number of men who, at full exertion (refer to problem 4–3), could develop 1 hp of external work.

4–5. In a room that is at 70 F, there are three 1-cu ft containers. One contains a metal alloy having a density of 600 lb/cu ft and a specific heat of 0.03 Btu/(lb)(°F). The second container is filled with water. The third contains a plastic having a density of 120 lb/cu ft and a specific heat of 0.5 Btu/(lb)(°F). If 100 Btu were to be removed from one of the containers, (a) from which container should the heat be extracted if it is desired to cause minimum immediate change in room temperature conditions? (b) From which container should the heat be extracted if it is desired to cause minimum permanent change in room temperature conditions?

4–6. Thermal stresses in a particular metal plate would lead to failure if the temperature gradient exceeded 10 F per inch. Thermal conductivity of the metal is 110 Btu/(hr)(sq ft)(°F/ft). Under steady-state conditions what would be the maximum permissible rate at which heat could be transferred through a $\frac{3}{4}$ in. thick plate?

4–7. A 20-ft by 10-ft wall of 4-in. common brick is faced on the inside with gypsum plaster. If inside and outside surfaces of the wall are at 68 F and 28 F when the rate of heat transfer is 8000 Btu/hr, calculate the thickness, in inches, of the plaster facing.

4–8. Determine the ratio of surface-to-surface thermal resistances of a 4-in. granite wall to a 4-in. common brick wall; to a solid yellow pine wall.

4–9. A thin-walled 4-in. diameter pipe carries water through a 100 ft long basement space in which the air temperature is 90 F. The water enters at 40 F and travels through the pipe at a velocity of 5 fps. Pipe insulation consists of a $2\frac{1}{2}$-in. layer of molded cork having thermal conductivity of 0.03 Btu/(hr)(sq ft) (°F/ft). (a) Calculate the leaving temperature of the water on the assumption that inside and outside surface temperatures of the insulation differ by little from the temperatures of the adjacent water and air. (b) Calculate the heat-transfer rate through the insulation.

4–10. For the insulated pipe of problem 4–9 calculate the temperature in the plane of the mean area.

4–11. A structure having homogeneous walls has inside and outside uniform wall-surface temperatures of 68 F and 28 F, respectively. Determine the temperature at the midpoint of a diagonal through a corner.

4–12. A room 12 ft by 12 ft has an 8-ft ceiling. Walls are of concrete [$k = 1$ Btu/(hr)(sq ft)(°F/ft)] and are 9 in. thick. (a) Calculate the total heat loss through the walls, assuming that inside and outside surface temperatures are uniformly at 70 F and 35 F, respectively. (b) What percentage of the loss is due to corner effect?

4–13. The outside surface of a corner is rounded, with the inside of the corner as center and with a radius of curvature equal to the wall thickness. Using the relaxation method with a network similar to that of Fig. 4–9a, (a) calculate the distance back from the inside of the corner (expressed in wall thicknesses) to which the corner effect is experienced; (b) calculate the increase in wall area (expressed in terms of wall thickness) to be used in calculating the additional heat loss through the walls, that is due to corner effect.

4–14. A flat plate 10 ft long and 6 in. wide is buried in a horizontal position 4 ft below the surface in moist earth having a thermal conductivity of 1 Btu/(hr)(sq ft)(°F/ft). The plate is electrically heated to a surface temperature of 250 F and the surface temperature of the earth is 60 F. (a) Calculate the total rate of heat loss from the plate. (b) Determine the rate of heat loss per square foot and compare it with the loss from a 6-in. diameter pipe under similar conditions. (The pipe heat loss is given in the solution of Example 4–10.)

4–15. In a particular structure the inside surface temperature of the homogeneous exterior wall is 68 F when inside air temperature is 73.5 F and outside air temperature is 0 F. (a) Calculate the film coefficient for convective transfer from room air to wall surface. (b) Assuming that radiant transfer from room to inside wall surface is negligible, calculate the inside surface temperature when the outside air temperature is 40 F (taking account of the change in value of the inside convective film coefficient).

4–16. Heat transfer is occurring to an unheated floor under conditions such that the rate of heat loss by convection is 465 Btu/hr. If the outside air temperature drops so that for the new equilibrium conditions, the temperature drop across the floor film is increased by 60 per cent, (a) calculate the percentage increase in the convective film coefficient, (b) calculate the new rate of heat loss to the floor.

4–17. Under conditions of design load, a particular structure has a temperature drop from room air to inside unheated ceiling surface of 8 F. If the outside air temperature drops until this room-to-ceiling temperature difference is reduced to 1.8 F, calculate the percentage reduction in the ceiling convective film coefficient and compare it with the percentage reduction in the ceiling film temperature drop.

4–18. Based on an arbitrarily selected convective film coefficient of unity for an unheated floor, calculate the ratio of heat transfer to wall, ceiling, and floor, for laminar flow conditions and for the same temperature drop across the three inside films.

4–19. An air space located in a wall behind a baseboard radiator is 2 in. wide and 21.2 in. high. Under design load conditions, the surface-to-surface temperature drop across this air space is 6 F. (a) Calculate the convective conductance of the air space. (b) Calculate the error that would result if the L/x ratio were not taken into account.

4–20. With all other conditions as in Example 4–17, calculate the film coefficient if the water is flowing through a tube of 3.23-in. inside diameter.

4–21. Determine the dimensions of a small rectangular conduit through which 100 F water is flowing at 10 fps; the conduit is twice as wide as it is deep, and the film coefficient is known to have the same value as that of the water in the 3.23-in. inside diameter tube of problem 4–20.

4–22. Water at 40 F is heated to 189 F while it is flowing through an annular space surrounding a pipe containing saturated steam at atmospheric pressure. (a) Calculate the temperature difference for use in evaluating the rate of heat transfer. (b) Evaluate the error in heat-transfer rate that would occur if the arithmetical temperature difference were used.

4–23. Under design conditions a structure is subjected to a wind velocity of 12 mph; the outside surface is very rough. If the outside surface were altered so that it became very smooth, what percentage increase in thermal resistance of the convective film would occur?

4-24. Calculate the rate at which energy is emitted from 1 sq ft of plastered wall at surface temperature of 70 F.

4-25. The distance from the center of a 0.4-sq ft surface to the center of a 0.3-sq ft surface is 12 ft. The line connecting the centers of these two surfaces makes a 60-deg angle with a normal to the 0.4-sq ft surface and a 45-deg angle with a normal to the 0.3-sq ft surface. (a) Calculate the shape factor $F_{0.3,0.4}$. (b) What fraction of radiant energy leaving the 0.3-sq ft surface strikes the 0.4-sq ft surface?

4-26. An inside room at 73.5 F has an exposed 20 ft by 20 ft ceiling, the inside surface temperature of which is 65.5 F under conditions of design load. Assuming that all other room surfaces are at 73.5 F and assuming that all surfaces (ceiling included) have unit emissivity, (a) calculate the equivalent film coefficient for radiant transfer to the ceiling, (b) calculate the rate of radiant transfer to the ceiling, (c) compare the rate of heat transfer to the ceiling by radiation with that by convection.

4-27. Air is being heated while passing through the annular space between two concentric tubes; the smaller tube has an outside diameter of 4 in. and the larger tube has an inside diameter of 6 in. The outside surface of the inner tube (at a given short section along its length) is at an average temperature of 208 F and has an emissivity of 0.73. The inside surface of the outer tube (at the same section) is at 115 F and has an emissivity of 0.85. Calculate the rate of net radiant transfer for a 1-ft length of the heater section for which data are given.

4-28. An 18-in. by 18-in. frosted glass plate (covering a light) is set flush with the ceiling at the midpoint of a 20-ft by 20-ft room that is 8 ft high. A 12-in. by 12-in. air grille is located at floor level and centered on the centerline of one wall. What fraction of light from the frosted plate (assuming that the emission of light is diffuse rather than specular) is received at the grille?

4-29. At a distance of 20 ft the human eye can readily discern a 1-in. diameter white button attached to a white background. Estimate the light-sensitive area of one of your eyes and calculate the shape factor of that area with respect to light received from a 1-in. diameter button at any specified position (assuming that light reflected from the button leaves diffusely).

4-30. In a room 20 ft by 40 ft with a 10-ft ceiling, a heating panel occupies a rectangular ceiling strip 4 ft wide and adjacent to one of the 40-ft walls. Calculate the fraction of radiation from the heating panel that (a) strikes the floor, (b) strikes the part of the floor area that is not directly under the panel, (c) strikes a 4-ft wide strip of floor that parallels the heating panel but is adjacent to the opposite 40-ft wall.

4-31. Refer to Fig. 4–22 and consider that area a represents a 4-ft by 7-ft door in a room that has a floor heating panel of area d which is 10 ft wide by 15 ft long. If the panel surface temperature is 85 F and if its emissivity is 0.92, calculate the loss by radiation from the panel through the open door.

4-32. A coffee table 18 in. high has a 24-in. diameter top. The table is located in the center of a 15-ft by 20-ft by 10-ft room in which the entire ceiling surface acts as a heating panel. Determine the percentage of the radiant energy emitted by the ceiling that is intercepted by the top of the table.

4–33. A man is seated in a room that has a 10-ft ceiling. Compare his reception of radiation from a unit-area ceiling heating panel located 3 ft in front of him and 6 ft to his right, with his reception of radiation from a unit-area ceiling panel at the same temperature and with the same emissivity but located 3 ft behind him and 6 ft to his right.

4–34. A standing subject is 6 ft from a wall that he is facing. At the 8-ft level on the wall and directly in front of him is a panel of unit area. What fraction of the energy leaving the panel strikes the subject?

4–35. Compare the transfer of radiation from unit area of panel in a 10-ft ceiling to a standing subject directly below the panel, with transfer to a seated subject directly under the same panel.

4–36. A 4-in. air space is located in the floor of a heated room. Surface temperatures of the air space are 70 F and 55 F, and each surface has an emissivity of 0.92. (a) Calculate the heat transfer per unit area by convection. (b) Calculate the heat transfer per unit area by radiation. (c) Calculate the total heat transfer per unit area across the air space. (d) Calculate the percentage of total heat transfer that occurs by radiation.

4–37. An exterior wall consists of 4 in. of granite on the outside, a 3-in. air space, and 8 in. of concrete on the inside. The value of h_r for the air space is 0.97, F_{ae} for the air space is 0.92, and a_c for the air space is 0.45. The value of F_e for inside and outside surfaces of the wall (with respect to their surrounds) is known to be 0.98 and 0.92, respectively, and the corresponding h_r values are 0.99 and 1.02. All room surfaces other than that of the one wall are inside surfaces and are at a uniform temperature approximately equal to room air temperature. The shape factor of the outside surround with respect to the outside wall surface is unity. The inside convective film coefficient is 0.6 and the outside film coefficient is determined by a design wind velocity of 14 mph. Evaluate the over-all coefficient of heat transfer.

4–38. For the wall of problem 4–37 calculate the temperature of the warm-side surface of the air space if room air temperature is 73.5 F and outside air temperature is −10 F.

4–39. Repeat problem 4–38, but solve for the warm-side surface temperature by using the graphical method discussed in Art. 4–8.

4–40. A laboratory "hot room" has a wall consisting of structural sections on each side of an 8-in. air space that is filled with glass wool insulation having a density of 1.5 lb/cu ft. The combined thermal resistance of the structural sections is 2.0, the combined inside film resistance is unity, and the value of h_r' for the outside surface is 0.6 Btu/(hr)(sq ft)(°F). The outside surface is smooth, and for design values of the inside and outside air temperature the outside wind velocity is 3 mph. (a) For design conditions, calculate the value of the combined outside film coefficient h_o. (b) If the wind increased to 30 mph, what would be the new value of h_o? (c) What percentage increase in the rate of heat loss (for the same inside and outside air temperatures) would occur as a result of the increased wind velocity? (d) For this system what constitutes the controlling thermal resistance?

4–41. A flat metal plate 1 ft by 1 ft is supported 2 ft above the earth in a horizontal position. The underside of the plate is highly polished; hence radiant transfer between the plate and the earth is negligible. The upper surface of the plate is covered with a very thin layer of lampblack. Air movement across top and bottom surfaces of the plate is such that the film coefficient for convective transfer is 3.0 Btu/(hr)(sq ft)(°F). Measurement shows that at a given time, the plate is irradiated with solar energy at a rate of 270 Btu/(hr)(sq ft). Calculate the equilibrium temperature of the plate if air temperature is 70 F.

4–42. A man seated in the shade places his hand flat on a table top that is in the sun. The hand receives solar irradiation at a rate of 270 Btu/(hr)(sq ft). Air movement is such that the convective film coefficient is 2 Btu/(hr)(sq ft)(°F). Air temperature is 70 F. Neglecting evaporation, (a) calculate the maximum temperature that could possibly be reached by the irradiated surface of the hand; (b) estimate the actual equilibrium temperature of the irradiated surface of the hand.

4–43. Repeat Example 4–8, assuming that the constant *air* temperature adjacent to the four edges is 120 F, 100 F, 80 F, and 60 F. Combined film coefficient for each edge is 2.0 Btu/(hr)(sq ft)(°F). The slab has dimensions of 5 ft by 5 ft by $\frac{1}{2}$ ft, and its thermal conductivity is 0.8 Btu/(hr)(sq ft)(°F/ft).

4–44. Repeat Example 4–9 with inside and outside air temperatures at 100 F and 0 F, respectively. Take h_i as 1.5 Btu/(hr)(sq ft)(°F) and h_o as 6.0 Btu/(hr) (sq ft)(°F). Calculate the percentage reduction in corner heat loss when air temperatures, rather than surface temperatures, are taken as constant. Take the wall thickness as 1 ft and the thermal conductivity as 0.7 Btu/(hr)(sq ft)(°F/ft).

5

TRANSMISSION HEATING LOAD

5–1. The Fundamental Transmission Equation. The design value of heat loss from any structure consists in part of energy lost by transmission through the walls, floor, ceiling, windows, and other exposed surfaces, and in part of heat carried away in exfiltration air either in latent or sensible form. The transmission fraction of the total loss can be evaluated for known inside and outside air temperatures by applying Eq. 4–145 to each of the exposed surfaces and adding the individual rates of transmission to determine total transmission losses. In the usual type of structure such losses occur through glass, g, exposed wall, w, floor, f, and ceiling, c. There is no loss through interior partitions that connect adjoining heated rooms, and in the case of multistoried houses there may be no loss through either the floor or the ceiling or both. The total transmission loss is therefore given by the equation

$$q_t = U_g A_g(t_a - t_o) + U_w A_w(t_a - t_o) + U_f A_f(t_a - t_b) + U_c A_c(t_a - t_o)$$

$$(5\text{--}1)$$

where t_b is the basement air temperature, U_c is the over-all coefficient of heat transfer for the combined ceiling and roof, and all other terms have significance as previously established.

Examination of Eq. 5–1 shows that the same temperature difference appears in all terms except the one for transmission through the floor. If this term were both multiplied and divided by the parenthetical $(t_a - t_o)$, the equation would simplify to the form

$$q_t = \left(U_g A_g + U_w A_w + U_c A_c + U_f A_f \frac{t_a - t_b}{t_a - t_o} \right)(t_a - t_o) \qquad (5\text{--}2)$$

Denoting the temperature ratio in the floor term by K_f, the equation can be rewritten as

$$q_t = (U_g A_g + U_w A_w + U_c A_c + U_f A_f K_f)(t_a - t_o) \qquad (5\text{--}3)$$

Eq. 5–3 is the most simple form of the over-all transmission equation as used conventionally in the evaluation of total transmission load. It is a generally valid and accurate equation, *provided* the design value of the inside air temperature is known. As discussed in Chapter 1, however, the value of t_a is related to the mean radiant temperature by the comfort equation (1–11); hence it depends on the thermal characteristics of the structure. For this reason the direct use of Eq. 5–3 would require an assumed value of t_a and could not be expected to provide accurate evaluation of transmission load. Before returning to the practical use of Eq. 5–3, it is therefore necessary to investigate means of accurately evaluating the inside design air temperature.

5–2. The Equivalent Over-all Coefficient. The total transmission losses from the actual room, as evaluated by Eq. 5–3, would be exactly equal to the transmission losses from an imaginary thermally homogeneous room having total inside surface area equal to that of the actual room, uniform construction, uniform exposure, and an equivalent over-all coefficient of heat transfer, U_e, defined by the equation

$$q_t = U_e A_e(t_a - t_o) = (U_g A_g + U_w A_w + U_c A_c + U_f A_f K_f)(t_a - t_o) \quad (5\text{–}4\text{a})$$

or
$$U_e = \frac{U_g A_g + U_w A_w + U_c A_c + U_f A_f K_f}{A_e} \quad (5\text{–}4\text{b})$$

where A_e is the total inside surface area of the enclosure, including interior partitions and any other surfaces through which no heat loss occurs. Thus for an ordinary rectangular room with flat ceiling, the value of A_e is given by

$$A_e = A_g + A_w + A_c + A_f + A_i$$
$$= 2(LW + LH + WH) \quad (5\text{–}5)$$

where L, W, and H are, respectively, the length, width, and height of the room in feet.

Rewriting Eq. 5–4b in terms of fractional areas gives

$$U_e = U_g\left(\frac{A_g}{A_e}\right) + U_w\left(\frac{A_w}{A_e}\right) + U_c\left(\frac{A_c}{A_e}\right) + U_f K_f\left(\frac{A_f}{A_e}\right) \quad (5\text{–}6)$$

where it is now evident that U_e is a weighted average of U values for the particular room.

EQUIVALENT COEFFICIENT AS A THERMAL CRITERION. The significance of the equivalent over-all coefficient of heat transfer is that it provides a single number which is a criterion of the thermal effectiveness of the particular room or structure. The U_e term is independent of both size and geographical location and hence permits direct comparison of the thermal "tightness" of the structure itself. Based on experience, the designer can determine at once from a knowledge of U_e whether or not the room or structure will have high, low, or average heat losses as compared with other structures of equal size in any one geographical location. Further, in dealing with heating systems in which radiation is an important factor, use of the equivalent concept eliminates need for shape-factor analysis and permits simple treatment of the problem in terms of an average inside surface temperature.

Of greater practical interest, however, is the fact that the equivalent over-all coefficient is determined as a step in the evaluation of transmission load and without need of any additional calculation. Thus the special information that it gives concerning the room or structure is, in effect, a dividend afforded the designer, without added effort or calculation, when he adopts this method of load calculation. The fundamental and significant relationship between U_e and transmission load and the consequent special significance of the equivalent coefficient is evident upon examination of Eq. 5–4a:

$$q_t = U_e A_e(t_a - t_o) \tag{5-7}$$

Eq. 5–7 is the basic equation for evaluation of transmission load; it shows that the total load q_t is related to the size of the structure (indicated by A_e), the location of the structure (indicated by the design outside air temperature t_o), and the thermal effectiveness of the structure as indicated by the equivalent over-all coefficient of heat transfer.

USE OF EQUIVALENT COEFFICIENT IN THE COMFORT EQUATION. Reverting to the concept of the thermally homogeneous room, the uniform value of the inside surface temperature is given by Eq. 4–147 as

$$t_{se} = t_a - r_{ie}U_e(t_a - t_o) \tag{5-8}$$

where t_{se} = inside surface temperature of all surfaces of the equivalent room.

  r_{ie} = equivalent combined inside film resistance.

  U_e = equivalent over-all coefficient of heat transfer, Btu/(hr)(sq ft)(°F).

For the imaginary room the uniform inside surface temperature is obviously equal to the mean radiant temperature; hence t_{se} can be substituted for *mrt* in Eq. 1–11 to give

$$t_a = 147 - t_a + r_{ie}U_e t_a - r_{ie}U_e t_o$$

or

$$t_a = \frac{147 - r_{ie}U_e t_o}{2 - r_{ie}U_e} \tag{5-9}$$

Eq. 5–9 can now be solved for t_a and the value thus determined then substituted into Eq. 5–7 to permit calculation of transmission load.

In many cases the required data can be more conveniently obtained in terms of the conductance of the equivalent room from inside surface to outside air. Thus, establishing a heat balance on the inside surface,

$$C_e(t_{se} - t_o) = h_e(t_a - t_{se}) \qquad (5\text{--}10)$$

where C_e = conductance, inside surface to outside air, of the equivalent room.

h_e = combined inside film coefficient for the equivalent room.

Solving Eq. 5–10 for t_{se} gives

$$t_{se} = \frac{h_e t_a + C_e t_o}{C_e + h_e} \qquad (5\text{--}11)$$

Substituting t_{se} for *mrt* in Eq. 1–11 and solving for t_a gives

$$t_a = \frac{147 - [C_e t_o/(C_e + h_e)]}{1 + [h_e/(C_e + h_e)]} \qquad (5\text{--}12)$$

Eq. 5–12 can also be obtained directly from Eq. 5–9 by noting that

$$C_e = \frac{1}{(1/U_e) - (1/h_e)} \qquad (5\text{--}13a)$$

and

$$r_{ie} = \frac{1}{h_e} \qquad (5\text{--}13b)$$

Thus evaluation of transmission load is accomplished by utilizing either Eq. 5–9 or 5–12 to determine the optimum inside air temperature that would be necessary at the time of steady-state, outside design air temperature; use of the calculated value of t_a in Eq. 5–7 will then give total transmission load. The calculated value of t_a for any convection-heated room will always exceed the thermal level (73.5 F when 147 is used as the constant in the comfort equation). For a poorly insulated structure, the required inside air temperature may be so high (in excess of 90 F for a U_e of 0.228 at t_o of 0 F; see Arts. 7–3 through 7–9) that comfort would not be realized even when the occupant experienced thermal equilibrium.

Direct use of Eqs. 5–9 or 5–12 requires evaluation of the convective and radiant conductances (or resistances) of the inside and outside air films and of any spaces that may exist within the transmitting wall, ceiling, or floor; conductances (or resistances) of each homogeneous series section of wall, floor, or ceiling must likewise be established.

5–3. Evaluation of Thermal Coefficients. A first step in the numerical calculation of transmission load is to determine the over-all coefficient of heat transfer for each type of transmitting surface that appears in Eq. 5–1. Considering a homogeneous exterior wall of a room, for example, the over-all coefficient of heat transfer, U_w, can be written in a form similar to that of the bracketed term of Eq. 4–143:

$$U_w = \frac{1}{r_i + r_{w_1} + r_a + r_{ins} + r_{w_2} + r_o} = \frac{1}{R_w} \qquad (5\text{–}14)$$

where r_i = combined convective and radiant resistance of equivalent inside film.

             $= 1/(h_c + h_r') = 1/h_i$.

   r_{w_1}, r_{w_2} = resistances of homogeneous structural sections of wall

             $= L_1/k_1, L_2/k_2$.

      r_a = combined convective and radiant resistance of air space

             $= 1/(a_c + a_r) = 1/a$.

    r_{ins} = resistance of non-structural insulation.

      r_o = combined convective and radiant resistance of equivalent outside film.

             $= 1/h_o$.

In many cases, for convenience in computation, a preferable form of Eq. 5–14 is

$$U_w = \frac{1}{r_i + (1/C_w)} \qquad (5\text{–}15)$$

where C_w = conductance from inside surface to outside air

          $= 1/(r_{w_1} + r_a + r_{ins} + r_{w_2} + r_o)$

All the terms in Eqs. 5–14 and 5–15 can be evaluated by the equations of Chapter 4 in terms of known thermal properties of the particular materials. As a matter of convenience, however, the task of evaluation can be very greatly simplified by use of various tabular arrangements.

COMBINED RESISTANCES OF OUTSIDE FILM. The convective fraction of the outside film conductance is given by Eqs. 4–81 through 4–84 as a function of wind velocity V'' in miles per hour and surface roughness. The equivalent radiant conductance can be evaluated from Eq. 4–113 (or Fig. 4–14), noting that for transfer from an outside surface to the entire surround, the shape factor and emissivity factor in Eq. 4–112 can each be taken as unity.

Exact evaluation of the radiant conductance would require knowledge of the outside surface temperature of the transmitting section and of the solid or *equivalent* solid surround seen by that surface. Fortunately, however, the variation in radiant conductance over the usual range of outside air temperatures is very small. Thus, between surfaces differing but slightly from 10 F, the value of radiant conductance is

$$h_r = \frac{0.1713\left[\left(\frac{470.5}{100}\right)^4 - \left(\frac{469.5}{100}\right)^4\right]}{470.5 - 469.5} = 0.7140$$

For temperatures close to 0 F the h_r value can be calculated in like manner as 0.669. For transfer from a 10 F surface to a 0 F surround, h_r is 0.689, whereas for transfer from a 20 F surface to a 0 F surround, h_r becomes 0.712. Thus it is evident that a single recommended value of

$$h_r = 0.7 \ \text{Btu}/(\text{hr})(\text{sq ft})(°\text{F})$$

can be used without serious error.

The recommended value of the combined outside film resistance is therefore given by an equation of the form

$$r_o = \frac{1}{h_o} = \frac{1}{h_c + h_r'} = \frac{1}{a + bV'' + 0.7} \tag{5-16}$$

where the constants a and b (given in Eqs. 4–81 through 4–84) depend on surface roughness. Further, the design value of the wind velocity can be taken as the average value during the months of December, January, and February; hence V'' is fixed by Weather Bureau data for the city in question. Table 5–1 gives design values of r_o for outside surfaces of varying degrees of roughness located in more than 100 representative cities in the United States.

RESISTANCES OF STRUCTURAL ELEMENTS OF EXTERIOR WALLS. The structural sections of most walls consist of some form of exterior construction, possible insulation or air space, and some form of interior finish. Structural sections are commonly of some standard type; hence it is possible to tabulate resistances and to group the most common types in tabular form. The *ASHRAE Guide*[1] provides tables that permit direct reading of the over-all

"Standard" Film or Air Space*	Combined Resistances for Winter Conditions
Outside film (based on 15-mph wind)	0.170
Air space in wall (winter)	0.9710†
Air space ($\frac{3}{4}$ in. to 4 in. space) in ceiling (winter)	0.8475
Air space ($1\frac{1}{2}$ in. space) in floor (winter)	1.150
Inside film for wall (winter)	0.6849
Inside film for ceiling (winter)	0.6135
Inside film for floor (winter)	0.9259

* Values used in *ASHRAE Guide* calculations (air-space conductance based on assumption that both faces of space are surfaced with material having emissivity of 0.90).

† The experimental data leading to the empirical equations from which these values are obtained do not justify more than two-place accuracy; as a convenience in obtaining consistency in mathematical computation, however, the extra places have been included.

coefficients of heat transfer for a multitude of wall types. Guide values necessarily include "standard" values of combined coefficients for inside films, for outside films, and air spaces as given in the table above.

[1] Bibliography, item 1.

TABLE 5–1
Outside Film Resistances, r_0, Based on Local Climatological Conditions

Station	Design Wind Velocity, mph	Type of Exterior Surface			
		Very Smooth*	Smooth*	Moderately Rough*	Rough*
Alabama					
Birmingham	7.4	0.288	0.262	0.202	0.172
Mobile	8.5	0.265	0.241	0.185	0.157
Arizona					
Kingman	8.6	0.263	0.239	0.184	0.156
Phoenix	5.6	0.337	0.305	0.236	0.204
Tucson	6.3	0.316	0.287	0.221	0.190
Winslow	7.5	0.286	0.260	0.200	0.171
Arkansas					
Little Rock	6.6	0.308	0.279	0.216	0.185
California					
Bakersfield	5.6	0.337	0.305	0.236	0.204
Burbank	4.9	0.361	0.326	0.253	0.220
Daggett	8.5	0.265	0.241	0.185	0.157
Fresno	4.5	0.376	0.339	0.263	0.230
Oakland	7.5	0.286	0.260	0.200	0.171
Redding	7.1	0.295	0.268	0.207	0.177
San Diego	5.8	0.331	0.299	0.231	0.200
Williams	8.3	0.269	0.244	0.188	0.160
Colorado					
Denver	8.8	0.259	0.236	0.181	0.154
Pueblo	6.4	0.313	0.284	0.219	0.189
Connecticut					
Hartford	8.3	0.269	0.244	0.188	0.160
New Haven	8.1	0.273	0.248	0.191	0.163
District of Columbia					
Washington	7.4	0.288	0.262	0.202	0.172
Florida					
Jacksonville	7.0	0.298	0.270	0.208	0.179
Miami	7.3	0.290	0.264	0.203	0.174
Titusville	6.5	0.311	0.282	0.217	0.187
Georgia					
Atlanta	10.2	0.235	0.215	0.164	0.139
Savannah	7.7	0.281	0.256	0.197	0.168
Idaho					
Boise	4.5	0.376	0.339	0.263	0.230
Burley	8.8	0.259	0.236	0.181	0.154
Idaho Falls	7.6	0.283	0.258	0.198	0.169
Pocatello	7.2	0.293	0.266	0.205	0.175
Illinois					
Chicago	11.7	0.214	0.196	0.150	0.126
Moline	10.8	0.226	0.207	0.158	0.133
Peoria	10.7	0.227	0.208	0.159	0.134
Springfield	11.6	0.215	0.197	0.151	0.127
Indiana					
Helmer	11.5	0.216	0.198	0.152	0.127
Indianapolis	11.4	0.218	0.199	0.152	0.128

* Very smooth (as glass); smooth (as planed wood); moderately rough (as finished concrete); rough (as stucco).

TABLE 5–I (continued)

Station	Design Wind Velocity, mph	Type of Exterior Surface			
		Very Smooth*	Smooth*	Moderately Rough*	Rough*
Iowa					
Des Moines	14.5	0.183	0.168	0.128	0.107
Kansas					
Wichita	14.7	0.181	0.166	0.127	0.106
Kentucky					
Louisville	8.8	0.259	0.236	0.181	0.154
Louisiana					
New Orleans	12.8	0.201	0.184	0.140	0.118
Shreveport	8.9	0.257	0.234	0.180	0.153
Maryland					
Baltimore	8.9	0.257	0.234	0.180	0.153
Massachusetts					
Boston	12.3	0.206	0.189	0.145	0.121
Michigan					
Detroit	11.0	0.223	0.204	0.156	0.132
Minnesota					
St. Paul	9.9	0.240	0.219	0.168	0.142
Missouri					
Kansas City	10.6	0.229	0.209	0.160	0.135
St. Louis	10.8	0.226	0.207	0.158	0.133
Springfield	11.0	0.223	0.204	0.156	0.132
Montana					
Billings	9.1	0.253	0.231	0.177	0.150
Butte	4.8	0.364	0.329	0.255	0.222
Miles City	8.4	0.267	0.243	0.187	0.159
Nebraska					
Lincoln	12.7	0.202	0.185	0.141	0.118
North Platte	10.7	0.227	0.208	0.159	0.134
Omaha	11.5	0.216	0.198	0.152	0.127
Nevada					
Elko	4.0	0.397	0.357	0.278	0.244
Las Vegas	5.3	0.347	0.313	0.243	0.211
Reno	3.6	0.415	0.373	0.291	0.256
New Jersey					
Camden	9.5	0.246	0.225	0.172	0.146
Newark	11.6	0.215	0.197	0.151	0.127
New Mexico					
Albuquerque	7.1	0.295	0.268	0.207	0.177
El Morro	4.6	0.372	0.336	0.260	0.227
Rodeo	8.4	0.267	0.243	0.187	0.159
Tucumcari	9.2	0.252	0.229	0.176	0.149
New York					
Albany	9.6	0.245	0.223	0.171	0.145
Buffalo	14.0	0.188	0.172	0.132	0.110
Elmira	8.0	0.275	0.250	0.192	0.164
Rochester	11.9	0.211	0.193	0.148	0.124
Syracuse	8.9	0.257	0.234	0.180	0.153
North Carolina					
Charlotte	7.5	0.286	0.260	0.200	0.171
Greensboro	7.8	0.279	0.254	0.195	0.167
Raleigh	8.5	0.265	0.241	0.185	0.157

TABLE 5-1 (continued)

Station	Design Wind Velocity, mph	Type of Exterior Surface			
		Very Smooth*	Smooth*	Moderately Rough*	Rough*
North Dakota					
Bismarck	7.1	0.295	0.268	0.207	0.177
Dickinson	12.4	0.205	0.188	0.144	0.120
Fargo	10.9	0.225	0.205	0.157	0.132
Pembina	11.9	0.211	0.193	0.148	0.124
Ohio					
Akron	10.6	0.229	0.209	0.160	0.135
Cincinnati	8.0	0.275	0.250	0.192	0.164
Cleveland	13.8	0.190	0.174	0.133	0.111
Columbus	10.5	0.230	0.211	0.161	0.136
Toledo	12.1	0.209	0.191	0.146	0.123
Oklahoma					
Ardmore	9.7	0.243	0.222	0.170	0.144
Oklahoma City	14.7	0.181	0.166	0.127	0.106
Tulsa	11.3	0.219	0.200	0.153	0.129
Waynoka	11.3	0.219	0.200	0.153	0.129
Oregon					
Arlington	7.8	0.279	0.254	0.195	0.167
Baker	6.4	0.313	0.284	0.219	0.189
Eugene	5.3	0.347	0.313	0.243	0.211
Medford	4.3	0.384	0.346	0.269	0.235
Portland	8.0	0.275	0.250	0.192	0.164
Pennsylvania					
Curwensville	13.5	0.193	0.177	0.135	0.113
Erie	12.1	0.209	0.191	0.146	0.123
Harrisburg	9.0	0.255	0.233	0.179	0.152
Pittsburgh	12.1	0.209	0.191	0.146	0.123
Sunbury	7.1	0.295	0.268	0.207	0.177
South Carolina					
Charleston	6.9	0.300	0.272	0.210	0.180
Tennessee					
Chattanooga	6.2	0.319	0.289	0.223	0.192
Memphis	8.9	0.257	0.234	0.180	0.153
Nashville	7.3	0.290	0.264	0.203	0.174
Texas					
Abilene	10.4	0.232	0.212	0.162	0.137
Amarillo	12.9	0.200	0.183	0.140	0.117
Dallas	8.8	0.259	0.236	0.181	0.154
El Paso	8.6	0.263	0.239	0.184	0.156
Houston	9.2	0.252	0.229	0.176	0.149
San Antonio	7.6	0.283	0.258	0.198	0.169
Waco	11.6	0.215	0.197	0.151	0.127
Wink	8.5	0.265	0.241	0.185	0.157
Utah					
Milford	7.7	0.281	0.256	0.197	0.168
Salt Lake City	7.4	0.288	0.262	0.202	0.172
Virginia					
Richmond	7.1	0.302	0.268	0.207	0.177
Roanoke	8.2	0.271	0.246	0.189	0.161

TABLE 5–1 (continued)

Station	Design Wind Velocity, mph	Type of Exterior Surface			
		Very Smooth*	Smooth*	Moderately Rough*	Rough*
Washington					
Ellensburg	3.8	0.406	0.365	0.284	0.250
Seattle	6.3	0.316	0.287	0.221	0.190
Spokane	5.1	0.354	0.319	0.248	0.215
Wisconsin					
La Crosse	6.9	0.300	0.272	0.210	0.180
Madison	9.1	0.253	0.231	0.177	0.150
Milwaukee	11.9	0.211	0.193	0.148	0.124
Wyoming					
Cheyenne	11.1	0.222	0.203	0.155	0.131
Rock Springs	9.1	0.253	0.231	0.177	0.150

In many cases the film or air-space resistance is small compared with the total air-to-air resistance of the wall, floor, or ceiling. Where this is the case, the "standard" values for films or air spaces can be used with small resultant error. In other cases, however, a difference in the convective or radiant transfer across a film or an air space may lead to an almost equal fractional difference in the rate of transmission through the surface. In order to permit maximum accuracy where this may be needed, the method presented in this chapter does not base over-all coefficients on the standard values of the accompanying table but rather establishes coefficients, using equations developed in Chapter 4, for the actual conditions of exposure.

Table 5–2 gives the resistances[2] of the four structural members that, in series, constitute the usual frame wall; hence homogeneous sections include those making up the exterior finish, sheathing, insulation, and interior finish. Thus one can write

$$r_w = r_{w_1} + r_{w_2} + r_{w_3} + r_{w_4}$$

$$= r_{\text{ext}} + r_{\text{sheath}} + r_{\text{ins}} + r_{\text{int}} \tag{5–17}$$

where r_w is total resistance of all parts of the wall except air spaces and surface films. (In the same way r_c and r_f will signify total resistances of ceiling and floors *except* for air spaces and surface films.)

The tabular resistances for insulation are for complete wall coverage by the insulation in a plane normal to heat flow; thus correction should be made for the effect of framing members. The insulation, however, is always so located between studs that there is an air space on one or both faces. Thus

---

[2] Resistances given in Tables 5–2 through 5–13 are taken (with permission) or calculated from values in the 1960 edition of the *ASHRAE Guide*.

TABLE 5–2
Thermal Resistances of Structural Elements of Frame Walls*

	Resistance, r
Exterior	
Wood siding	
drop, 1 in. by 8 in.	0.79
bevel, $\frac{1}{2}$ in. by 8 in.	0.81
Wood shingles, $7\frac{1}{2}$ in. exposure	0.87
Wood panels, $\frac{3}{4}$ in.	0.94
Face-brick veneer	0.44
Plywood, $\frac{3}{8}$ in.	0.47
Wood shingles over insulation:	
backer board, $\frac{5}{16}$ in.	1.40
Asphalt insulating siding	1.45
Asbestos-cement siding	0.21
Stucco, 1 in.	0.20
Asphalt roll siding	0.15
Sheathing	
None (building paper)	0.06
Gypsum board, $\frac{1}{2}$ in.	0.45
Plywood, $\frac{5}{16}$ in.	0.39
Wood, $\frac{25}{32}$ in., and building paper	1.04
Insulation board, $\frac{1}{2}$ in.	1.32
$\frac{25}{32}$ in.	2.06
Fibrous Insulation	
$k = 0.27$ Btu/(hr)(sq ft)(°F/in.)	
$\frac{1}{2}$ in. thick	1.85
1 in. thick	3.70
2 in. thick	7.40
3 in. thick	11.10
Interior Finish	
Gypsum board, $\frac{3}{8}$ in.	0.32
Gypsum lath, $\frac{3}{8}$ in., and $\frac{1}{2}$-in. plaster (lightweight aggregate) . . .	0.64
Gypsum lath, $\frac{3}{8}$ in., and $\frac{1}{2}$-in. plaster (sand aggregate)	0.41
Metal lath and $\frac{3}{4}$-in. plaster (lightweight aggregate)	0.47
Metal lath and $\frac{3}{4}$-in. plaster (sand aggregate)	0.13
Insulating board, $\frac{1}{2}$ in.	1.43
Insulating board lath, $\frac{1}{2}$ in., and $\frac{1}{2}$ in. plaster (sand aggregate) . . .	1.52
Plywood, $\frac{1}{4}$ in.	0.31
Wood panels, $\frac{3}{4}$ in.	0.94
Wood lath and $\frac{1}{2}$-in. plaster (sand aggregate)	0.40

* For non-structural elements (air spaces and air films) refer to Tables 5–14, 5–18, 5–19, 5–20, and 5–23. From *ASHRAE Guide*.

the framing correction should be based on parallel heat transfer through the wall area backed by studs and through the combination insulation and air-space area between studs. This subject will be quantitatively discussed in connection with air space resistances (see discussion in this article on page 183).

TABLE 5-3

Thermal Resistances of Structural Elements of Solid Masonry Walls*

				Resistance, r			
Exterior	4 in.	6 in.	8 in.	10 in.	12 in.	16 in.	24 in.
Brick (face and common) . . .	—	0.61	1.24	—	2.04	2.84	—
Brick (common only)	—	—	1.60	—	2.40	3.20	—
Stone (lime and sand)	—	—	0.64	—	0.96	1.28	1.92
Hollow clay tile	—	—	1.85	2.22	2.50	—	—
Poured concrete							
30 lb/cu ft	4.44	6.66	8.88	11.10	—	—	—
80 lb/cu ft	—	2.40	3.20	4.00	4.80	—	—
140 lb/cu ft	—	0.48	0.64	0.80	0.96	—	—
Concrete block							
gravel aggregate	—	—	1.11	—	1.28	—	—
cinder aggregate	—	—	1.72	—	1.89	—	—
light weight aggregate . . .	—	—	2.00	—	2.27	—	—

	Resistance, r
Fibrous Insulation	
$k = 0.27$ Btu/(hr)(sq ft)(°F/in.)	
$\frac{1}{2}$ in. thick	1.85
1 in. thick	3.70
2 in. thick	7.40
3 in. thick	11.10

	Resistance, r		
Interior Finish	No Plaster	Sand Aggregate	Light-weight Aggregate
Plaster, $\frac{5}{8}$ in. on wall	—	0.11	0.39
Metal lath and $\frac{3}{4}$-in. plaster on furring . . .	—	0.13	0.47
Gypsum lath, $\frac{3}{8}$ in., and $\frac{1}{2}$-in. plaster on furring	0.32	0.41	0.64
Insulating board lath, $\frac{1}{2}$ in., and $\frac{1}{2}$-in. plaster on furring	1.43	1.52	—
Wood lath and $\frac{1}{2}$-in. plaster	—	0.40	—

* For non-structural elements (air spaces and air films) refer to Tables 5–14, 5–18, 5–19, 5–20, and 5–23. From *ASHRAE Guide.*

Table 5–3 gives resistances of structural members for solid masonry walls; Table 5–4 gives values for masonry walls; and Table 5–5 applies to masonry walls of the cavity type. Note that in all cases the tabular resistances are for structural sections only and do not include film resistances, air-space resistances (except for air spaces built into the structural members, as for hollow concrete blocks), or the minor thermal resistances that may occur at interfaces.

TABLE 5–4
Thermal Resistances of Structural Elements of Masonry Walls*

	Resistance, r
Exterior Facing	
Face brick, 4 in.	0.44
Stone, 4 in.　.	0.32
Precast concrete (sand aggregate)	
4 in.	0.32
6 in.	0.48
8 in.　.	0.64
Common brick, 4 in. . . . .ʹ.	0.80

	Resistance, r			
	4 in.	*6 in.*	*8 in.*	*12 in.*
Backing				
Concrete block				
cinder aggregate	1.11	—	1.72	1.89
lightweight aggregate	1.50	—	2.00	2.27
sand aggregate　.	0.71	—	1.11	1.28
Hollow clay tile	1.11	—	1.85	2.50
Concrete (sand aggregate)	0.32	0.48	0.64	—

	Resistance, r
Fibrous Insulation	
$k = 0.27$ Btu/(hr)(sq ft)(°F/in.)	
$\frac{1}{2}$ in. thick　.	1.85
1 in. thick　.	3.70
2 in. thick　.	7.40
3 in. thick　.	11.10

	Resistance, r		
	No Plaster	*Sand Aggregate*	*Light-weight Aggregate*
Interior Finish			
Plaster, $\frac{5}{8}$ in. on wall	—	0.11	0.39
Metal lath and $\frac{3}{4}$-in. plaster on furring . . .	—	0.13	0.47
Gypsum lath, $\frac{3}{8}$ in., and $\frac{1}{2}$-in. plaster on furring	0.32	0.41	0.64
Insulating board lath, $\frac{1}{2}$ in., and $\frac{1}{2}$-in. plaster on furring	1.43	1.52	—
Wood lath and $\frac{1}{2}$-in. plaster	—	0.40	—

* For non-structural elements (air spaces and air films) refer to Tables 5–14, 5–18, 5–19, 5–20, and 5–23. From *ASHRAE Guide*.

TABLE 5–5
Thermal Resistances of Structural Elements of Masonry Cavity Walls*

	Resistance, r
Exterior	
Face brick, 4 in.	0.44
Common brick, 4 in.	0.80
Concrete block (gravel aggregate), 4 in.	0.71
Concrete block (cinder aggregate), 4 in.	1.11
Inner Section	
Concrete block, 4 in.	
gravel aggregate	0.71
cinder aggregate	1.11
lightweight aggregate	1.50
Common brick, 4 in.	0.80
Clay tile, 4 in.	1.11
Fibrous Insulation	
$k = 0.27$ Btu/(hr)(sq ft)(°F/in.)	
$\frac{1}{2}$ in. thick	1.85
1 in. thick	3.70
2 in. thick	7.40
3 in. thick	11.10

	Resistance, r		
			Light-weight
	No	*Sand*	*weight*
Interior Finish	*Plaster*	*Aggregate*	*Aggregate*
Plaster, $\frac{5}{8}$ in. on wall	—	0.11	0.39
Metal lath and $\frac{3}{4}$-in. plaster on furring	—	0.13	0.47
Gypsum lath, $\frac{3}{8}$ in., and $\frac{1}{2}$-in. plaster on furring	0.32	0.41	0.64
Insulation board lath and $\frac{1}{2}$-in. plaster on furring	1.43	1.52	—
Wood lath and $\frac{1}{2}$-in. plaster	—	0.40	—

* For non-structural elements (air spaces and air films) refer to Tables 5–14, 5–18, 5–19, 5–20, and 5–23. From *ASHRAE Guide*.

RESISTANCES OF STRUCTURAL SECTIONS OF INTERIOR WALLS AND PARTITIONS. Tables 5–6 and 5–7, for frame or masonry partitions, respectively, will usually be needed only in cases where the air temperature differs on opposite sides of the partition. In very unusual circumstances, however, there might be a large difference in reception or loss of radiant energy on the two sides even though air temperatures were the same; when this occurs, the partition resistance would be needed in setting up a heat balance of the form

(Radiant transfer to warm side) − (convective loss from warm side)

= conductive transfer through partition

= (radiant transfer from cool side) + (convective transfer from cool side)

(5–18)

TABLE 5–6
Thermal Resistances of Structural Elements of Frame Partitions or Interior Walls*

Interior Partition Finish	Resistance, r	
	Finish, One Side of Studs	Finish, Both Sides of Studs
Gypsum board, $\frac{3}{8}$ in.	0.32	0.64
Gypsum lath, $\frac{3}{8}$ in., and $\frac{1}{2}$-in. plaster (lightweight aggregate)	0.64	1.28
Gypsum lath, $\frac{3}{8}$ in., and $\frac{1}{2}$-in. plaster (sand aggregate) .	0.41	0.82
Metal lath and $\frac{3}{4}$-in. plaster (lightweight aggregate) .	0.47	0.94
Metal lath and $\frac{3}{4}$-in. plaster (sand aggregate) . . .	0.13	0.26
Insulation board, $\frac{1}{2}$ in.	1.43	2.86
Insulation board lath, $\frac{1}{2}$ in., and $\frac{1}{2}$-in. plaster (sand aggregate)	1.52	3.04
Plywood		
$\frac{1}{4}$ in.	0.31	0.62
$\frac{3}{8}$ in.	0.47	0.94
$\frac{1}{2}$ in.	0.63	1.26
Wood panels, $\frac{3}{4}$ in.	0.94	1.88
Wood-lath and $\frac{1}{2}$-in. plaster (sand aggregate) . . .	0.40	0.80

* For non-structural elements (air spaces and air films) refer to Tables 5–14, 5–18, 5–19, 5–20, and 5–23. From *ASHRAE Guide.*

When an air temperature difference exists in rooms on opposite sides of an interior wall, the term $U_i A_i (t_a - t_{a'})$ would be added to Eq. 5–1 and the corresponding term $U_i A_i (t_a - t_{a'})/(t_a - t_o)$ added to Eq. 5–2 (where $t_{a'}$ is the temperature on the "outside" of the interior wall as determined by the location of the room for which t_a is defined). The term K_i, equal to $(t_a - t_{a'})/(t_a - t_o)$, then appears, with an added $U_i A_i K_i$ term in Eqs. 5–3, 5–4, and 5–6.

RESISTANCES OF STRUCTURAL SECTIONS OF CEILINGS, FLOORS, AND FLOOR-CEILING COMBINATIONS. Table 5–8 gives thermal resistances of frame construction ceilings, floors, and floor-ceiling combinations. When used for a ceiling (without floor above), the situation would be comparable to that of heat loss through a ceiling to an unfinished attic space overhead. In this case, taking attic space temperature as $t_{a''}$, a K_c temperature ratio correction of $[K_c = (t_a - t_{a''})/(t_a - t_o)]$ should be added to the ceiling term in Eqs. 5–3, 5–4, and 5–6.

Table 5–9 is comparable to Table 5–8 but is applicable to concrete rather than frame construction.

RESISTANCES OF STRUCTURAL SECTIONS OF ROOFS AND CEILING-ROOF COMBINATIONS. Table 5–10 gives resistances of various types of flat masonry roofs with built-up roofing and with or without suspended ceilings. The built-up roofing is assumed to be $\frac{3}{8}$ in. thick with a thermal resistance of 0.33.

TABLE 5–7

Thermal Resistances of Structural Elements of Masonry Partitions*

	Resistance, r				
Interior Partition	*3 in.*	*4 in.*	*6 in.*	*8 in.*	*12 in.*
Hollow concrete block					
cinder aggregate	0.86	1.11	—	1.72	1.89
lightweight aggregate	1.27	1.50	—	2.00	2.27
gravel aggregate	—	—	—	1.11	1.28
Hollow clay tile	0.80	1.11	1.52	1.85	—
Hollow gypsum tile	1.35	1.67	—	—	—

	Resistance, r
Solid plaster walls, $\frac{1}{2}$ in.	
gypsum lath, $\frac{1}{2}$ in., and plaster	
$\frac{3}{4}$ in. each side	
lightweight aggregate	1.39
sand aggregate	0.71
1 in. each side	
lightweight aggregate	1.73
sand aggregate	0.81
metal lath and plaster	
2 in. total thickness	
lightweight aggregate	1.28
sand aggregate	0.36
$2\frac{1}{2}$ in. total thickness	
lightweight aggregate	1.60
sand aggregate	0.45

	Resistance, r	
Surface Finish	*One Side*	*Two Sides*
Plaster (lightweight aggregate) $\frac{5}{8}$ in.	0.39	0.78
Plaster (sand aggregate) $\frac{5}{8}$ in.	0.11	0.22

   * For non-structural elements (air spaces and air films) refer to Tables 5–14, 5–18, 5–19, 5–20, and 5–23. From *ASHRAE Guide.*

   This value is included in the resistances given for various types of deck construction; hence if there is a difference in the resistance of the built-up roofing actually used, a correction should be made to the value of deck resistance. If r_d is tabular deck resistance and r_{br} is resistance of the built-up roof actually used, then the *corrected* deck resistance, r'_d, would be

$$r'_d = r_d + r_{br} - 0.33 \qquad\qquad (5\text{–}19)$$

   Table 5–11 is similar in form to Table 5–10 but is used for wood or metal roofs with or without ceiling. When special forms of built-up roofing are used, the deck resistances of Table 5–11 can be corrected in the same manner (Eq. 5–19) as applies to Table 5–10.

TABLE 5–8
Thermal Resistances of Structural Elements of Frame
Construction Ceilings and Floors*

	Resistances, r
Ceiling	
Gypsum board, $\frac{3}{8}$ in.	0.32
Gypsum lath, $\frac{3}{8}$ in., and $\frac{1}{2}$-in. plaster	
lightweight aggregate	0.64
sand aggregate	0.41
Metal lath and $\frac{3}{4}$-in. plaster	
lightweight aggregate	0.47
sand aggregate	0.13
Insulating board, $\frac{1}{2}$ in.	1.43
Insulating board lath, $\frac{1}{2}$ in., and $\frac{1}{2}$-in. plaster (sand aggregate) . .	1.52
Acoustical tile	
$\frac{1}{2}$ in. on $\frac{3}{8}$ in. gypsum board	1.51
$\frac{1}{2}$ in. on furring	1.19
$\frac{3}{4}$ in. on $\frac{3}{8}$ in. gypsum board	2.10
$\frac{3}{4}$ in. on furring	1.78
Wood lath and $\frac{1}{2}$-in.	
plaster (sand aggregate)	0.40
Fibrous Insulation	
$k = 0.27$ Btu/(hr)(sq ft)(°F/in.)	
$\frac{1}{2}$ in. thick	1.85
1 in. thick	3.70
2 in. thick	7.40
3 in. thick	11.10
Floor	
Wood subfloor, $\frac{25}{32}$ in..	0.98
Wood subfloor, $\frac{25}{32}$ in., felt and cement, $1\frac{1}{2}$ in., and ceramic tile, $\frac{1}{2}$ in. .	1.38
hardwood floor, $\frac{3}{4}$ in.	1.72
plywood, $\frac{5}{8}$ in., and floor tile or linoleum, $\frac{1}{8}$ in.	1.87
insulating board, $\frac{3}{8}$ in., and hard board, $\frac{1}{4}$ in., and floor tile	
or linoleum, $\frac{1}{8}$ in.	2.26

* For non-structural elements (air spaces and air films) refer to Tables 5–15, 5–16, 5–17, 5–18, 5–19, 5–21, 5–22, and 5–23. From *ASHRAE Guide.*

Table 5–12 gives resistances for structural elements of pitched roofs. In cases where the attic space between a pitched roof and the ceiling of the room below is neither heated nor ventilated, the thermal combination of pitched roof, attic space, and ceiling can be treated as a unit. This method requires prior determination of the equivalent air-space resistance of the attic and hence will be discussed later (Art. 5–10).

RESISTANCES OF DOORS AND WINDOWS. Table 5–13 gives surface-to-surface resistances of solid wood doors and inside surface-to-outside surface resistances (but not inside or outside air film resistances) of solid-door–storm-door combinations. In this case the resistance of the air space between solid door and storm door is included, owing to the fact that difference in closure would undoubtedly have so great an effect on air-space conductance that use of the refinements of the air-space conductance relationship would not

TABLE 5–9

Thermal Resistances of Structural Elements of Concrete Floor-Ceiling Constructions*

	Resistances, r
Ceiling (applied directly to slab)	
Plaster	
lightweight aggregate, $\frac{1}{8}$ in.	0.08
sand aggregate, $\frac{1}{8}$ in.	0.02
Acoustical tile, glued, $\frac{1}{2}$ in.	1.19
$\frac{3}{4}$ in.	1.78

	Resistances, r		
	No Plaster	Lightweight Aggregate, $\frac{1}{2}$ in.	Sand Aggregate, $\frac{3}{4}$ in.
Ceiling (suspended)			
Gypsum board, $\frac{3}{8}$ in., and plaster . .	0.32	0.64	0.41
Metal lath and plaster	—	0.47	0.13

	Resistances, r	
	$\frac{1}{2}$ in.	$\frac{3}{4}$ in.
Ceiling (acoustical tile)		
On furring or channels	1.19	1.78
On gypsum board, $\frac{3}{8}$ in.	1.51	2.10

	Resistances, r
Fibrous Insulation	
$k = 0.27$ Btu/(hr)(sq ft)(°F/in.)	
$\frac{1}{2}$ in. thick.	1.85
1 in. thick.	3.70
2 in. thick.	7.40
3 in. thick.	11.10

	Resistances, r			
	4 in.	6 in.	8 in.	10 in.
Deck				
Concrete (sand aggregate)	0.32	0.48	0.64	0.80

	Resistances, r
Finish Floor	
Floor tile or linoleum, $\frac{1}{8}$ in.	0.05
Wood block, $\frac{13}{16}$ in., on slab	0.74
Floor on sleepers	
plywood subfloor, $\frac{5}{8}$ in., felt and floor tile or linoleum, $\frac{1}{8}$ in. . .	0.89
wood subfloor, $\frac{25}{32}$ in., felt and hardwood, $\frac{3}{4}$ in.	1.72

* For non-structural elements (air spaces and air films) refer to Tables 5–15, 5–16, 5–17, 5–18, 5–19, 5–21, 5–22, and 5–23. From *ASHRAE Guide.*

TABLE 5–10
Thermal Resistances of Structural Elements of Flat Masonry Roofs With Built-up Roofing, With and Without Suspended Ceilings*

	Resistances, r Conductance of Roof Insulation, Btu/(hr)(sq ft)(°F)					
	0.12	*0.15*	*0.19*	*0.24*	*0.36*	*0.72*
No ceiling (insulated roof)	8.33	6.67	5.26	4.17	2.78	1.39

	Resistances, r		
	0 in.	*½ in.*	*¾ in.*
Suspended Ceiling			
Gypsum board, ⅜ in., and plaster			
no plaster	0.32	—	—
lightweight aggregate	—	0.64	—
sand aggregate	—	0.41	—
Metal lath and plaster			
lightweight aggregate	—	—	0.47
sand aggregate	—	—	0.13
Acoustical tile			
on furring or channels	—	1.19	1.75
on gypsum board, ⅜ in.	—	1.51	2.10

	Resistances, r
Fibrous Insulation	
$k = 0.27$ Btu/(hr)(sq ft)(°F/in.)	
½ in. thick	1.85
1 in. thick	3.70
2 in. thick	7.40
3 in. thick	11.10
Subdeck (Form)	
Corrugated metal	0
Insulation board, 1 in.	2.78
1½ in.	4.17
Glass fiber board, 1 in.	4.00
Gypsum board, ½ in.	0.45
Asbestos cement board, ¼ in.	0.06

	Resistances, r				
Deck (including ⅜-in. built-up roofing, $r = 0.33$)					
Concrete slab	*2 in.*	*3 in.*	*4 in.*	*6 in.*	*8 in.*
gravel aggregate	—	—	0.65	0.81	0.97
lightweight aggregate	2.55	3.66	4.77	—	—
Gypsum slab	1.53	2.13	2.73	—	—

* For non-structural elements (air spaces and air films) refer to Tables 5–17, 5–18, 5–19, 5–22, and 5–23. From *ASHRAE Guide*.

TABLE 5–11
Thermal Resistances of Structural Elements of Wood or Metal Construction Flat Roofs and Ceilings*

	Resistances, r
Ceiling	
Gypsum board, $\frac{3}{8}$ in., and plaster	
none	0.32
lightweight aggregate, $\frac{1}{4}$ in.	0.64
sand aggregate, $\frac{1}{2}$ in.	0.41
Metal lath and plaster	
lightweight aggregate, $\frac{3}{4}$ in.	0.47
sand aggregate, $\frac{3}{4}$ in.	0.13
Insulating board $\frac{1}{2}$ in.	
plain	1.43
$\frac{1}{2}$-in. plaster (sand aggregate)	1.52
Acoustical tile	
on furring, $\frac{1}{2}$ in.	1.19
$\frac{3}{4}$ in.	1.78
on $\frac{3}{8}$ in. gypsum board, $\frac{1}{2}$ in.	1.51
$\frac{3}{4}$ in.	2.10

	Resistances, r Conductance of Roof Insulation Btu/(hr)(sq ft)(°F)					
	0.12	0.15	0.19	0.24	0.36	0.72
Roof Insulation						
Applied on top of deck	8.33	6.67	5.26	4.17	2.78	1.39

	Resistances, r		
	1 in.	*2 in.*	*3 in.*
Deck (including $\frac{3}{8}$ in. built-up roofing, $r = 0.33$)			
Wood	1.31	2.36	3.61
Preformed slabs; wood fiber and cement binder	—	3.93	5.73

	Resistance, r
Flat metal roof deck	0.33

* For non-structural elements (air spaces and air films) refer to Tables 5–17, 5–18, 5–19, 5–22, and 5–23. From *ASHRAE Guide*.

be justified. The air space between doors has been taken as having a resistance of 0.97, corresponding to a combined conductance of 1.03 Btu/(hr)(sq ft)(°F); if particular conditions dictate use of a different value of air-space resistance, the correction can be made readily by adding to the tabular value the algebraic difference between actual air-space resistance and 0.97.

The thermal resistance of glass is very low. For average single-glazed windows, the surface-to-surface resistance of the glass can be taken as 0.112,

TABLE 5–12

Thermal Resistances of Structural Elements for Pitched Roofs*

	Resistances, r
Ceiling (applied directly to roof rafters)	
Gypsum board, $\frac{3}{8}$ in.	0.32
Gypsum lath, $\frac{3}{8}$ in., and $\frac{1}{2}$-in. plaster	
lightweight aggregate	0.64
sand aggregate	0.41
Metal lath and $\frac{3}{4}$-in. plaster	
lightweight aggregate	0.47
sand aggregate	0.13
Insulating board, $\frac{1}{2}$ in.	1.43
Insulating board lath and $\frac{1}{2}$-in. plaster	
sand aggregate	1.52
Acoustical tile	
$\frac{1}{2}$ in. on $\frac{3}{8}$ in. gypsum board	1.51
$\frac{1}{2}$ in. on furring	1.19
$\frac{3}{4}$ in. on $\frac{3}{8}$ in. gypsum board	2.10
$\frac{3}{4}$ in. on furring	1.78
Wood lath and $\frac{1}{2}$-in. plaster (sand aggregate)	0.40
Fibrous Insulation†	
$k = 0.27$ Btu/(hr)(sq ft)(°F/in.)	
$\frac{1}{2}$ in. thick	1.85
1 in. thick	3.70
2 in. thick	7.40
3 in. thick	11.10
Roof (for unventilated and uninsulated rafter space)†	
Asphalt shingles building paper	
on plywood sheathing, $\frac{5}{16}$ in.	0.95
on wood sheathing, $\frac{25}{32}$ in.	1.48
Asbestos-cement slate, or tile shingles, building	
paper on wood sheathing, $\frac{25}{32}$ in.	1.09
Wood shingles on 1-in. by 4-in. wood strips, 6-in. centers	0.87

* For non-structural elements (air spaces and air films) refer to Tables 5–17, 5–18, 5–19, 5–22, and 5–23.

† When insulation is installed between rafters, the space above should be ventilated, and in this case the roof construction is disregarded in calculation of total resistance. From *ASHRAE Guide*.

corresponding to a thermal conductance of approximately 9 Btu/(hr)(sq ft)(°F). For multiple sheets of glass, the total resistance will then be 0.112 per sheet plus film and air-space resistances.

RESISTANCES OF AIR SPACES. Heat transfer across an air space occurs by the parallel mechanisms of convection and radiation. The combined conductance a is therefore the sum of the conductances for convective and for radiant transfer:

$$a = a_c + a_r$$

and the combined resistance is the reciprocal of the conductance or

$$r_a = \frac{1}{a} = \frac{1}{a_c + a_r} \qquad (5\text{--}20)$$

TABLE 5–13

Thermal Resistances of Structural Elements of Solid Wood Doors*

Resistances, r

Nominal Thickness, in.	Actual Thickness, in.	Exposed Door	With Glass Storm Door (50% glass and 50% thin wood panels)
1	$\frac{25}{32}$	0.711	1.848
$1\frac{1}{4}$	$1\frac{1}{16}$	0.965	2.088
$1\frac{1}{2}$	$1\frac{5}{16}$	1.188	2.273
$1\frac{3}{4}$	$1\frac{3}{8}$	1.230	2.372
2	$1\frac{5}{8}$	1.473	2.716
$2\frac{1}{2}$	$2\frac{1}{8}$	1.923	2.993
3	$2\frac{5}{8}$	2.372	3.493

* For non-structural elements (air spaces and air films) refer to Tables 5–20 and 5–23. From *ASHRAE Guide*.

Thus determination of r_a first requires evaluation of a_c and of a_r. But the variables significant in fixing a_c and a_r are not the same, so convenience dictates that they be investigated separately.

Convective Transfer Across Air Spaces in Walls. The recommended equation (4–68) for evaluating the convective film coefficient for air spaces in vertical walls is

$$a_c = 0.093(\Delta t_a)^{1/3} \qquad (5\text{–}21)$$

But by analogy with Eq. 4–146 (using r_w as defined in Eq. 5–17),

$$\frac{\Delta t_a}{t_a - t_o} = \frac{r_a}{R} = \frac{r_a}{r_i + r_w + r_a + r_o} \qquad (5\text{–}22)$$

where r_a is combined resistance of the air space, R the over-all (air-to-air) resistance of the structural section (as wall, ceiling, or floor) through which heat is being transmitted. The value of r_w is obtainable from an equation analogous to Eq. 5–17, using data on individual resistances as given in Table 5–2 through 5–5. The value of r_o is obtained from Table 5–1.

From Eqs. 5–21 and 5–22 it is evident that the convective conductance of an air space can be evaluated only in terms of prior knowledge of both the combined conductance of the air space and the combined conductance of the inside film; both of the latter terms are themselves functions of the convective conductance of the air space; hence evaluation of a_c must be carried out by a trial-and-error procedure. Fortunately, however, the influence of r_a and r_o on a_c is not great, and it will often be found that a first trial will provide a close approximation and a second trial will establish a_c with accuracy as great as other conditions will justify.

As a first approximation, the value of r_a will be taken as 0.9710 and the value of h_i as 0.6849, each as used (refer Table in Art. 5–3) for calculating

TABLE 5–14
Convective Film Coefficient for Wall Air Spaces*

| $r_w + r_0$ | Outside Design Air Temperature | | | | | |
| | −20 F | | 0 F | | +20 F | |
	Δt	a_c	Δt	a_c	Δt	a_c
0.30	46.4	0.33	36.5	0.31	26.6	0.28
0.40	44.2	0.33	34.7	0.30	25.3	0.27
0.50	42.1	0.32	33.1	0.30	24.1	0.27
0.60	40.3	0.32	31.6	0.29	23.0	0.26
0.70	38.5	0.31	30.3	0.29	22.0	0.26
0.80	37.0	0.31	29.1	0.28	21.2	0.26
0.90	35.5	0.31	27.9	0.28	20.3	0.25
1.00	34.2	0.30	26.9	0.28	19.6	0.25
1.10	33.0	0.30	25.9	0.27	18.8	0.25
1.20	31.8	0.30	25.0	0.27	18.2	0.25
1.30	30.7	0.29	24.1	0.27	17.6	0.24
1.40	29.7	0.29	23.4	0.26	17.0	0.24
1.60	27.9	0.28	21.9	0.26	16.0	0.23
1.80	26.3	0.28	20.7	0.26	15.0	0.23
2.00	24.8	0.27	19.5	0.25	14.2	0.23
2.25	23.3	0.26	18.3	0.25	13.3	0.22
2.50	21.9	0.26	17.2	0.24	13.2	0.22
2.75	20.6	0.25	16.2	0.24	11.8	0.21
3.00	19.5	0.25	15.3	0.23	11.2	0.21
3.25	18.5	0.25	14.6	0.23	10.6	0.20
3.50	17.6	0.24	13.8	0.22	10.1	0.20
3.75	16.8	0.24	13.2	0.22	9.6	0.20
4.00	16.1	0.24	12.6	0.22	9.2	0.19
4.50	14.8	0.23	11.6	0.21	8.4	0.19
5.00	13.6	0.22	10.7	0.21	7.8	0.18
6.00	11.9	0.21	9.3	0.20	6.8	0.17
8.00	9.4	0.20	7.4	0.18	5.4	0.16
10.00	7.8	0.18	6.1	0.17	4.5	0.15
15.00	5.4	0.16	4.3	0.15	3.1	0.13
20.00	4.2	0.15	3.3	0.14	2.4	0.12
25.00	3.4	0.14	2.7	0.13	2.0	0.11

* Calculated from Eq. 4–68.

the "standard" over-all coefficients tabulated in the *ASHRAE Guide*.[3] On this basis Eq. 5–22 becomes

$$\frac{\Delta t_a}{t_a - t_o} = \frac{0.971}{(r_w + r_o) + 0.9710 + 0.6849} = \frac{0.971}{(r_w + r_o) + 1.6559}$$

If t_a is arbitrarily taken at the recommended thermal level of 73.5 F (this approximation can likewise, if necessary, be adjusted in a second trial), then

$$\Delta t_a = \frac{71.37 - 0.971 t_o}{(r_w + r_o) + 1.6559} \qquad (5\text{–}23)$$

Table 5–14 provides a solution of Eqs. 5–23 and 5–21 for outside design air temperatures of −20 F, 0 F, and +20 F and for a wide range of values

[3] Bibliography, item 1.

of $(r_w + r_o)$. By interpolation or extrapolation it is possible to obtain from Table 5–14 the value of Δt_a and the corresponding value of the convective film coefficient a_c, for any likely outside design air temperature or any thermally reasonable value of $(r_w + r_o)$.

Convective Transfer Across Air Spaces in Floors. In this case the width of the air space has a significant influence on the convective conductance. For Δt_a of $13\frac{1}{2}$ F and for an air space of 4-in. width,

$$x^3 \, \Delta t_a = \left(\frac{4}{12}\right)^3 (13.5) = 0.5$$

For any Δt_a greater than $13\frac{1}{2}$ F with any width greater than 4 in.,

$$x^3 \, \Delta t_a > 0.5$$

and Eq. 4–70 is applicable to evaluation of the convective conductance

$$a_c = 0.112(\Delta t_a)^{1/3} \tag{5–24}$$

The *ASHRAE Guide* value of r_a for a 4-in. floor air space is 1.2340 (slightly greater than the value of 1.150 shown in the table of Art. 5–3) and the value of r_i for a floor is 0.9259. Then, by analogy with Eq. 5–23,

$$\Delta t_a = \frac{90.70 - 1.2340}{(r_f + r_o) + 2.1599} \tag{5–25}$$

Solutions of Eqs. 5–24 and 5–25 are given for -20 F, 0 F, and $+20$ F outside air design temperature in the columns of Table 5–15, which are for 4-in. air spaces; the same values are equally applicable to air spaces of any width greater than 4 in. It will be noted that in those cases where Δt_a is less than $13\frac{1}{2}$ F, the accuracy of the result may be in question, since the criterion that $x^3 \, \Delta t_a$ be greater than 0.5 no longer holds. In all such cases, however, the corresponding value of $(r_f + r_o)$ is so great compared with the convective film resistance, $(1/a_c)$, that the practical effect of this error is negligible.

For air spaces of $2\frac{1}{2}$-in. width or less, $x^3 \, \Delta t_a$ is equal to $(2.5/12)^3 \, \Delta t_a$ or $\Delta t_a/110.6$. For any value of Δt less than 55 F, the value of $x^3 \, \Delta t_a$ would be less than 0.5, and for any value of x less than $2\frac{1}{2}$ in., the $x^3 \, \Delta t_a$ product would be even smaller. Thus under all conditions applicable to air spaces narrower than $2\frac{1}{2}$ in., the $x^3 \, \Delta t_a$ product will be less than 0.5. For these conditions, Eq. 4–69 applies; hence for a $2\frac{1}{2}$-in. air space,

$$a_c = 0.117\left(\frac{12}{2.5}\right)^{0.25} (\Delta t_a)^{0.25} = 0.173(\Delta t_a)^{0.25} \tag{5–26}$$

Neglecting the difference (on the first approximation) in the "standard" r_a for $2\frac{1}{2}$-in. and 4-in. air spaces permits utilizing Eq. 5–25 for determination of Δt_a and Eq. 5–26 for evaluation of a_c for $2\frac{1}{2}$-in. air spaces. Table 5–15 gives a_c values for $2\frac{1}{2}$-in. air spaces calculated from these equations.

TABLE 5–15
Convective Film Coefficient for Floor Air Space*

	Outside Design Air Temperature								
	−20 F			0 F			+20 F		
	Δt	a_c width		Δt	a_c width		Δt	a_c width	
$r_f + r_o$		$2\frac{1}{2}''$	$4''$		$2\frac{1}{2}''$	$4''$		$2\frac{1}{2}''$	$4''$
0.30	46.9	0.45	0.40	36.9	0.43	0.38	26.9	0.39	0.33
0.40	45.1	0.45	0.40	35.4	0.42	0.37	25.8	0.39	0.33
0.50	43.4	0.44	0.39	34.1	0.42	0.37	24.8	0.38	0.32
0.60	41.8	0.44	0.39	32.9	0.41	0.36	23.9	0.38	0.32
0.70	40.4	0.43	0.38	31.7	0.41	0.36	23.1	0.38	0.32
0.80	39.0	0.43	0.38	30.6	0.41	0.35	22.3	0.38	0.31
0.90	37.7	0.43	0.38	29.6	0.40	0.35	21.6	0.37	0.31
1.00	36.5	0.43	0.37	28.7	0.40	0.34	20.9	0.37	0.31
1.10	35.4	0.42	0.37	27.8	0.40	0.34	20.3	0.37	0.31
1.20	34.3	0.42	0.37	27.0	0.39	0.33	19.7	0.36	0.30
1.30	33.3	0.41	0.36	26.2	0.39	0.33	19.1	0.36	0.30
1.40	32.4	0.41	0.36	25.5	0.39	0.33	18.6	0.36	0.30
1.60	30.7	0.41	0.35	24.1	0.38	0.32	17.6	0.35	0.29
1.80	29.1	0.40	0.35	22.9	0.38	0.31	16.7	0.35	0.29
2.00	27.7	0.40	0.34	21.8	0.37	0.31	15.9	0.35	0.28
2.25	26.1	0.39	0.33	20.6	0.37	0.31	15.0	0.34	0.28
2.50	24.8	0.38	0.32	19.5	0.36	0.30	14.2	0.34	0.27
2.75	23.5	0.38	0.32	18.5	0.36	0.30	13.5	0.33	0.27
3.00	22.4	0.38	0.31	17.6	0.35	0.29	12.8	0.33	0.26
3.25	21.3	0.37	0.31	16.8	0.35	0.29	12.2	0.32	0.26
3.50	20.4	0.37	0.31	16.0	0.35	0.28	11.7	0.32	0.25
3.75	19.5	0.36	0.30	15.4	0.34	0.28	11.2	0.32	0.25
4.00	18.7	0.36	0.30	14.7	0.34	0.27	10.7	0.31	0.25
4.50	17.3	0.35	0.29	13.6	0.33	0.27	9.9	0.31	0.24
5.00	16.1	0.35	0.29	12.7	0.33	0.26	9.2	0.30	0.24
6.00	14.1	0.34	0.27	11.1	0.32	0.25	8.1	0.29	0.23
8.00	11.4	0.32	0.25	8.9	0.30	0.23	6.5	0.28	0.21
10.00	9.5	0.30	0.24	7.5	0.29	0.22	5.4	0.26	0.19
15.00	6.7	0.28	0.21	5.3	0.26	0.19	3.9	0.24	0.17
20.00	5.2	0.26	0.19	4.1	0.24	0.17	3.0	0.23	0.16
25.00	4.3	0.25	0.18	3.3	0.23	0.16	2.4	0.22	0.14

* Eq. 5–26 for $2\frac{1}{2}$-in. width; Eq. 5–24 for 4-in. width. For air-space widths greater than 4-in. the 4-in. values are applicable; for widths less than $2\frac{1}{2}$ in. refer to Table 5–16.

For air spaces less than $2\frac{1}{2}$ in. wide, Eq. 4–69 applies and Eq. 5–26 can therefore be corrected to the form

$$a_c = \left(\frac{2.5}{x}\right)^{0.25} (0.173)(\Delta t_a)^{0.25} \qquad (5\text{–}27)$$

where $(2.5/x)^{0.25}$ is a correction factor that is applicable to the Table 5–15 values of a_c as given for a $2\frac{1}{2}$-in. air space. Table 5–16 gives values of this correction factor for air spaces in the width range from $\frac{3}{4}$ in. to $2\frac{1}{2}$ in. Then, for an air space less than $2\frac{1}{2}$ in. wide, the Δt_a and a_c values for a $2\frac{1}{2}$-in. air space are obtained from Table 5–15 for known values of t_o and $(r_f + r_o)$. The Δt_a value given in the table is applicable to the air space in question, but the tabular a_c value must be corrected by multiplying it by the factor given in Table 5–16.

TABLE 5–16

Correction Factors for Floor Air Spaces of Width
Less than $2\frac{1}{2}$ Inches

Width of floor air space, in.	$2\frac{1}{2}$	$2\frac{1}{4}$	2	$1\frac{3}{4}$	$1\frac{1}{2}$	$1\frac{1}{4}$	1	$\frac{3}{4}$
Correction factors, for use with a_c values for $2\frac{1}{2}$-in. width, from Table 5–15	1.00	1.03	1.08	1.09	1.13	1.19	1.26	1.35

Convective Transfer Across Air Spaces in Ceilings. For Δt_a of 2.7 F and for a ceiling air space of 4-in. width,

$$x^3 \, \Delta t_a = \left(\frac{4}{12}\right)^3 (2.7) = 0.1$$

For any Δt_a greater than 2.7 with an air space width in excess of 4 in.

$$x^3 \, \Delta t_a > 0.11$$

which is the criterion for establishing the applicability of Eq. 4–72,

$$a_c = 0.140(\Delta t_a)^{1/3} \qquad (5\text{--}28)$$

Evaluation of Δt_a is accomplished by noting (table in Art. 5–3, page 168) that "standard" values of r_a and r_i for ceiling air space and film are, respectively, 0.8475 and 0.6135. Use of these values, by analogy with Eq. 5–23, establishes the equation

$$\Delta t_a = \frac{62.29 - 0.8475t_o}{(r_c + r_o) + 1.4610} \qquad (5\text{--}29)$$

Table 5–17 provides a tabular solution of Eqs. 5–28 and 5–29, giving the temperature drop and the convective film coefficient for ceiling air spaces as a function of outside design temperature and of $(r_c + r_o)$; r_c is now the sum of resistances of all solid structural elements constituting the ceiling (r_c is thus analogous to r_w for a wall as defined in Eq. 5–17).

Radiant Transfer Across Air Spaces. The equivalent film coefficient for radiant transfer is given by Eq. 4–113, but that relationship can be considerably simplified by noting that

$$
\begin{aligned}
T_1^4 - T_2^4 &= (T_1^2 + T_2^2)(T_1 + T_2)(T_1 - T_2) \\
&= (T_1^3 + T_1 T_2^2 + T_1^2 T_2 + T_2^3)(t_1 - t_2) \qquad (5\text{--}30)
\end{aligned}
$$

TABLE 5–17
Convective Film Coefficient for Ceiling Air Space*

$r_c + r_o$	Outside Design Air Temperature					
	−20 F		0 F		+20 F	
	Δt	a_c	Δt	a_c	Δt	a_c
0.30	45.0	0.50	35.4	0.46	25.8	0.41
0.40	42.6	0.49	33.5	0.45	24.4	0.40
0.50	40.4	0.48	31.8	0.45	23.2	0.40
0.60	38.4	0.47	30.2	0.44	22.0	0.39
0.70	36.7	0.46	28.8	0.43	21.0	0.39
0.80	35.1	0.46	27.6	0.42	20.1	0.38
0.90	33.6	0.46	26.4	0.41	19.2	0.38
1.00	32.2	0.45	25.3	0.41	18.4	0.37
1.10	31.0	0.44	24.3	0.40	17.7	0.37
1.20	29.8	0.43	23.4	0.40	17.1	0.36
1.30	28.6	0.43	22.6	0.39	16.4	0.36
1.40	27.7	0.42	21.8	0.39	15.9	0.35
1.60	25.9	0.41	20.4	0.38	14.8	0.34
1.80	24.3	0.40	19.1	0.38	13.9	0.34
2.00	22.9	0.40	18.0	0.37	13.1	0.33
2.25	21.4	0.39	16.8	0.36	12.3	0.32
2.50	20.0	0.38	15.7	0.35	11.5	0.32
2.75	18.8	0.38	14.8	0.34	10.8	0.31
3.00	17.8	0.37	14.0	0.34	10.2	0.30
3.25	16.8	0.36	13.2	0.33	9.6	0.30
3.50	16.0	0.35	12.6	0.33	9.1	0.29
3.75	15.2	0.35	12.0	0.32	8.7	0.29
4.00	14.5	0.34	11.4	0.32	8.3	0.28
4.50	13.3	0.33	10.5	0.30	7.6	0.27
5.00	12.3	0.32	9.6	0.30	7.0	0.26
6.00	10.6	0.30	8.4	0.28	6.1	0.25
8.00	8.4	0.28	6.6	0.26	4.8	0.24
10.00	6.9	0.26	5.4	0.24	4.0	0.22
15.00	4.8	0.24	3.8	0.21	2.8	0.19
20.00	3.7	0.22	2.9	0.20	2.1	0.17
25.00	3.0	0.20	2.4	0.18	1.7	0.16

* Eq. 4–72.

Further,

$$T_1^3 + T_1 T_2^2 + T_1^2 T_2 + T_2^3$$
$$= (0.5 T_1^3 + 1.5 T_1 T_2^2 + 1.5 T_1^2 T_2 + 0.5 T_2^3)$$
$$+ (0.5 T_1^3 - 0.5 T_1^2 T_2 - 0.5 T_1 T_2^2 + 0.5 T_2^3)$$
$$= 4 \left(\frac{T_1 + T_2}{2} \right)^3 + \frac{T_1^3 + T_2^3 - T_1^2 T_2 - T_1 T_2^2}{2}$$
$$= 4 T_m^3 + \frac{T_1^3 + T_2^3 - T_1^2 T_2 - T_1 T_2^2}{2} \tag{5–31}$$

where

$$T_m = \frac{T_1 + T_2}{2} \tag{5–32}$$

As T_1 approaches T_2, the second term in Eq. 5–31 approaches zero; hence $(T_1^4 - T_2^4)$ approaches $4T_m^3(t_1 - t_2)$. This shows that when the ratio of T_1 to T_2 is small, the equivalent radiant coefficient as exactly calculated by Eq. 4–113 will be a function primarily of the arithmetical average of the temperatures of surfaces between which net radiant transfer is occurring.

Consider, for example, a wall air space having a surface temperature of 70 F on one side and 0 F on the other. For this case,

$$T_1^4 - T_2^4 = (460 + 70)^4 - (460 + 0)^4$$
$$= (789.05 - 447.75)10^8$$
$$= (341.30)10^8$$

and

$$4T_m^3(t_1 - t_2) = 4(460 + 35)^3(70) = (339.60)10^8$$

Thus, if the equivalent radiant coefficient were calculated by using the mean temperature of the air space, the result would differ from the exact value by $(341.30 - 339.60)/341.30$, or less than one-half of 1 per cent.

TABLE 5–18

Equivalent Radiation Coefficient for Non-reflective (Black) Air Spaces*

t_o	−20	−16	−12	−8	−4	0	+4	+8	+12	+16	+20
a_r	0.79	0.80	0.81	0.82	0.83	0.84	0.85	0.86	0.87	0.88	0.89

* Refer to Table 5–19 for emissivity factor for reflective air spaces.

From the above discussion it follows that the h_r value exactly calculated for a $\frac{1}{2}$ F temperature difference on either side of a given temperature (as between 59.5 F and 60.5 F, for a mean of 60 F) will be applicable to any other temperature difference that will occur in structural air spaces when the mean temperature has the same value (as an air-space surface-to-surface temperature difference corresponding to 70 F at one surface and 50 F at the other surface). As a first approximation it will be assumed that the air space is located at the thermal center of the wall, floor, or ceiling. In this case the mean temperature of the air space would be the arithmetical average of inside and outside air temperatures.

Table 5–18 gives the value of the equivalent coefficient as a function of outside air temperature based on the assumption that inside air temperature is 73.5 F and that the air space is located at the thermal center of the structural section. Thus the value of h_r given in Table 5–18 for an outside design air temperature of −20 F was obtained by using Eq. 4–113 with temperatures ±0.5 F from the mean value of

$$t_m = \frac{73.5 + 20}{2} - 20 = 26.75 \text{ F}$$

giving

$$h_r = \frac{0.1713\left[\left(\dfrac{460 + 27.25}{100}\right)^4 - \left(\dfrac{460 + 26.25}{100}\right)^4\right]}{27.25 - 26.25}$$

$$= 0.7873 = 0.79$$

The geometrical arrangement of the transfer surfaces in air spaces is approximated by that of infinite parallel planes; hence the equivalent radiant conductance for an air space is given by

$$a_r = F_{ae}h_r = \left[\frac{e_1 e_2}{e_1 + e_2 - e_1 e_2}\right]h_r \qquad (5\text{–}33)$$

where h_r = equivalent radiant coefficient (from Table 5–18).

e_1 = emissivity of warm surface of air space.

e_2 = emissivity of cool surface of air space.

Table 5–19 gives values of F_{ae} for air spaces as calculated by the bracketed term of Eq. 5–33. From the tabular values it is evident that use of a reflective surface (as aluminum sheet with emissivity of 0.12) on one side of an air space

TABLE 5–19
Emissivity Factor for Air Spaces*

e_1 / e_2	0.05	0.10	0.15	0.20	0.25	0.50	0.90	1
0.05	0.03	0.03	0.04	0.04	0.04	0.05	0.05	0.05
0.10	—	0.05	0.06	0.07	0.08	0.09	0.10	0.11
0.15	—	—	0.08	0.09	0.10	0.13	0.15	0.15
0.20	—	—	—	0.11	0.13	0.17	0.20	0.20
0.25	—	—	—	—	0.14	0.20	0.24	0.25
0.50	—	—	—	—	—	0.33	0.47	0.50
0.90	—	—	—	—	—	—	0.82	0.90
1.00	—	—	—	—	—	—	—	1.0

* For use with equivalent radiation coefficients from Table 5–18.

for which the other side has an emissivity of 0.9 would establish an F_{ae} value of 0.12 (or exact value of 0.1184), thus reducing radiant transfer (based on the same temperature difference) by 88 per cent. Use of two surfaces with emissivity of 0.12 would give (by double interpolation in Table 5–19) an F_{ae} value of approximately 0.6 and hence a reduction in radiant transfer of 94 per cent.

Resistance of Air Spaces. The total resistance of any air space can now be written as a modified form of Eq. 5–20:

$$r_a = \frac{1}{a_c + F_{ae}h_r} \qquad (5\text{–}34)$$

where a_c is determinable from Table 5–14, 5–15, or 5–17, depending on the location of the air space in wall, floor, or ceiling; F_{ae} is determinable from Table 5–19; and h_r is determinable from Table 5–18.

Multiple Air Spaces. In cases where more than one air space exists in a wall, floor, or ceiling, the resistance of each space is obtained by the method of this article, page 191. If an air space is divided into two parts by a splitter (having the same emissivity as the surfaces of the single space), the resistance to radiant transfer will be doubled. If the splitter emissivity differs from that of the original surfaces, the new resistance of each half of the space must be evaluated.

Correction for Framing. The concept of unidimensional heat transfer does not strictly apply in cases where two parallel paths are not insulated from one another. Thus in a frame wall there is heat transfer by conduction through the framing members and by convection through the air space that separates such members. The framing members conduct heat from the warm side to the cooler; hence there must be a continuous temperature drop in the direction of heat flow. The air space, on the contrary, provides major resistance at the two surface films and is otherwise at a practically uniform temperature. Under these conditions it is evident that the heat transfer will occur between the framing and the air space, and therefore the actual rate of heat transfer through each of the structurally parallel paths will be influenced by the interchange between them. Further, the rate of heat transfer per unit area will differ between framing and air space, so it would be expected that the temperature on the warm and the cool sides would not be the same for these two paths.

In spite of the complications indicated above, the steady-state thermal system consisting of framing and air space would necessarily have a pattern of isotherms that would remain fixed with time. For known inside and outside air temperature and with resistances of all other parts of the system established (as siding, inside finish, and the inside and outside surface films), the modified relaxation procedure described in Art. 4–8, page 156, can be used to establish the temperature pattern, locate the isotherms, and calculate the resultant transmission load for any particular type of frame construction. Usually, however, the effect of two-dimensional heat flow is either conservative or self-compensating, so it is rarely necessary to calculate the correction. Thus, in the case of transfer between studs and an air space, the stud temperature would exceed the air-space temperature on the warm side but would be less than air-space temperature on the cool side. In this case heat would first flow by convection from stud to air space and return by convection from air space to stud, the combined processes acting in such a way that the air space acts, in part, as a regenerator with respect to energy received from the studs.

The most commonly used simplification in correcting for framing is to assume parallel flow through the framing and through the air space. Based on this assumption, the corrected air-space resistance is

$$r_a' = \frac{1}{(1/r_a)X + (1/r_s)(1 - X)} \tag{5-35}$$

where $r_a' =$ average combined resistance of an air space with correction to include the fraction of total transmitting area that is backed by framing members.

      $X =$ fraction of wall area (or floor or ceiling area) not backed by framing members.

      $r_s =$ resistance of studs (or other framing member) based on unidirectional heat flow (no heat transfer between framing and air space).

When partial insulation is installed adjacent to one side of an air space, the resistance of the series system consisting of insulation and reduced-size air space becomes

$$r_a'' = r_a + r_{\text{ins.}} \tag{5-36}$$

where r_a'' is the resistance of the wall (or floor, or ceiling) area between framing members. The corrected resistance of the area between framing members is then given by Eq. 5–35, with r_a'' substituted for r_a.

A very common wall framing is that using nominal 2-in. by 4-in. studs on 16-in. centers. The actual width of the stud is $1\frac{5}{8}$ in.; hence X is equal to 1.625/16, or approximately 0.1. For this case Eq. 5–35 simplifies to

$$r_a' = \frac{1}{(0.9/r_a) + (0.1/r_s)} \tag{5-37}$$

or (when insulation is included)

$$r_a' = \frac{1}{(0.9/r_a^n) + (0.1/r_s)} \tag{5-38}$$

COMBINED RESISTANCES OF INSIDE FILMS. Just as with outside films and air spaces, the heat transfer to the inside surface of a transmitting section of the structure occurs by the parallel mechanisms of convection and radiation. The convective fraction varies with the orientation of the surface and as an exponential function of the temperature drop across the inside film. The radiation fraction depends on the temperature of the surface and on the temperatures and orientations of all the other surfaces which make up the enclosure. Unlike the situation with respect to air spaces, the emissivity of the inside surface is of no consequence, and all such surfaces can be treated as though they had emissivities of unity (refer to Art. 8–2, page 325).

Convective Transfer Across Wall Film. For heat transfer by free convection in the streamline region to an unheated wall of average height, the laminar flow condition is given by Eq. 4–53:

$$h_{cw} = 0.274(\Delta t_f)^{0.25} \tag{5-39}$$

where Δt_f is the temperature drop across the inside film. This equation is applicable for values of the Nusselt number between 6.0 and 100 and (as shown in Example 4–13) it would be expected to apply for values of Δt_f up to a maximum of 52 F. Using the ASHRAE value of the combined inside film resistance for a wall ($r_i = 0.6849$) as a first approximation permits evaluation of Δt_f by an expression analogous to Eq. 5–22:

$$\frac{\Delta t_f}{t - t_o} = \frac{r_i}{(r_o + r_w + r_a) + r_i} = \frac{r_i}{(1/C_w) + r_i}$$

$$= \frac{0.6849}{(1/C_w) + 0.6849} \qquad (5\text{–}40)$$

where r_w is as defined in Eq. 5–17 and C_w is as defined in Eq. 5–15. Substituting 73.5 F as a first approximation to t_a (see the preceding discussion, page 190) and solving for the temperature drop across the film gives

$$\Delta t_f = \frac{50.34 - 0.6849t_o}{(1/C_w) + 0.6849} \qquad (5\text{–}41)$$

Table 5–20 provides a tabular solution of Eqs. 5–39 and 5–41 for outside design air temperatures of -20 F, 0 F, and $+20$ F and for a range of conductances (inside wall surface to outside air) from 0.30 to 25.00 Btu/(hr)(sq ft)(°F). By interpolation between given values of C_w and by interpolation or limited extrapolation from given values of t_o, it is readily possible to obtain from the table the temperature drop across the film and the film coefficient corresponding to any likely values of t_o and of C_w.

In comparing Table 5–20 with Table 5–14, it should be noted that the resistance term in the latter table does not include the air-space resistance. Thus

$$r_w + r_o = \frac{1}{C_w} - r_a \qquad (5\text{–}42)$$

The film coefficients given in Table 5–20 are based on the laminar flow equation (5–39), and it has been shown that the condition of laminar flow does not hold for values of Δt_f greater than 52 F. For $1/C_w$ values of 0.3, 0.4, and 0.5 at outside design air temperatures of -20 F, the tabulated Δt_f values exceed 52 F. In these three cases it is probable that the free-convection-flow condition has undergone transformation from streamline to turbulent and that Eq. 4–55 would therefore apply more accurately than would Eq. 4–53. The corrected values of these three coefficients could be obtained from the equation

$$h_{cw\text{corrected}} = \left[\frac{0.241(\Delta t_f)^{1/3}}{0.274(\Delta t_f)^{1/4}}\right] h_{cw\text{tab}}$$

$$= 0.880(\Delta t)^{4/3} h_{cw\text{tab}} \qquad (5\text{–}43)$$

In the (Δt_f) range between 28 F and 52 F, the flow pattern has been shown to be indeterminate (Example 4–13). Therefore, if circumstances of a

TABLE 5–20
Convective Film Coefficient for Walls*

| | Outside Design Air Temperature | | | | | |
| | −20 F | | 0 F | | +20 F | |
$1/C_w$	Δt	h_c	Δt	h_c	Δt	h_c
0.30	65.0	0.78	51.1	0.73	37.2	0.68
0.40	59.0	0.76	46.4	0.71	33.8	0.66
0.50	54.0	0.74	42.3	0.70	30.9	0.64
0.60	49.8	0.73	39.2	0.69	28.5	0.63
0.70	46.2	0.71	36.3	0.67	26.5	0.62
0.80	43.1	0.70	33.9	0.66	24.7	0.61
0.90	40.0	0.69	31.8	0.65	23.1	0.60
1.00	38.0	0.68	29.9	0.64	21.8	0.59
1.10	35.9	0.67	28.2	0.63	20.5	0.58
1.20	34.0	0.66	26.7	0.62	19.4	0.58
1.30	32.2	0.65	25.4	0.61	18.4	0.57
1.40	30.7	0.64	24.2	0.61	17.6	0.56
1.60	28.0	0.63	22.0	0.59	16.1	0.55
1.80	25.8	0.62	20.3	0.58	14.7	0.54
2.00	23.8	0.60	18.8	0.57	13.7	0.53
2.25	21.8	0.59	17.2	0.56	12.5	0.52
2.50	20.0	0.58	15.8	0.55	11.4	0.51
2.75	18.6	0.57	14.7	0.54	10.7	0.49
3.00	17.4	0.56	13.7	0.53	9.9	0.48
3.25	16.3	0.55	12.8	0.52	9.3	0.47
3.50	15.3	0.54	12.0	0.51	8.7	0.47
4.00	13.7	0.53	10.8	0.50	8.3	0.46
4.50	12.4	0.52	9.7	0.49	7.1	0.45
5.00	11.3	0.50	8.9	0.47	6.4	0.44
6.00	9.6	0.48	7.5	0.44	5.5	0.42
8.00	7.4	0.45	5.8	0.43	4.2	0.39
10.00	6.0	0.43	4.7	0.40	3.4	0.37
15.00	4.1	0.39	3.2	0.37	2.3	0.34
20.00	3.1	0.36	2.4	0.34	1.8	0.32
25.00	2.5	0.35	2.0	0.32	1.4	0.32

* Laminar flow, Eq. 4–53.

particular design are such as to suggest the probability of turbulent flow, the tabular film coefficient can be corrected from the laminar to the turbulent condition by use of Eq. 5–43.

Convective Transfer Across Floor Film. The free convection flow pattern for convective heat loss through floor films is always laminar rather than turbulent; hence Eq. 4–61 is applicable:

$$h_{cf} = 0.126(\Delta t_f)^{0.25} \tag{5–44}$$

Using the ASHRAE value of the combined inside film resistance ($r_i = 0.9259$) and assigning t_a a value of 73.5 F gives an equation for Δt_f that is analogous to Eq. 5–41:

$$\Delta t_f = \frac{68.05 - 0.9259 t_o}{(1/C_f) + 0.9259} \tag{5–45}$$

TABLE 5-21
Convective Film Coefficient for Floors*

| | Outside Design Air Temperature | | | | | |
| | −20 F | | 0 F | | +20 F | |
$1/C_f$	Δt	h_c	Δt	h_c	Δt	h_c
0.30	70.6	0.37	55.5	0.34	40.4	0.32
0.40	65.2	0.36	51.3	0.34	37.4	0.31
0.50	60.8	0.35	47.7	0.33	34.7	0.31
0.60	56.8	0.35	44.6	0.33	32.5	0.30
0.70	53.2	0.34	41.9	0.32	30.5	0.30
0.80	50.2	0.34	39.4	0.32	28.7	0.29
0.90	47.4	0.33	37.3	0.31	27.1	0.29
1.00	44.9	0.33	35.3	0.31	25.7	0.28
1.10	42.7	0.32	33.6	0.30	24.4	0.28
1.20	40.7	0.32	32.0	0.30	23.3	0.28
1.30	38.9	0.31	30.6	0.30	22.2	0.27
1.40	37.3	0.31	29.3	0.29	21.3	0.27
1.60	34.3	0.31	26.9	0.29	19.6	0.27
1.80	31.7	0.30	25.0	0.28	18.2	0.26
2.00	29.6	0.29	23.3	0.28	16.9	0.26
2.25	27.3	0.29	21.4	0.27	15.6	0.25
2.50	25.3	0.28	19.9	0.27	14.5	0.25
2.75	23.6	0.28	18.5	0.26	13.5	0.24
3.00	22.0	0.27	17.3	0.26	12.7	0.24
3.25	20.7	0.27	16.3	0.25	11.9	0.23
3.50	19.6	0.27	15.4	0.25	11.2	0.23
4.00	17.6	0.26	13.8	0.24	10.1	0.23
4.50	16.0	0.25	12.5	0.24	9.1	0.22
5.00	14.6	0.25	11.5	0.23	8.4	0.21
6.00	12.5	0.24	9.8	0.22	7.1	0.20
8.00	9.7	0.22	7.6	0.21	5.5	0.19
10.00	7.9	0.21	6.2	0.20	4.5	0.18
15.00	5.4	0.19	4.3	0.18	3.1	0.17
20.00	4.1	0.18	3.3	0.17	2.4	0.16
25.00	3.3	0.17	2.6	0.16	1.9	0.15

* Laminar flow, Eq. 4–61.

Table 5–21 tabulates solutions of Eqs. 5–44 and 5–45, based on the assumed values of r_i and of t_a. In cases where the actual value of Δt_f is known, the exact value of h_{cf} can be obtained by entering the table at known Δt_f and reading the corresponding value (regardless of t_o or of C_f) of h_{cf}.

Convective Transfer Across Ceiling Film. For heat loss through ceilings the free-convective flow pattern has been established (see Art. 4–6, page 98) as turbulent, and Eq. 4–59 applies:

$$h_{cc} = 0.259(\Delta t_f)^{1/3} \qquad (5\text{–}46)$$

The corresponding equation for Δt_f based on the ASHRAE value of combined inside film resistance for ceilings as 0.6135 and t_a as 73.5 F, is analogous to Eq. 5–45:

$$\Delta t_f = \frac{45.09 - 0.6135t_o}{(1/C_c) + 0.6135} \qquad (5\text{–}47)$$

TABLE 5-22
Convective Film Coefficient for Ceilings*

| | Outside Design Air Temperature | | | | | |
| | −20 F | | 0 F | | +20 F | |
$1/C_c$	Δt	h_c	Δt	h_c	Δt	h_c
0.30	62.8	1.03	49.4	0.95	35.9	0.86
0.40	56.6	1.00	44.5	0.92	32.4	0.83
0.50	51.5	0.96	40.5	0.89	29.5	0.80
0.60	47.3	0.94	37.2	0.87	27.0	0.76
0.70	43.7	0.91	34.3	0.85	25.0	0.75
0.80	40.6	0.89	31.9	0.82	23.2	0.74
0.90	37.9	0.87	29.8	0.81	21.7	0.72
1.00	35.6	0.85	28.0	0.78	20.4	0.71
1.10	33.5	0.84	26.3	0.77	19.2	0.70
1.20	31.6	0.82	24.9	0.75	18.1	0.68
1.30	30.0	0.81	23.6	0.74	17.1	0.67
1.40	28.5	0.80	22.4	0.73	16.3	0.66
1.60	25.9	0.79	20.4	0.71	14.8	0.64
1.80	23.8	0.74	18.7	0.69	13.6	0.62
2.00	21.9	0.73	17.3	0.67	12.6	0.61
2.25	20.0	0.70	15.8	0.65	11.5	0.58
2.50	18.4	0.69	14.5	0.63	10.5	0.57
2.75	17.1	0.67	13.4	0.62	9.8	0.56
3.00	15.9	0.65	12.5	0.60	9.1	0.54
3.25	14.8	0.64	11.7	0.59	8.4	0.53
3.50	13.9	0.63	11.0	0.58	8.0	0.52
4.00	12.4	0.60	9.8	0.55	7.1	0.50
4.50	11.2	0.58	8.8	0.54	6.4	0.48
5.00	10.2	0.56	8.0	0.52	5.8	0.46
6.00	8.7	0.53	6.8	0.49	5.0	0.44
8.00	6.6	0.48	5.2	0.45	3.8	0.40
10.00	5.4	0.45	4.3	0.42	3.1	0.37
15.00	3.7	0.39	2.9	0.36	2.1	0.33
20.00	2.8	0.36	2.2	0.33	1.6	0.30
25.00	2.2	0.33	1.8	0.31	1.3	0.28

* Turbulent flow, Eq. 4–59.

Table 5–22 presents solutions of Eqs. 5–46 and 5–47; the form and use of Table 5–22 is similar to that of Tables 5–20 and 5–21.

Radiant Transfer Across Films. The transfer by radiation between any two surfaces of a room is given by an equation similar to Eq. 4–112;

$$q = F_e F_{A_1 A_2} h_{r12} A_2 (t_1 - t_2) \qquad (5\text{–}48)$$

But for any two surfaces which constitute part of an enclosure, the inter-reflections are such that the effective emissivities are unity (see Art. 8–2, page 326); hence the F_e term drops out of Eq. 5–48. The net reception of radiant energy at the inside surface of a transmitting wall is therefore

$$q = [F_{A_i A_w} h_{riw}(t_i - t_w) + F_{A_g A_w} h_{rgw}(t_g - t_w)$$
$$+ F_{A_c A_w} h_{rcw}(t_c - t_w) + F_{A_f A_w} h_{rfw}(t_f - t_w)] A_w \qquad (5\text{–}49)$$

where $F_{A_x A_w}$ = shape factor of surface x with respect to energy reception from the wall and based on wall area.

h_{rxw} = equivalent film coefficient for radiant transfer (Eq. 4–113) between surface x and the wall.

The basic need, however, is to express net radiant transfer to the wall by the equation

$$q = h'_{rw} A_w (t_a - t_w) \qquad (5\text{-}50)$$

where h'_{rw} is the corrected equivalent radiant component of heat transfer for addition to h_{cw} to establish the combined inside film coefficient h_i, as used in Eq. 5–14. From Eqs. 5–49 and 5–50 it follows that

$$h'_{rw} = F_{A_i A_w} h_{riw}(t_i - t_w) + F_{A_g A_w} h_{rgw}(t_g - t_w)$$
$$+ \frac{F_{A_c A_w} h_{rcw}(t_c - t_w) + F_{A_f A_w} h_{rfw}(t_f - t_w)}{t_a - t_w} \qquad (5\text{-}51)$$

Eq. 5–51 brings out the significant fact that h'_{rw} is largely dependent on the inside surface temperatures of the enclosure. Thus, if a one-room structure were so constructed that the inside convective film coefficient and the over-all coefficient of heat transfer were the same for walls, floor, and ceiling, it would follow that h'_{rw} would be zero, since the inside surface temperature would be equal over all the room surfaces. In such a room, even though a substantial temperature difference might exist between inside air temperature and inside surface temperature, there would be no energy loss by radiation.

An opposite situation would occur in a room where transmission loss occurred only through one wall. In this case the floor, ceiling, and three interior walls would reach equilibrium temperatures approaching, but less than, the inside air temperature. If the exposed wall were of low thermal resistance, the inside surface temperature of this wall would be very much lower than the inside air temperature. Therefore the difference between inside air temperature and the surface temperature of non-transmitting surfaces would become of less significance and, as an approximation, the uniform surface temperature of floor, ceiling, and three walls could be taken as equal to the inside air temperature. In this case Eq. 5–51 would simplify to

$$h'_{rw} = \frac{F_{A_i A_w} h_{riw}(t_i - t_w)}{t_a - t_w} \doteq h_{rw} \qquad (5\text{-}52)$$

where t_i = the uniform inside surface temperature of all surfaces of the enclosure except the one transmitting wall ($t_i \doteq t_a$).

h_{rw} = the equivalent coefficient for radiant transfer from all non-transmitting surfaces of the enclosure to the single transmitting wall.

$F_{A_i A_w}$ = fraction of radiant energy leaving the transmitting surface which is received by the non-transmitting surfaces = 1 for this case.

Thus for this condition h'_{rw} is equal to h_{rw} as evaluated by Eq. 4–113, with t_1 and t_2 taken as t_a and t_w, respectively.

From the discussion of the two preceding paragraphs it follows that heat loss by radiation from unit area of transmitting surface varies from zero in a uniformly exposed enclosure to a maximum in an enclosure with a single transmitting wall. Thus the value of h'_{rw} would be expected to increase as the number of non-transmitting planes increased.

For a room having a single inside partition and equal exposure of the other three walls and floor and ceiling, the only net reception of radiation at the inside surface of the five transmitting sections would be that from the single inside partition. Then,

$$q = h_{rwi} F_{A_{(f+c+w)}A_i} A_i (t_i - t_t)$$
$$= h_{rwi} F_{A_i A_{(f+c+w)}} A_{(f+c+w)} (t_i - t_t) \qquad (5\text{–}53)$$

where t_t is the uniform inside surface temperature of all transmitting sections of the enclosure.

From Eq. 5–53,

$$F_{A_i A_{(f+c+w)}} = F_{A_{(f+c+w)}A_i} \frac{A_i}{A_{(f+c+w)}} \qquad (5\text{–}54)$$

But the single partition is wholly enclosed; hence

$$F_{A_{(f+c+w)}A_i} = 1 \qquad (5\text{–}55)$$

and therefore

$$F_{A_i A_{(f+c+w)}} = \frac{A_i}{A_{(f+c+w)}} \qquad (5\text{–}56)$$

Thus the fraction of radiant energy leaving the floor, ceiling, and three exposed walls and reaching the inside partition is equal to the ratio of partition area to total exposed area. If the room were cubical, the same ratio would then be equal to the fraction of radiation received at the inside partition from the floor alone, the ceiling alone, or the walls alone. Thus, for a cubical room with a single inside partition but with *differently* exposed floor and ceiling and outside walls, the fraction of net radiant transfer to the wall from the partition would be given by a simplified form of Eq. 5–49, with the shape factor evaluated from Eq. 5–56,

$$q_{riw} = h_{riw} F_{A_i A_w} A_w (t_i - t_w)$$
$$= h_{riw} \left[\frac{A_i}{A_{(f+c+w)}} \right] A_w (t_i - t_w)$$
$$= h''_{riw} A_w (t_i - t_w) \qquad (5\text{–}57)$$

where

$$h''_{riw} = h_{riw} \left[\frac{A_i}{A_{(f+c+w)}} \right] \qquad (5\text{–}58)$$

Note that the h''_r term is based on surface-to-surface temperature difference, whereas the h'_r term, from Eq. 5–50, is based on air-to-surface temperature difference.

Eq. 5–58 (exactly true only for a cubical room) evaluates the h_r'' term for transfer from any exposed surface to total area A_i of the interior partitions. In similar manner, equations can be written for the h_r'' terms applicable to transfer between transmitting surfaces. But all transmitting surfaces have inside surface temperatures less than room air temperatures; therefore if there is a net loss by radiation from an inside surface, it follows that this energy must have been received at the surface either from room air (by convection) or from inside partitions (by radiation). As an approximation, therefore, radiant transfer between transmitting surfaces can be neglected and heat loss from the room evaluated on the assumption that the total net reception of radiation at all inside transmitting surfaces is equal to the net loss of radiation from the total area of inside partitions.

On the above basis the equivalent radiation coefficient for any room transmitting surface of area A_x would be in a form obtainable from Eq. 5–58:

$$h_{rx}'' = h_{rix} \frac{A_i}{A_{e-i}} = h_{rix} \frac{A_i}{A_t} \qquad (5\text{--}59)$$

where A_e is total surface of the enclosure and A_{e-i} (equal to A_t) is the total transmitting area. Due to the fact that equally exposed surfaces in adjacent or in opposite walls "see themselves," the rational shape factors (obtainable as in Art. 4–7, page 115) are less than the area ratio of Eq. 5–59 and are more closely approached by using the ratio of inside area to total area, A_i/A_e. A comparison of such shape factors for a cubical room shows the data given in the accompanying table.

Number of Non-transmitting Room Surfaces	Rational Value of $F_{A_iA_w}$	A_i/A_e
1	0.2	0.17
2	0.4	0.33
3	0.6	0.50
4	0.8	0.67
5	1.0	0.83

For the great majority of practical design problems in rooms of average geometry, shape factor $F_{A_iA_w}$ can be approximated as A_i/A_e rather than evaluated by the rational procedure. Thus

$$h_{rw}'' = h_{rw} \frac{A_i}{A_e} \qquad (5\text{--}60)$$

$$h_{rf}'' = h_{rf} \frac{A_i}{A_e} \qquad (5\text{--}61)$$

$$h_{rc}'' = h_{rc} \frac{A_i}{A_e} \qquad (5\text{--}62)$$

$$h_{rg}'' = h_{rg} \frac{A_i}{A_e} \qquad (5\text{--}63)$$

A remaining problem is that of establishing the corrected radiation coefficient h'_r, based on air temperature. Recalling that net radiation to transmitting surfaces equals net radiation from interior partitions, it follows that this energy rate must also equal the convective transfer from room air to inside partitions. Thus

$$h_{rti}F_{A_tA_i}(t_i - t_t)A_i = h_{ci}(t_a - t_i)A_i \qquad (5\text{–}64)$$

where h_{rti} = equivalent radiation coefficient (Eq. 4–113) for net transfer from inside partitions to the transmitting surfaces of the room.

$F_{A_tA_i}$ = shape factor of the transmitting surfaces with respect to energy emitted by the inside partitions.

h_{ci} = film coefficient for convective transfer from room air to inside partitions.

Solving Eq. 5–64 for $(t_a - t_i)$,

$$t_a - t_i = \frac{h_{rti}F_{A_tA_i}}{h_{ci}}(t_i - t_t) \qquad (5\text{–}65)$$

Adding $(t_i - t_t)$ to both sides of the equation,

$$(t_a - t_i) + (t_i - t_t) = t_a - t_t = \left(1 + \frac{h_{rti}F_{A_tA_i}}{h_{ci}}\right)(t_i - t_t)$$

or

$$t_a - t_t = \frac{h_{ci} + h_{rti}F_{A_tA_i}}{h_{ci}}(t_i - t_t) \qquad (5\text{–}66)$$

Dividing each side of Eq. 5–65 by each side of Eq. 5–66,

$$\frac{t_a - t_i}{t_a - t_t} = \frac{h_{rti}F_{A_tA_i}}{h_{ci} + h_{rti}F_{A_tA_i}} \qquad (5\text{–}67)$$

The order of magnitude of h_{ci} can be established as 0.4 and the order of magnitude of h_{rti} as unity. Then

$$\frac{t_a - t_i}{t_a - t_t} = \frac{F_{A_tA_i}}{0.4 + F_{A_tA_i}} \qquad (5\text{–}68)$$

In a room with one inside partition $F_{A_tA_i}$ is unity; hence

$$\left(\frac{t_a - t_i}{t_a - t_t}\right)_{\text{(1 non-transmitting surface)}} = \frac{1}{0.4 + 1} = \frac{1}{1.4} \qquad (5\text{–}69)$$

The required condition for establishing h'_r is that

$$h''_r(t_i - t_t) = h'_r(t_a - t_t)$$

or

$$h'_r = \left(\frac{t_i - t_t}{t_a - t_t}\right)h''_r = \left(1 - \frac{t_a - t_i}{t_a - t_t}\right)h''_r \qquad (5\text{–}70)$$

Substituting for $(t_a - t_i)/(t_a - t_t)$ from Eq. 5–69 into 5–70 gives

$$h'_{r\,\text{(1 non-transmitting surface)}} = \left(1 - \frac{1}{1.4}\right)h''_r = 0.286h''_r \qquad (5\text{–}71)$$

When two or more room surfaces are inside partitions, the value of $F_{A_t A_i}$ is obtained from the reciprocity theorem as

$$F_{A_t A_i} = \frac{A_t}{A_i} F_{A_i A_t} \qquad (5\text{-}72)$$

But $F_{A_i A_t}$ is approximated by A_i / A_e; hence

$$F_{A_t A_i} = \frac{A_t}{A_i} \frac{A_i}{A_e} \qquad (5\text{-}73)$$

For a cubical room, or as an approximation for a room of any average geometry,

$$F_{A_t A_{i(2\ \text{non-transmitting surfaces})}} = \frac{4}{2} \frac{2}{6} = 0.67 \qquad (5\text{-}74a)$$

$$F_{A_t A_{i(3\ \text{non-transmitting surfaces})}} = \frac{3}{3} \frac{3}{6} = 0.50 \qquad (5\text{-}74b)$$

$$F_{A_t A_{i(4\ \text{non-transmitting surfaces})}} = \frac{2}{4} \frac{4}{6} = 0.33 \qquad (5\text{-}74c)$$

$$F_{A_t A_{i(5\ \text{non-transmitting surfaces})}} = \frac{1}{5} \frac{5}{6} = 0.17 \qquad (5\text{-}74d)$$

Substituting each of the above values into Eq. 5–68, and then substituting the resultant numerical value of this temperature ratio into Eq. 5–70, gives

$$h'_{r(1\ \text{non-transmitting surface})} = 0.286 h''_r \qquad (5\text{-}75a)$$

$$h'_{r(2\ \text{non-transmitting surfaces})} = 0.374 h''_r \qquad (5\text{-}75b)$$

$$h'_{r(3\ \text{non-transmitting surfaces})} = 0.445 h''_r \qquad (5\text{-}75c)$$

$$h'_{r(4\ \text{non-transmitting surfaces})} = 0.548 h''_r \qquad (5\text{-}75d)$$

$$h'_{r(5\ \text{non-transmitting surfaces})} = 0.702 h''_r \qquad (5\text{-}75e)$$

Then substituting for h''_r from the equation (general case of the relationship given by Eqs. 5–60 through 5–63),

$$h''_r = h_r \frac{A_i}{A_e} \qquad (5\text{-}76)$$

into the above equations for h'_r,

$$h'_{r(1\ \text{non-transmitting surface})} = (0.286)(1/6)h_r = 0.048 h_r \qquad (5\text{-}77a)$$

$$h'_{r(2\ \text{non-transmitting surfaces})} = 0.125 h_r \qquad (5\text{-}77b)$$

$$h'_{r(3\ \text{non-transmitting surfaces})} = 0.223 h_r \qquad (5\text{-}77c)$$

$$h'_{r(4\ \text{non-transmitting surfaces})} = 0.365 h_r \qquad (5\text{-}77d)$$

$$h'_{r(5\ \text{non-transmitting surfaces})} = 0.585 h_r \qquad (5\text{-}77e)$$

The h'_r values given above are specifically applicable to a transmitting surface that has an over-all coefficient of the same order of magnitude as the average value U_t. These values can be used without significant error for walls, floor, ceiling, or double-glazed windows, but for single-glazed windows a correction should be applied. The magnitude of the correction will depend on the value of U_t; hence it is convenient to establish correction limits between U_t values for an average poorly insulated room and an average well-insulated room.

For the poorly insulated room, the U_t value will be selected as 0.3 and the combined inside film coefficient for the transmitting surfaces approximated as $h_t = 0.65$. For the glass, the over-all coefficient and the combined inside film coefficient will be taken as 0.8 and 1.2. Then

$$\frac{t_a - t_t}{t_a - t_o} = \frac{1/0.65}{1/0.3} = 0.462 \tag{5–78}$$

and

$$\frac{t_a - t_g}{t_a - t_o} = \frac{1/1.2}{1/0.8} = 0.667 \tag{5–79}$$

Dividing Eq. 5–79 by Eq. 5–78,

$$\frac{t_a - t_g}{t_a - t_t} = \frac{0.667}{0.462} = 1.444 \tag{5–80}$$

But from Eq. 5–68,

$$t_a - t_t = \frac{0.4 + F_{A_t A_i}}{F_{A_t A_i}} (t_a - t_i) \tag{5–81}$$

and substituting the expression for $(t_a - t_i)$ into Eq. 5–80,

$$\frac{t_a - t_i}{t_a - t_g} = \frac{F_{A_t A_i}}{1.444(0.4 + F_{A_t A_i})} \tag{5–82}$$

Then by analogy with Eq. 5–70,

$$h'_{rg} = \left(1 - \frac{t_a - t_i}{t_a - t_g}\right) h''_r \tag{5–83}$$

and

$$\frac{h'_{rg}}{h'_r} = \frac{1 - [F_{A_t A_i}/1.444(0.4 + F_{A_t A_i})]}{K} \tag{5–84}$$

where K is the coefficient in each of Eqs. 5–75a through 5–75e. Therefore

$$\left(\frac{h'_{rg}}{h'_r}\right)_{(1 \text{ non-transmitting surface})} = 1.77 \tag{5–85a}$$

$$\left(\frac{h'_{rg}}{h'_r}\right)_{(2 \text{ non-transmitting surfaces})} = 1.51 \tag{5–85b}$$

$$\left(\frac{h'_{rg}}{h'_r}\right)_{(3 \text{ non-transmitting surfaces})} = 1.38 \tag{5–85c}$$

$$\left(\frac{h'_{r\beta}}{h'_r}\right)_{(4 \text{ non-transmitting surfaces})} = 1.25 \tag{5–85d}$$

$$\left(\frac{h'_{rg}}{h'_r}\right)_{(5 \text{ non-transmitting surfaces})} = 1.13 \tag{5–85e}$$

For a well-insulated room, the U_t value will be taken as 0.1, all other terms having the same values as for the poorly insulated room. In this case, by the same procedure as above,

$$\frac{t_a - t_g}{t_a - t_t} = 4.337 \tag{5-86}$$

$$\frac{h'_{rg}}{h'_r} = \frac{1 - [F_{A_tA_i}/4.337(0.4 + F_{A_tA_i})]}{K} \tag{5-87}$$

and

$$\left(\frac{h'_{rg}}{h'_r}\right)_{\text{(1 non-transmitting surface)}} = 2.92 \tag{5-88a}$$

$$\left(\frac{h'_{rg}}{h'_r}\right)_{\text{(2 non-transmitting surfaces)}} = 2.29 \tag{5-88b}$$

$$\left(\frac{h'_{rg}}{h'_r}\right)_{\text{(3 non-transmitting surfaces)}} = 1.96 \tag{5-88c}$$

$$\left(\frac{h'_{rg}}{h'_r}\right)_{\text{(4 non-transmitting surfaces)}} = 1.63 \tag{5-88d}$$

$$\left(\frac{h'_{rg}}{h'_r}\right)_{\text{(5 non-transmitting surfaces)}} = 1.33 \tag{5-88e}$$

Table 5–23 provides a simplified means of evaluating h_r and h'_r. Previous discussion (Art. 5–3, page 190) has established that h_r is determined primarily as a function of the arithmetical mean of the temperatures of the two surfaces that are exchanging radiation. In the present case, however, the warmer surface is assumed to be at approximately the room air temperature (closely true for rooms with many non-transmitting surfaces); hence the arithmetical average of the two surface temperatures is

$$t_m = t_a - \frac{\Delta t_f}{2} \tag{5-89}$$

where t_m = arithmetical average surface temperature, °F.
        t_a = room air temperature.
        Δt_f = temperature drop across the inside film adjacent to the transmitting surface for which h_r is being evaluated.

As a first approximation the inside air temperature can be taken at the comfort level of 73.5 F. The value of Δt_f has already been obtained for walls, floors, and ceiling as given in Tables 5–20, 5–21, and 5–22, respectively. Thus entering Table 5–23 at known value of Δt_f permits reading the value of h_r corresponding to

$$h_r = (0.1713)(4)(t_m + 460)^3(10)^{-8} \tag{5-90}$$

As a further aid, the last five columns of Table 5–23, calculated from equations 5–77a through 5–77e, provide direct values of h'_r as a function of h_r and of the number of non-transmitting surfaces of the room.

TABLE 5–23

Equivalent Radiation Coefficient

		Values of h'_r Number of Non-transmitting Surfaces				
Δt_f	h_r	1	2	3	4	5
1	1.04	0.05	0.13	0.23	0.38	0.60
3	1.03	0.05	0.13	0.23	0.38	0.60
7	1.02	0.05	0.13	0.23	0.37	0.60
11	1.01	0.05	0.13	0.23	0.37	0.59
15	1.00	0.05	0.13	0.22	0.37	0.59
18	0.99	0.05	0.12	0.22	0.36	0.58
22	0.98	0.05	0.12	0.22	0.36	0.57
25	0.97	0.05	0.12	0.22	0.35	0.57
29	0.96	0.05	0.12	0.21	0.35	0.56
33	0.95	0.05	0.12	0.21	0.35	0.56
37	0.94	0.05	0.12	0.21	0.34	0.55
40	0.93	0.04	0.12	0.21	0.34	0.54
44	0.92	0.04	0.12	0.21	0.34	0.54
47	0.91	0.04	0.11	0.20	0.33	0.53
51	0.90	0.04	0.11	0.20	0.33	0.53
55	0.89	0.04	0.11	0.20	0.32	0.52
59	0.88	0.04	0.11	0.20	0.32	0.51
62	0.87	0.04	0.11	0.19	0.32	0.51
66	0.86	0.04	0.11	0.19	0.31	0.50
70	0.85	0.04	0.11	0.19	0.31	0.50

5–4. Evaluation of Equivalent Combined Inside Film Coefficient.

In Art. 5–2 the equivalent over-all coefficient was defined (Eq. 5–4b) and a procedure was established for evaluating transmission load in terms of an equivalent uniformly constructed room. In order for the equivalent room to have the same comfort characteristics as the actual room, it is necessary that the uniform inside surface temperature of the equivalent room equal the mean radiant temperature of the actual room. The average inside surface temperature, t_t, of transmitting sections of the enclosure (thus not taking account of interior partitions or other non-transmitting sections) is given by an equation in the form of Eq. 4–146:

$$\frac{t_a - t_t}{t_a - t_o} = \frac{1/h_t}{1/U_t} = r_{it}U_t \tag{5-91}$$

where r_{it} = average inside film resistance of all transmitting sections of the enclosure.

U_t = average over-all coefficient of heat transfer of all transmitting sections of the enclosure.

But

$$r_{it}U_t = \frac{r_{ig}U_gA_g}{A_t} + \frac{r_{iw}U_wA_w}{A_t} + \frac{r_{ic}U_cA_c}{A_t} + \frac{r_{if}U_fA_f}{A_t} \tag{5-92}$$

where A_t = total area of transmitting surface = $A_w + A_f + A_c + A_g$
$\qquad\qquad = A_e - A_i$

Then, substituting from Eq. 5–92 into Eq. 5–91 and solving for the average combined inside film coefficient h_t for all transmitting surfaces of the enclosure,

$$h_t = \frac{1}{r_{it}} = \frac{U_t}{(U_gA_g/A_t)/h_g + (U_wA_w/A_t)/h_w + (U_cA_c/A_t)/h_c + (U_fA_f/A_t)/h_f}$$
$$\tag{5-93}$$

Comparison of Eqs. 5–93 and 5–6 and noting that

$$U_t = \frac{A_e}{A_t} U_e \tag{5-94}$$

show that each term in the denominator on the right side of Eq. 5–93 consists of the combined film coefficient for the surface in question, divided into the corresponding term on the right side of Eq. 5–6 when multiplied by A_e/A_t; thus

$$h_t = \frac{(A_e/A_t)U_e}{[(K_g/h_g) + (K_w/h_w) + (K_c/h_c) + (K_f/h_f)](A_e/A_t)}$$
$$= \frac{U_e}{(K_g/h_g) + (K_w/h_w) + (K_c/h_c) + (K_f/h_f)} \tag{5-95}$$

where K terms are of the form $K_x = U_xA_x/A_e$. $\qquad\qquad\qquad$ (5–96)

With h_t and U_t known, it is now possible to calculate an equivalent inside film coefficient h_e for which the uniform inside surface temperature of the equivalent room will be equal to the mean radiant temperature (approximated by the average surface temperature) of the actual room:

$$\frac{t_a - ast}{t_a - t_o} = \frac{1/h_e}{1/U_e} = r_{ie}U_e \tag{5-97}$$

But

$$r_{ie}U_e = \frac{r_{it}U_tA_t}{A_e} + \frac{[(t_a - t_i)/(t_a - t_o)]A_i}{A_e} \tag{5-98}$$

From Eq. 5–68,

$$t_a - t_i = \frac{F_{A_tA_i}}{0.4 + F_{A_tA_i}} (t_a - t_t) \tag{5-99}$$

But

$$t_a - t_t = r_{it}U_t(t_a - t_o) \tag{5-100}$$

so

$$t_a - t_i = \frac{F_{A_tA_i}}{0.4 + F_{A_tA_i}} (r_{it}U_t)(t_a - t_o) \tag{5-101}$$

Substituting U_t from Eq. 5–94 into Eq. 5–101 and $(t_a - t_i)$ from Eq. 5–101 into Eq. 5–98 and solving for h_e give

$$h_e = \frac{1}{r_{ie}} = \frac{U_e}{[r_{it}U_e(A_e/A_t)(A_t/A_e)] + [F_{A_tA_i}/(0.4 + F_{A_tA_i})][r_{it}U_e(A_e/A_t)(A_i/A_e)]}$$

$$= \frac{1}{r_{it} + [F_{A_tA_i}/(0.4 + F_{A_tA_i})]r_{it}(A_i/A_\cdot)} \tag{5–102}$$

Values of $F_{A_tA_i}$ have been established as functions of the number of non-transmitting sections of room surface (refer to Art. 5–3); hence on substitution into Eq. 5–102,

$$h_{e_{(1 \text{ non-transmitting surface})}} = 0.875h_t \tag{5–103a}$$

$$h_{e_{(2 \text{ non-transmitting surfaces})}} = 0.762h_t \tag{5–103b}$$

$$h_{e_{(3 \text{ non-transmitting surfaces})}} = 0.643h_t \tag{5–103c}$$

$$h_{e_{(4 \text{ non-transmitting surfaces})}} = 0.525h_t \tag{5–103d}$$

$$h_{e_{(5 \text{ non-transmitting surfaces})}} = 0.401h_t \tag{5–103e}$$

5–5. Summary of Transmission-Load Relationships. With transmitting areas and over-all coefficients known, U_e is calculated by Eq. 5–6, h_t by Eq. 5–95, and h_e by the applicable form of Eqs. 5–103. With U_e and h_e known, the optimum comfort air temperature is calculated from Eq. 5–9 and the transmission load evaluated by Eq. 5–7.

5–6. Examples of Transmission-Load Calculation. A group of numerical examples will be presented to illustrate the procedures discussed in preceding articles. To emphasize the influence of particular factors, it will be convenient in some cases to use conditions much more extreme than would occur in actual practice. Thus, by comparison of a very poorly insulated enclosure with a very well insulated enclosure, the boundary conditions can be recognized and the effect of intermediate degrees of insulation then more readily estimated.

EXAMPLE 5–1. A room 20 ft by 20 ft by 10 ft high has interior partitions adjacent to identically heated rooms on two sides and has one 56.8 sq ft window in each exterior wall (see Fig. 7–1). Outside design air temperature of 0 F is applicable to roof, floor, and both exposed walls, and test has shown that the outside combined film resistance is likewise the same for roof, floor, and walls and is equal to 0.248. For the wall, r_w is equal to 1.71 and the wall contains one non-reflective air space. For the roof-ceiling combination, $r_c = 1.78$ and there is one non-reflective air space. The floor has a resistance r_f of 1.72; it is unfinished on the under side and so does not contain an air space. Glass resistance, r_g, is 0.112. Noting that this room is subject to extreme conditions of exposure and is uninsulated, calculate: (a) the equivalent over-all coefficient of heat transfer; (b) the optimum inside air temperature for thermal comfort based on t_c of 73.5 F; (c) the rate of heat loss by transmission.

Solution,[4] *First Approximation:* A first step is to determine the various unknown thermal coefficients.

The wall area is $(2)(20)(10)$ minus $(2)(56.8)$ or 286.4 sq ft, and $r_w + r_o = 1.71 + 0.248 = 1.958$.

Entering Table 5–14 for $r_w + r_o$ of 1.958 at t_o of 0 F gives the temperature drop across the air space (by interpolation) as 19.7 F and the convective conductance of the air space as 0.26. For a non-reflective air space, Table 5–18 gives the radiant conductance as 0.84 at t_o of 0 F. The air-space combined conductance is then 0.26 plus 0.84, or 1.10 Btu/(hr)(sq ft)(°F), and its resistance r_a is $1/1.10$, or 0.909. Then

$$\frac{1}{C_w} = 1.958 + 0.909 = 2.867$$

Entering Table 5–20 at $1/C_w$ of 2.867 and t_o of 0 F gives (by interpolation) the inside film temperature drop as 14.2 F and the convective film coefficient for the inside surface of the wall as 0.535. From Table 5–23, entering at Δt_f of 14.2 F, the corrected equivalent radiant coefficient for a room with two inside partitions is 0.13. Then, for the wall,

$$h_w = h_{cw} + h'_{rw} = 0.535 + 0.13 = 0.67$$

and

$$\frac{1}{U_w} = \frac{1}{C_w} + \frac{1}{h_w} = 2.867 + \frac{1}{0.67}$$

$$= 2.867 + 1.493 = 4.360$$

giving

$$U_w = \frac{1}{4.360} = 0.229$$

The roof-ceiling area is 400 sq ft and $r_c + r_o = 1.78 + 0.248 = 2.028$. From Table 5–17, at t_o of 0 F, the corresponding values of Δt and a_c for the air space are 18.0 F and 0.37. From Table 5–18 the value of a_r is 0.84; so,

$$a = a_c + a_r = 0.37 + 0.84 = 1.21$$

and

$$\frac{1}{C_c} = 2.028 + \frac{1}{1.21} = 2.854$$

From Table 5–22, Δt is 12.9 F and h_{cc} is 0.61, and from Table 5–23, h'_{rc} is 0.13. Therefore

$$h_c = h_{cc} + h'_{rc} = 0.61 + 0.13 = 0.74$$

and

$$\frac{1}{U_c} = \frac{1}{C_c} + \frac{1}{h_c} = 2.854 + \frac{1}{0.74}$$

$$= 2.854 + 1.351 = 4.205$$

giving

$$U_c = 0.238$$

[4] The accuracy of the data on which the thermal coefficients are based is not sufficient to justify more than two-place significance. As a matter of arithmetical convenience, however (in order to show the influence of different variables), the calculations in the examples are given to a greater number of places.

The floor area is 400 sq ft and $r_f + r_o = 1/C_f = 1.72 + 0.248 = 1.968$; from Table 5–21, Δt is 23.4 F and h_{cf} is 0.28, whereas from Table 5–23, h'_{rf} is 0.12. Then

$$\frac{1}{U_f} = 1.968 + \frac{1}{0.28 + 0.12} = 1.968 + 2.500 = 4.468$$

giving

$$U_f = 0.224$$

The glass area is $(2)(56.8)$, or 113.6 sq ft, and $r_g + r_o = 1/C_g = 0.112 + 0.248 = 0.3\ 0$; from Table 5–20, Δt is 49 F and h_{cg} is 0.72, whereas from Table 5–23, h'_{rg} is 0.11. The h'_{rg} value should be corrected, however, by a factor of 1.51, as given in Eq. 5–85b; thus $h'_{rg} = (1.51)(0.11) = 0.166$.

$$\frac{1}{U_g} = 0.360 + \frac{1}{0.72 + 0.166} = 0.360 + 1.129 = 1.489$$

giving

$$U_g = 0.672$$

(a) By Eq. 5–6,

$$U_e = \left[0.672\left(\frac{113.6}{1600}\right)\right] + \left[0.229\left(\frac{286.4}{1600}\right)\right] + \left[0.238\left(\frac{400}{1600}\right)\right]$$
$$+ \left[0.224\left(\frac{400}{1600}\right)\right]$$

$$= 0.04771 + 0.0410 + 0.0595 + 0.0560$$
$$= 0.2042 \text{ Btu/(hr)(sq ft)(}^\circ\text{F)}$$

(b) The equivalent combined inside film coefficient for the transmitting surfaces is given by Eq. 5–95 with the K_x terms as evaluated in part (a) of the solution:

$$h_t = \frac{0.2042}{\begin{array}{c}[0.0477/(0.72 + 0.166)] + [0.0410/(0.535 + 0.13)] \\ + [0.0595/(0.61 + 0.13)] + [0.0560/(0.28 + 0.12)]\end{array}}$$

$$= \frac{0.2042}{0.0538 + 0.0617 + 0.0804 + 0.1400}$$

$$= \frac{0.2042}{0.3359} = 0.608$$

Then, by Eq. 5–103b,

$$h_e = 0.762 h_t = (0.762)(0.608) = 0.463$$

and by Eq. 5–13a,

$$C_e = \frac{1}{(1/U_e) - (1/h_e)} = \frac{1}{(1/0.2042) - (1/0.463)}$$

$$= \frac{1}{4.897 - 2.160} = \frac{1}{2.737}$$

$$= 0.365 \text{ Btu/(hr)(sq ft)(}^\circ\text{F)}$$

The optimum air temperature (by Eq. 5–9) is

$$t_a = \frac{147 - 0}{2 - (1/0.463)(0.2042)}$$

$$= \frac{147}{1.559} = 94.3 \text{ F}$$

The excessively high inside temperature is due to the fact that the room is uninsulated and therefore has large heat losses. Obviously the occupants would not be comfortable at this temperature, but with average clothing they would not be "thermally" comfortable at any lower temperature. Thus the example establishes the fact that a poorly insulated structure located in a region of cold climate cannot be comfortably heated.

(c) Transmission loss (by Eq. 5–7) amounts to

$$q_t = U_e A_e (t_a - t_o) = (0.2042)(1600)(94.3) = 30{,}810 \text{ Btu/hr}$$

The above solution uses values of convective coefficients based on an assumed 73.5 F inside air temperature and is calculated from assumed "standard" film and air-space coefficients. A revised solution will utilize correction coefficients based on the calculated inside air temperature of 94.3 F and on the film and air-space coefficients obtained in the first solution.

Second Approximation: For the wall,

$$\Delta t_{\text{air space}} = \frac{r_a}{1/U_w} (t_a - t_o) = (0.909)(0.229)(94.3)$$

$$= 19.6 \text{ F}$$

and the corresponding value of a_c from Table 5–14 is 0.25. The increase of inside air temperature by $94.3 - 73.5$, or 20.8 F, is equivalent (in using Table 5–18) to an outside air temperature rise of equal amount; hence a_r is read at 20.8 F as 0.89. Then

$$a = 0.25 + 0.89 = 1.14$$

$$r_a = \frac{1}{1.14} = 0.877$$

$$\frac{1}{C_w} = 1.958 + 0.877 = 2.835$$

Also

$$\Delta t_{\text{film}} = \left(\frac{1}{0.67}\right)(0.229)(94.3) = 32.2 \text{ F}$$

and the corresponding value of h_c from Table 5–20 is 0.65; h_r' from Table 5–23 is 0.12; then h_w is 0.65 plus 0.12, or 0.77.

$$\frac{1}{U_w} = \frac{1}{C_w} + \frac{1}{h_w} = 2.835 + \frac{1}{0.77}$$

$$= 2.835 + 1.299 = 4.134$$

$$U_w = 0.242$$

For the roof-ceiling,

$$\Delta t_{\text{air space}} = \left(\frac{1}{1.21}\right)(0.238)(94.3) = 18.5 \text{ F}$$

so, a_c is unchanged at 0.37. The value of a_r (from Table 5–18 for $t_o = 20.8$ F) is 0.89; hence

$$a = 0.37 + 0.89 = 1.26$$

$$r_a = \frac{1}{1.26} = 0.79$$

$$\frac{1}{C_c} = 2.028 + 0.79 = 2.818$$

Also

$$\Delta t_{\text{film}} = \left(\frac{1}{0.74}\right)(0.238)(94.3) = 30.3 \text{ F}$$

and hence $h_{cc} = 0.81$ and $h_c = 0.81 + 0.12 = 0.93$.

$$\frac{1}{U_c} = \frac{1}{C_c} + \frac{1}{h_c} = 2.818 + \frac{1}{0.93}$$

$$= 2.818 + 1.075 = 3.993$$

$$U_c = 0.250$$

For the floor,

$$\Delta t_{\text{film}} = \left(\frac{1}{0.40}\right)(0.224)(94.3) = 52.8 \text{ F}$$

and hence $h_{cf} = 0.34$ and $h_f = 0.34 + 0.11 = 0.45$.

$$\frac{1}{U_f} = \frac{1}{C_c} + \frac{1}{h_c} = 1.968 + \frac{1}{0.45}$$

$$= 1.968 + 2.222 = 4.190$$

$$U_f = 0.239$$

For the glass,

$$\Delta t_{\text{film}} = \left(\frac{1}{0.886}\right)(0.672)(94.3) = 71.5 \text{ F}$$

and hence $h_{cg} = 0.80$ and $h_g = 0.80 + 0.166 = 0.97$.

$$\frac{1}{U_g} = \frac{1}{C_g} + \frac{1}{h_g} = 0.360 + \frac{1}{0.97}$$

$$= 0.360 + 1.031 = 1.391$$

$$U_g = 0.719$$

Then

$$U_e = \left[0.719\,\frac{113.6}{1600}\right] + \left[0.242\,\frac{286.4}{1600}\right] + \left[0.250\,\frac{400}{1600}\right] + \left[0.239\,\frac{400}{1600}\right]$$

$$= 0.0510 + 0.0433 + 0.0625 + 0.0598 = 0.2166$$

$$h_t = \frac{0.2166}{(0.0510/0.91) + (0.0433/0.77) + (0.0625/0.93) + (0.0598/0.45)}$$

$$= \frac{0.2166}{0.0560 + 0.0562 + 0.0672 + 0.1329} = \frac{0.2166}{0.3123}$$

$$= 0.694$$

$$h_e = 0.762h_t = (0.762)(0.694) = 0.529$$

$$C_e = \frac{1}{(1/0.2166) - (1/0.529)}$$

$$= \frac{1}{4.6168 - 1.8904} = \frac{1}{2.7264} = 0.367$$

$$t_a = \frac{147 - 0}{2 - (1/0.529)(0.2166)}$$

$$= \frac{147}{1.591} = 92.4\ \text{F}$$

$$q_t = (0.2166)(1600)(92.4) = 32{,}022\ \text{Btu/hr}$$

In order to show the close approach of the second trial, a third solution will be obtained, using the data of the second solution.

Third Approximation: For the wall,

$$\Delta t_{\text{air space}} = (0.877)(0.242)(92.4) = 19.6\ \text{F}$$

which is the same value as before.

$$\Delta t_{\text{film}} = \left(\frac{1}{0.77}\right)(0.242)(92.4) = 29.0\ \text{F}$$

giving h_c of 0.63. Then

$$\frac{1}{U_w} = 2.835 + \frac{1}{0.75} = 4.168$$

$$U_w = 0.240$$

For the roof-ceiling,

$$\Delta t_{\text{air space}} = (0.79)(0.250)(92.4) = 18.2\ \text{F}$$

so, a_c is unchanged; a_r is also unchanged.

$$\Delta t_{\text{film}} = \left(\frac{1}{0.93}\right)(0.250)(92.4) = 24.8\ \text{F}$$

so, h_{cc} is 0.75 and h_c is 0.87. Thus

$$\frac{1}{U_c} = 2.818 + \frac{1}{0.87} = 3.967$$

$$U_c = 0.252.$$

For the floor,

$$\Delta t_{\text{film}} = \left(\frac{1}{0.45}\right)(0.239)(92.4) = 49.1 \text{ F}$$

so, the coefficients remain unchanged.

For the glass,

$$\Delta t_{\text{film}} = \left(\frac{1}{0.97}\right)(0.719)(92.4) = 68.5 \text{ F}$$

and the coefficients remain unchanged.

$$U_e = 0.0510 + \left[0.240 \left(\frac{286.4}{1600}\right)\right] + \left[0.252 \left(\frac{400}{1600}\right)\right] + 0.0598$$

$$= 0.0510 + 0.0430 + 0.0630 + 0.0598 = 0.2168$$

$$h_t = \frac{0.2168}{0.0560 + (0.0430/0.75) + (0.0625/0.87) + 0.1329}$$

$$= \frac{0.2168}{0.0560 + 0.0573 + 0.0718 + 0.1329}$$

$$= \frac{0.2168}{0.3180} = 0.682$$

$$h_e = (0.762)(0.682) = 0.520$$

$$t_a = \frac{147 - 0}{2 - (1/0.520)(0.2168)}$$

$$= \frac{147}{1.583} = 92.9 \text{ F}$$

$$q_t = (0.2168)(1600)(92.9) = 32,225 \text{ Btu/hr}$$

The difference between results for the second and third trials is negligible and, since this example is for an extreme case, it follows that a third approximation will never be required.

This same room is used in Chapter 7 and the transmission load is calculated (Art. 7–4) by the more complex rational method. The result from the second approximation above agrees within 96 per cent with the transmission load as calculated by the rational method.

EXAMPLE 5–2. For the room of Example 5–1 evaluate the over-all coefficients, using ASHRAE "standard" values of air-space conductances and film coefficients; (note that the ASHRAE values of the corresponding resistances are given in a table in Art. 5–3, page 168). Determine the corresponding value of U_e and calculate the optimum comfort temperature and the rate of transmission loss.

Solution:

$$U_w = \frac{1}{r_i + r_w + r_a + r_o} = \frac{1}{0.6849 + 1.71 + 0.9710 + 0.170}$$

$$= \frac{1}{3.5359} = 0.2828$$

$$h_{iw} = 1.46$$

$$U_c = \frac{1}{0.6135 + 1.78 + 0.8475 + 0.170}$$

$$= \frac{1}{3.4110} = 0.2932$$

$$h_{ic} = 1.63$$

$$U_f = \frac{1}{0.9259 + 1.72 + 0.170}$$

$$= \frac{1}{2.8159} = 0.3551$$

$$h_{if} = 1.08$$

$$U_g = 1.13 \quad \text{and} \quad h_{ig} = 1.5 \text{ (from } ASHRAE \text{ } Guide)$$

Then

$$U_e = \left[(1.13)\left(\frac{113.6}{1600}\right) \right] + \left[(0.2828)\left(\frac{286.4}{1600}\right) \right]$$

$$+ \left[(0.2932)\left(\frac{400}{1600}\right) \right] + \left[(0.3551)\left(\frac{400}{1600}\right) \right]$$

$$= 0.0802 + 0.0506 + 0.0733 + 0.0888$$

$$= 0.2929$$

$$h_t = \frac{0.2929}{(0.0802/1.50) + (0.0506/1.46) + (0.0733/1.63) + (0.0888/1.08)}$$

$$= \frac{0.2929}{0.0535 + 0.0347 + 0.0450 + 0.0822} = \frac{0.2929}{0.2154}$$

$$= 1.3598$$

$$h_e = (0.762)(1.3598) = 1.0362$$

$$t_a = \frac{147 - 0}{2 - (1/1.0362)(0.2929)} = \frac{147}{1.717}$$

$$= 85.6 \text{ F}$$

$$q_t = (0.2929)(1600)(85.6) = 40,116 \text{ Btu/hr}$$

The lower air temperature and increased transmission loss resulting from use of "standard" coefficients are both attributable to the use of combined inside film coefficients which greatly overemphasize the effect of radiation. An exact quantitative evaluation of such coefficients is carried out in Chapter 7 (see Art. 7–5), and it is there established that the procedure on which

Table 5–23 is based is in close agreement with the results of a rational heat-balance analysis of this same room. Note that the U_e value for the "standard" room is $(0.2929/0.2166)100$, or 135 per cent of that for the room of Example 5–1, but the transmission loss in the first case is $(40,116/32,022)100$, or 125 per cent greater; the difference is, of course, due to the lower calculated inside air temperature in the latter case.

In one other respect the comparison of results of Example 5–1 and 5–2 is interesting. In many cases the dependence of optimum inside air tempera-ture on outside air temperature is not taken into account, and design trans-mission load is erroneously calculated by using the inside air temperature as equal to the optimum inside thermal level. If this were done for the room of Example 5–2, the resultant transmission loss would be $(73.5/85.6)40,116$, or 34,443 Btu/hr. This value is 8 per cent greater than the value obtained in Example 5–1 by use of the recommended procedure.

EXAMPLE 5–3. As the outside air temperature rises, the temperature drop across films and air spaces decreases, and the values of h_c and a_c decrease, whereas h_r and a_r increase. For the room of Example 5–1, evaluate U_e when the outside air temperature is close to the inside temperature and the temperature drops across all films and air spaces are of the order of 2 F.

Solution: From Table 5–14 for a Δt of 2 F, the corresponding value of a_c for the wall air space is 0.11, and from Table 5–23, the value of h_r (equal to a_r for the non-reflective air space) is 1.04. Then $a = 0.11 + 1.04 = 1.15$, and

$$\frac{1}{C_w} = 1.958 + \left(\frac{1}{1.15}\right) = 2.828$$

From Table 5–20 at Δt of 2 F, h_{cw} is 0.32, and from Table 5–23, h_r' is 0.13; so, $h_w = 0.45$ and

$$\frac{1}{U_w} = 2.828 + \left(\frac{1}{0.45}\right) = 5.050$$

$$U_w = 0.198$$

For the roof-ceiling, Table 5–17 gives a_c as 0.17 and a_r is the same as for the wall (1.04); so, a is equal to 1.21, which is the same value as for 0 F. From Table 5–22 at 2 F, read h_{cc} as 0.32; so, $h_c = 0.32 + 0.13 = 0.45$, and

$$\frac{1}{U_c} = 2.854 + \left(\frac{1}{0.45}\right) = 5.076$$

$$U_c = 0.197$$

For the floor, from Table 5–21, h_{cf} is 0.15; hence $h_f = 0.15 + 0.13 = 0.28$, and

$$\frac{1}{U_f} = 1.968 + \left(\frac{1}{0.28}\right) = 5.539$$

$$U_f = 0.181$$

For the glass,

$$h_g = 1.51 h_w = (1.51)(0.45) = 0.680$$

$$\frac{1}{U_g} = 0.360 + \left(\frac{1}{0.680}\right) = 1.831$$

$$U_g = 0.546$$

$$U_e = \left[(0.546)\left(\frac{116.4}{1600}\right)\right] + \left[(0.198)\left(\frac{283.6}{1600}\right)\right]$$

$$+ \left[(0.197)\left(\frac{400}{1600}\right)\right] + \left[(0.181)\left(\frac{400}{1600}\right)\right]$$

$$= 0.0397 + 0.0351 + 0.0493 + 0.0453$$

$$= 0.1694$$

Thus in warm weather the rate of transmission loss per degree inside-to-outside air temperature difference for this room is $[(0.2168 - 0.1694)/0.2168]100$, or 22 per cent less than the corresponding transmission loss at 0 F.

EXAMPLE 5–4. For the room of Example 5–1 determine the ratio of transmission losses for steady-state conditions with outside air temperature at 0 F and at 72.5 F.

Solution: With outside air temperature at 72.5 F, the optimum inside air temperature would be practically equal to the optimum thermal level, or 73.5 F. The equivalent over-all coefficient at t_o of 72.5 F would be very close to the value of 0.1694, as calculated in Example 5–3. With outside air temperature at 0 F as in Example 5–1, the corresponding values of U_e and t_a are 0.2168 and 92.9 F. The ratio of transmission losses is therefore

$$\frac{U_{e_1}(t_a - t_o)_1}{U_{e_2}(t_a - t_o)_2} = \frac{0.2168(92.9 - 0)}{0.1694(73.5 - 72.5)} = \frac{20.1}{0.169} = 119$$

This result strikingly demonstrates that the rate of transmission loss increases with decreasing temperature at a rate far greater than the rate of change of the nominal temperature difference between assumed, fixed inside-air temperature and outside-air temperature. Thus, if the inside-air temperature were assumed fixed at 73.5 F, the ratio of temperature difference would be $(73.5 - 0)/(73.5 - 72.5)$, or 73.5, which is less than two-thirds of the ratio of transmission load. In this particular case the room is uninsulated; so, the situation is extreme but is indicative of the effect of both increasing t_a and increasing U_e with decreasing t_o.

EXAMPLE 5–5. The enclosure of Example 5–1 is to be altered by adding 3 in. of insulation with $k = 0.27$ Btu/(hr)(sq ft)(°F/ft) as used in Table 5–2, in the wall air space, and 2 in. of fibrous insulation together with one layer of aluminum foil as facing on one side of the ceiling-roof air space. The crawl space under the floor will be closed, so that design air temperature under the floor can be taken as 40 F and the film coefficient under the floor will be evaluated in the same way as the ceiling film coefficient. Windows will be double-glazed. Determine optimum inside-air comfort temperature and transmission losses.

Solution: The revised wall resistance, including the resistance of the 3 in. of insulation, is

$$r_w = 1.71 + \frac{3}{0.27} = 12.82$$

and

$$r_w + r_o = 12.82 + 0.248 = 13.07$$

From Table 5–14, a_c is 0.16; so, $a = 0.16 + 0.84 = 1.00$, and

$$\frac{1}{C_w} = 13.07 + 1.00 = 14.07$$

From Table 5–20, h_{cw} is 0.38 and Δt is 4 F, and from Table 5–23 at 4 F, h'_{rw} is 0.13; so, h_w is 0.51.

$$\frac{1}{U_w} = 14.07 + \frac{1}{0.51} = 16.03$$

$$U_w = 0.0624$$

For the roof-ceiling combination, the resistance of the insulation is 2/0.27, or 7.41. The air-space convective conductance, from Table 5–17, is 0.27. The equivalent radiation coefficient (Table 5–18) would be 0.84 if the air space were black, but since one side is of aluminum foil, the emissivity for the air space (based on e_1 of 0.05 and e_2 of 0.90) is, from Table 5–19, 0.05: thus $a_r = (0.05)$ $(0.84) = 0.0420$, and the combined air-space conductance is $0.27 + 0.04$ or 0.31. Then

$$\frac{1}{C_c} = 1.78 + 0.248 + 7.41 + \frac{1}{0.31} = 12.66$$

From Table 5–22, Δt at $1/C_c$ of 12.66 is 4 F and h_{cc} is 0.39; then $h_c = 0.39 + 0.13 = 0.52$, and

$$\frac{1}{U_c}' = 12.66 + \frac{1}{0.52} = 14.58$$

$$U_c = 0.0686$$

For the floor the convective film coefficient in the crawl space will be taken at the same value that applied to the ceiling (0.39) and the radiation fraction will be of the order of 0.81, giving a combined h of 1.20 and $1/C_f$ of 1.72 plus 1/1.2, or 2.55. The value of h_{cf} is obtained by entering Table 5–21 at $1/C_f$ of 2.55 and extrapolating to t_o of +40 F to estimate h_{cf} as 0.21, giving $h_f = 0.21 + 0.13 = 0.34$. Then

$$\frac{1}{U_f} = 2.55 + \frac{1}{0.34} = 5.49$$

$$U_f = 0.182$$

For the double-glazed window,

$$r_g + r_o = 0.112 + 0.112 + 0.248 = 0.472$$

From Table 5–14, a_{cg} is 0.30, and from Table 5–18, a_r is 0.84; so, a is $0.30 + 0.84 = 1.14$. Then

$$\frac{1}{C_g} = 0.472 + \frac{1}{1.14} = 1.349$$

From Table 5–20 Δt is 8 F and $h_{cg} = 0.45$. From Table 5–23, h_r' is 0.13, but this should be corrected by 2.29, as shown in Eq. 5–88b; hence

$$h_{rg}' = (2.29)(0.13) = 0.298$$

Then $h_g = 0.45 + 0.298 = 0.748$, and

$$\frac{1}{U_g} = 1.349 + \frac{1}{0.748} = 2.686$$

$$U_g = 0.372$$

By Eq. 5–6,

$$U_e = \left[0.372\left(\frac{113.6}{1600}\right) \right] + \left[0.0624\left(\frac{286.4}{1600}\right) \right]$$

$$+ \left[0.0686\left(\frac{400}{1600}\right) \right] + \left[0.182\left(\frac{73.5 - 40}{73.5 - 0}\right)\left(\frac{400}{1600}\right) \right]$$

$$= 0.0264 + 0.0112 + 0.0172 + 0.0207$$

$$= 0.07550$$

By Eq. 5–95,

$$h_t = \frac{0.0755}{(0.0264/1.14) + (0.0112/0.51) + (0.0172/0.52) + (0.0207/0.34)}$$

$$= \frac{0.0755}{0.02316 + 0.02196 + 0.03308 + 0.06088}$$

$$= \frac{0.0755}{0.1391} = 0.543$$

$$h_e = (0.762)(0.543) = 0.414$$

$$t_a = \frac{147 - 0}{2 - (1/0.414)(0.0755)}$$

$$= \frac{147}{1.818} = 80.9 \text{ F}$$

The transmission load is

$$q_t = (0.0743)(1600)(80.9) = 9617 \text{ Btu/hr}$$

Comparing the above results with those from Example 5–1 brings out the fact that the addition of insulation has led to a much more reasonable value of the inside air temperature. Further, the transmission losses for the insulated room are only 9617/32,022, or 30.0 per cent of those for the uninsulated room (second approximation) even though the revised, equivalent over-all coefficient is 0.0755/0.2166, or 34.9 per cent of the value for the uninsulated enclosure. Then the lower inside air temperature of the insulated house is responsible for a reduction in transmission load substantially greater than the reduction due to increased insulation alone.

EXAMPLE 5–6. If the thermal level in the room used in Examples 5–1 and 5–5 were lowered from 73.5 F to 68 F, what would be the corresponding optimum inside-air comfort temperatures when outside air temperature is 0 F?

Solution: The quotient of temperature drop from inside air to thermal level divided by temperature drop from inside air to outside air will be a constant for any given structure. Thus, for the uninsulated enclosure of Example 5–1,

$$\frac{t_a - t_c}{t_a - t_o} = \frac{92.4 - 73.5}{92.4 - 0} = 0.205$$

Hence, as either t_c or t_o changes,

$$t_a = \frac{(t_c - 0.205 t_o)}{0.795}$$

For a 68 F thermal level with t_o of 0 F,

$$t_{a_{\text{uninsul}}} = \frac{68}{0.795} = 85.5 \text{ F}$$

For the insulated structure of Example 5–5,

$$\frac{t_a - t_c}{t_a - t_o} = \frac{80.9 - 68}{80.9 - 0} = 0.159$$

hence as either t_c or t_a changes,

$$t_a = \frac{t_c - 0.159 t_o}{0.841}$$

and if the thermal level were lowered to 68 F, with $t_o = 0$ F,

$$t_{a_{\text{insul}}} = \frac{68}{0.841} = 80.9 \text{ F}$$

EXAMPLE 5–7. The relatively high, design inside-air temperatures obtained in Examples 5–1 and 5–5 may seem somewhat unrealistic. Realizing that design outside-air temperature occurs only a small percentage of the time, it will be helpful to calculate the optimum inside-air temperature that would be applicable during the greater part of the heating season. For outside-air temperature of 40 F, determine the corresponding inside-air temperature for the enclosure when uninsulated (Example 5–1) and when well insulated (Example 5–5).

Solution: By the method used in the solution of Example 5–6, but holding the thermal level constant while changing t_o,

$$t_{a_{\text{uninsul}}} = \frac{t_c - 0.205 t_o}{0.795}$$

$$= \frac{73.5 - (0.205)(40)}{0.795} = 82.1 \text{ F}$$

$$t_{a_{\text{insul}}} = \frac{73.5 - (0.159)(40)}{0.841} = 79.8 \text{ F}$$

EXAMPLE 5–8. For the same room with thermal level at 68 F, calculate t_a when $t_o = 40$ F.

Solution: As in the solution of Example 5–6,

$$t_{a_{\text{uninsul}}} = \frac{68 - (0.205)(40)}{0.795} = 75.2 \text{ F}$$

$$t_{a_{\text{insul}}} = \frac{68 - (0.159)(40)}{0.841} = 73.3 \text{ F}$$

EXAMPLE 5–9. For the insulated room (Example 5–5) calculate the optimum inside air temperature and the transmission load when over-all coefficients are evaluated but using the "standard" values of air-space conductances and of film conductances.

Solution: Using "standard" values from the table in Art. 5–3, page 168, and using other thermal coefficients as evaluated in the solutions of Examples 5–1 and 5–5,

$$U_w = \frac{1}{r_i + r_w + r_{\text{ins}} + r_a + r_o}$$

$$= \frac{1}{0.6849 + 1.71 + 11.11 + 0.971 + 0.170} = \frac{1}{14.64}$$

$$= 0.0683$$

$$U_c = \frac{1}{r_i + r_c + r_{\text{ins}} + r_a + r_o}$$

$$= \frac{1}{0.6135 + 1.78 + 7.41 + 3.52 + 0.170} = \frac{1}{13.49}$$

$$= 0.0741$$

$$U_f = \frac{1}{r_i + r_f + r_o} = \frac{1}{0.9259 + 1.72 + 0.6135} = \frac{1}{3.259}$$

$$= 0.307$$

$$U_g = 0.55 \quad \text{and} \quad h_{ig} = 1.5 \quad \text{(from } ASHRAE \text{ } Guide)$$

Then

$$U_e = \left[(0.55)\left(\frac{113.6}{1600}\right) \right] + \left[(0.0682)\left(\frac{286.4}{1600}\right) \right] + \left[(0.0741)\left(\frac{400}{1600}\right) \right]$$

$$+ \left[(0.307)\left(\frac{73.5 - 40}{73.5 - 0}\right)\left(\frac{400}{1600}\right) \right]$$

$$= 0.0391 + 0.0122 + 0.0185 + 0.0350 = 0.1048$$

$$h_t = \frac{0.1048}{(0.0391/1.5) + (0.0122/1.46) + (0.0185/1.63) + (0.0350/1.08)}$$

$$= \frac{0.1048}{0.0261 + 0.00836 + 0.0113 + 0.0324}$$

$$= \frac{0.1048}{0.0782} = 1.340$$

$$h_e = (0.762)(1.340) = 1.021$$

$$t_a = \frac{147 - 0}{2 - 1/(1.021)(0.1048)} = \frac{147}{1.897} = 77.5 \text{ F}$$

$$q_t = (0.1048)(1600)(77.5) = 12,995 \text{ Btu/hr}$$

The above results, as compared with the transmission load of 9617 Btu/hr from Example 5–5, show that the excessive radiant transfer assumed in the "standard" film coefficients causes them to be much too conservative when used for well-insulated structures. In this case the added transmission load due to use of "standard" values is 12,995 − 9617, or 3378 Btu/hr, which is 35.1 per cent higher than the losses calculated (in Example 5–5) by the method which the authors recommend. The 35 per cent greater loss is in close agreement with the $[(0.1048 − 0.0755)/0.0755]100$, or 39 per cent, increase in U_e when using "standard" coefficients, but it has increased over the 25 per cent greater loss that was noted for the use of "standard" coefficients with the uninsulated structure. The increase results from the smaller difference between calculated inside air temperature for the insulated structure.

If the "standard" coefficients were used in an analysis in which t_a was assumed at the 73.5 F thermal level, the resultant transmission loss would be

$$q_t = (0.1048)(1600)(73.5) = 12,324 \text{ Btu/hr}$$

Thus it is evident that in calculations made by the customary method (using "standard" coefficients and an assigned design inside-air temperature), the percentage error will be greater in insulated than in uninsulated structures, and the compensating effect of fixed air temperature will decrease in significance as the degree of insulation increases.

EXAMPLE 5–10. The structure of Example 5–1 is poorly insulated; that of Example 5–5 is well insulated except for the floor. Consider now, as an extreme example of an enclosure with low heat loss, that the flooring with thermal resistance of 1.72 now has 3 in. of fibrous insulation added. It is again considered, as in Example 5–1, to be over an open crawl space in which air temperature is 0 F and film resistance is 0.248; the floor has no air space. (a) Evaluate t_a and U_e for film coefficients derived by the recommended method. (b) Repeat a with "standard" coefficients. (c) Compare results of a and b.

Solution: (a) The only over-all coefficient that differs from those obtained in the solution of Example 5–5 is that of the floor. Thus

$$\frac{1}{C_f} = r_f + r_{\text{ins}} + r_o = 1.72 + \frac{3}{0.27} + 0.248 = 13.08$$

From Table 5–21 at $1/C_f$ of 13.08 and t_o of 0 F, read the floor film temperature drop as 5 F and h_{cf} as 0.19. From Table 5–23 at Δt of 5 F and for two non-transmitting room surfaces, read h'_{rf} as 0.13. The combined floor film is therefore 0.19 plus 0.13, or 0.32, and

$$\frac{1}{U_f} = 13.08 + \frac{1}{0.32} = 13.08 + 3.13 = 16.21$$

$$U_f = 0.0617$$

The value of U_e is then obtained from that of Example 5–5 by correction.

$$U_e = 0.0755 - 0.0207 + 0.0617\left(\frac{400}{1600}\right)$$

$$= 0.0755 - 0.0207 + 0.0154 = 0.0702$$

and h_t is likewise obtained by correction.

$$h_t = \frac{0.0702}{0.1391 - 0.06088 + (0.0154/0.32)}$$

$$= \frac{0.0702}{0.1263} = 0.556$$

$$h_e = (0.762)(0.556) = 0.424$$

$$t_a = \frac{147 - 0}{2 - (1/0.424)(0.0702)}$$

$$= \frac{147}{1.834} = 80.2 \text{ F}$$

The transmission load is

$$q_t = (0.0702)(1600)(80.2) = 9008 \text{ Btu/hr}$$

(b) Using the "standard" inside and outside film coefficients,

$$\frac{1}{U_f} = \frac{1}{r_i + r_f + r_{\text{ins}} + r_o} = \frac{1}{0.9259 + 1.72 + (3/0.27) + 0.6135}$$

$$= \frac{1}{14.37} = 0.0696$$

The value of U_e is obtained from that of Example 5–9 by correction.

$$U_e = 0.1048 - 0.0350 + 0.0696\left(\frac{400}{1600}\right)$$

$$= 0.1048 - 0.0350 + 0.0174 = 0.0872$$

$$h_t = 0.0872/(0.0261 + 0.00836 + 0.0113 + 0.0174/1.08)$$

$$= 0.0872/0.0619 = 1.409$$

$$h_e = (0.762)(1.409) = 1.074$$

$$t_a = (147 - 0)/[2 - (1/1.074)(0.0872)]$$

$$= 147/1.919 = 76.6 \text{ F}$$

$$q_t = (0.0872)(1600)(76.6) = 10{,}687 \text{ Btu/hr}$$

(c) As a result of the floor insulation the U_e and the transmission losses for the room with "standard" coefficients have become $(0.0872/0.0702)100$, or 124 per cent, and $(10{,}687/9008)100$, or 119 per cent, respectively, of the values for the same room with film coefficients and air-space coefficients evaluated by the method of Example 5–1. If transmission losses were calculated with "standard" coefficients on the basis of an inside air temperature at the comfort level of 73.5 F,

$$q_t = (0.0872)(1600)(73.5) = 10,255 \text{ Btu/hr}$$

or $(10,255/9008)100 = 114$ per cent of the value based on the recommended procedure.

EXAMPLE 5–11. The over-all coefficient of heat transfer for the wall of the enclosure in Examples 5–1 and 5–5 was computed by neglecting the effect of the studs. Recompute U_w on the assumption of parallel heat transfer through the studs and air space of Example 5–1 and through the series path consisting of insulation and air space of Example 5–5. The pine studs are nominally 2 in. by 4 in. (actually $1\frac{5}{8}$ in. by $3\frac{5}{8}$ in.) on 16-in. centers and have a thermal conductivity of 0.80 Btu/(hr)(sq ft)(°F/in.).

Solution: In Example 5–1 the conductance a of the air space was found as 1.1. Then, by Eq. 5–37,

$$r'_a = \frac{1}{(0.9)(1.1) + [0.1/(3.58/0.8)]} = 0.988$$

$$a_{\text{corrected}} = 1.012$$

Then

$$\frac{1}{C_w} = r_o + r_w + r_a = 0.248 + 1.71 + 0.988 = 2.946$$

The value of h_w remains unchanged at 0.67; hence

$$\frac{1}{U_w} = 2.946 + \frac{1}{0.67} = 2.946 + 1.493 = 4.439$$

$$U_w = \frac{1}{4.439} = 0.225$$

The corrected value of U_w for the uninsulated wall is within 2 per cent of the uncorrected value; hence, for such a wall, the framing can be neglected. This is particularly true because neglect of framing *for the uninsulated wall* gives a higher, and hence a more conservative, value of U_w.

For the insulated wall of Example 5–5 the resistance of the 3 in. of insulation was determined as 3/0.27, or 11.11, and the resistance of the adjacent air space was 1.00. The resistance across insulation plus air space is given by Eq. 5–36 as

$$r''_a = r_a + r_{\text{ins}} = 1.00 + 11.11 = 12.11$$

Then, by Eq. 5–38,

$$r'_a = \frac{1}{0.0966} = 10.35$$

$$a_{\text{corrected}} = 0.0966$$

Then

$$\frac{1}{C_w} = 1.71 + 10.35 + 0.248 = 12.31$$

and h_w is found to remain unchanged at 0.51. Thus

$$\frac{1}{U_w} = 12.31 + \frac{1}{0.51} = 14.27$$

$$U_w = 0.0701$$

The corrected U_w is greater than the uncorrected value; hence use of the uncorrected value would lead to a non-conservative error of

$$[(0.0701 - 0.0624)/0.0701]100,$$

or 11 per cent, in wall transmission losses. Thus, for uninsulated air spaces, a framing correction can be safely neglected, but for insulated framing spaces—whether insulation is fibrous or reflective—a correction is desirable.

Note: The additional heat transmission through the wall would be of the order of

$$\Delta q_t = (0.0701 - 0.0624)(286.4)(80.9) = 232 \text{ Btu/hr}$$

indicating that the total transmission load, as calculated in Example 5–5, is in error by approximately $[232/(9617 + 232)]100$, or 2 per cent.

EXAMPLE 5–12. As a thermal condition intermediate between those of the enclosure of Examples 5–1 and 5–5, consider that the room is insulated as in Example 5–5 but that the closed crawl space below the floor is at outside temperature (0 F).

Solution: All coefficients have the same values as in Example 5–5; in calculating U_e, however, the term for the floor is not corrected for higher crawl-space temperature. Thus

$$U_e = 0.0264 + 0.0112 + 0.0172 + 0.0455 = 0.1003$$

$$h_t = \frac{0.1003}{0.02316 + 0.02196 + 0.03308 + (0.0455/0.34)}$$

$$= \frac{0.1003}{0.213} = 0.471$$

$$h_e = (0.762)(0.471) = 0.359$$

$$t_a = \frac{147 - 0}{2 - (1/0.359)(0.1003)}$$

$$= \frac{147}{1.7206} = 85.4 \text{ F}$$

$$q_t = (0.1003)(1600)(85.4) = 13,705 \text{ Btu/hr}$$

EXAMPLE 5–13. To complete the investigation of the enclosure in question, consider that it is insulated as in Example 5–10 and that the crawl space is closed with a combined film on the underside of the floor of 1.20 (Example 5–5) and an air temperature of 40 F.

Solution: All coefficients except that of the floor have the same values as in Example 5–10a.

$$\frac{1}{C_f} = r_f + r_{\text{ins}} + r_o = 1.72 + \frac{3}{0.27} + \frac{1}{1.2} = 13.66$$

$$\frac{1}{U_f} = 13.66 + \frac{1}{0.32} = 16.79$$

$$U_f = 0.0596$$

$$U_e = 0.0264 + 0.0112 + 0.0172 + 0.0596\left(\frac{73.5 - 40}{73.5 - 0}\right)\left(\frac{400}{1600}\right)$$

$$= 0.0616$$

$$h_t = \frac{0.0616}{0.02316 + 0.02196 + 0.03308 + (0.00679/0.34)}$$

$$= \frac{0.0616}{0.09817} = 0.627$$

$$h_e = (0.762)(0.627) = 0.478$$

$$t_a = \frac{147 - 0}{2 - (1/0.478)(0.0616)}$$

$$= \frac{147}{1.871} = 78.6 \text{ F}$$

$$q_t = (0.0616)(1600)(78\ 6) = 7747 \text{ Btu/hr}$$

EXAMPLE 5–14. Calculate transmission losses for the enclosures of Examples 5–11 and 5–12, using the "standard" coefficients.

Solution: For the enclosure of Example 5–11, all over-all coefficients, when expressed in terms of "standard" coefficients, have the same values as in Example 5–9. In evaluating U_e, however, the correction for higher crawl-space temperature (applied in the solution of Example 5–9) is now eliminated. Thus

$$U_e = 0.0391 + 0.0122 + 0.0185 + 0.0768 = 0.1466$$

$$h_t = \frac{0.1466}{0.0261 + 0.00836 + 0.0133 + (0.0768/1.08)}$$

$$= \frac{0.1466}{0.1189} = 1.233$$

$$h_e = (0.762)(1.233) = 0.940$$

$$t_a = \frac{147 - 0}{2 - (1/0.940)(0.1466)}$$

$$= \frac{147}{1.844} = 79.71 \text{ F}$$

$$q_t = (0.1466)(1600)(79.71) = 18,697 \text{ Btu/hr}$$

For the enclosure of Example 5–13, all over-all coefficients except that of the floor have the same values as in Example 5–10b:

$$\frac{1}{C_f} = r_f + r_{\text{ins}} + r_o = 1.72 + \frac{3}{0.27} + \frac{1}{1.2} = 13.66$$

$$\frac{1}{U_f} = 13.66 + \frac{1}{0.9259} = 15.74$$

$$U_f = 0.0635$$

In evaluating U_e, the floor term must also be corrected for the crawl-space temperature of 40 F rather than the 0 F value that applied in Example 5–10b. Thus

$$U_e = 0.0872 - 0.0174 + 0.0635 \left(\frac{73.5 - 40}{73.5 - 0}\right) \left(\frac{400}{1600}\right)$$

$$= 0.0770$$

$$h_t = \frac{0.0770}{0.0619 - (0.0174/1.08) + (0.0072/1.2)}$$

$$= \frac{0.0770}{0.0518} = 1.486$$

$$h_e = (0.762)(1.486) = 1.132$$

$$t_a = \frac{147 - 0}{2 - (1/1.132)(0.0770)}$$

$$= \frac{147}{1.932} = 76.1 \text{ F}$$

$$q_t = (0.0770)(1600)(76.1) = 9376 \text{ Btu/hr}$$

5–7. Comparison of Recommended Procedure with Conventional Procedure.

In Art. 5–6, Examples 5–1, 5–12, 5–5, 5–10a, and 5–13 analyze transmission losses by the recommended method for the same enclosure under conditions of progressively increasing thermal effectiveness. For the same outside design conditions, the optimum inside-air comfort temperature is found to decrease from a 92.4 F maximum for the uninsulated room of Example 5–1 to 78.6 F for the fully insulated room of Example 5–13. The corresponding transmission-load reduction is from 40,116 Btu/hr to 9376 Btu/hr. For the uninsulated room, it is important to note that cold-wall effect, requiring increase of room air temperature, is directly responsible for [(92.4 − 73.5)/92.4]30,022, or 6548 Btu/hr, of the load. This is an increase of [6548/(32,022 − 6548)]100, or 25.6 per cent, over the transmission load that would occur if cold-wall effect were eliminated.

Examples 5–2, 5–14 (first part), 5–9, 5–10b, and 5–14 (second part) analyze the same enclosure in the same progression of change in thermal effectiveness but use inside and outside film coefficients as provided in the "standard" over-all coefficients given in the *ASHRAE Guide*. The "standard" film coefficients in all cases are practically double the recommended values, since they include an h_r term of the order of 0.7 to 0.9 rather than the recommended value of h_r, which is of the order of 0.1 to 0.2 (refer to Art. 7–5 for detailed analysis). Because of the reduced film resistance, the ratio of film temperature drop to air-to-air temperature drop is less when the "standard" coefficients are used; hence the calculated mean radiant temperature is higher and the optimum air temperature is lower. This means that transmission losses are based on a lower air-to-air temperature drop. If results of the recommended procedure are considered correct, then the effect of using the "standard" coefficients is to:

1. Establish a design value of inside-air temperature that is too low by from 2 F to 7 F, the error increasing with the equivalent over-all coefficient for the structure.
2. Establish a transmission loss, based on calculated inside-air design temperature, of from 19 per cent (Example 5–10a versus 5–10b) to 36 per cent (Example 5–12 versus 5–14) more than that obtained by the recommended procedure.
3. Establish a transmission loss, if erroneously calculated (as is done by the conventional procedure) on the assumption that inside air temperature is equal to the thermal level, of from 8 to 28 per cent more than that obtained by the recommended procedure.

Thus it would appear that use of "standard" coefficients results in an overdesign of from 8 to 36 per cent.

5–8. Inside Air Temperature Gradients. In all steps of load analysis up to this point, the inside-air temperature t_a has been referred to as though it were equal at all points in the enclosure. Actually, the variation of t_a in any horizontal plane is negligible up to a distance of a few inches, or less, from vertical transmitting surfaces. In a vertical plane, however, variation of t_a may be significant.

Vertical gradient is due to the buoyant effect of warmer air and its consequent tendency to stratify. Thus the magnitude of the vertical gradient would be expected to vary as a function of temperature drop across the inside films and as a function of the method of distributing the heat which is introduced into the enclosure. For panel heating or baseboard heating systems, experiment has established that no appreciable gradient exists. For forced-flow air-heating systems, the *ASHRAE Guide* recommends basing the gradient on an increase of 1 per cent of breathing zone (5 ft above the floor) temperature per foot of height up to a height of 15 ft and an increase of $\frac{1}{10}$ F per foot for heights greater than 15 ft. The gradient below the breathing level is assumed to be the same as that above it; so, for a room with 10-ft ceiling and 73.5 F breathing-level temperature, the air temperature just below the ceiling and just above the floor would be $73.5 + (5)(0.735) = 77.2$ F and $73.5 - (5)(0.735) = 69.8$ F, respectively.

For a gravity warm-air system or for a heating system using cast-iron radiators, the recommended gradient is 1.5 per cent per foot up to 15 ft and 0.15 F per foot for greater heights.

Correction of transmission load for vertical gradient can be made by utilizing K terms in Eq. 5–4b for those transmitting surfaces that are subjected to an average inside air temperature different from t_a. Except where extraordinary accuracy is needed, the K term can utilize an added or subtracted temperature difference based on 73.5 F rather than on the unknown optimum value of t_a.

EXAMPLE 5–15. For the enclosure of Example 5–1 assume use of a forced-circulation air-heating system and calculate: (a) the air temperature below the ceiling; (b) the air temperature above the floor; (c) the corrected value of the transmission loss.

Solution: Base the correction on the calculated optimum air temperature of 92.4 F.

(a) Room height is 10 ft; therefore the same temperature correction applies to floor as to ceiling. Thus

$$\Delta t_{\text{correction}} = (5)(0.924) = 4.62$$

Air temperature below ceiling is $92.4 + 4.62 = 97.0$ F.

The K term for the ceiling is then

$$\frac{t_a + \Delta t - t_o}{t_a - t_o} = \frac{97.0}{92.4} = 1.05$$

(b) Air temperature near the floor is $92.4 - 4.62 - 87.8$ F and the K term is

$$\frac{t_a - \Delta t - t_o}{t_a - t_o} = \frac{87.8}{92.4} = 0.95$$

(c) The revised value of U_e (refer to solution of Example 5–1, second trial, for data) is

$$U_e = 0.0510 + 0.0430 + [(0.0630)(1.05)] + [(0.0598)(0.95)]$$
$$= 0.2170$$

The corrected U_e differs by only two parts in 2168 from the original value; hence it is evident that, for this structure, the increased ceiling loss is practically compensated for by the decreased floor loss; the change in transmission loss is negligible.

5–9. Influence of Ventilation or Infiltration on Transmission-Load Analysis.

In the recommended procedure for evaluating optimum inside air temperature no mention was made of the rate at which outside air is being introduced into the heated enclosure. With most types of heating systems, ventilation load can be investigated independently of transmission load. Thus, when energy distribution is accomplished by use of convectors, radiators, baseboard radiators, or warm air, the total heat input into the room (neglecting possible internal sources) is equal to the sum of transmission and ventilation loads. Under these conditions the ventilation rate, or infiltration rate, has no influence on thermal conditions within the room.

An exception to the above condition is represented by panel heating. In this case large sections of the enclosure surface area are used as the heat source to supply both transmission and ventilation losses; hence the required panel temperature is a function of ventilation as well as transmission load. This requires that the mean radiant temperature change with ventilation load; therefore the optimum air temperature is likewise dependent on the infiltration rate. Thus, for panel heating systems in which outside air is introduced (or infiltrates) at a temperature less than room temperature, it follows that the procedure that has been recommended for evaluating transmission loss must be modified; this subject is covered in Chapter 8.

Another type of enclosure in which ventilation rate affects transmission-load analysis is that of an unheated enclosure such as an attic; the modified procedure for this case is discussed in Art. 5–11.

5–10. Equilibrium Air Temperature in Unheated and Unventilated Spaces.

The equilibrium air temperature in any unheated and unventilated space can be calculated by setting up a heat balance on that space. This procedure is equally applicable to individual rooms, whether unheated or partially heated, to attics and to basements.

EXAMPLE 5–16. A utility room in an office building measures 10 ft by 8 ft by 9 ft high. It is surrounded on three sides and on top and bottom by rooms in which the air temperature is 75 F. One 10-ft side is exposed to outside air at a temperature of -10 F. If the air-to-air thermal resistance of the exposed wall is one-fifth of that of the other walls, floor, and ceiling, what will be the temperature in the unheated room?

Solution: The area of the transmitting wall is 90 sq ft and the area of all other surfaces is $90 + (2)(9)(8) + (2)(10)(8)$, or 394 sq ft. Writing a heat balance equation,

$$q = \left(\frac{A}{R}\right)(t_x - t_y) = \left(\frac{90}{R}\right)(t_a + 10) = \left(\frac{394}{5R}\right)(75 - t_a)$$

$$90t_a + 900 = 5910 - 78.8t_a$$

$$t_a = 29.68 \text{ F}$$

EXAMPLE 5–17. A 20-ft by 40-ft house has a 45-deg pitched roof consisting of asbestos-cement slate and building paper on $\frac{25}{32}$-in. wood sheathing; the underside of the roof is unfinished. Attic walls are 3 ft high and consist of wood shingles ($7\frac{1}{2}$-in. exposure) over building paper, with 3 in. of fibrous insulation, and an interior finish of $\frac{3}{8}$-in. gypsum board. The attic floor is $\frac{1}{8}$-in. linoleum over a wood subfloor ($\frac{25}{32}$ in.) and felt. The ceiling under the attic is $\frac{3}{8}$-in. gypsum board, and there is an air space. The residence is located at Peoria, Illinois. The attic is unheated and unventilated and is over rooms with 12-ft ceiling height and with breathing-level air temperature of 76 F. The heating system utilizes cast-iron radiators for energy distribution. Calculate: (a) the attic temperature;

(b) the attic transmission loss; (c) the combined over-all coefficient for the attic based on heated room air temperature to outside-air temperature.

Solution: The exterior surfaces of roof and walls are rough; so, from Table 5–1, for Peoria, the combined outside film resistance is 0.134 and is based on a design wind velocity of 10.7 mph. From Table 3-1 the design outside-air temperature selected on a 13-year probability basis is −13 F.

From Table 5–2 the resistance of shingles, building paper, and insulation are 0.87, 0.06, and 11.10, respectively; so,

$$\frac{1}{C_w} = 0.87 + 0.06 + 11.10 + 0.134 = 12.16$$

From Table 5–20 at $1/C_w$ of 12.16 and t_o of −13 F, determine Δt as 4.5 F and h_{cw} as 0.40. The attic space can be treated as equivalent to a room with one inside partition (the attic floor being a heat source rather than a transmitting surface); hence h_r, from Table 5–23, is 0.05. Thus

$$h_w = 0.40 + 0.05 = 0.45$$

and

$$\frac{1}{U_w} = 12.16 + \frac{1}{0.45} = 14.38$$

$$U_w = 0.0695$$

The temperature beneath the attic floor is

$$t_a = 76 + (12 - 5)(0.015)(76) = 84.0 \text{ F}$$

Area of the side walls is $(3)(40 + 40)$ or 240 sq ft.

Area of the end walls is $(3)(20 + 20) + (0.5)(20)(10)(2)$, or 320 sq ft; so, total wall area is 560 sq ft.

The resistance of the structural element of the roof is obtained from Table 5–12 as 1.09; hence

$$\frac{1}{C_r} = 1.09 + 0.134 = 1.224$$

The convective film coefficient for under the roof can be estimated from the values for vertical wall and flat ceiling (Tables 5–20 and 5–22) as 0.7; hence h_r is equal to $0.7 + 0.05$, and

$$\frac{1}{U_r} = 1.224 + \frac{1}{0.75} = 2.557$$

$$U_r = 0.3911$$

Roof area is $(2)(40)(200)^{1/2}$ or 1130 sq ft.

For the floor-ceiling, the structural resistances from Table 5–8 are 1.87 for the floor and 0.32 for the ceiling, or 2.19 total, giving $r_c + r_o$ of 2.32. The convective coefficient for the air space, Table 5–17 (since heat flow is upward), is 0.36 and a_r (Table 5–18) is 0.81; so, air-space combined conductance is 1.17. Thus

$$\frac{1}{C_w} = 2.32 + \frac{1}{1.17} + 0.134 = 3.309$$

The convective fraction of the inside film coefficient, from Table 5–21, is 0.26, and with the radiant fraction taken as 0.05, the combined film coefficient is 0.31, giving

$$\frac{1}{U_f} = 3.309 + \frac{1}{0.31} = 6.535$$

$$U_f = 0.1530$$

Floor area is (20)(40) or 800 sq ft.
Summarizing the data:

$$h_w = 0.45 \qquad U_w = 0.0695 \qquad A_w = 560$$

$$h_r = 0.75 \qquad U_r = 0.3911 \qquad A_r = 1130$$

$$h_f = 0.31 \qquad U_f = 0.1530 \qquad A_f = 800$$

(a) The attic temperature is now determinable by setting up a heat balance:

$$U_f A_f (t_a - t_{\text{attic}}) = U_w A_w (t_{\text{attic}} - t_o) + U_r A_r (t_{\text{attic}} - t_o)$$

$$t_{\text{attic}} = \frac{U_f A_f t_a + (U_w A_w + U_r A_r) t_o}{U_f A_f + U_w A_w + U_r A_r}$$

$$= \frac{[(0.1530)(800)(84.0)] - [(0.0695)(560)(13)] - [(0.3911)(1130)(13)]}{[(0.1530)(800)] + [(0.0695)(560)] + [(0.3911)(1130)]}$$

$$= \frac{4031}{603.2} = 6.7 \text{ F}$$

(b) The transmission loss is equal to the heat flow to the attic:

$$q_t = U_f A_f (t_a - t_{\text{attic}}) = (0.1530)(800)(84.0 - 6.7)$$
$$= 9461 \text{ Btu/hr}$$

(c) The combined over-all coefficient, based on attic floor area, is obtained by noting that parallel flow occurs through walls and roof, whereas series flow occurs through floor in conjunction with the wall-roof combination:

$$U = \frac{1}{\dfrac{1}{U_f} + \dfrac{1}{U_w(A_w/A_f) + U_r(A_r/A_f)}}$$

$$= \frac{1}{\dfrac{1}{0.1530} + \dfrac{1}{[0.0695(560/800)] + [0.3911(1130/800)]}} = 0.1220$$

The combined coefficient can be checked by noting that

$$q_t = U A_f (t_a - t_o) = (0.1220)(800)(84.0 + 13) = 9467 \text{ Btu/hr}$$

5–11. Equilibrium Temperature in Ventilated Unheated Spaces.

When untempered outside air is introduced into (or infiltrated into) an unheated enclosure, the equilibrium air temperature within the enclosure will

necessarily be lowered. A heat balance on such an enclosure would be of
the form

$$q_{t_{in}} = q_{t_{out}} + q_v = q_{t_{out}} + 0.2411W(t_a - t_o) \qquad (5\text{--}104)$$

where q_t represents transmission load, q_v ventilation load, and W is the flow
rate of ventilation air in pounds per hour.

EXAMPLE 5–18. Consider that vents or louvers are installed in the attic of
Example 5–17 so that outside air is introduced at a rate of 0.5 cfm/sq ft of
attic floor space. Taking the specific volume of ventilation air as 12.5 cu ft/lb,
calculate the attic equilibrium air temperature.

Solution: Writing a heat balance in the form of Eq. 5–104,

$$U_f A_f(t_a - t_{\text{attic}}) = (U_w A_w + U_r A_r + 0.2411W)(t_{\text{attic}} - t_o)$$

$$t_{\text{attic}} = \frac{U_f A_f t_a + (U_w A_w + U_r A_r + 0.2411W)t_o}{U_f A_f + U_w A_w + U_r A_r + 0.2411W}$$

Substituting the data from Example 5–17,

$$t_{\text{attic}} = \{(0.1530)(800)(84.0) - [(0.0695)(560) + (0.3911)(1130)$$
$$+ (0.2411)(0.5)(800)(60)/12.5]13\} \div$$
$$\{(0.1530)(800) + (0.0695)(560) + (0.3911)(1130)$$
$$+ (0.2411)(0.5)(800)(60)/12.5\}$$
$$= -1.9\,\text{F}$$

Thus the effect of ventilation has been to reduce the attic temperature from
6.7 F to -1.9 F; the increase in transmission loss to the attic is therefore
$[(6.7 + 1.9)/(84 - 6.7)]100$, or 11.1 per cent.

5–12. Direct Transmission Losses to Earth.

For basements that are
below grade and for concrete floor slabs poured on grade, the heat loss at
steady state would be two-dimensional; therefore rational analysis would
require application of some procedure such as that of the relaxation method
(Arts. 4–5, page 76, and 4–8, page 156). In using the relaxation method,
a temperature pattern in the earth under the slab or adjacent to the below-
grade wall would be assumed and the pattern then corrected by the usual
step-by-step method. With the correct temperature pattern established, the
transmission loss could then be readily evaluated.

In most cases, however, steady-state transmission to the earth will be
unlikely, since changes in load due to weather variation will occur much more
rapidly than will the thermal response of the relatively large earth mass under
the slab or adjacent to an underground wall. Further, the rates of heat loss
to the earth are usually small as compared with transmission losses to the
outside air; hence approximate methods of calculation can be safely used.

For underground uninsulated basement floors the *ASHRAE Guide*
recommends using a conductance of 0.1 Btu/(hr)(sq ft)(degree temperature
difference from basement air to earth). When more precise data on ground

temperatures are not available, a common approximation is to assume a value equal to that of ground water at the 30-ft level; this temperature ranges from a low of 40 F in northern Maine through 55 F for San Francisco, Chicago, and New York to a high of 75 F in southern Texas and in Florida.

For underground uninsulated basement walls, the same conductance as for floors is recommended, but in this case the earth temperature is approximated as the average of ground-water temperature and design outside-air temperature.

For concrete floors poured on gravel over grade, the major heat loss occurs at the edges, and a commonly used procedure is to neglect downward loss and to evaluate total floor transmission as a function of the perimeter. The *ASHRAE Guide* suggests a perimeter coefficient of 0.81 Btu/(hr)(lin ft)(°F) for a floor without edge insulation and 0.50 Btu/(hr)(sq ft)(°F) for a floor with edges insulated; the coefficient is expressed in terms of inside-to-outside air temperature difference. In general, transmission losses through the floor are only a small fraction of total room losses, provided drainage conditions are such that excess losses due to a wet slab do not occur.

5–13. Conclusion. The procedure for transmission load calculation, which has been developed in this chapter, is applicable to all types of heating systems, with or without ventilation, except panel heating (panel-system analysis is covered in Chapter 8). The method differs from conventional procedures in two important respects:

1. The design value of the inside air temperature is calculated rather than assumed and is based on a selected thermal level which includes cold-wall effect as well as air temperature.
2. Radiant transfer across inside films is evaluated in terms of the number of non-transmitting sections of the enclosure and is, for most cases, much less than the value commonly used (use of the lower values of the coefficients is justified in the rational analysis presented in Chapter 7).

PROBLEMS

5–1. A one-room storage house is 15 ft by 20 ft by 8 ft. The windowless walls have an over-all coefficient of 0.20, the roof-ceiling combination has an over-all coefficient of 0.15, and the floor (over a basement) has an over-all coefficient of 0.25 Btu/(hr)(sq ft)(°F). Inside air temperature is to be held at 60 F when outside air temperature is 15 F and basement air temperature is 35 F. (a) Calculate the rate of heat loss by transmission. (b) Evaluate the equivalent over-all coefficient of heat transfer.

5–2. A residence located in Boston, Massachusetts, has a total shell area, A_e, of 3800 sq ft. Steady-state rate of heat loss is 63,000 Btu/hr when inside and outside air temperatures are 77 F and −2 F. A store located in Shreveport, Louisiana, has a total shell area of 8200 sq ft, and its steady-state rate of heat loss is 107,000 Btu/hr when inside and outside temperatures are 74 F and +12 F. How does the thermal effectiveness of these two structures compare?

5-3. For a given structure the values of C_e and h_e are 0.40 and 0.90 Btu/(hr) (sq ft)(°F), respectively. If t_o is equal to $+15$ F, calculate the optimum inside air temperature corresponding to a comfort temperature, t_c, of 73.5 F.

5-4. For the conditions of problem 5–3, show that Eqs. 5–9 and 5–12 give identical values of the optimum inside air temperature.

5-5. For the conditions of problem 5–3, calculate the inside surface temperature of the thermally equivalent enclosure.

5-6. Table 5–1 gives 0.184 as the combined outside film coefficient for the moderately rough exterior surface of a wall located in Kingman, Arizona. Check this value by calculation.

5-7. The exterior walls of a frame structure consist of face-brick veneer on $\frac{25}{32}$-in. sheathing with building paper; 3 in. of fibrous insulation completely fill the space between the sheathing and the inside surfacing, the latter consisting of $\frac{3}{8}$-in. gypsum lath and $\frac{1}{2}$-in. lightweight aggregate plaster. The structure is located at Pocatello, Idaho. The heating system is designed to maintain a 72 F inside air temperature with design outside-air temperature selected on the TAC $97\frac{1}{2}$ per cent basis. There are no inside partitions. (a) Determine the combined outside film coefficient. (b) Calculate the surface-to-surface thermal resistance of the wall. (c) Evaluate the approximate combined inside film coefficient. (d) Calculate the over-all coefficient of heat transfer.

5-8. For the conditions of problem 5–7, (a) determine the *exact* value of the combined inside film coefficient, (b) determine the over-all coefficient of heat transfer based on the exact value of the combined inside film coefficient, (c) determine the percentage error that occurs in the over-all coefficient, owing to use of an approximate value of the combined inside film coefficient.

5-9. Data from a heating research project are based on tests in a cubical room 10 ft by 10 ft by 10 ft. The claim is made that a comfort temperature, t_c, of 72 F exists in the test room when air temperature is 76 F and five of the room surfaces are held at a uniform temperature of 66.3 F; thesixth surface is non-conducting. Investigate, quantitatively, the validity of the claim.

5-10. The equivalent over-all coefficient of heat transfer is said to be indicative of the thermal effectiveness of a structure regardless of its size or geographical location. Consider a test room in which the inside air temperature is to be held at 73.5 F regardless of outside air temperature. The room is of uniform construction and has a surface-to-surface conductance of 0.25 Btu/(hr)(sq ft)(°F). Outside surface is smooth. (a) Calculate the value of U_e for this room if it is located at Pueblo, Colorado, and if the design value of the outside air temperature is selected on a 20-year probability basis. (b) Repeat part (a) on the assumption that the room is located in Augusta, Georgia. (c) What percentage change occur in U_e for the same structure when its location changes from Pueblo to Augusta?

5-11. A roof deck consists of a 4-in. slab of concrete (gravel aggregate) with special built-up roofing having a thermal resistance of 0.45. The subdeck is corrugated metal, and between the subdeck and the ceiling there is a 3-in. layer of fibrous insulation (no air space). Ceiling consists of $\frac{3}{4}$-in. metal lath and plaster (lightweight aggregate). Determine the surface-to-surface conductance of the roof-ceiling combination.

5-12. Using tabular values of the resistances, calculate the over-all coefficient of heat transfer for a triple pane window when inside air temperature is 77 F and outside air temperature is $+20$ F. Wind velocity is 9 mph. The window is in a room that has three non-transmitting surfaces.

5–13. For the window of problem 5–12, carry out second and third approximations to the exact value of the over-all coefficient. By what percentage does the value of U_e from tabular data differ from the exact value?

5–14. A floor has a thermal resistance, r_f, of 0.5 when r_o is 0.2 and outside air temperature is $+20$ F. The room is at a comfort temperature of 73.5 F and contains two inside partitions. An air space located in the floor is 4 in. wide and is surfaced on both sides with a material having an emissivity of 0.15. (a) Determine the over-all coefficient of heat transfer for the floor. (b) If the air space were reduced in width to $1\frac{1}{4}$ in., what percentage change would occur in U_f?

5–15. If both sides of Eq. 5–92 are divided by r_{ig} and multiplied by A_t/A_e, the resultant expression for U_e differs from that given in Eq. 5–6. Using data from Example 5–1, check the equality of these two expressions for U_e.

5–16. The temperature of the inside surface of a 2-in. by 4-in. wall stud is 70 F and the temperature of its outside surface is 50 F; the thermal conductivity of the stud is 0.09 Btu/(hr)(sq ft)(°F/ft). The air spaces between studs are at 60 F, and the combined film coefficient for possible heat transfer between the sides of the studs and the adjoining air spaces is 0.7 Btu/(hr)(sq ft)(°F). Assuming that there is no vertical heat transfer along the length of the stud, apply the relaxation method to (a) determine the equilibrium temperatures at the center of each $\frac{1}{2}$-in. by $\frac{1}{2}$-in. square of an arbitrary network established over a horizontal cross-section through the stud; (b) determine the rate of heat transfer from the inner surface of the stud to its outer surface; (c) determine the percentage difference between actual heat-transfer rate and transfer rate based on the assumption of uni-directional heat flow from warmer to cooler surface of the stud.

5–17. A two-room structure has a 4-in. concrete floor poured on gravel over grade. Inside air temperature is 75 F when outside air temperature is $+15$ F. Calculate the rate of heat loss from the floor if edges are not insulated and if area is 20 ft by 30 ft.

5–18. A structure identical to that of problem 5–17 is constructed so that the floor slab is raised 1 ft above the ground. The underslab space is ventilated to an extent such that the underslab air temperature is practically equal to the outside air temperature, but air movement is negligible. (a) Calculate the rate of heat loss through the floor. (b) Compare the heat loss through this raised slab to that from the slab that was investigated in problem 5–17.

5–19. A center-line partition is installed in the room of Example 5–1 (refer to Fig. 7–1). The partition establishes two rooms, one with a single 5-ft by 5.68-ft window and the other with two windows, one 10 ft by 5.68 ft and the other 5 ft by 5.68 ft. (a) For the conditions of Example 5–1, calculate *by the equivalent conductance method* the optimum air and surface temperatures in each of the two rooms. (b) Calculate the total transmission load for the structure. (c) Discuss the influence of the partition on load and on thermal comfort.

5–20. Repeat problem 5–19 for the conditions of Example 5–5.

5–21. Repeat problem 5–19 for the conditions of Example 5–10.

5–22. Repeat problem 5–19 for the conditions of Example 5–12.

5–23. Repeat problem 5–19 for the conditions of Example 5–13.

6

VENTILATION HEATING LOAD

In addition to the loss of heat by transmission, all actual structures lose heat through outward leakage (exfiltration) of warmed room air. Since for every cubic foot of exfiltration there must be an equal admission of infiltration air, it is evident that the amount of heat carried away in the leaving air stream will depend on the inside and outside air temperatures and on the exfiltration rate (or ventilation rate) for the room or the structure.

In one respect ventilation losses are twice as serious as transmission losses, since the leaving air carries away not only sensible heat (based on temperature) but latent heat (based on humidity) also. Thus, for every unit of ventilation air which leaves a room, there will be need for an additional sensible heat supply to the room and for a supply of both heat and water to the humidifier. The relative magnitude of ventilation losses, as compared with transmission losses, varies widely, but in most cases such losses are a substantial fraction of the total load and in some cases (as inside rooms with outside air requirements for odor control) the ventilation loss may constitute the entire load.

6–1. Thermal Air Changes. In mechanical ventilating systems, outside air is usually tempered before being admitted to the heated space, but irrespective of where the heat addition occurs, the quantity of energy needed to raise each unit weight of outside air to room conditions is, of course, the same. Thus, for purposes of total load calculation, the designer need not concern himself with how, when, or where either the heating or humidifying of outside air takes place; his sole concern is the weight of outside air introduced and its change of thermal state from outside-to-room conditions. In systems that utilize recirculation, or a combination of recirculation with outside air, the recirculated fraction is of no significance whatever as far as thermal load is concerned. Recirculation *is* of importance in those processes of the heating system which are concerned with transportation and with distribution. To differentiate the thermally important fraction of outside ventilation air, it is sometimes desirable to separate the total ventilation rate for a structure into its thermal and non-thermal fractions; in some cases the division may require three classifications:

1. The non-thermal fraction, determined by the amount of recirculation.

2. The thermal fraction, determined by the tempering (and/or humidi-fying) of outside air by means of conditioning units located outside of the occupied room.

3. The thermal fraction corresponding to the heating of outside air by means of units located within the occupied space.

The above distinctions can be clarified by considering a room in which mechanical ventilation provides one-half air change per hour of outside air. This air is considered to be tempered to 60 F before being mixed with one-half air change per hour of recirculated room air; room air temperature is 70 F and outside air is at 0 F.

In this case equal weights of outside and recirculated air mix before admission to the occupied room so that the temperature of entering air is halfway between 60 F and 70 F; hence, 65 F.[1] The mixing process, however, has no thermal significance, so that in this system the non-thermal fraction of total ventilation is 50 per cent. Of the remaining 50 per cent, part of the heating is done by the tempering unit and part by the room heating units. The tempering fraction amounts to $(60 - 0)/(70 - 0)$, or $\frac{6}{7}$, and is therefore $(\frac{6}{7})(0.5)$, or 0.43, equivalent thermal change per hour, based on outside air. The remaining 0.07 equivalent thermal change per hour represents ventilation heating load as it appears within the room. Thus, in evaluating the room heat load for this case (to be carried by room heating units as convectors, radiators, or radiant panels), the ventilation would be taken as 0.07 thermal air change per hour, but an additional 0.43 thermal air change would be charged against the room and carried as added load to be handled by a separate tempering system.

When humidification is provided, the latent load is usually carried by equipment operated in conjunction with the tempering of outside air. In this case the humidification load would be chargeable to the structure but would not be included in the heat losses to be met by the heating units located within the room. Thus, in evaluation of ventilation load, a problem arises that does not exist with transmission losses: determination of that part of the load which is chargeable to the room and will be carried by equipment in the room as against the fraction that occurs because of conditions existing in the room but which is carried by equipment that is not within the room. Total ventilation load must therefore be evaluated in three parts:

1. Sensible load carried by room units.
2. Sensible load carried by tempering equipment.
3. Latent load carried by the humidifying system.

Before proceeding with the numerical evaluation of sensible and latent ventilation load, it is necessary to investigate the thermal properties of the atmosphere.

[1] Approximation based on neglect of humidity difference between inside air and outside air.

119889758

6–2. Basic Principles. Air and water vapor, the normal atmosphere, is the "working substance" in all heating and humidifying systems. Whether the equipment in question is a fan, a grille, a duct, an extended surface coil, a radiator, or an air washer, the designer must determine the physical properties of the air-water vapor atmospheric mixture as it enters, passes through, and leaves that equipment. Obviously, therefore, a thorough and sound understanding of the physical and thermal properties of the ambient atmosphere is a fundamental requirement for any engineer working in the field of heating and air conditioning.

The following treatment of air-water vapor mixtures (psychrometrics) starts with a review of basic principles, from which the construction of a typical psychrometric chart is developed, and in subsequent articles the assumptions and approximations involved in the use of such a chart are critically examined.

The ambient atmosphere consists of a mechanical mixture of gases plus a variable quantity of water vapor. Taken together, the mixture of gases acts as, and has specific properties equivalent to, a single homogeneous gas. Essentially, therefore, the atmosphere can be treated thermodynamically as a gas-vapor mixture. This requires some knowledge of the thermodynamic properties of a vapor, of a gas, and of a mixture of the two.

For all psychrometric purposes, dry air can be considered a perfect gas. Within the temperature range used in comfort heating, the specific heat of dry air (for constant pressure) is substantially constant: ($c_p = 0.2411$ Btu/(lb)(°F)). All other data needed for psychrometric calculations involving dry air are obtainable from the perfect gas law

$$Pv = RT \tag{6-1}$$

where P = pressure, lb/sq ft.
  v = specific volume, cu ft/lb.
  T = temperature in degrees Fahrenheit absolute (= °F + 460).
  R = gas constant (= 53.3 for dry air).

If the atmosphere with which the engineer worked were free of water vapor, there would be little or no need for tables or charts of air properties, since the relationship of pressure, specific volume, and temperature would be readily obtainable from Eq. 6-1, and the energy associated with a warm, moving air stream (enthalpy h in Btu/lb based on zero enthalpy at °F for dry air) would in every case be equal to 0.2411 multiplied by the air temperature in degrees Fahrenheit. Since water vapor is invariably present, a less direct method of property evaluation is necessary.

The properties of water vapor cannot be expressed so simply as those of dry air. Though empirical equations are available for expressing the variation of vapor properties over limited ranges, greater facility and accuracy in calculations are possible through use of vapor tables or graphical representation of vapor properties. A complete pressure-enthalpy chart of the properties of water vapor is given in Fig. 6-1. From this figure it is evident that the constant temperature lines (isothermals) for low-pressure vapor (less than 1 psia) in the superheat region are substantially parallel to the lines of constant enthalpy. This fact is of enormous value to the engineer because it enables him to determine the enthalpy of the superheated water vapor by reading directly from Fig. 6-1 the corresponding enthalpy of saturated vapor at the same temperature. It also shows that low-pressure superheated vapor closely obeys the perfect gas law, since one identifying characteristic of a perfect gas is that its enthalpy is a function of temperature but not of pressure or specific volume. For psychrometric purposes, therefore, a table or chart of saturated steam properties provides all the data needed for a thermodynamic evaluation of the properties of such vapor as is present in the atmosphere.

Before evaluating the properties of the air-water vapor mixture, one additional thermodynamic point must be considered: the effect, if any, of the presence of a gas on the properties of a vapor. Fortunately, this influence is so small that for psychrometric purposes it can be considered negligible, and evaluation of properties can be accurately carried out on the assumption that the gas and vapor jointly and independently occupy the same volume. The only additional equation needed in dealing with such mixtures is Dalton's law of partial pressures, which states that the total pressure of the mixture is equal to the sum of the partial pressures of the gas and vapor present:

$$p_t = p_g + p_v \qquad (6\text{-}2)$$

where the subscripts refer to total, gas, and vapor, respectively.

Summarizing, all data essential to a complete thermodynamic and psychrometric analysis of an air-with-water vapor atmosphere are available from two equations (6-1 and 6-2), a table of saturated steam properties (Appendix Table A-1), and two physical constants (R and c_p). A recognition of the simplicity of these basic data is essential to the engineer, since otherwise he may fail to comprehend that the sole justification for a psychrometric chart is that it can, if properly constructed, reduce to a minimum the effort needed to calculate atmospheric properties.

6-3. Thermodynamic Properties on the Psychrometric Chart.

Many forms of psychrometric chart are in use at the present time. Differences in construction occur as a result of varying choice in the selection of basic variables or because consideration has been given to the dynamic characteristics of special processes involving the humidification or dehumidification of a given atmosphere. The typical chart presented in Fig. 6-5 is constructed on the basis of the simplest and most fundamental thermodynamic considerations.

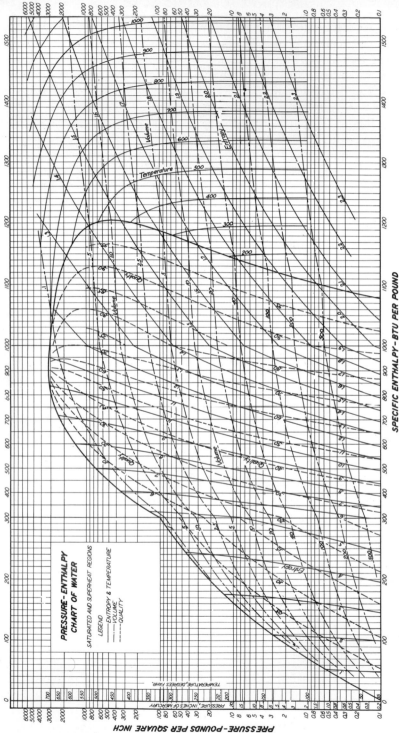

SPECIFIC ENTHALPY-BTU PER POUND

Fig. 6–1. Pressure-enthalpy chart for water.

240

The chart is constructed for standard atmospheric pressure (14.696 psia), and properties are expressed in terms of a basic, arbitrarily defined atmospheric unit of 1 lb of dry air plus the weight of water vapor associated with it. For convenience, the x-axis is selected as the *scale of temperature* and the y-axis as the *scale of moisture content*, or *specific humidity* W, expressed in grains per pound of dry air (7000 grains = 1 lb).

SATURATION LINE. As a first state to be fixed on the chart, consider an atmosphere at 70 F and saturation. The vapor pressure of saturated water

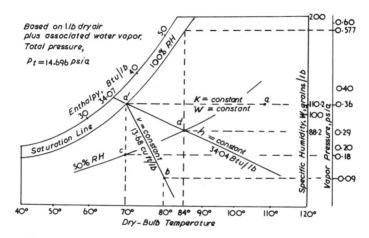

Fig. 6–2. Psychrometric representation of thermodynamic properties.

vapor at 70 F is 0.3631 psia (from Table A–1). Then, by Eq. 6–2, the pressure of the dry air in this atmosphere is $14.696 - 0.3631 = 14.333$, and the volume of 1 lb of such dry air is (by Eq. 6–1)

$$v = \frac{53.3(70 + 460)}{(14.333)(144)} = 13.68 \text{ cu ft}$$

The weight of saturated vapor associated with a pound of dry air (reading the specific volume at 70 F as 867.9 cu ft/lb from Table A–1) is therefore

$$W' = \frac{13.68}{867.9} = 0.01574 \text{ lb vapor/lb dry air}$$

or

$$W = (0.01574)(7000) = 110.2 \text{ grains vapor/lb dry air}$$

Accordingly, the state of 70 F saturated air is given at the intersection (a' on Fig. 6–2) of a horizontal line through 110.2 on the specific humidity scale and a vertical line through 70 F on the temperature scale. In exactly the same way enough additional points are determined to permit fixing the saturation line.

VAPOR PRESSURE SCALE. The vapor pressure at each point on the saturation line is the saturation pressure at the particular temperature (as 0.3631 psia at 70 F). But horizontal lines on the chart are lines of constant specific humidity; hence along any such line the total pressure, weight of vapor, and weight of dry air are all constant. It follows, therefore, that the partial pressures of the dry air and of the associated water vapor must also be constant along horizontals. Thus a scale of vapor pressure can be set up on the right side of the chart parallel to the specific humidity scale. As each point on the saturation line is established, the corresponding vapor pressure is then transferred (along the horizontal) to the vertical scale. Note particularly that the vapor pressure scale is not linear but is established by transposition of steam table data. Examination of the scale (refer Fig. 6–5) will show that the scale interval between equal increments of vapor pressure is greater at high values than at low.

CONSTANT SPECIFIC VOLUME LINES. The second step is the construction of lines representing the loci of states for which the specific volume of the atmosphere is constant. The method can be demonstrated by determining that state of an 80 F atmosphere for which the specific volume is the same as that of the 70 F saturated atmosphere ($v = 13.68$). The necessary dry-air pressure, from Eq. 6–1, is

$$p_g = \frac{53.3(80 + 460)}{(13.68)(144)} = 14.60 \text{ psia}$$

and the vapor pressure must be $14.696 - 14.60 = 0.096$ psia. The desired state is therefore on the 80 F vertical at intersection (b on Fig. 6–2) with a constant-pressure line for water vapor at 0.096 psia.

By the method already described, sufficient points having the same specific volume are established to permit drawing a curve through them ($a'b$ on Fig. 6–2). Additional lines established provide adequate coverage of the entire chart area and permit ready interpolation of the specific volume of points not falling directly on a plotted line.

RELATIVE HUMIDITY LINES. Relative humidity (RH) is defined as the ratio of the actual vapor pressure in an air-vapor mixture to the vapor pressure which would exist in a saturated mixture at the same temperature. The saturation line on the chart is therefore the line of 100 per cent RH. Lines on the chart for any desired value of the relative humidity can be constructed as follows: Taking 50 per cent RH as an example, the point on the 70 F line corresponding to this relative humidity must be at the intersection (c on Fig. 6–2) with the line representing a vapor pressure of $(0.5)(0.3631) = 0.1816$ psia. In a similar manner, states on the 50 per cent line at other temperatures are determined, and the curve cd is then drawn through these points (Fig. 6–2). By proceeding in this way, as many lines of constant relative humidity can be established as may be needed.

LINES OF CONSTANT ENTHALPY. The enthalpy of an air-vapor mixture, based on 1 lb of dry air plus associated water vapor, is commonly taken as including the enthalpy of the air above 0 F plus the enthalpy of the vapor above 32 F. The energy associated with water vapor in the water vapor includes that necessary to raise the liquid from 32 F to the temperature corresponding to the saturation pressure, plus the latent heat of vaporization at saturation pressure, plus energy required to superheat the vapor from the saturation temperature to the actual temperature of the mixture. As already pointed out, the fortunate circumstance that constant-enthalpy lines in the low-pressure region of the pressure-enthalpy chart are approximately parallel to constant temperature lines greatly simplifies the psychrometric construction, since it permits fixing the enthalpy of vapor in a mixture by determining the enthalpy of saturated vapor at the temperature of the mixture. Thus, on any vertical line on the psychrometric chart, the enthalpy of the associated water vapor is constant and is equal to the enthalpy of the saturated vapor which would exist at the intersection of that vertical with the saturation line. This relationship (exact only for a perfect gas but a very close approximation at vapor pressures less than 1 psia) permits determination of lines of constant-mixture enthalpy on the chart without need of taking into account the variation of latent heat of vaporization with pressure.

As an example, consider the state at 70 F and saturation which was previously investigated. The enthalpy of the dry air at 70 F is $(0.2411)(70) = 16.88$ Btu/lb. The weight of vapor present was calculated as 0.01574, and the enthalpy of saturated vapor at 70 F (steam tables) is 1092.3 Btu/lb. The enthalpy of water vapor associated with 1 lb of dry air is then $(0.01574)(1092.3) = 17.19$, and the total enthalpy of the air-vapor mixture is $16.88 + 17.19 = 34.07$ Btu/lb of dry air present.

To fix the state for some temperature, other than 70 F, at which the enthalpy of the mixture is also 34.07, note that the dry-air enthalpy of the new temperature (taking 84 F as an example) is $(0.2411)(84) = 20.24$, and the enthalpy of associated vapor at the unknown state point must then be $34.07 - 20.24 = 13.83$. But the enthalpy of vapor at any state on the 84 F line is the same as that of saturated vapor at 84 F. The enthalpy of vapor at the unknown state must therefore, from steam table, Appendix A–1, be 1098.4 Btu/lb for saturated vapor at 84 F. The weight of vapor present is then $(13.83/1098.4)(7000) = 88.2$ grains/lb, and the state is fixed at the intersection (d on Fig. 6–2) of the 88.2 grains/lb horizontal and the 84 F vertical. In the same way, other points having a mixture enthalpy of 34.07 Btu/lb can be determined and the constant enthalpy line thereby located on the chart. Other lines of constant enthalpy can be similarly located.

For convenience in psychrometric measurement the constant-enthalpy lines as plotted on the chart are not for even values of the enthalpy but are for arbitrarily selected values corresponding to even increments in the temperature of the saturated mixture. Thus a constant-enthalpy line is shown passing through 70 F and saturation (Fig. 6–5) where the enthalpy is 34.07, rather than through the lower fractional saturated temperature for which the enthalpy would be an even 34.00. The reason for such an apparently irrational procedure will be discussed in detail in the later article on methods of psychrometric measurement. Because of the above condition, the numerical values of enthalpy are not marked on the chart lines but can be interpolated from the enthalpy scale which appears just above the saturation line (Fig. 6–5).

SUMMARY. All needed thermodynamic properties of an air-vapor mixture have now been appropriately indicated on the chart. A knowledge of any two of the following properties will permit fixing the state and consequent determination of all other properties: temperature, grains per pound of dry air or vapor pressure, specific volume, relative humidity, or enthalpy.

EXAMPLE 6–1. Investigate the properties of saturated air at 70 F in a location (as Mexico City) where the altitude is 7500 ft. Compare these properties with the corresponding values for sea level.

Solution: Atmospheric pressure at an elevation of 7500 ft is approximately 22.65 in. of mercury as compared with 29.92 in. of mercury at sea level. Total pressure is therefore

$$p_t = \left(\frac{22.65}{29.92}\right)(14.696) = 11.12 \text{ psia}$$

From the steam tables (Appendix A–1) at 70 F (as previously determined) for saturated vapor,

$$p_v = 0.3631 \text{ psia}$$
$$v_v = 867.9 \text{ cu ft/lb}$$
$$h_v = 1092.3 \text{ Btu/lb}$$

Then

$$p_a = p_t - p_v = 11.12 - 0.3631 = 10.76 \text{ psia}$$

$$v_a = \frac{53.3(70 + 460)}{(10.76)(144)} = 18.22 \text{ cu ft/lb}$$

$$W' = \frac{18.22}{867.9} = 0.021 \text{ lb vapor/lb dry air}$$

or

$$W = (0.021)(7000) = 147.0 \text{ grains vapor/lb dry air}$$

$$h = [(0.2411)(70)] + [(0.021)(1092.3)] = 40.79 \text{ Btu/lb dry air plus}$$
associated water vapor

Thus a comparison of thermodynamic properties shows

Altitude	p_t	p_v	p_a	v_a	W	h
Sea level	14.696	0.3631	14.333	13.68	110.2	34.04
7500 ft	11.12	0.3631	10.76	18.22	147.0	40.79

The differences due to altitude are sufficiently great to require either use of a special psychrometric chart for the particular altitude or evaluation of the properties by computation.

6–4. Psychrometric Properties.

In order for the chart of thermodynamic properties of air-water vapor mixtures to become a useful tool, there is obvious need for some method of experimentally determining the numerical value of at least two of the above mentioned properties. It was with respect to this adaptation of the thermodynamic relationships to interpretation from psychrometric measurements that Carrier[2] made his important pioneering contribution to the rational advance of air-conditioning techniques with a paper presented to the American Society of Mechanical Engineers in 1911. In his paper the concepts of *wet-bulb temperature* and *dew-point temperature* were developed and their relationship to the basic chart properties indicated.

DRY-BULB TEMPERATURE. Of the five properties recorded on the chart, the only one amenable to direct measurement is temperature. For many practical purposes the temperature can be measured with sufficient accuracy by inserting a thermometer in the air-vapor mixture. To distinguish this reading from others to be discussed, it is referred to as the *dry-bulb* temperature (dbt).

Where the temperature of walls enclosing the mixture differs from that of the mixture, the unshielded thermometer gives an erroneous reading, owing to radiant transfer between the bulb and the surrounding surfaces. In precise work the radiation error may be too large to neglect, and it then becomes necessary to use either a specially shielded thermometer or to apply a correction to the reading of the unshielded instrument. Based on laboratory tests, Dropkin[3] recommends the following empirical equation for correcting unshielded dry-bulb temperature readings:

$$t_a = t - \left[\left(\frac{T_w}{100} \right)^4 - \left(\frac{T}{100} \right)^4 \right] \left(\frac{d}{0.235} \right)^{0.44} \left(\frac{0.3105}{V_m^{0.56}} \right) \tag{6–3}$$

where t_a = true temperature of the air, °F.

t = temperature of the thermometer bulb exposed to radiation, °F.

T_w = temperature of the wall of the enclosure, °F abs.

T = temperature of the thermometer bulb exposed to radiation, ° F abs.

d = diameter of the thermometer bulb, in.

V_m = air velocity, fpm at a barometric pressure of 29.92 in. of mercury and temperature of 70 F.

[2] W. H. Carrier, "Rational Psychrometric Formulae," *Trans. ASME*, 1911.
[3] David Dropkin, "Effect of Radiation on Psychrometric Readings," *Bulletin 26*, Cornell, 1939.

In cases where the average surface temperature of the surround is known and where the convective film coefficient for the thermometer bulb can be calculated, the true air temperature can be determined be applying the rational heat-balance procedure (refer to Art. 4–8, page 155).

EXAMPLE 6–2. The general air movement in an average heated room is of the order of 20 fpm. In a room having an average over-all coefficient of heat transfer of 0.24 Btu/(hr)(sq ft)(°F) and combined inside film coefficient of 1.65 Btu/(hr)(sq ft)(°F), the inside air temperature is approximately 72 F when outside air temperature is 0 F. If a suspended, unshielded mercury thermometer with $\frac{1}{4}$-in. bulb reads 70 F, calculate the room air temperature.

Solution: The average inside surface temperature, based on approximate air temperature of 72 F. is calculable by Eq. 4–147:

$$t_{si} = t_i - r_i U(t_i - t_o) = 72 - \left(\frac{1}{1.65}\right)(0.24)(70 - 0)$$

$$= 72 - 10.2 = 61.8 \text{ F}$$

Room air temperature, by Eq. 6–3, is therefore

$$t_a = 70 - \left[\left(\frac{61.8 + 460}{100}\right)^4 - \left(\frac{70 + 460}{100}\right)^4\right]\left(\frac{0.25}{0.235}\right)^{0.44}\left(\frac{0.3105}{20^{0.56}}\right)$$

$$= 70 + (47)(1.027)(0.058)$$

$$= 70 + 2.8$$

$$= 72.8 \text{ F}$$

Since this example is for a low outside temperature (0 F) and for an uninsulated wall ($U = 0.24$), it follows that under ordinary conditions an unshielded thermometer will agree within 2 deg with true room air temperature.

DEW-POINT TEMPERATURE. To fix the state of an air-vapor mixture on the psychrometric chart, at least one property in addition to the dry-bulb temperature must be known. A second such measurable characteristic is the *dew-point temperature* (dpt). If the pressure of a superheated vapor remains constant and heat is removed, the temperature decreases until desuperheating is complete; further heat extraction causes condensation. Determination of the temperature at which condensation starts, therefore, fixes the saturation temperature and the vapor pressure of the unsaturated mixture. Instruments for measuring dew-point temperature are commercially available, but because of difficulties in achieving precision of control, they are of limited practical usefulness outside the laboratory.

With the dry-bulb and dew-point temperatures known (t_z and $t_{a'}$, respectively, in Fig. 6–3), the state of the original mixture is fixed at the intersection x of the dry-bulb vertical with the line of constant vapor pressure which originates at the dew-point temperature on the saturation line.

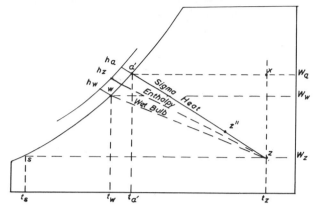

Fig. 6–3. Representation of psychrometric properties.

TEMPERATURE OF ADIABATIC SATURATION. An air-vapor mixture at a state, such as z (Fig. 6–3), when allowed to remain in contact with a body of water (at temperature in excess of the dew point of the mixture), will undergo an increase in humidity until eventually it reaches a saturated state. When the water is supplied at a temperature equal to the final temperature of the saturated mixture, provided no energy enters or leaves the system during the humidifying process, the final mixture temperature is defined as the *temperature of adiabatic saturation*. Refer to Fig. 6–3 and let a' represent the final state of a mixture originally at some unknown state such as z, from which it was adiabatically humidified to a' as a result of contact with water supplied at temperature $t_{a'}$. For an energy balance on the system, the enthalpy of the mixture at z plus heat of the liquid evaporated must equal the enthalpy at a':

$$h_z + (W'_{a'} - W'_z)(t_{a'} - 32) = h_{a'} \qquad (6\text{--}4)$$

From this equation the temperature (hence the state) at z, corresponding to any particular initial value of the specific humidity, can be calculated when the saturation temperature $t_{a'}$ is known. As an example, consider an air-vapor mixture at unknown state z which contains 50 grains/lb and after adiabatic saturation reaches state a' at 72 F. The enthalpy and humidity at a' are (from the chart) 35.9 Btu/lb and 118 grains/lb. Then, from Eq. 6–4,

$$h_z = 35.9 - \frac{(118 - 50)(72 - 32)}{7000}$$
$$= 35.9 - 0.389$$
$$= 35.5 \text{ Btu/lb}$$

and the percentage of change in enthalpy during the process of adiabatic saturation is, for this example, $0.389/35.5 = 1.1$ per cent. For most practical problems, 1 per cent accuracy is well within the limit of experimental error, and in such cases it is permissible to regard the constant enthalpy lines as equivalent to lines of constant temperature of adiabatic saturation.

If greater accuracy were required, it would be readily possible to plot true lines of adiabatic saturation (from Eq. 6–4 by the same method as in the above example). Psychrometric charts have been published which show adiabatic saturation lines in place of constant enthalpy lines.

By regrouping the terms of Eq. 6–4,

$$h_z - W'_z(t_{a'} - 32) = h_{a'} - W'_{a'}(t_{a'} - 32) \qquad (6-5)$$

Referring again to Fig. 6–3, suppose that the mixture at z is adiabatically humidified to any non-saturated state z'' as a result of contact with water at the temperature of adiabatic saturation, $t_{a'}$. By a heat balance on the system,

$$h_z + (W'_{z''} - W'_z)(t_{a'} - 32) = h_{z''} \qquad (6-6)$$

and by rearranging terms,

$$h_z - W'_z(t_{a'} - 32) = h_{z''} - W'_{z''}(t_{a'} - 32) \qquad (6-7)$$

By comparing Eqs. 6–5 and 6–7 and noting that the state z'' was taken as *any* point on the line of adiabatic saturation, it is evident that this line is characterized by constancy of the term

$$h - W'(t_{a'} - 32) = \Sigma \qquad (6-8)$$

where h is the enthalpy of any mixture having a specific humidity W and a temperature of adiabatic saturation $t_{a'}$. The above equation states that the enthalpy of an air-vapor mixture less the heat of its associated liquid at the temperature of adiabatic saturation is constant along any path of adiabatic humidification. This term appears so frequently in heating and air-conditioning calculations that it has been given a name, the *sigma heat content*, Σ. On some psychrometric charts, lines of constant sigma heat content are plotted instead of lines of constant enthalpy. Note, however, that if either lines of constant h or of constant Σ are shown, the values of the other property (h or Σ) can be readily calculated from Eq. 6–8.

Eq. 6–8 is usually written in somewhat different form. The enthalpy of the mixture is equal to the enthalpy of the dry air ($c_{pa}t_a$) plus that of associated water vapor ($W'h_v$). But it has been shown (Art. 6–2) that the enthalpy of the superheated vapor at z is approximately the same as at x (Fig. 6–3), or

$$h_{v_z} = h_{v_x} = (t_{a'} - 32) + h_{fg_{a'}} + c_{ps}(t_z - t_{a'}) \qquad (6-9)$$

where $h_{fg_{a'}}$ is the latent heat of vaporization at the pressure corresponding to a saturation temperature of $t_{a'}$, and c_{ps} is the specific heat at constant pressure of superheated steam. Then, substituting in Eq. 6–8,

$$\begin{aligned} \Sigma &= c_{pa}t_z + W'_z[(t_{a'} - 32) + h_{fg_{a'}} + c_{ps}(t_z - t_{a'})] - W'_z(t_{a'} - 32) \\ &= c_{pa}t_z + W'_z[h_{fg_{a'}} + c_{ps}(t_z - t_{a'})] \end{aligned} \qquad (6-10)$$

By equating the sigma heat contents for points z and a',

$$\Sigma = c_{pa}t_z + W'_z[h_{fg_{a'}} + c_{ps}(t_z - t_{a'})]$$
$$= c_{pa}t_{a'} + W'_{a'}[h_{fg_{a'}} + c_{ps}(t_{a'} - t_{a'})] \qquad (6\text{–}11a)$$

Rearranging terms gives an equation similar to that originally established by Carrier:

$$h_{fg_{a'}}(W'_{a'} - W'_z) = c_{pa}(t_z - t_{a'}) + W'_z c_{ps}(t_z - t_{a'})$$

or

$$h_{fg_{a'}}(W'_{a'} - W'_z) = (c_{pa} + W'_z c_{ps})(t_z - t_{a'}) \qquad (6\text{–}11b)$$

Eq. 6–11b is applicable only when the final state a' is on the saturation line. Eq. 6–11b is often written in the form

$$h_{fg_{a'}}(W'_{a'} - W'_z) = c_H(t_z - t_{a'}) \qquad (6\text{–}11c)$$

where

$$c_H = c_{pa} + W'_z c_{ps} = \text{humid specific heat, Btu/(lb)(°F)} \qquad (6\text{–}12)$$

Note: In the general case c_H is evaluated in terms of the average specific humidity of the humid air that is undergoing a psychrometric process.

The left side of Eq. 6–11c is a quantitative statement of the amount of energy that must be obtained during adiabatic humidification from the sensible heat present in the mixture at z (Fig. 6–3), but it is *not* equal to the difference in energy stored as latent heat between state points a' and z. The true latent heat difference is

$$h_{fg_{a'}}W'_{a'} - h_{fg_z}W'_z$$

but this quantity is less than the left side of Eq. 6–11b by an amount equal to W'_z times the difference between the increased heat of the liquid (from z to a') in Btu per pound and the decreased superheat in Btu per pound; thus

$$h_{fg_{a'}}(W'_{a'} - W'_z) = (h_{fg_{a'}}W'_{a'} - h_{fg_z}W'_z) + W'_z[(t_{a'} - t_s) - c_{ps}(t_{a'} - t_s)] \qquad (6\text{–}13)$$

where t_s is the dew-point temperature of air at state z.

Summarizing, lines of constant enthalpy (as on the chart of Fig. 6–5) are not identical with lines representing constancy of the temperature of adiabatic saturation, but the deviation is of the order of 1 per cent and for most practical problems can be safely neglected. The sigma heat content Σ is constant along an adiabatic path (provided water is supplied at the temperature of adiabatic saturation).

The temperature of adiabatic saturation is the third measurable characteristic from which a thermodynamic property can be established. Refer to Fig. 6–3 and assume that an air-vapor mixture has known dry-bulb temperature t_z but that its state point z is not known. By adiabatically saturating this atmosphere, it would come to a temperature which, as already shown, would very closely approach the dry-bulb temperature of a saturated atmosphere of equal enthalpy. Thus the state of any atmosphere can be closely approximated by measuring its dry-bulb temperature, then adiabatically humidifying a sample of the atmosphere and measuring its new dry-bulb temperature. The state is fixed by entering the chart at the temperature of adiabatic saturation (on dry-bulb temperature scale), rising to saturation line, and then moving down a constant-enthalpy line to intersection with the original dry-bulb temperature.

WET-BULB TEMPERATURE. The principal disadvantage of using the temperature of adiabatic saturation as a psychrometric measurement is the obvious difficulty of isolating and adiabatically humidifying a sample of the air-vapor mixture. To solve this problem, the concept of *wet-bulb temperature* (wbt) has been established. If an unsaturated mixture (z on Fig. 6–3) is passed over a wetted surface, as the radiation-shielded wick-covered bulb of a thermometer, a condition of dynamic equilibrium must be reached such that the sensible heat flowing from the passing air-vapor stream will be exactly equal to the latent heat carried from the surface in the diffusing vapor. If M' (lb/hr) is the rate at which diffusion occurs, the conditions necessary for a dynamic balance will be

$$h_{fg_w}M' = h_c A(t_z - t_w) \qquad (6\text{--}14)$$

where h_{fg_w} = latent heat of vaporization, Btu/lb at the saturation pressure corresponding to t_w.

t_z = dry-bulb temperature of passing air stream.

t_w = temperature of the wetted surface when dynamic equilibrium has been reached; t_w is, by definition, the *wet-bulb temperature* of the passing stream.

h_c = film coefficient of heat transfer by convection, Btu/(sq ft)(hr)(°F).

But it is necessary also to satisfy the diffusion equation,

$$M' = KA(p_w - p_z) \qquad (6\text{--}15)$$

where K = diffusion coefficient through the gas film on the wetted surface in lb/(sq ft surface)(hr)(unit difference in vapor pressure) across the film.

p_w = pressure (psia) of saturated vapor at t_w.

p_z = pressure of vapor in the passing stream.

By substituting from Eq. 6–15 into Eq. 6–14,

$$h_{fg_w}K(p_w - p_z) = h_c(t_z - t_w) \qquad (6\text{--}16)$$

or by re-expressing the diffusion coefficient in terms of specific humidity differences,

$$h_{fg_w}K'(W'_w - W'_z) = h_c(t_z - t_w) \qquad (6\text{--}17)$$

Comparing Eq. 6–11b (for the temperature of adiabatic saturation, $t_{a'}$) and Eq. 6–17 (for the wet-bulb temperature t_w), it is evident that if h_c/K' were equal to the humid specific heat of the unsaturated air, ($c_{pa} + W'c_{ps}$), the wet-bulb temperature would always be exactly equal to the temperature of adiabatic saturation. There is no theoretical reason for expecting the above equality to hold, but experiment has shown that for water vapor in air, it does very closely apply. Thus, for air-water vapor mixtures,

$$\frac{h_c}{K'c_H} = 1 \tag{6–18}$$

and this dimensionless parameter is known as the *Lewis number*.

Fortuitously, therefore, the wet-bulb temperature of an air-vapor mixture is a close approximation to the true temperature of adiabatic saturation and can be used as such in psychrometric measurements. Thus the dynamic equilibrium temperature reached by a wet-bulb thermometer, over which an air-with-vapor stream is passing at moderate velocity, can be used as a third psychrometric measurement from which to determine the thermodynamic properties requisite to fixing the state of such a mixture.

For some special types of problems arising in industrial air conditioning, the difference between wet-bulb and adiabatic saturation temperatures may be of great importance. Consider, for example, the air-vapor mixture in an oil storage tank: Since the vapor present is not water, the fortuitous h_c/K' relationship no longer holds, and the humid specific heat may not even closely approach equality with h_c/K'. For atmospheres of this kind a special psychrometric chart must be constructed and consideration given to the deviation of wet-bulb from adiabatic saturation temperatures.

EXAMPLE 6–3. The wick of a recording radiation-shielded wet-bulb thermometer ($\frac{1}{4}$-in. outside diameter by 2-in. long) is connected to a jar containing water at wet-bulb temperature. Calculate the weight of water evaporated in a 24-hr period if room state is at 75 F dbt with 30 per cent RH and if air movement is such that the convective film coefficient, h_c, is 0.65 Btu/(hr)(sq ft)(°F).

Solution: The specific humidity at room state (from Fig. 6–5) is 39 grains/lb, the wet-bulb temperature is 56.5 F, and the specific humidity in the film adjacent to the wick (saturated air at 56.5 F) is 69 grains/lb. By taking h_c/K' as equal to the humid specific heat at room state (refer to Art. 6–4) and using the nomenclature of Eq. 6–12,

$$\frac{h}{K'} = (c_{pa} + W'_z c_{ps})$$

From the steam table (Appendix, Table A–1) the value of c_{ps} at 56.5 F and saturation is 0.5 Btu/(lb)(°F); so,

$$K' = \frac{h_c}{c_{pa} + W'_z c_{ps}}$$

$$= \frac{0.65}{0.2411 + [(39/7000)(0.5)]}$$

$$= \frac{0.65}{0.2411 + 0.0028}$$

$$= \frac{0.65}{0.2439} = 2.66 \text{ lb/(hr)(sq ft)(unit difference in specific humidity)}$$

Surface area of the wetted thermometer bulb is

$$A = \pi DL = \frac{(\pi)(0.25)(2)}{144} = 0.0109 \text{ sq ft}$$

$$\text{Evaporation loss} = K'A(W_w' - W_z')(24)$$

$$= \frac{(2.66)(0.0109)(69 - 39)(24)}{7000}$$

$$= 0.004 \text{ lb/24 hr}$$

Thus it follows that a 1-pt reservoir would supply makeup water to the wick for almost a year.

EXAMPLE 6–4. A 75-ft by 30-ft heated outdoor swimming pool is maintained at 75 F when ambient air is at 60 F with 50 per cent RH. The convective film coefficient for a day with still air is approximately 0.65 Btu/(hr)(sq ft)(°F). Calculate the rate of evaporative loss in gallons per day.

Solution: Specific humidities in the water film (75 F, saturated) and in the ambient air are (from Fig. 6–5) 131 and 47 grains/lb, respectively, and the specific heat of the vapor is 0.5 Btu/(lb)(°F). Then, since h_c/K' for an air-water vapor mixture is approximately equal to the humid specific heat of the room air,

$$K' = \frac{0.65}{0.2411 + (47/7000)(0.5)}$$

$$= \frac{0.65}{0.2411 + 0.0034} = \frac{0.65}{0.2445}$$

$$= 2.62 \text{ lb/(hr)(sq ft)(unit difference in specific humidity)}$$

$$\text{Evaporation loss} = K'A(131 - 47)(24)$$

$$= \frac{(2.62)(75)(30)(84)(24)}{7000} = 1700 \text{ lb/24 hr}$$

$$= \frac{1700}{8.345} \approx 200 \text{ gal/24 hr}$$

EXAMPLE 6–5. Calculate the quantity of heat that must be added to 1 lb of saturated air at 56.5 F to raise its temperature to 75 F; determine the error that would occur if this heat addition were calculated in terms of the specific heat of dry air.

Solution: From Example 6–3, the humid specific heat of air having a specific humidity equal to that at 56.5 F and saturation is

$$c_p = 0.2411 + 0.00493 = 0.2460 \text{ Btu/(lb)(°F)}$$

The required heat addition is

$$Q_{56.5 \text{ F to 75 F}} = 0.2460(75 - 56.5) = 4.55 \text{ Btu}$$

If the heat requirement were calculated in terms of the specific heat of dry air, the error would be

$$\text{Error due to use of } c_{pa} = \frac{0.00493}{0.2460}$$

$$= 0.020, \text{ or } 2.0 \text{ per cent}$$

EXAMPLE 6–6. Determine the error involved in using the specific heat of dry air instead of the humid specific heat when calculating heating requirements for saturated air at 100 F.

Solution: The specific humidity at 100 F, 100 per cent RH, is 300 grains/lb. Then

$$c_H = 0.2411 + \left(\frac{300}{7000}\right)(0.5) = 0.2411 + 0.0214 = 0.2625$$

The error would therefore be

$$\text{Error due to use of } c_{pa} = \frac{0.0214}{0.2625} = 0.082, \text{ or } 8.2 \text{ per cent}$$

A comparison of the results of Examples 6–5 and 6–6 shows that the importance of using the c_H rather than the c_{pa} increases rapidly with specific humidity. For high-temperature industrial processes, as in drying, very large errors would occur if c_H were not used.

EXAMPLE 6–7. Dry air at 119 F is adiabatically saturated. Calculate the enthalpy change.

Solution: Dry air at 119 F has an enthalpy (from Fig. 6–5) of 29.4 Btu/lb and, by Eq. 6–8, this is also its sigma heat content. If the adiabatic process occurred at constant enthalpy, the specific humidity gain would be 89 − 0, or 89 grains/lb, and the temperature of the saturated air would be 64.0 F. Associated with this humidity gain would be an enthalpy increase, due to heat of the liquid, of (89/7000)(64 − 0), or 0.814 Btu/lb. Then, as a first approximation, the adiabatically saturated air will be assumed to be at 66 F with an enthalpy of 30.8 Btu/lb and a specific humidity of 96 grains/lb. If the assumed final state were correct, the sigma heat content at saturation would equal that for dry air at 119 F; hence, by Eq. 6–8,

$$\Sigma = 29.4 \doteq 30.8 - \left(\frac{96}{7000}\right)(66 - 32) = 30.8 - 0.47 \doteq 30.3$$

The assumed value of the saturation temperature is evidently too large. As a second assumption, take the saturation temperature as 65 F with corresponding enthalpy of 29.9 Btu/lb and specific humidity of 92 grains/lb. Then

$$\Sigma = 29.4 \doteq 29.9 - \left(\frac{92}{7000}\right)(65 - 32) = 29.9 - 0.43 = 29.47$$

The value for the second approximation is slightly high by 0.07; noting that a 1 F change between first and second approximations provided a 30.3 − 29.47 = 0.83 change in the sigma heat content, it follows that a further sigma reduction of 0.07 would correspond to a temperature reduction of approximately (0.07/0.83)(1), or about 0.1 F. Thus the adiabatic saturation temperature would be close to 64.9 F and the corresponding enthalpy would be close to 29.8. The enthalpy gain during adiabatic saturation is therefore approximately 29.8 − 29.4, or 0.4 Btu/lb. The wet-bulb temperature of this atmosphere would be very close to the temperature of adiabatic saturation; hence, would be 64.9 F. If a constant enthalpy line were followed from 64.9 F and saturation to intersection with the vertical for 119 F dbt, the corresponding specific humidity would be read as 5 grains/lb rather than the true value of 0 grains/lb.

COMFORT REGION ON THE PSYCHROMETRIC CHART. The discussion in Art. 1–10 led to the recommendation of 73.5 F dbt at 50 per cent RH as the optimum indoor air state during the heating season for an enclosure in which the average inside surface temperature is equal to the inside air temperature; this state is indicated with an x on the psychrometric chart. By following a line of constant specific volume (approximating a line of constant effective temperature, as discussed in Art. 1–9) to the saturation line, the corresponding optimum value of effective temperature is read as 68 F.

As indications of the range of inside comfort conditions, lines WW and $W'W'$ (on Fig. 6–5) correspond, respectively, to effective temperatures of 66 F and 63 F and are the loci of states for which 95 and 50 per cent, respectively, of the occupants will be comfortable in a heated enclosure (average surface temperature being equal to room air temperature), whereas 5 and 50 per cent, respectively, will be too warm. To permit a comparison of the shift in preferred inside states from winter to summer, lines SS and $S'S'$ have been drawn on Fig. 6–5 to show the loci of states at which 98 and 50 per cent, respectively, of occupants would be thermally comfortable in summer. Intersection of the SS line with the line of 50 per cent RH establishes 76.5 F (at 50 per cent RH) as the optimum summer inside air state: thus for the same relative humidity, the optimum dry-bulb temperature is 3 F greater in summer than in winter. All four of the loci lines shown on the psychrometric chart terminate at relative humidities of 30 and 70 per cent; for RH values below 30 per cent or above 70 per cent, thermal comfort would be unchanged (along a line of fixed effective temperature), but at humidities less than 30 per cent, undesirable drying effects would occur, whereas at RH values greater than 70 per cent an unpleasant sensation of clamminess is likely to be experienced.

Adjustment of the optimum winter inside state, x, to take account of cold-wall effect is accomplished by raising the dry-bulb temperature while maintaining the inside specific humidity at the value (62 grains/lb) corresponding to state x. Adjustment of the dry-bulb temperature is evaluated from the comfort equation (Eq. 1–11) by the method discussed in Art. 5–2.

EXAMPLE 6–8. Analysis of a particular enclosure establishes that, for design conditions, the uniform inside surface temperature will be 71 F. Determine the optimum value of the inside relative humidity.

Solution: The optimum inside dry-bulb temperature is calculable from Eq. 1–11:

$$t_a = 147 - mrt = 147 - 71 = 76 \text{ F}$$

Optimum inside specific humidity (equal to that at state C on Fig. 6–5) is 62 grains/lb; hence the optimum relative humidity is read at the intersection of known specific humidity and dry-bulb temperature lines as 45 per cent.

SENSIBLE HEAT—TOTAL HEAT RATIO. Around the outside border of the psychrometric chart (Fig. 6–5) a scale has been established which permits graphical separation of the fractions of ventilation load due to simple heating (the sensible heat load) and to humidification (the latent heat load). Referring to Fig. 6–4, let point r represent the selected inside air state and point o the design value of the outside air state. Assume that sensible and latent transmission losses from the enclosure are to be made up by means of a system separate from that used for tempering outside air. Also assume that the tempering process changes the state of the mechanically introduced outside air from o to r.

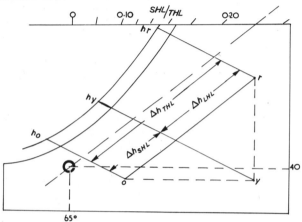

Fig. 6–4. Psychrometric representation of ratio of sensible heat load to total heat load.

The enthalpy of outside air is read from the psychrometric chart by following a constant-enthalpy line from state o to the enthalpy scale above the saturation line; the value is h_o Btu/lb. The enthalpy of room air is similarly determined as h_r. The total heat load for tempering ventilation air is therefore

$$\Delta h_{\mathrm{THL}} = h_r - h_o \quad \mathrm{Btu/lb} \tag{6–19}$$

Two methods are available for separating total load into sensible and latent loads. By one method the process of tempering from o to r is considered to occur in two steps: heating at constant specific humidity from o to y (Fig. 6–4) with corresponding enthalpy gain of

$$\Delta h_{\mathrm{SHL}} = h_y - h_o \tag{6–20}$$

followed by humidification at constant dry-bulb temperature from y to r with corresponding enthalpy gain of

$$\Delta h_{\mathrm{LHL}} = h_r - h_y \ . \tag{6–21}$$

Then

$$\Delta h_{\mathrm{THL}} = \Delta h_{\mathrm{SHL}} + \Delta h_{\mathrm{LHL}} = (h_y - h_o) + (h_r - h_y) = h_r - h_o \tag{6–22}$$

and

$$\frac{\mathrm{SHL}}{\mathrm{THL}} = \frac{\Delta h_{\mathrm{SHL}}}{\Delta h_{\mathrm{LHL}}} = \frac{h_y - h_o}{h_r - h_o} \tag{6–23}$$

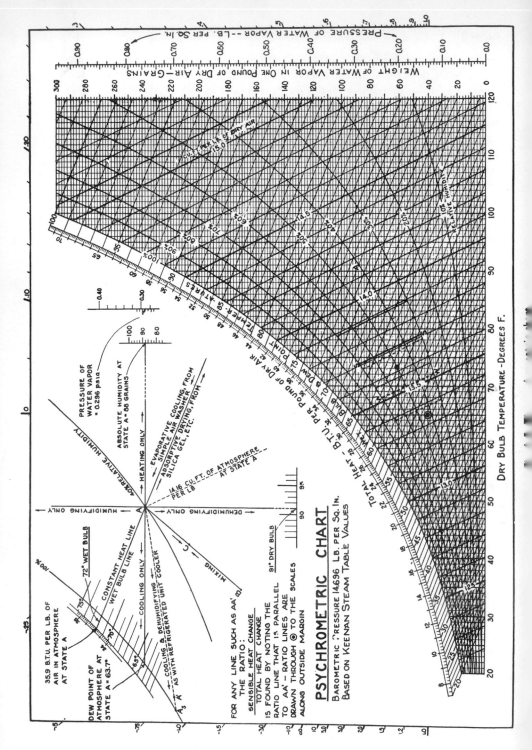

PSYCHROMETRIC CHART

BAROMETRIC PRESSURE 14.696 LB. PER SQ. IN.
BASED ON KEENAN STEAM TABLE VALUES

FOR ANY LINE SUCH AS AA'
THE RATIO:

$$\frac{\text{SENSIBLE HEAT CHANGE}}{\text{TOTAL HEAT CHANGE}}$$

IS FOUND BY NOTING THE
RATIO LINE THAT IS PARALLEL
TO AA' — RATIO LINES ARE
DRAWN THROUGH ⊙ TO THE SCALES
ALONG OUTSIDE MARGIN

35.9 B.T.U. PER LB. OF
AIR IN ATMOSPHERE
AT STATE A

DEW POINT OF
ATMOSPHERE AT
STATE A = 63.7°

72° WET BULB

ABSOLUTE HUMIDITY AT
STATE A = 88 GRAINS

PRESSURE OF
WATER VAPOR
= 0.296 psia

14.16 CU. FT. OF ATMOSPHERE
PER LB. OF DRY AIR
AT STATE A

40% RELATIVE HUMIDITY

CONSTANT HEAT LINE

WET BULB LINE

HEATING ONLY

HUMIDIFYING ONLY

DEHUMIDIFYING ONLY

COOLING ONLY

COOLING & DEHUMIDIFYING
AS WITH REFRIGERATED UNIT COOLER

EVAPORATIVE COOLING, FROM
SIMPLE AIR WASHER

ADSORPTIVE DRYING, FROM
SILICA GEL, ETC.

MIXING

91° DRY BULB

DRY BULB TEMPERATURE - DEGREES F.

PRESSURE OF WATER VAPOR — LB. PER SQ. IN.

WEIGHT OF WATER VAPOR IN ONE POUND OF DRY AIR — GRAINS

TOTAL HEAT — B.T.U. PER POUND OF DRY AIR

CU. FT. OF DRY AIR
15.0

RELATIVE HUMIDITY

The second method of evaluating the SHL/THL ratio is carried out graphically by drawing a straight line (Fig. 6–4) from o to r. A second line, parallel to or is then drawn through the reference point which is shown on the chart at the intersection of the 65 F dbt line with the horizontal for a specific humidity of 40 grains/lb. The line through the reference point is extended upward to the scale around the border of the psychrometric chart, where intersection determines a decimal value that is numerically equal to the SHL/THL ratio. With known total load, the sensible and latent fraction are then directly calculable.

EXAMPLE 6–9. An auditorium seating 500 people is to be maintained at 75 F dbt with specific humidity of 62 grains/lb when outside air state is at 30 F dbt with 20 per cent RH. Outside air is tempered to room state and then introduced to the auditorium at a rate of 30 cfm/(min)(occupant). Calculate (a) the sensible heating load on the tempering unit, (b) the latent heat load on the tempering unit, (c) the required water supply to the humidifier in gallons per day.

Solution: (a) The enthalpies at inside and outside states are read from Fig. 6–5 as 28 Btu/lb and 8 Btu/lb, respectively. The inside and outside specific humidities are 62 grains/lb and 5 grains/lb, and the specific volume at the inside state is 13.66 cu ft/lb. The weight of air tempered per hour is therefore

$$w = \frac{(500)(30)}{13.66} \, 60 = 65{,}900 \text{ lb/hr}$$

and the total heat load for tempering is

$$\text{THL} = w(\Delta h_{\text{THL}}) = 65{,}900(28 - 8) = 1{,}318{,}000 \text{ Btu/hr}$$

To determine the SHL/THL ratio, draw a line through the reference point on Fig. 6–5 parallel to or and extend it to intersect the border scale at 0.535. Then

$$\text{SHL} = \Delta h_{\text{SHL}} = \left(\frac{\text{SHL}}{\text{THL}}\right)\text{THL}$$

$$= (0.535)(1{,}318{,}000) = 705{,}000 \text{ Btu/hr}$$

(b) Similarly,

$$\text{LHL} = \Delta h_{\text{LHL}} = \left[1 - \left(\frac{\text{SHL}}{\text{THL}}\right)\right](\text{THL})$$

$$= (1 - 0.535)(1{,}318{,}000) = 613{,}000 \text{ Btu/hr}$$

or, from part (a),

$$\text{LHL} = \text{THL} - \text{SHL} = 1{,}318{,}000 - 705{,}000 = 613{,}000 \text{ Btu/hr}$$

(c) The water supply to the humidifier would be

$$gpd = \frac{w(W_r' - W_o')24}{8.345}$$

$$= \frac{65{,}900(62 - 5)(24)}{(7000)(8.345)}$$

$$540 \text{ gal/24 hr}$$

The inside and outside states used in this example are closely approached for many design conditions, and therefore it is interesting to note that, for these conditions, the heating and humidifying fractions of total load approach equality.

6–5. Summary. The psychrometric chart (Fig. 6–5) is a plotting of the basic thermodynamic properties of air-water vapor mixtures at fixed total pressure. A necessary preliminary to use of the chart is determination of the state of the atmosphere in question; this requires a knowledge of at least two independent properties.

The only thermodynamic property subject to direct and simple measurement is temperature. This is usually determined with an ordinary thermometer, and when necessary the experimental reading is corrected for radiation.

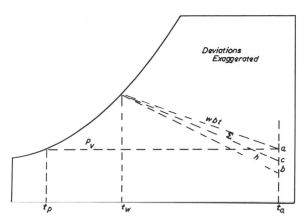

Fig. 6–6. Psychrometric properties for determination of state point.

The corrected reading is called the *dry-bulb temperature* and appears as the x-coordinate of the chart. Referring to Fig. 6–6, knowledge of the dry-bulb temperature t_a fixes the state of an unknown atmosphere as somewhere along the vertical through t_a.

The dew-point temperature (t_p in Fig. 6–6 fixes the specific humidity and locates the state of the mixture at point a.

The enthalpy is not subject to direct measurement but has been shown to be approximately constant along a line representing a fixed value of the temperature of adiabatic saturation. The latter temperature has also been shown to remain approximately constant along a line of fixed wet-bulb temperature. Thus measuring the wet-bulb temperature fixes the approximate enthalpy of the mixture. By referring to Fig. 6–6, the known wet-bulb temperature t_w fixes the mixture state at a if lines of constant wet-bulb temperatures are available on the chart. If lines of constant sigma heat content are used, the state fixed from the wet-bulb temperature will be at c, and the error ac will be due to the deviation of the true temperature of adiabatic saturation from the wet-bulb temperature. If lines of constant enthalpy are used, the state will be fixed at *b*, with a consequent error of *ab*. As already discussed, the error *ab* is usually negligible for mixtures of water vapor in air but may be very serious for mixtures of other vapors and gases.

Summarizing, the state of any air-water vapor mixture can be fixed on the chart with accuracy sufficient for most heating and humidifying problems by means of any two of the three following measurable psychrometric characteristics: dry-bulb temperature, wet-bulb temperature, dew-point temperature. For most practical purposes the first two characteristics are used because they are simplest to determine experimentally.

6–6. Required Ventilation. The heating and humidifying load attributable to the introduction into the enclosure of outside air depends on the ventilation rate and on the differences in temperature and of specific humidity of air at the inside and outside states. With the two states fixed, the sensible, latent, and total heat loads per pound of outside air are obtained from the psychrometric chart by the method discussed in Art. 6–4, page 254. When tempering is not used, the entire ventilation load is added to the transmission load to obtain the total heat loss for the enclosure. When the outside air is tempered to room state before introduction, the ventilation load is treated separately from transmission load and is supplied by a secondary heating and humidifying system consisting of special tempering equipment. If the outside air is tempered to a state having an enthalpy less than that of room air, the tempering fraction of load is separately treated, but the difference between total ventilation load and tempering load is added to the transmission load to obtain the total load on the primary heating system.

Determination of the rate of introduction of outside air starts with an investigation of *requirements* and proceeds to an analysis of availability.

For occupied enclosures in which there are no unusual sources of heat, humidity, odor, smoke, or other objectionable contaminant, the required outdoor air supply will be that needed to prevent noticeable odor; this subject was discussed in Art. 2–3 and recommended rates of ventilation were given in Fig. 2–1.

When tobacco smoke is a significant factor in contributing to the need for ventilation, the rate of introduction of outside air (refer to Art. 2–3) should not be less than 25 cfm per smoker.

For spaces with odor or contaminant sources, the required ventilation rate varies widely, dependent on the rate at which the odor or contaminant is released and on the volume of the space. Whenever possible, quantitative data on the particular installation should be used in estimating required ventilation, but as an approximate guide for typical types of spaces under average conditions, the rates in Table 6–1 are suggested.

If the released contaminants are toxic (as in some industrial processes), determination of ventilation requirements will require calculation of the dilution needed to reduce the concentration in the occupied space to a safe value.

TABLE 6–1

Average Ventilation Requirements

Type of Space	Air Changes/Hr
Bathrooms (in residences)	3
Locker rooms	6
Restaurants	10
Toilets (in public buildings)	12
Kitchens (residential or commercial)	30

6–7. Available Ventilation. Once the required outside air supply rate has been evaluated, the next problem is that of determining how it is to be obtained. Three mechanisms can be used to provide some of or all the required ventilation air.

1. *Infiltration* is the uncontrolled leakage of outside air into the structure through porous walls or through cracks around windows and doors. The infiltration rate varies as a function of the inside-outside total pressure differential, and this differential is itself a function of both wind velocity and difference in density between inside and outside air.

2. *Natural ventilation* is the partially controlled introduction of outside air into the room through designed openings of variable size (such as partially open windows), due to an inside-outside pressure differential of natural causation.

3. *Mechanical ventilation* is the fully controlled introduction of outside air into an enclosure, due to the imposition of a pressure differential caused by a fan or blower.

INFILTRATION RATES. For most residential installations need does not exist for a positive, mechanically provided air supply. Normal leakage into and out of the structure (infiltration and associated exfiltration) through cracks, around doors and windows, by direct transfer through porous walls, and through opening of doors will provide more than the required volume of outside air. In such cases the infiltration air volume should be determined and checked against the required ventilation rate. This volume, if adequate for control of odor or other contaminant, can then be used in evaluating the ventilation heating load.

Effect of Wind Velocity. The influence of wind velocity on rate of infiltration is due to the static or bursting pressure that is produced when a moving air stream comes to rest. The kinetic energy stored in an air stream is a function of the velocity squared and is given by the equation

$$\text{KE} = \frac{V^2}{2g} = h'_{v,\,\text{air}} \tag{6–24}$$

where V = velocity, fps.

  g = acceleration due to gravity, ft/sq sec.

  KE = kinetic energy in units of ft-lb/lb air.

  h'_v air = velocity pressure expressed as head of air in feet.

Assuming complete conversion of velocity head to pressure head, it follows that the inside-outside pressure difference caused by wind velocity will be proportional to the square of that velocity. But infiltration is proportional to pressure difference; so,

$$\frac{I}{I_{15}} = \left(\frac{V''}{15}\right)^2 \tag{6–25}$$

where
I = infiltration rate at wind velocity of V mph.
I_{15} = infiltration rate at wind velocity of 15 mph.
V'' = wind velocity, mph.

Thus experimental evaluation of infiltration rate at one wind velocity, usually 15 mph, permits calculation of the corresponding infiltration rate for greater or lesser wind velocities.

Effect of Temperature Difference. The influence on infiltration rate of inside-to-outside air-temperature difference can be determined by investigating the chimney effect of the room-height column of warm low-density inside air as compared with a column of equal height of cool higher-density outside air. The density of air is given by the perfect gas law (Eq. 6–1) as

$$\rho = \frac{1}{v} = \frac{P}{RT} \quad \text{lb/cu ft} \tag{6–26}$$

The difference in density between room air and outside air is therefore

$$\Delta\rho = \frac{P}{R}\left(\frac{1}{T_o} - \frac{1}{T_r}\right) = \frac{P}{(R)(T_r)(T_o)}(t_r - t_o) \quad \text{lb/cu ft} \tag{6–27}$$

and the pressure difference is the product of ceiling height H and density difference:

$$\Delta P = H\,\Delta\rho = \frac{P}{(R)(T_r)(T_o)}H(t_r - t_o) \tag{6–28}$$

In many cases it is more convenient to express pressure difference as static head of water, $h''_{s,\text{water}}$ in inches. Then

$$h''_{s,\text{water}} = \frac{\Delta P}{\rho_{\text{water}}/12}$$

$$= \left[\frac{12P}{(\rho_{\text{water}})(R)(T_r)(T_o)}\right]H(t_r - t_o) \tag{6–29}$$

Similarly the velocity pressure head of Eq. 6–24 can be converted from feet of air to inches of water:

$$h''_{v,\text{water}} = \frac{12\rho_{\text{air}}h'_{v,\text{air}}}{\rho_{\text{water}}} = \frac{12h'_{v,\text{air}}}{(\rho_{\text{water}})(v_{\text{air}})}$$

giving

$$h''_{v,\text{water}} = \frac{12V^2}{(2g)(\rho_{\text{water}})(v_{\text{air}})} \tag{6–30}$$

The effect of temperature difference on infiltration can be expressed in terms of an equivalent velocity, V_e, by equating Eqs. 6–29 and 6–30 and solving for V_e:

$$V_e = \left[\frac{(2g)(\rho_{\text{water}})(v_{\text{air}})(12P)}{(12)(\rho_{\text{water}})(R)(T_r)(T_o)} \right]^{\frac{1}{2}} [H(t_r - t_o)]^{\frac{1}{2}} \tag{6–31}$$

By substituting standard densities for water (62.3 lb/cu ft at 68 F) and air (0.075 lb/cu ft at 70 F and 0 per cent RH), 53.3 for the gas constant R, and $460 + 40$, or 500 F abs as an average of the inside and outside absolute air temperature,

$$V_e = \left[\frac{(2)(32.2)(62.3)(13.33)(12)(14.696)(144)}{(12)(62.3)(53.3)(500)^2} \right]^{\frac{1}{2}} [H(t_r - t_o)]^{\frac{1}{2}}$$

$$= 0.368[H(t_r - t_o)]^{\frac{1}{2}} \tag{6–32}$$

For convenience the equivalent wind velocity is usually expressed as V_e'' in units of miles per hour. Then

$$V_e'' = \left(\frac{3600}{5280} \right) V_e = \left(\frac{3600}{5280} \right)(0.368)[H(t_r - t_o)]^{\frac{1}{2}}$$

$$= 0.251[H(t_r - t_o)]^{\frac{1}{2}} \tag{6–33}$$

where V_e'' = equivalent wind velocity, mph.

H = cciling height, ft.

t_r, t_o = room and outside air temperature, °F.

Eq. 6–33 gives the theoretical equivalent wind velocity to temperature difference across a single wall, for an enclosure flow at equal rate occurs by both infiltration and exfiltration; hence some modification of the coefficient 0.251 would be expected. For a single-story building (or for one story of a multistory building in which there is no air flow between stories) the *ASHRAE Guide* recommends taking V_e'' as 48 per cent of the theoretical value, or

$$V_e'' = 0.12[H(t_r - t_o)]^{\frac{1}{2}} \tag{6–34}$$

whereas for average single-story frame buildings with attic and ceiling, the recommended coefficient is approximately four times the theoretical value, giving

$$V_e'' = [H(t_r - t_o)]^{\frac{1}{2}} \tag{6–35}$$

With V_e'' known, the infiltration due to inside-to-outside temperature difference is calculated in terms of I_{15} by use of Eq. 6–25 with V_e'' substituted for V''.

Infiltration Rate Through Solid Walls. For a basic wind velocity of 15-mph infiltration through an average frame wall with lath and plaster (bevel siding painted or cedar shingles, sheathing, building paper, wood lath, and three coats of gypsum plaster) is given by the *ASHRAE Guide*, based on test values, as 0.13 cu ft/(hr)(sq ft). For poorly constructed porous brick and lime mortar walls of $8\frac{1}{2}$ in. and 13 in. thickness, respectively, the same source gives 8 and 7 cu ft/(hr)(sq ft) as the 15-mph infiltration rates. For a brick wall with furred space and an inside finish consisting of lath and two coats of prepared gypsum plaster, the infiltration rate can be conservatively taken as 3 per cent of that for a plain brick wall of equal thickness. If the wall is finished with two coats of prepared plaster directly on the brick, the infiltration can be conservatively taken as 1 per cent of that for the unplastered wall.

Infiltration Rate Through Windows. Although a large body of test data is available on infiltration through many types of doors and windows (refer to research publications of the ASHRAE), the variations in the quality of construction and in care during installation of such units is so great that test data on a "standard" door or window may differ widely from experience with a particular door or window of the same type. Lacking other information, however, the engineer can use the following values as a guide:

For an unlocked, non-weatherstripped, double-hung, wood sash window having $\frac{1}{16}$-in. crack and $\frac{3}{64}$-n. clearance the basic, (15 mph) infiltration rate can be taken as 39 cu ft/(hr)(lin ft of crack); this value includes frame leakage. The effect of weatherstripping a window of this type is to reduce the infiltration by approximately one-third. For a poorly fitted ($\frac{3}{32}$-in. crack and clearance) window, the infiltration approximately triples, 111 cu ft/(hr) (lin ft of crack), if the window is not weatherstripped, whereas with weatherstripping the poorly fitted window has an infiltration rate, 34 cu ft/(hr)(lin ft of crack length), about 40 per cent greater than an average fitted weatherstripped window. The crack length of a double-hung window is taken as three times the width plus twice the height.

Rolled section, steel-sash windows of the type widely used in industrial buildings (pivoted, with $\frac{1}{16}$-in. crack) have a very high infiltration rate: 176 cu ft/(hr)(lin ft of crack length) with 15-mph wind velocity; length of crack is equal to the perimeter of the movable section of the window. Average rolled section, steel-sash windows for residential use have $\frac{1}{64}$ in. to $\frac{1}{32}$ in. crack with infiltration rate of the order of 40 cu ft/(hr)(lin ft of crack).

Infiltration Rate Through Doors. For an average well-fitted door, the infiltration rate can be taken as 100 cu ft/(hr)(lin ft of crack), and for a poorly fitted door the rate is twice this value; weatherstripping reduces the infiltration for either type of door by about 50 per cent.

Total Infiltration Rate. To maintain pressure equilibrium within an enclosure, the rate of infiltration in cubic feet per hour must equal the rate of exfiltration; hence air will not be entering the structure through all the door and window cracks. Thus, if a room were entirely airtight except for the crack around a window located in one wall, there would be very little infiltration through the crack and no *net* infiltration. Rather than correct the rate of flow through crack for variations in location within the enclosure, a more common procedure is to use fixed flow rates but to vary the fraction of total crack length for use in estimating total infiltration. In estimating total infiltration *available* for ventilation purposes, the rates should be based on the minimum wind velocity likely to occur for an extended period during the heating season. If data are lacking on the particular location, it is suggested that 5 mph be used.

When windows or exterior doors are located in only one wall of a room, the recommendation is to base infiltration on the total crack length in that wall. This recommendation is made on the assumption that the infiltering air leaves the room through interior doors or door cracks and flows to an adjoining enclosure. If there are windows or exterior doors in two walls, the length of crack to be used is that for the wall in which the crack length is greater; if there are windows or exterior doors in three or four walls, the length used is either half the total or that for the single wall with greatest crack, whichever is the larger.

The method of the preceding paragraph is used to determine the outside air *available* by infiltration for purposes of ventilation. When continuing to the next step in the design, ventilation load evaluation, some adjustment is necessary. Thus, for the structure as a whole, air will enter on the windward side and exit on the leeward. If the structure is divided into rooms, those on the windward side will receive outside air by infiltration, but those on the leeward side will receive air at room temperature through interior doors or door cracks from the windward-side rooms. Under these circumstances infiltration will be responsible for a heating and humidifying load in the windward-side rooms only. But as the direction of the wind changes, the rooms experiencing ventilation load will also change. The recommended procedure is therefore to include ventilation heating load for *each* room when sizing the heating or humidifying equipment, or both, for that room but to calculate the total heating and humidifying load on the entire structure as though the structure were a single room. Thus over-all infiltration rate is taken as that occurring through the wall of the structure which has the greatest crack length or through one-half the total crack length of all four walls, whichever is greater. Total infiltration for the structure is therefore less than the sum of the infiltration rates for individual rooms.

The wind velocity for use in calculating the design value of the heating and humidifying ventilation loads will usually exceed the 5-mph value which was recommended for estimating *available* ventilation. Table 5–1 gives the maximum wind velocity that is likely to occur in a given city when outside air temperature is equal to or less than the design value. This velocity should be used in calculating the design value of infiltration load.

The crack-length method is at best only a rough approximation, since actual infiltration will vary with wind direction and with arrangement of rooms with respect to one another. Many engineers prefer to estimate the infiltration rate for design conditions (but *not* for *available* ventilation) in terms of assumed air changes per hour. There is not exact agreement as to what values should be used, but for an average structure under average conditions of winter exposure, the following values are representative of common practice:

1. If windows on one side, allow $\frac{1}{2}$ air change.
2. If windows on two sides, allow 1 air change.
3. If windows on three sides, allow $1\frac{1}{2}$ air change.
4. If windows on four sides, allow 2 air changes.

The above recommendations must be used with judgment and the values altered in terms of experience with structures similar to the one for which the design is being made. Thus the rates given would be expected to apply to rooms having windows of usual construction, size, and frequency but would not apply if large plate-glass "solar" windows were used or if the fraction of wall surface occupied by ordinary windows departed greatly from average practice. Wherever accurate determination of crack type and length is possible, the crack method of infiltration evaluation should be used in preference to the air-change method.

NATURAL VENTILATION. An open window or any other relatively large (as compared with window crack) wall opening on the windward side of a structure will admit outside air. Rate of flow through such an opening will vary directly as the first power of the wind velocity and will decrease (though not in direct proportion) with increase in the angle between wind direction and a normal to the opening. Flow through the opening will also be materially influenced by the size and location of the openings or cracks through which the entering air escapes from the room. If data on the particular installation are lacking, an approximation to flow through an average opening can be taken as

$$Q = 18A V'' \quad \text{cu ft/hr} \tag{6-36}$$

where

A = free area of inlet.

V'' = wind velocity, mph.

MECHANICAL VENTILATION. When the rate of introduction of outside air is established by positive means, the heating and humidifying loads for each room and for the structure as a whole can be readily determined. In this case the ventilation load will be part of room load if the air is introduced at its outside state but will be considered separate from room load if tempered to the room state before introduction.

6-8. Step-by-Step Ventilation Load Evaluation. In summarizing the discussions of the preceding articles, the entire procedure for determination of ventilation load can now be presented in simplified and orderly arrangement. The steps to be followed are as follows:

1. By reference to the architectural drawings for each room of a structure, determine the length of each type of window and exterior door crack that is located in each exposed wall. If the structure is of brick or frame wall construction, determine the net area (less doors and windows) of each exposed wall.

2. Repeat step 1, with the structure considered as a single room.

3. Select the infiltration rate, based on a 15-mph wind, for each type of crack and sum the products of crack length and infiltration rate for all types of cracks that occur in any one wall. If the wall is of brick or frame, select the infiltration rate through the wall and multiply by net area to obtain wall infiltration. Add crack and wall infiltration to obtain total infiltration for each exposed wall.

4. Based on the number of exposed walls of a given room, determine (from data of step 3) the total infiltration rate (based on 15-mph wind) for that room. Similarly, determine the total infiltration rate for the structure as a whole (noting that this will be less than the sum of room infiltration rates).

5. Calculate the ventilation rate for each room, using Eq. 6–25, for a 5-mph wind:

$$I = (5/15)^2 I_{15} = 0.111 I_{15} \quad \text{cu ft/hr} \tag{6–37}$$

where I_{15} is the total wind-induced infiltration rate based on 15-mph wind (calculated in step 4).

6. Evaluate the equivalent wind velocity due to inside-to-outside air-temperature difference (Eq. 6–34 or 6–35) and use this value as V'' in Eq. 6–25 to calculate the additional infiltration caused by chimney effect.

7. Add the infiltration rates from steps 5 and 6 for each room, to determine the *available* ventilation rates, and compare these, room by room, with the *required* rates. If required ventilation exceeds available infiltration, the need for mechanical ventilation will be indicated; in this case omit steps 8 through 10 following, and go to step 11.

8. If mechanical ventilation is not used, calculate the design infiltration rate by repeating step 5 for each room and for the structure as a whole, using Eq. 6–25 with the design wind velocity V'', as given in Table 5–1.

9. For each room and for the structure as a whole, add the infiltration rates from steps 6 and 8 to determine the total infiltration rates responsible for design values of the ventilation heating and humidifying loads.

10. For known inside and outside design states, read the corresponding enthalpies from the psychrometric chart (Fig. 6–5) and subtract to obtain the total load in Btu per pound of outside air. Establish the SHL/THL ratio (refer to Art. 6–4, page 254) and use it to calculate the sensible and latent loads in Btu per pound.

11. Convert individual room and over-all structure ventilation rates (whether due to infiltration or mechanical ventilation) from a volume basis to a weight basis. This is done by dividing the volume in cubic feet per hour by the specific volume of standard air (13.35 cu ft/lb).

12. If ventilation is by infiltration, multiply the pound per hour infiltration rate for each room by sensible, latent, and total heat enthalpy gains to obtain SHL, LHL, and THL values for each room due to ventilation. In the same way obtain SHL, LHL, and THL values for the structure as a whole (noting that each of these loads for the structure is less than the sum of corresponding loads for the rooms).

13. If ventilation is by mechanical means, determine whether the outside air is to be tempered prior to introduction into the rooms.

a. If outside air is untempered, the sensible, latent, and total heat loads due to ventilation must be calculated for each room. Note that for a mechanical ventilation system, unlike infiltration, the sum of loads for the various rooms is equal to the total load for the structure.

b. If outside air is tempered to inside state, there will not be individual room loads due to ventilation, but the SHL, LHL, and THL due to ventilation of the entire structure will be carried by the tempering equipment.

c. If outside air is partially tempered (to a state t), read the enthalpy at t and determine the SHL/THL ratios for lines ot and tr on the psychrometric chart. Values of SHL, LHL, and THL for the tempering equipment will then be calculated from the total ventilation rate and from the enthalpy gains for sensible, latent, and total heat addition between states o and t. Values of SHL, LHL, and THL for each room will be calculated from the ventilation rate for that room and from the enthalpy gain for sensible, latent, and total heat addition between states t and r.

EXAMPLE 6–10. A 20-ft by 40-ft single-room structure has a ceiling height of 9 ft. Walls are of 8-in. porous brick without inside finish. Floor and ceiling are airtight, and the equivalent over-all coefficient of heat transfer, U_e, for the structure is 0.24 Btu/(hr)(sq ft)(°F); combined inside film coefficient is known to be 1.65 Btu/(hr)(sq ft)(°F). Window and door arrangement is as shown in Fig. 6–7. The structure is located in Raleigh, North Carolina, and the inside design state for winter conditions is to correspond to conditions of optimum comfort. Normal occupancy consists of 15 people. Determine whether or not infiltration will provide adequate ventilation for odor control, and calculate the sensible, latent, and total loads that would occur if ventilation were solely by infiltration.

Solution: Proceeding according to the step-by-step procedure developed above, the following data are recorded:

1. (a) North wall crack: one door plus four windows is calculated as 20 ft for the door plus (4)(15), or 60 ft, for the windows.
   (b) East wall crack: one window, 15 ft.
   (c) South wall crack: three windows, 45 ft.
   (d) West wall crack, 0.

   (e) Net area of north brick wall, $(9)(40) - 20 - 4(10) = 300$ sq ft.
   (f) Net area of east brick wall, $(9)(20) - 10 = 170$ sq ft.
   (g) Net area of south brick wall, $(9)(40) - 3(10) = 330$ sq ft.
   (h) Net area of west brick wall, $(9)(20) - 0 = 180$ sq ft.
   2. Same as step 1 for single-room structure.

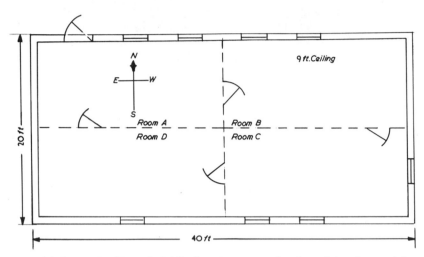

Fig. 6–7. Room plan (Example 6–10). Exterior average-fitted wood door has crack length of 20 ft and area of 21 sq ft. Windows are all unlocked, non-weatherstripped, double-hung wood sash with crack of 1/16 in. and clearance of 3/64 in. All windows are of equal size, each having a glass area of 10 sq ft and a crack length of 15 ft.

   3. Infiltration rate for wall (Art. 6–7, page 263) is taken as 8 cu ft/(hr)(sq ft) for a 15-mph wind. Infiltration rate for windows (Art. 6–7) is taken as 39 cu ft/(hr)(lin ft of crack). Infiltration rate through the exterior door is 100 cu ft/(hr)(lin ft of crack). Total infiltration is therefore:
   (a) North wall: wall plus door plus window, $(300)(8) + (20)(100) + (60)(39)$
      $= 2400 + 4340 = 6740$ cu ft/hr.
   (b) East wall: wall plus window, $(170)(8) + (15)(39) = 1360 + 585 = 1945$
      cu ft/hr.
   (c) South wall: wall plus windows, $(330)(8) + (45)(39) = 2640 + 1755$
      $= 4395$ cu ft/hr.
   (d) West wall: wall only, $(180)(8) = 1440$ cu ft/hr.
(Note that for this structure the infiltration through the wall constitutes a large fraction of the total infiltration.)
   4. The total infiltration rate is $6740 + 1945 + 4395 + 1440$, or 14,520 cu ft/hr. The rate through the wall having greatest infiltration is 6740 cu ft/hr. Since four walls are exposed and since one-half the total infiltration rate exceeds the maximum rate for a single wall, the one-half total value of 7260 cu ft/hr will be used.
   5. For a wind velocity of 5 mph the available ventilation due to infiltration caused by the wind will be

$$I = (0.111)(7260) = 806 \text{ cu ft/hr}$$

6. In order to evaluate infiltration due to inside-to-outside air-temperature difference, it is first necessary to determine the design value of inside air temperature. Assuming that the outside design temperature is selected as the value in common use, Table 3–1 gives 13 F for Raleigh, North Carolina. Then, by Eq. 4–147, the average inside surface temperature is

$$t_{si} = t_i - \left(\frac{1}{1.65}\right)(0.24)(t_i - 13) = 0.85t_i + 1.89$$

Substituting in the comfort equation (1–11),

$$t_i = 147 - 0.85t_i - 1.89$$

giving

$$t_i = 78.4 \text{ F}$$

The equivalent wind velocity (by Eq. 6–34) is

$$V'_e = 0.12[9(78.4 - 13)]^{\frac{1}{2}} = 2.9 \text{ mph}$$

and the infiltration rate (Eq. 6–25) is

$$I = \left(\frac{2.9}{15}\right)^2 7260 = 271 \text{ cu ft/hr}$$

In a strict sense the I value calculated above is irrational for use in determining available ventilation, since lesser infiltration would occur at higher outside temperatures; in practice, however, the error in that total will not be great.

7. *Available* infiltration is (from steps 5 and 6) at a rate of 806 plus 271, or 1077 cu ft/hr. *Required* ventilation for odor control, based on occupancy by sedentary adults of average socioeconomic status, is determinable from Fig. 2–1. Air space per occupant amounts to (20)(40)(9)/15, or 480 cu ft. The required outdoor supply is 7 cfm per occupant, which amounts to (7)(15)(60), or 6300 cu ft/hr. The required ventilation rate is approximately six times as great as the available infiltration rate, so mechanical ventilation should be used.

8. If mechanical ventilation were not provided for this structure, it would be necessary to provide natural ventilation through partially open windows during periods when the wind velocity was low. With closed windows, the infiltration under design conditions would be based on a wind velocity of 8.5 mph (from Table 5–1) for Raleigh, North Carolina. The infiltration due to wind would therefore be (Eq. 6–25).

$$I = \left(\frac{8.5}{15}\right)^2 (7260) = 2330 \text{ cu ft/hr}$$

9. The rate due to temperature difference would be, as before, 271 cu ft/hr. Total infiltration rate for design conditions would therefore amount to 2330 plus 271, or 2601 cu ft/hr.

10. For room conditions equivalent to those of optimum comfort, the inside dry-bulb temperature would be 78.4 F and the inside specific humidity would be maintained at a value equal to that at 73.5 F and 50 per cent RH, or 62 grains/lb. Air at the inside state, 78.4 F dbt and 62 grains/lb, has an enthalpy of 28.6 Btu/lb. The outside state can conservatively be taken at 13 F and 0 per cent RH, giving

an enthalpy of $(0.2411)(13)$, or 3.13 Btu/lb. After locating points o and r on the psychrometric chart (o being fixed approximately by extrapolation down to 13 F), a line or is drawn between them. A line through the reference point and parallel to or intersects the marginal scale at an SHL/THL value of 0.63. Therefore

$$THL = 28.6 - 3.1 = 25.5 \text{ Btu/lb}$$
$$SHL = (0.63)(25.5) = 16.1 \text{ Btu/lb}$$
$$LHL = 25.5 - 16.1 = 9.4 \text{ Btu/lb}$$

11. Design infiltration rate on a weight basis is equal to 2601 cu ft/hr divided by 13.35 cu ft/lb, giving 194.8 lb/hr.

12.
$$SHL = (194.8)(16.1) = 3140 \text{ Btu/hr}$$
$$LHL = (194.8)(9.4) = 1830 \text{ Btu/hr}$$
$$THL = (194.8)(25.5) = 4970 \text{ Btu/hr}$$

EXAMPLE 6–11. For the structure of the above example determine the infiltration loads in each of four equal area rooms, A, B, C, and D, if partitions are installed as shown by the dotted lines of Fig. 6–7.

Solution: Using data from Example 6–10, the infiltration due to wind velocity from room A will be that through the north wall, or

$$I_{A,15} = [(9)(20) - 20 - 2(10)](8) + (20)(100) + (2)(15)(39)$$
$$= 4290 \text{ cu ft/hr}$$

$$I_{A,8.5} = \left(\frac{8.5}{15}\right)^2 (4290) = 1375 \text{ cu ft/hr}$$

The infiltration due to temperature difference will be

$$I_{A,2.9} = \left(\frac{2.9}{15}\right)^2 (4290) = 160 \text{ cu ft/hr}$$

Total infiltration rate in room A is therefore

$$I_A = 1375 + 160 = 1535 \text{ cu ft/hr}$$

which is equal to 1535/13.35, or 115 lb/hr.

If design inside state is taken as the same as in Example 6–10 (neglecting the radiant shielding effect of the inside partitions), the ventilation loads in room A are

$$SHL_A = (115)(16.1) = 1852 \text{ Btu/hr}$$
$$LHL_A = (115)(9.4) = 1080 \text{ Btu/hr}$$
$$THL_A = (115)(25.5) = 2932 \text{ Btu/hr}$$

Similarly, for room B, infiltration will be taken as that through the north wall, giving

$$I_{B,15} = [(9)(20) - (2)(10)](8) + (2)(15)(39) = 2450 \text{ cu ft/hr}$$

giving

$$I_{B,8.5} = \left(\frac{8.5}{15}\right)^2 (2450) = 785 \text{ cu ft/hr}$$

The infiltration due to temperature difference is

$$I_{B,2.9} = \left(\frac{2.9}{15}\right)^2 (2450) = 92 \text{ cu ft/hr}$$

Total infiltration is equal to 785 plus 92, or 877 cu ft/hr, which is equivalent to a weight rate of 65.7 lb/hr. Then

$$\text{SHL}_B = (65.7)(16.1) = 1058 \text{ Btu/hr}$$
$$\text{LHL}_B = (65.7)(9.4) = 618 \text{ Btu/hr}$$
$$\text{THL}_B = (65.7)(25.5) = 1676 \text{ Btu/hr}$$

For room C, infiltration will be based on the south wall and the ventilation load will be identical with that for room B.

For room D, infiltration will be based on the south wall, giving

$$I_{D,15} = [(9)(20) - 10](8) + (15)(39) = 1945 \text{ cu ft/hr}$$

giving

$$I_{D,8.5} = \left(\frac{8.5}{15}\right)^2 (1945) = 623 \text{ cu ft/hr}$$

The infiltration due to temperature difference is

$$I_{D,2.9} = \left(\frac{2.9}{15}\right)^2 (1945) = 72 \text{ cu ft/hr}$$

Total infiltration is equal to 623 plus 72, or 695 cu ft/hr, which is equivalent to a weight rate of 52 lb/hr. Then

$$\text{SHL}_D = (52.0)(16.1) = 837 \text{ Btu/hr}$$
$$\text{LHL}_D = (52.0)(9.4) = 489 \text{ Btu/hr}$$
$$\text{THL}_D = (52.0)(25.5) = 1326 \text{ Btu/hr}$$

The total capacity of heating and humidifying equipments for the four rooms is

$$\sum \text{SHL} = 1852 + 1058 + 1058 + 837 = 4805 \text{ Btu/hr}$$
$$\sum \text{LHL} = 1080 + 618 + 618 + 489 = 2805 \text{ Btu/hr}$$
$$\sum \text{THL} = 4805 + 2805 = 7610 \text{ Btu/hr}$$

Note that the over-all capacity of the heating and humidifying system (from Example 6–10) was

$$\text{SHL} = 3140 \text{ Btu/hr}$$
$$\text{LHL} = 1830 \text{ Btu/hr}$$
$$\text{THL} = 4970 \text{ Btu/hr}$$

The surround totals are much larger than the over-all totals; this is due to the fact that for wind from any fixed direction, not more than two of the rooms will be under maximum load. Regardless of wind direction, the over-all load values will always be sufficient to supply the heating and humidifying needs of all four rooms.

6–9. Summary. Minimum ventilation requirements for an occupied space are determined from considerations of odor prevention or contamination dilution as discussed in Chapter 2. For most residential construction the minimum requirements for odor will be met and surpassed by air flow through the structure due to infiltration. Infiltration volume is calculated either in terms of crack lengths and average flow rates for different types of windows and doors or in terms of arbitrarily selected values of the hourly air change. An experienced designer will usually prefer the air-change method, but unless one possesses sufficient background of experience to permit accurate judgment of relative infiltration as a function of location and structural arrangement, it will usually be safer to make use of the crack method. Evaluation of *available* infiltration is based on a low wind velocity (such as 5 mph), whereas evaluation of the heating and humidity loads due to infiltration is based on the design value of the wind velocity as given in Table 5–1.

PROBLEMS

6–1. In a mechanical ventilation system, 150 cfm of air are exhausted from a 30-ft by 20-ft by 10-ft room. Of the volume of air handled, 85 cfm are recirculated and the remainder is discharged to the atmosphere and replaced with outside air. Assuming that the room is sufficiently tight so that exfiltration can be neglected, determine the number of thermal air changes per hour.

6–2. The state of air in a 20-ft by 20-ft by 8-ft room is 80 F and 30 per cent RH. Calculate the weight of dry air in the room (do not use Fig. 6–5).

6–3. Solve problem 6–2 by using data from Fig. 6–5.

6–4. A storage tank 50 ft in diameter and 20 ft high is half full of a chemical which has a saturation vapor pressure of 1.5 psia at 90 F. What will be the weight of chemical in vapor form when equilibrium is reached?

6–5. A tank containing air at 50 F, 30 per cent RH, and 14.696 psia is rapidly filled with 150 F water until only a small air space exists near the top of the tank. During filling of the tank, air escapes through a valve at the top and tank pressure remains constant at 14.696 psia. The air and water values are closed when the tank is almost full. Assuming perfect insulation, calculate the pressure that will exist in the tank when equilibrium is reached.

6–6. Determine (using Fig. 6–5) the enthalpy of an atmosphere in which the relative humidity is 65 per cent and vapor pressure is 0.46 psia.

6–7. Room air has a specific volume of 14.5 cu ft/lb and a specific humidity of 160 grains/lb. Determine (using Fig. 6–5) the air temperature.

6–8. Assuming unavailability of steam tables, use Fig. 6–5 to determine the enthalpy of superheated steam at 90 F and at unknown pressure.

6–9. Calculate the specific humidity of a 70 F hydrogen atmosphere that is saturated with water vapor; the total pressure is 14.696 psia. (The gas constant R for hydrogen is 386.6.) Compare this humidity with that of an air-vapor atmosphere at the same state.

6–10. One wall of a windowless room has a combined inside film resistance of 2 and an air-to-air over-all resistance of 10. Inside air temperature is automatically controlled at a fixed value of 70 F. Condensation starts to form on the inside wall surface when the outside air temperature, dropping slowly, reaches +5 F. Estimate the relative humidity of the room air.

6–11. Air at 120 F dbt undergoes adiabatic saturation and reaches a saturated state at 75 F. Calculate (do not use Fig. 6–5) the specific humidity of the air at the initial (120 F dbt) state.

6–12. For the conditions of problem 6–11, if adiabatic saturation were assumed to occur along a constant-enthalpy line, what would be the error in fixing the dew-point temperature at the initial state?

6–13. Calculate the sigma heat content of air at 120 F dry-bulb temperature and 56 grains/lb specific humidity.

6–14. Two hundred cubic feet of air at 90 F dbt and 80 F dpt are to be heated to 120 F dbt. (a) Calculate the required heat addition [taking the specific heat of low-pressure superheated vapor as 0.5 Btu/(lb)(°F)]. (b) What percentage of error would result if the calculation in part (a) were based on the specific heat of dry air?

6–15. The latent heat of vaporization at 70 F (from Appendix, Table A-1) is 1054.3 Btu/lb. Taking the specific heat of low-pressure superheated water vapor as 0.5 Btu/(lb)(°F), calculate (using *only* data from Fig. 6–5) the latent heat of vaporization of saturated steam at 35 F.

6–16. Derive an equation comparable to Eq. 6–17 for a wetted thermometer bulb that is exposed to radiation and has a combined film coefficient of $h = h_c + h_r'$.

6–17. For the swimming pool of Example 6–4 assume that the corrected equivalent coefficient for radiant transfer is 0.8 Btu/(hr)(sq ft)(°F). Calculate the total rate of evaporation loss due to the combined effects of convection and radiation.

6–18. An unshielded, wetted, mercury thermometer bulb has a combined film coefficient of $h = h_c + h_r' = 0.4 + 0.5 = 0.9$ Btu/(hr)(sq ft)(°F). (a) Calculate the equilibrium temperature of the thermometer when in a room with air at 70 F and 50 per cent RH. (b) Calculate the magnitude of the error if the temperature determined in part (a) were used as the wet-bulb temperature of room air.

6–19. A factory work room is maintained at 61 F wbt and 57.5 F dpt. In order to expedite a drying process, it is decided to reduce the specific humidity of room air to 20 grains/lb. If, under the new conditions the occupants are to experience the same degree of thermal comfort that was experienced originally, what must be the value of the new dry-bulb temperature?

6–20. Under design conditions a given structure has a latent heat load of 23,000 Btu/hr and a known sensible heat-total heat ratio of 0.3. (a) Calculate the total load under design conditions. (b) Calculate the required wet-bulb temperature of supply air from a warm-air heating system if supply dry-bulb temperature is 100 F and if the state of air in the room is 65 F dbt and 43 F dpt.

6–21. For the structure of Example 6–10, (a) calculate the total sensible transmission and ventilation heating load if ventilation is by infiltration only, (b) calculate the ratio of total sensible load to total load, (c) calculate the ratio total ventilation load to total load.

6–22. If the structure of Example 6–10 were adequately ventilated by mechanical means, (a) calculate the total sensible load, (b) calculate the ratio of total sensible load to total load, (c) calculate the ratio of total ventilation load to total load.

6-23. Transmission load for a given room is 7000 Btu/hr and infiltration load is 5000 Btu/hr, of which 3600 Btu/hr is latent heat load. Room state is at 70 F dpt. If a recirculating warm-air heating and humidifying system is used, what would be the required dry-bulb and wet-bulb temperatures of the supply air if the rate of air flow to the return duct were 200 cfm?

6-24. During a severe storm a residential heating and humidifying system that was designed for 0 F at 10 mph is subjected to outside conditions of 0 F at 25 mph. The structure is well insulated, so the increased wind velocity (hence greater outside convective film coefficient) has negligible influence on design value (65,000 Btu/hr) of the transmission load. Design value of the ventilation load is 30,000 Btu/hr and design inside-air temperature is 76 F. Calculate the equilibrium value of the inside air temperature for storm conditions.

Part III

LOAD DETERMINATION FOR SPECIAL DESIGN CONDITIONS

7

RATIONAL BASIS OF LOAD EVALUATION

The methods established in Chapters 5 and 6 are commonly used for all types of heating systems installed in all types of structures and located in all kinds of climates. Although satisfactory in the great majority of cases, these methods can lead to serious error in performance when applied to extremes of construction or of climate and can result in serious penalty of equipment cost when applied to large structures. In order to assist the professional engineer in recognizing limitations of the usual load-analysis procedure, the present chapter will investigate in considerable detail a number of the simplifications that are customarily accepted as providing adequate accuracy.

The rational analysis is long, time-consuming, and in many respects tedious. Thorough understanding of it will, however, enable the engineer to estimate with much greater confidence the applicability (within specified limits of accuracy) of conventional and less complex procedures. Thus familiarity with rational procedures affords two advantages: (1) develops judgment to permit recognizing the extreme cases that should be treated by this method; (2) develops confidence to enable selection of conventional methods for the great majority of cases to which they are safely applicable.

In its broadest application the rational procedure requires that a heat balance be established on each thermally different structural section of a room. Thus differences in location (such as ceiling, wall, or floor), differences in surface-to-surface conductance (as for different types of exposed wall area), and differences in exposure (such as ceiling, inside partitions, and windows) all require consideration. To minimize the calculations without loss of generality, a geometrically simple room will be selected.

The room to be considered is 20 ft by 20 ft in plan with a 10-ft ceiling and with an identical window in each of two outside walls; each window is 10 ft long by 5.68 ft high with its sill 2.50 ft above the floor and its vertical center line superimposed on the vertical center line of the wall. Fig. 7–1a is a three-dimensional view of the room; Fig. 7–1b is an expanded view with each different surface identified. Exterior walls w_1 and w_2 have the same construction and exposure; walls i_1 and i_2 are interior partitions, and since they are non-transmitting, the door located in one partition can be treated as thermally identical to the partition. Thermal characteristics and film conductances for all surfaces will be discussed in Art. 7–3, page 295.

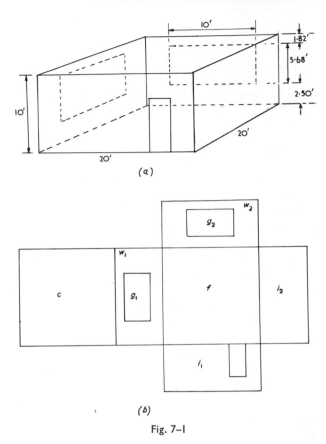

Fig. 7–I

7–I. Shape-Factor Analysis of Room Surfaces.

Each different type of surface will necessarily be exchanging radiant energy with each other surface. As a first step in the analysis, the required shape factors will be separated into groups arranged according to the type of problem involved in their respective evaluation. The simplest type has equal, opposite rectangles in parallel planes; F_{cf} is of this group and hence can be evaluated directly from Fig. 4–15 for $D/L = 2$, and $W/L = 2$, giving $F_{cf} = 0.41$. By the reciprocity theorem, $F_{fc} = F_{cf} = 0.41$.

The second type of problem consists of simple rectangles in perpendicular planes which have one side in common. Problems of this kind can be directly solved from Fig. 4–20 and are represented by the shape factors F_{if}, F_{fi}, F_{ii}, F_{ci}, and F_{ic}. For $F_{i_1 f}$ note that $Y = 1$, $Z = 0.5$, and from Fig. 4–20 the corresponding shape factor is read as 0.15. By observation $F_{i_2 f} = F_{i_1 f}$, and since both these areas are the same, $F_{if} = 2F_{i_1 f} = 0.30$ (where the subscript i without further identification refers to the total inside wall area). The areas of i and f are equal; therefore F_{if} is equal to F_{fi}. Further, observation shows that $F_{ci} = F_{ic} = F_{if}$. The one remaining factor of this type is F_{ii}; here $Y = Z = 2$, and so F_{ii} is read as 0.15.

All the remaining groups of shape factors involve more complex conditions. Consider first the evaluation of the shape factor for one of the windows

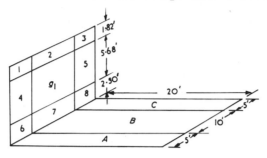

Fig. 7–2

(such as g_1) with respect to the floor. Referring to Fig. 7–2, divide both wall and floor into the component areas shown, and note that

$$F_{(g_1)f} = \frac{F_{(g_1)A}A_A + F_{(g_1)B}A_B + F_{(g_1)C}A_C}{A_f}$$

$$= \frac{F_{(g_1)B}A_B + 2F_{(g_1)C}A_C}{A_f} \tag{7-1}$$

But

$$F_{(g_1)B} = F_{(g_17)B} - F_{7B} \tag{7-2}$$

where $F_{(g_17)B}$ is read from Fig. 4–20 (for $Y = 2$ and $Z = 0.818$) as 0.108, and F_{7B} (for $Y = 2$ and $Z = 0.25$) is 0.047; therefore, by Eq. 7–2,

$$F_{(g_1)B} = 0.108 - 0.047 = 0.061$$

The factor $F_{(g_1)C}$ is given by a reduced form of Eq. 4–135:

$$F_{(g_1)C} = F_{(g_17)C} - F_{7C} \tag{7-3}$$

in which the two factors on the right can be evaluated by equations of the form of Eq. 4–134:

$$F_{(g_17)C} = \frac{F_{(g_1578)BC}A_{BC} - F_{(58)C}A_C - F_{(g_17)B}A_B}{2A_C} \tag{7-4}$$

where $F_{(g_1578)BC}$ is obtained from Fig. 4–20 (for $Y = 20/15 = 1.33$, $Z = 8.18/15 = 0.545$) as 0.121; $F_{(58)C}$ (for $Y = 4$, $Z = 8.18/5 = 1.636$) as 0.077; and $F_{(g_17)B}$ (for $Y = 2$, $Z = 0.818$) as 0.108.

Then, by Eq. 7–4,

$$F_{(g_17)C} = \frac{[(0.121)(300)] - [(0.077)(100)] - [(0.108)(200)]}{(2)(100)} = 0.035$$

Similarly,

$$F_{7C} = \frac{F_{(78)(BC)}A_{BC} - F_{8C}A_C - F_{7B}A_B}{2A_C} \quad (7\text{-}5)$$

where $F_{(78)(BC)}$ (for $Y = 20/15 = 1.33$, $Z = 2.5/15 = 0.167$) as 0.05; F_{8C}(for $Y = 4$, $Z = 0.5$) as 0.04; and F_{7B}(for $Y = 2$, $Z = 0.25$) as 0.045, so that, by Eq. 7–5,

$$F_{7C} = \frac{[(0.05)(300)] - [(0.04)(100)] - [(0.045)(200)]}{(2)(100)} = 0.01$$

Then, substituting in Eq. 7–3 gives

$$F_{(g_1)C} = 0.035 - 0.01 = 0.025$$

and by Eq. 7–1,

$$F_{(g_1)f} = \frac{[(0.061)(200)] + [(2)(0.025)(100)]}{400} = 0.043$$

Then $F_{gf} = 2F_{(g_1)f} = 0.086$, and by the reciprocity theorem, (Eq. 4–99),

$$F_{fg} = F_{gf}\frac{A_f}{A_g} = 0.086\,\frac{400}{113.6} = 0.304$$

The shape factor of the outside wall with respect to the floor is now easily obtained.

$$F_{(w_1)f} = F_{(w_1 g_1)f} - F_{(g_1)f}$$

where $F_{(y_1)f}$ is already known and $F_{(w_1 g_1)f} = F_{i_1 f} = 0.15$. Thus

$$F_{(w_1)f} = 0.15 - 0.043 = 0.107$$

and

$$F_{wf} = 2F_{(w_1)f} = (2)(0.107) = 0.214$$

so that

$$F_{fw} = 0.214\,\frac{400}{286.4} = 0.299$$

The procedure for determining the shape factor of glass with respect to ceiling is exactly the same as that developed above for evaluating F_{gf}. Refer to Fig. 7–3 and note that the nomenclature is arranged to permit direct use of Eqs. 7–1 through 7–5; Eq. 7–1 becomes

$$F_{(g_1)c} = \frac{F_{(g_1)B}A_B + 2F_{(g_1)C}A_C}{A_c} \quad (7\text{-}1a)$$

But

$$F_{(g_1)B} = F_{(g_1 7)B} - F_{7B} \quad (7\text{-}2a)$$

where $F_{(g_1 7)B}$ (for $Y = 2$, $Z = 0.75$) is 0.10 and F_{7B} (for $Y = 2$, $Z = 0.182$) is 0.035; and so,

$$F_{(g_1)B} = 0.100 - 0.035 = 0.065$$

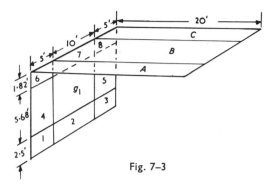

Fig. 7–3

The factor $F_{(g_1)C}$ is given by Eq. 7–3:

$$F_{(g_1)C} = F_{(g_1 7)C} - F_{7C} \qquad (7\text{–}3a)$$

in which the two factors on the right can be evaluated by equations of the form of Eq. 7–4:

$$F_{(g_1 7)C} = \frac{F_{(g_1 578)BC} A_{BC} - F_{(58)C} A_C - F_{(g_1 7)B} A_B}{2A_C} \qquad (7\text{–}4a)$$

where $F_{(g_1 578)BC}$ (for $Y = 1.33$, $Z = 0.5$) is 0.115; $F_{(58)C}$ (for $Y = 4$, $Z = 1.5$) is 0.075; and $F_{(g_1 7)B}$ (for $Y = 2$, $Z = 0.75$) is 0.10. Then

$$F_{(g_1 7)C} = \frac{[(0.115)(300)] - [(0.075)(100)] - [(0.100)(200)]}{(2)(100)}$$

$$= \frac{34.5 - 7.5 - 20}{200} = 0.035$$

Similarly,

$$F_{7C} = \frac{F_{(78)(BC)} A_{BC} - F_{8C} A_C - F_{7B} A_B}{2A_C} \qquad (7\text{–}5a)$$

where $F_{(78)(BC)}$ (for $Y = 1.33$, $Z = 0.121$) is 0.039; F_{8C} (for $Y = 4$, $Z = 0.363$) is 0.03; and F_{7B} (for $Y = 2$, $Z = 0.182$) is 0.034; and so,

$$F_{7C} = \frac{[(0.039)(300)] - [(0.03)(100)] - [(0.034)(200)]}{(2)(100)}$$

$$= \frac{11.73 - 6.8}{200} = 0.009$$

Then, by Eq. 7–3a,

$$F_{(g_1)c} = \frac{[(0.065)(200)] + [(2)(0.026)(100)]}{400} = \frac{13 + 5.2}{400} = 0.046$$

Then

$$F_{gc} = 2F_{(g_1)c} = (2)(0.046) = 0.092$$

and, by the reciprocity theorem,

$$F_{cg} = 0.092\left(\frac{400}{113.6}\right) = 0.325$$

The shape factor of the outside wall with respect to the ceiling is now easily obtained:

$$F_{wc} = 2F_{(w_1)c} = 2[F_{(w_1 g_1)c} - F_{(g_1)c}] \tag{7-6}$$

where $F_{(g_1)c}$ is already known and

$$F_{(w_1 g_1)c} = F_{i_1 c} = \frac{F_{ic}}{2} = 0.150$$

Thus

$$F_{wc} = 2(0.150 - 0.046) = (2)(0.104) = 0.208$$

and

$$F_{cw} = 0.208\left(\frac{400}{286.4}\right) = 0.290$$

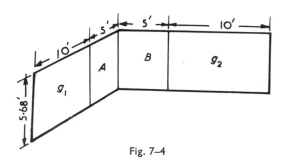

Fig. 7-4

The shape factor of glass with respect to glass is next obtained. Refer to Fig. 7-4;

$$F_{g_2 g_1} = \frac{F_{(g_2 B)(g_1 A)}A_{(g_1 A)} - F_{B(g_1 A)}A_{(g_1 A)} - F_{(g_2 B)A}A_A + F_{(BA)}A_A}{A_{g_1}}$$

$$= \frac{F_{(g_2 B)(g_1 A)} - 2F_{B(g_1 A)}A_{(g_1 A)} + F_{(BA)}A_A}{A_{g_1}} \tag{7-7}$$

where $F_{(g_2 B)(g_1 A)}$ (for $Y = 2.64$, $Z = 2.64$) is 0.131; $F_{B(g_1 A)}$ (for $Y = 2.64$, $Z = 0.88$) is 0.086; and F_{BA} (for $Y = 0.88$, $Z = 0.88$) is 0.21; and so,

$$F_{g_2 g_1} = F_{gg} = \frac{(0.131) - [(2)(0.086)(85.2)] + [(0.21)(28.4)]}{56.8}$$

$$= \frac{-3.49 + 5.96}{56.8} = 0.043$$

To evaluate the shape factor of wall area with respect to glass area, the methods of extending the use of Figs. 4–15 and 4–20 could be followed again, but a more rapid and direct method is to divide the glass area into small sections and then to evaluate the shape factor of the entire adjacent wall (including window) with respect to points in the center of these smaller areas. Refer to Fig. 7–5 and read all shape factors from Fig. 4–25.

For point A, $H/D = 20/12.5 = 1.60$, and the values of W/D for the areas above and below A are $3.23/12.5 = 0.2585$ and $6.77/12.5 = 0.542$, giving as

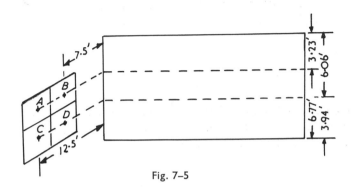

Fig. 7–5

the respective shape factors of these areas, with respect to A, 0.030 and 0.057, or a total of 0.087.

For point B, $H/D = 2.67$, and W/D is $3.23/7.5 = 0.431$ and $6.77/7.5 = 0.903$, giving shape factors of 0.054 and 0.098, or a total of 0.152.

For point C, $H/D = 20/12.5 = 1.60$, and W/D is $6.06/12.5 = 0.485$ and $3.94/12.5 = 0.315$, giving shape factors of 0.052 and 0.038, or a total of 0.090.

For point D, $H/D = 20/7.5 = 2.67$, and $W/D = 6.06/7.5 = 0.808$ and $3.94/7.5 = 0.525$, giving shape factors of 0.094 and 0.068, or a total of 0.162.

The over-all shape factor of the adjacent wall with respect to the glass is the average of the values for points A, B, C, and D, or

$$\frac{0.087 + 0.152 + 0.090 + 0.162}{4} = 0.123$$

That is,

$$F_{i_1 g_1} = 0.123$$

Then

$$F_{wg} = F_{i_1 g_1} - F_{gg} = 0.123 - 0.043 = 0.080$$

and, by the reciprocity theorem,

$$F_{gw} = 0.080 \frac{113.6}{286.4} = 0.032$$

By a similar procedure of evaluating shape factors of each of four rectangular areas with respect to the center points of a series of relatively small

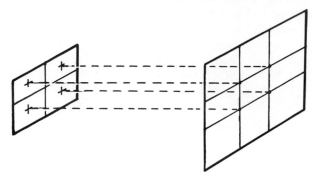

Fig. 7–6

areas (refer to Fig. 7–6), the shape factor of one inside partition with respect to glass in the opposite wall can be obtained. All shape factors are read from Fig. 4–29, and the final result is

$$F_{i_2 g_1} = 0.130$$

Then

$$F_{ig_1} = F_{i_1 g_1} + F_{i_2 g_1} = 0.123 + 0.130 = 0.253$$

which, by observation, is equal to F_{ig}. Then, by the reciprocity theorem,

$$F_{gi} = 0.253 \frac{113.6}{400} = 0.072$$

The shape factor of wall area with respect to inside partition can next be obtained by noting that

$$F_{wi} = F_{wi_1} + F_{w_1 i_1} + F_{w_2 i_1} \tag{7–8}$$

where

$$F_{w_1 i_1} = F_{i_2 i_1} - F_{g_1 i_1} = 0.150 - 0.035 = 0.115$$

Similarly,

$$F_{i_1 w_1} = 0.115 \left(\frac{400}{286.4} \right) = 0.1605$$

Likewise,

$$F_{w_2 i_1} = F_{(w_2 g_2) i_1} - F_{g_2 i_1}$$

From Fig. 4–15, $F_{(w_2 g_2) i_1}$ for $L/D = 0.5$, and $W/D = 1.0$ is found as 0.11; and so,

$$F_{w_2 i_1} = 0.11 - 0.037 = 0.073$$

and

$$F_{wi} = 0.115 + 0.073 = 0.188$$

Then, by the reciprocity theorem,

$$F_{iw} = 0.188 \frac{400}{286.4} = 0.262$$

Finally,

$$F_{ww} = F_{w_2 w_1} = F_{i_1 w_1} - F_{gw} = 0.1605 - 0.032 = 0.128$$

All the required shape factors have now been determined. The results may be tabulated:

$$
\begin{aligned}
&F_{fi} = 0.300 \quad && F_{if} = 0.300 \quad && F_{iw} = 0.262 \quad && F_{wi} = 0.188 \\
&F_{fc} = 0.410 \quad && F_{cf} = 0.410 \quad && F_{ww} = 0.128 \\
&F_{fw} = 0.299 \quad && F_{wf} = 0.214 \quad && F_{wc} = 0.208 \quad && F_{cw} = 0.290 \\
&F_{fg} = 0.304 \quad && F_{gf} = 0.086 \quad && F_{wg} = 0.080 \quad && F_{gw} = 0.032 \\
&F_{ii} = 0.150 \quad && && F_{gg} = 0.043 \\
&F_{ic} = 0.300 \quad && F_{ci} = 0.300 \quad && F_{gc} = 0.092 \quad && F_{cg} = 0.325 \\
&F_{ig} = 0.253 \quad && F_{gi} = 0.072
\end{aligned}
$$

The accuracy of the computed shape factors can be checked by investigating whether the sum of all shape factors with respect to a particular area is equal to unity:

For the floor:
$$F_{cf} + F_{if} + F_{wf} + F_{gf} = 1.000$$
$$0.410 + 0.300 + 0.214 + 0.086 = 1.010$$

For the wall:
$$F_{cw} + F_{iw} + F_{fw} + F_{gw} + F_{ww} = 1.000$$
$$0.290 + 0.262 + 0.299 + 0.032 + 0.128 = 1.011$$

For the inside partition:
$$F_{ci} + F_{ii} + F_{wi} + F_{gi} + F_{fi} = 1.000$$
$$0.300 + 0.150 + 0.188 + 0.072 + 0.300 = 1.010$$

For the glass:
$$F_{cg} + F_{ig} + F_{wg} + F_{gg} + F_{fg} = 1.000$$
$$0.325 + 0.253 + 0.080 + 0.043 + 0.304 = 1.005$$

For the ceiling:
$$F_{ic} + F_{wc} + F_{gc} + F_{fc} = 1.000$$
$$0.300 + 0.208 + 0.092 + 0.410 = 1.010$$

The maximum deviation noted above is 1 per cent, which is as close agreement as could be expected and is within the limit of accuracy possible from readings of the shape-factor curves. Note that each check equation could have been used to determine one shape factor, but this procedure was not followed because it would have precluded checking the results.

7–2. Evaluation of Mean Radiant Temperature. The first requirement of a thermally satisfactory occupied enclosure is to satisfy the comfort equation (Eq. 1–11),

$$t_a = 147 - mrt \tag{7–9}$$

As previously defined (Art. 1–5), the *mean radiant temperature mrt* is the imaginary, uniform, inside, surface temperature of a large room for which the rate of radiant exchange between the occupant and the enclosing surface is numerically equal to the radiant exchange experienced by the occupant in the actual room which has a non-uniformly heated inside surface. Practically all actual rooms are surfaced with materials having reflectivities of less than 10 per cent. In all such rooms, 90 per cent of the energy emitted by any surface is absorbed at the first surface which that energy strikes, while the remaining 10 per cent is reflected back to the emitter or to other surfaces that make up the surround. The reflected energy is likewise 90 per cent absorbed at the first surface which it strikes, so that in actual rooms, 99 per cent of all energy emitted by an average surface will be absorbed either directly or after one reflection.

Since the reflected energy is *damped out* so rapidly, the assumption is frequently made that radiant exchange rates within an enclosure with surfaces having various emissivities between 90 and 100 per cent are practically the same as if all surfaces were thermally black. The effect of this assumption is to increase the quantity of energy transferred directly from one surface to another and to eliminate the quantity of energy that would be received at the second surface as a result of re-reflections between surfaces one and two or of interreflections among the various other surfaces constituting the surround. These two effects alter the exchange rate in opposite directions; the accuracy of the result will obviously depend on the extent to which the errors cancel one another. In very unusual problems where this assumption may not appear to be valid (as when surfaces are present which have emissivities substantially less than 90 per cent), resort should be made to the rational procedure for reflection analysis as developed in Art. 8–2.

Based on the above assumption, a relatively simple equation can now be set up for establishing the mean radiant temperature in a room having many surfaces at various temperatures but all of which have emissivities in excess of 90 per cent. To evaluate the mean radiant temperature of a room with respect to an occupant at a given location and in a given position (as sitting or standing), use must be made of the basic equation for the net rate of radiant transfer between two thermally black surfaces. This equation can be written (from Eq. 4–112) as

$$q = h_r A_1 F_{21}(t_1 - t_2) \tag{7-10}$$

where, as previously defined, the term h_r is an equivalent coefficient for radiant transfer and can be obtained directly from the graphical solution of Fig. 4–14.

In order to determine the mean radiant temperature, the net radiant-transfer rate must be established between a given surface (with respect to which *mrt* is being evaluated) and its surround. Equating this rate to the net transfer that would occur between the same surface and a uniform surround at unknown temperature *mrt* gives an equation which can then be solved for the mean radiant temperature. Such an equation to define the *mrt* with respect to a surface, A_s, which is within an enclosure made up of any number of other uniformly heated surfaces A_1, A_2, A_3, etc., is

$$h_{r_{s1}} A_1 F_{s1}(t_1 - t_s) + h_{r_{s2}} A_2 F_{s2}(t_2 - t_s) + h_{r_{s3}} A_3 F_{s3}(t_3 - t_s) + \cdots$$
$$= h_{r_{se}} A_e F_{se}(mrt - t_s) \tag{7-11}$$

where the subscript e represents the uniformly heated enclosure (equal in area to $A_1 + A_2 + A_3 + \cdots$) and the double subscripts on the h_r and F terms indicate the two surfaces for which the equivalent coefficient, or the shape factor, is to be evaluated. Usually the variation of h_r is negligibly small for the range of surface-temperature differences occurring in an actual room; hence this term can be canceled from the above equation. By the reciprocity theorem, $F_{s1}A_1 = F_{1s}A_s$; therefore, making a substitution of this form in each term of Eq. 7–11 and canceling the area A_s from the equation give

$$F_{1s}(t_1 - t_s) + F_{2s}(t_2 - t_s) + F_{3s}(t_3 - t_s) + \cdots = F_{es}(mrt - t_s) \quad (7\text{–}12)$$

Solving for mrt gives

$$mrt = \frac{[(F_{1s}t_1 + F_{2s}t_2 + F_{3s}t_3 + \cdots)] - [(F_{1s} + F_{2s} + F_{3s} + \cdots)t_s]}{F_{es}} + t_s$$

$$(7\text{–}13)$$

The sum of the shape factors of the various enclosuring surfaces with respect to the surface A_s must be equal to F_{es} and this term must itself be equal to unity, since all energy emitted by the surface A_s must remain within the enclosure. Making these substitutions in Eq. 7–13 gives

$$mrt = F_{1s}t_1 + F_{2s}t_2 + F_{3s}t_3 + \cdots \quad (7\text{–}14)$$

Eq. 7–14 is the fundamental relationship from which the mean radiant temperature at any given point, or with respect to any given surface of an enclosure, can be evaluated. The only type of problem for which Eq. 7–14 cannot be satisfactorily used is one involving a very small room surfaced on walls, floor, and ceiling with polished unprotected metal; such a problem is remote from the interests of the practical designer.

Application of Eq. 7–14 requires knowledge of the number of surfaces at different temperatures that exist within the enclosure and the shape factors of each of these surfaces with respect to the point or surface for which the mrt of the enclosure is to be determined. The temperature problem is too complex to permit of an exact rational solution. Brief consideration of any room will show that no finite surface exists over which the temperature has a fixed value. Even for surfaces of uniform construction, like an uncovered floor, the temperature is a point function, since it varies as the point moves with respect to the walls, the windows, or the heating panel. Thus exact evaluation of the mrt would necessitate an infinite number of terms in Eq. 7–14 and an infinite number of surface temperatures.

The practical application of Eq. 7–14 requires that it include the smallest possible number of terms. Since the surface temperature is a point function and since the major variations in surface temperature occur because of change in the construction or orientation, or external exposure, a first approximation would be to limit the number of terms to the number of differently constructed or oriented, or exposed surfaces within the room. For the general case of a room such as that of Fig. 7–1 with ceiling c, exposed wall w, windows g, and inside partitions i, and floor f, Eq. 7–14 takes the form

$$mrt = F_{cs}t_c + F_{ws}t_w + F_{gs}t_g + F_{is}t_i + F_{fs}t_f \qquad (7\text{–}15)$$

where the subscript s identifies the point or surface (usually the occupant) with respect to which the mean radiant temperature is being evaluated.

The sum of the various shape factors that appear in Eq. 7–15 must under all conditions be equal to unity, but the individual factors will show wide variation as the point or area A_s is moved to different places within the same enclosure. Thus the mean radiant temperature evaluated with respect to an occupant standing at the midpoint of the floor may have a decidedly different value from the mean radiant temperature of the same room when evaluated with respect to an occupant standing near one corner of the room. Fortunately, the problem of variable mean radiant temperature is somewhat less of a complicating factor than the above discussion would indicate. In order for any heating system to provide comfort, the heat sources must be distributed in such a manner that the heating effect for the occupant is reasonably uniform regardless of his posture or movement through the room. If such uniformity is attained, the mean radiant temperature of the room with respect to the occupant must be approximately the same for all normal locations and postures of the occupant. One major problem in heating design is, therefore, to provide distribution of heating elements such that the value of the mean radiant temperature of the room with respect to the occupant will not vary appreciably as the occupant moves from place to place or alters his bodily position.

MEAN RADIANT TEMPERATURE WITH RESPECT TO STANDING SUBJECT. For an occupant standing at the center of a room, the true mean radiant temperature for substitution in the comfort equation (Eq. 1–11) can be determined by use of the actual shape factors of the various enclosure surfaces with respect to the subject. Thus for the 20-ft by 20-ft by 10-ft room considered in Art. 7–1, the shape factors of each surface with respect to a standing subject at the room center can be obtained from the equation

$$F_{sc}A_c + F_{sw}A_w + F_{sg}A_g + F_{si}A_i + F_{sf}A_f$$
$$= A_s(F_{cs} + F_{ws} + F_{gs} + F_{is} + F_{fs}) = A_s \qquad (7\text{–}16)$$

where each of the shape factors on the left side can be evaluated from the graphs and the areas on the left side are already known. Thus the equivalent area of the subject, A_s, can be readily determined, and the shape factors of the various surfaces with respect to the subject can then be calculated by means of the reciprocity theorem.

Evaluation of Shape Factors. The shape factor, with respect to the ceiling, of a subject standing in the center of the room is the same as the shape factor of the subject with respect to any one of the 10-ft by 10-ft quarters of the ceiling; this latter shape factor is the average of point values taken at the centers of equal-area sections of any quarter. Fig. 7–7 shows one such quarter divided into 25 elements of 4 sq ft each, the subject standing at point P and his approximate distance from the center of each area being given by the number shown just above the midpoint of that area. The shape factor of the subject with respect to each midpoint can then be taken directly from Fig. 4–32 for a 10-ft ceiling and for a subject in semiprofile; numerical values are recorded on Fig. 7–7 just below the midpoints of elementary areas. The

P

1′ 6″	3′ 3″	5′ 2″	7′ 0″	9′ 0″
0.017	0.019	0.0145	0.0105	0.0
(0.060)	(0.050)	(0.017)	(0.0099)	(0.0057)
3′ 3″	4′ 3″	6′ 0″	7′ 6″	9′ 6″
0.019	0.017	0.0125	0.010	0.007
(0.050)	(0.0225)	(0.0125)	(0.0090)	(0.0050)
5′ 3″	6′ 0″	7′ 0″	8′ 6″	10′ 3″
0.014	0.0125	0.0105	0.010	0.007
(0.017)	(0.0125)	(0.0080)	(0.0064)	(0.0045)
7′ 0″	7′ 6″	8′ 6″	10′ 0″	11′ 6″
0.0105	0.010	0.010	0.007	0.006
(0.0099)	(0.090)	(0.0064)	(0.0043)	(0.0030)
9′ 0″	10′ 3″	10′ 6″	11′ 6″	12′ 9″
0.008	0.007	0.007	0.006	0.004
(0.0050)	(0.0054)	(0.0045)	(0.0030)	(0.0023)

Fig. 7–7

over-all shape factor of the occupant with respect to this quarter of the ceiling (and hence with respect to the entire ceiling) is then $\frac{1}{25}$ of the sum of 25 point factors (as recorded on Fig. 7–7), or

$$F_{sc} = \frac{0.2640}{25} = 0.0106$$

By the same method, taking values from Fig. 4–34, the point shape factors of the subject with respect to midpoints of elementary floor areas can be determined (they are recorded on Fig. 7–7 below the ceiling point factors and in parentheses), and the over-all shape factor of the subject with respect to this quarter of the floor, hence also with respect to the entire floor, can then be obtained as $\frac{1}{25}$ of the sum of point factors, or

$$F_{sf} = \frac{0.3431}{25} = 0.0137$$

The shape factor of the subject with respect to either of the interior partitions can be determined as the average of point factors determined for 4-sq ft elementary areas.

From Table 4–8 for full face and for $L = 10$:

H, ft	0	2	4	6	8	10
$\frac{1}{2}(0 + 10)$	0.014	0.0135	0.013	0.012	0.011	0.010
2	0.017	0.016	0.015	0.014	0.013	0.011
4	0.016	0.015	0.014	0.013	0.012	0.011
6	0.017	0.017	0.016	0.014	0.013	0.012
8	0.015	0.014	0.014	0.013	0.012	0.010
	(1)(0.079)	(2)(0.076)	(2)(0.072)	(2)(0.066)	(2)(0.061)	(1)(0.054)
	= 0.079	= 0.152	= 0.144	= 0.132	= 0.122	= 0.054

The over-all full-face shape factor is

$$\frac{0.079 + 0.152 + 0.144 + 0.132 + 0.122 + 0.054}{50} = 0.0137$$

From Table 4–9 for full profile and for $L = 10$:

H, ft	0	2	4	6	8	10
$\frac{1}{2}(0 + 10)$	0.0085	0.008	0.007	0.007	0.006	0.0055
2	0.011	0.010	0.010	0.009	0.008	0.007
4	0.010	0.010	0.009	0.009	0.008	0.007
6	0.011	0.011	0.010	0.009	0.008	0.008
8	0.009	0.008	0.008	0.008	0.007	0.006
	(1)(0.049)	(2)(0.048)	(2)(0.044)	(2)(0.041)	(2)(0.037)	(1)(0.033)
	= 0.049	= 0.096	= 0.088	= 0.082	= 0.074	= 0.033

The over-all full-profile shape factor is

$$\frac{0.049 + 0.096 + 0.088 + 0.082 + 0.074 + 0.033}{50} = 0.008$$

The over-all semiprofile shape factor is the average of full face and full profile and is therefore $F_{si} = (0.0137 + 0.008)/2 = 0.0109$, or approximately 0.011.

The shape factor of the subject with respect to the glass area can likewise be obtained as the average of point shape factors as follows: divide one-half of one window into small areas and note that the shape factor of subject with respect to this section is the same as that with respect to both full windows.

From Table 4–8 for full face and $L = 10$:

	D, ft		
H, ft	0	2	4
$\frac{1}{2}(2 + 8)$	0.016	0.015	0.0145
4	0.016	0.015	0.014
6	0.0175	0.017	0.016
	(1)(0.0495)	(2)(0.047)	(2)(0.0445)
	= 0.0495	= 0.094	= 0.089

The over-all full-face shape factor is then: $(1/15)(0.0495 + 0.094 + 0.089) = 0.0155$.

From Table 4–9 for full profile and $L = 10$:

	D, ft		
H, ft	0	2	4
$\frac{1}{2}(2 + 8)$	0.010	0.0095	0.009
4	0.011	0.010	0.009
6	0.012	0.011	0.010
	(1)(0.033)	(2)(0.0305)	(2)(0.028)
	= 0.033	= 0.061	= 0.056

The over-all full-profile shape factor is then: $(1/15)(0.033 + 0.061 + 0.056) = 0.010$.

The over-all semiprofile shape factor is the average of full face and full profile and is therefore

$$F_{sg} = \frac{0.0155 + 0.010}{2} = 0.01275 \quad \text{(approx 0.013)}$$

The shape factor of occupant with respect to total outside wall area is the same as that with respect to the exterior wall surface in either outside wall, which, in turn, is calculable from the known shape factors with respect to the inside partition and the glass area:

$$F_{sw} = \frac{F_{si}A_i - F_{sg}A_g}{A_w} = \frac{[(0.011)(400)] - [(0.013)(113.6)]}{286.4}$$

$$= 0.0102 \quad \text{(approx. 0.010)}$$

As all required shape factors have now been determined, Eq. 7–16 can be solved for A_s:

$$A_s = [(0.0106)(400)] + [(0.010)(286.4)] + [(0.013)(113.6)] + [(0.011)(400)] + [(0.0137)(400)]$$

$$= 4.24 + 2.86 + 1.48 + 4.40 + 5.48 = 18.46 \qquad (7\text{–}17)$$

Dividing each term on the right side of Eq. 7–17 by 18.46 gives the shape factor of all of the surrounding surfaces with respect to the subject:

$$A_s = 18.46(0.2298 + 0.1549 + 0.0803 + 0.2383 + 0.2968) = (18.46)(1)$$

$$= A_s(F_{cs} + F_{ws} + F_{gs} + F_{is} + F_{fs}) = A_s(1) \qquad (7\text{–}18)$$

Explicit Form of the Comfort Equation. The mean radiant temperature can now be expressed in terms of the unknown room surface temperatures. By Eq. 7–15, substituting values of shape factors from Eq. 7–18,

$$mrt = 0.2298t_c + 0.1549t_w + 0.0803t_g + 0.2383t_i + 0.2968t_f \quad (7\text{–}19)$$

Then, substituting for *mrt* from Eq. 7–19 into Eq. 7–9 establishes the comfort equation as an explicit relationship between the unknown optimum dry-bulb temperature t_a and the five unknown inside surface temperatures:

$$t_a = 147 - 0.2298t_c - 0.1549t_w - 0.0803t_g - 0.2383t_i - 0.2968t_f \quad (7\text{–}20)$$

In order to evaluate numerically the optimum inside air temperature, it will be necessary to obtain five more independent equations, each involving the six unknown temperatures. Simultaneous solution of all six equations will then fix the value of the room air temperature and of each inside surface temperature; heating load can then be readily evaluated.

MEAN RADIANT TEMPERATURE WITH RESPECT TO A SPHERE. A small sphere is sometimes used to determine the mean radiant temperature experi-

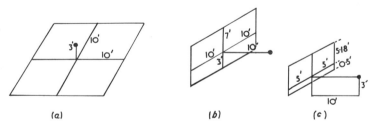

Fig. 7–8

mentally. In order to investigate the accuracy with which radiant exchange between such a sphere and the enclosure approximates exchange between a standing occupant and the enclosure, a complete analysis will be made of shape factors of the various room surfaces with respect to a sphere located 3 ft above the floor at the center of the room.

Refer to Fig. 7–8a; the shape factor of the floor with respect to the sphere is equal to four times the shape factor of a quarter of the floor, which can be read from Fig. 4–30 (for $L_1/D = L_2/D = 10/3$) as 0.09; thus

$$F_{fs'} = (4)(0.091) = 0.364$$

Similarly, the shape factor of ceiling with respect to the sphere is

$$F_{cs'} = (4)(0.058) = 0.232$$

where 0.058 is read from Fig. 4–30 for $L_1/D = L_2/D = 10/7$.

The shape factor of one inside partition with respect to the sphere (see Fig. 7–8b) is $2(0.016 + 0.033) = 0.098$, where 0.016 and 0.033 are read from Fig. 4–30 for $L_1/D = 3/10$, $L_2/D = 10/10$ and $L_1/D = 7/10$, $L_2/D = 10/10$, respectively; thus

$$F_{is'} = 0.196$$

The shape factor of one window with respect to the sphere is (refer to Fig. 7–8c) $2(0.0024 + 0.017) = 0.0388$, where 0.0024 and 0.017 are read from

TABLE 7–I
Shape Factors with Respect to:

	Subject	Sphere	Area
F_{cs}	0.2298	0.235	0.250
F_{ws}	0.1549	0.121	0.179
F_{gs}	0.0803	0.078	0.071
F_{is}	0.2383	0.200	0.250
F_{fs}	0.2968	0.366	0.250

Fig. 4–30 for $L_1/D = 0.05$, $L_2/D = 0.5$ and $L_1/D = 0.518$, $L_2/D = 0.50$, respectively; then

$$F_{gs'} = 0.0776$$

The shape factor of exterior wall with respect to the sphere is

$$F_{ws'} = F_{is} - F_{gs} = 0.196 - 0.0776 = 0.1184$$

The sum of surface shape factors with respect to the sphere is then

$$F_{cs'} + F_{ws'} + F_{gs'} + F_{is'} + F_{fs'} = 0.232 + 0.1184 + 0.0776$$
$$+ 0.196 + 0.364 = 0.988 \quad (7\text{–}21)$$

But the sum must be unity, and so an arbitrary correction will be applied to each of the factors, giving

$$F_{cs'} + F_{ws'} + F_{gs'} + F_{is'} + F_{fs'} = 0.235 + 0.121 + 0.078$$
$$+ 0.200 + 0.366 = 1.00 \quad (7\text{–}22)$$

Table 7–1 permits a direct comparison of shape factors with respect to the sphere and with respect to a subject standing at the center of the room. The fourth column of Table 7–1 lists approximate shape factors taken as ratios of the area of one type of surface to the total surface area of the room. The significance of the difference is discussed in the last paragraph of the next discussion on page 294.

COMPARISON OF MEAN RADIANT TEMPERATURE WITH AVERAGE SURFACE TEMPERATURE. To reduce the work needed in evaluating the shape factors within an enclosure, many attempts have been made to devise simplified approximate relationships that would in some measure be representative of the actual shape factors. One of the most widely used of these approximations is based on the assumption that all infinitesimal areas within the enclosure have the same shape factor with respect to the occupant, and hence that the shape factors of finite surfaces are proportional to their areas. This assumption permits substitution of A_c/A_e (where A_e is the total surface area of the enclosure) for the shape factor F_{cs} in Eq. 7–18 and similar substitutions for all the other shape factors in that equation. The resultant simplified approximate form of Eq. 7–19 is

$$ast = \frac{A_c t_c + A_w t_w + A_g t_g + A_i t_i + A_f t_f}{A_e} \doteq mrt \qquad (7\text{--}23)$$

where $A_e = A_c + A_w + A_g + A_i + A_f$.

Since the right side of Eq. 7–23 is numerically equal to the average surface temperature of the enclosure, this equation states, in effect, that the average surface temperature is approximately equal to the mean radiant temperature. By examining this suggested equality more closely, evidence can be collected to assist in defining the conditions under which the average surface temperature *ast* can with adequate accuracy be taken as equivalent to the mean radiant temperature. Thus, for the room for which the load analysis is to be made,

$$F_{cs} \doteq \frac{A_c}{A_e} = \frac{400}{1600} = 0.250$$

$$F_{ws} \doteq \frac{A_w}{A_e} = \frac{286.4}{1600} = 0.179$$

$$F_{gs} \doteq \frac{A_g}{A_e} = \frac{113.6}{1600} = 0.071$$

$$F_{is} \doteq \frac{A_i}{A_e} = \frac{400}{1600} = 0.250$$

$$F_{fs} \doteq \frac{A_f}{A_e} = \frac{400}{1600} = 0.250$$

The above values are tabulated for purposes of comparison in Table 7–1.

For rooms of height not greater than 12 ft, the assumption that shape factors are proportional to area will usually be found satisfactory for practical design purposes, but for auditoriums, churches, entrance halls of public buildings, or other very high enclosures, the area method will overemphasize the effect of the ceiling and underestimate the influence of the floor; for all such enclosures the true mean radiant temperature should be based on either a standing occupant, or as an adequate approximation, a centrally located sphere 3 ft above the floor.

7–3. Heat-Balance Equations for Room Surfaces.   Corresponding to a given value of the outside air temperature, and for a room in which the total energy input and ventilation rate are fixed, the inside air and each type of inside surface will reach equilibrium temperatures, which will be fixed with respect to time, at values determined by the heat-transfer characteristics of the room.   For a particular room, a heat-balance relationship can be established, giving the equilibrium temperature of any one type of surface in terms of the equilibrium temperatures of the inside air and of each of the other surface areas that constitute the enclosure.

HEAT BALANCE ON THE EXTERIOR WALL.   When equilibrium exists, the exterior wall area must dissipate heat as rapidly as it is received.   A heat balance on the exterior wall area is of the form

$$\text{Energy dissipated} = \text{energy received}$$

or

$$\begin{pmatrix} \text{Loss by conduction through the inside} \\ \text{surface to the outside air} \end{pmatrix}$$

$$= \begin{pmatrix} \text{net gain at the inside surface by radiation from surrounding} \\ \text{surfaces} + \text{gain by convection from room air} \end{pmatrix}$$

$$q_c = q_v + q_r \qquad (7\text{–}24)$$

Conduction Through the Surface.   This loss is of the form

$$q_c = C_w(t_w - t_o)A_w \qquad (7\text{–}25)$$

in which

$$C_w = \frac{1}{(L_1/k_1) + \cdots + (1/a) + \cdots + (1/h_o)} \qquad (7\text{–}26)$$

where L is the thickness, inches, of each homogeneous section of wall having a conductivity of k, Btu/(hr)(sq ft)(°F/in.); a is the conductance in Btu/(hr)(sq ft)(°F) of each air space in the wall; h_o is the equivalent film coefficient of heat transfer by convection and radiation for the outside of the wall, Btu/(hr)(sq ft)(°F); and C_w is the wall conductance, Btu/(hr)(sq ft)(°F), from the inside surface to the outside air.

Surface Gain by Convection.   Heat flows from room air to exterior wall surface by convection,

$$q_v = h_{cw}(t_a - t_w)A_w \qquad (7\text{–}27)$$

where h_{cw} is the *convective* film coefficient for inside surface of exterior *wall*, Btu/(hr)(sq ft)(°F).

Surface Gain by Radiation.   A net heat transfer by radiation occurs from other types of interior surfaces to the inside surface of the exterior wall.   This transfer rate is (based on the previously discussed reasons for omitting emissivity factors, Art. 7–2)

$$q_r = [F_{iw}h_{riw}(t_i - t_w) + F_{gw}h_{rgw}(t_g - t_w) + F_{cw}h_{rcw}(t_c - t_w)$$
$$+ F_{fw}h_{rfw}(t_f - t_w)]A_w \qquad (7\text{–}28)$$

where h_{rxy} is the equivalent *radiation* coefficient for transfer between surfaces x and y.

Heat Balance Equation for Exterior Wall. A heat balance on the exterior wall is now obtained by substituting from Eqs. 7–25, 7–27, and 7–28 into Eq. 7–24:

$$C_w(t_w - t_o)A_w = h_{cw}(t_a - t_w)A_w + [F_{iw}h_{riw}(t_i - t_w) + F_{gw}h_{rgw}(t_g - t_w)$$
$$+ F_{cw}h_{rcw}(t_c - t_w) + F_{fw}h_{rfw}(t_f - t_w)]A_w \qquad (7\text{–}29)$$

Solving for the inside surface temperature of the exterior wall,

$$t_w = \frac{(F_{fw}h_{rfw}t_f + F_{iw}h_{riw}t_i + F_{gw}h_{rgw}t_g + F_{cw}h_{rcw}t_c) + h_{cw}t_a + C_w t_o}{(F_{fw}h_{rfw} + F_{iw}h_{riw} + F_{gw}h_{rgw} + F_{cw}h_{rcw}) + h_{cw} + C_w}$$
$$(7\text{–}30)$$

HEAT BALANCE ON OTHER FOUR ROOM SURFACES. By a method similar to that above, heat-balance equations can be established on each of the other four types of surface and the equilibrium temperatures determined, or written by analogy with Eq. 7–30:

$$t_f = \frac{(F_{if}h_{rif}t_i + F_{gf}h_{rgf}t_g + F_{wf}h_{rwf}t_w + F_{cf}h_{rcf}t_c) + h_{cf}t_a + C_f t_o}{(F_{if}h_{rif} + F_{gf}h_{rgf} + F_{wf}h_{rwf} + F_{cf}h_{rcf}) + h_{cf} + C_f} \qquad (7\text{–}31)$$

$$t_g = \frac{(F_{wg}h_{rwg}t_w + F_{fg}h_{rfg}t_f + F_{ig}h_{rig}t_i + F_{cg}h_{rcg}t_c) + h_{cg}t_a + C_g t_o}{(F_{wg}h_{rwg} + F_{fg}h_{rfg} + F_{ig}h_{rig} + F_{cg}h_{rcg}) + h_{cg} + C_g} \qquad (7\text{–}32)$$

$$t_i = \frac{(F_{gi}h_{rgi}t_g + F_{wi}h_{rwi}t_w + F_{fi}h_{rfi}t_f + F_{ci}h_{rci}t_c) + h_{ci}t_a + C_i t_o}{(F_{gi}h_{rgi} + F_{wi}h_{rwi} + F_{fi}h_{rfi} + F_{ci}h_{rci}) + h_{ci} + C_i} \qquad (7\text{–}33)$$

$$t_c = \frac{(F_{gc}h_{rgc}t_g + F_{wc}h_{rwc}t_w + F_{fc}h_{rfc}t_f + F_{ic}h_{ric}t_i) + h_{cc}t_a + C_c t_o}{(F_{gc}h_{rgc} + F_{wc}h_{rwc} + F_{fc}h_{rfc} + F_{ic}h_{ric}) + h_{cc} + C_c} \qquad (7\text{–}34)$$

For a fixed outside temperature t_o, Eqs. 7–30 through 7–34 together with Eq. 7–20 relate the five unknown surface temperatures and the unknown air temperature. Before seeking a simultaneous solution of the above equations, it will be helpful to investigate the convective and radiant coefficients to see if identity among some groups of coefficients will permit reducing the number of separate cases which need be evaluated.

EVALUATION OF COEFFICIENTS FOR USE IN THE HEAT-BALANCE EQUATIONS. A numerical solution of the heat-balance equations requires that all terms other than inside air and inside surface temperatures be given explicit numerical values. The area and shape-factor terms are determinable from the geometry of the room. Outside temperature is fixed by location. Conductances are fixed by the type of construction. This leaves the inside and outside surface coefficients for convective and radiant transfer to be evaluated.

Equivalent Radiation Coefficients. Exact evaluation of the various radiation coefficients, such as h_{rig}, h_{rcw}, etc., depends on a knowledge of the individual surface temperatures and hence can only be estimated before a trial solution. However, the range of variation of these coefficients is so small for certain groups of room surfaces as to permit use of a single value for all exchange terms involving each such group. Thus all inside room surfaces other than glass areas, for structures of average thermal resistance, will be found to fall within the surface temperature range from 67.5 F to 73.5 F; referring to Art. 5–3, page 190 (or by approximation from Fig. 4–14), the corresponding range of h_r variation is

$$\left(\begin{array}{l}\text{Radiation coefficient for exchange}\\\text{between two 67.5 F surfaces}\end{array}\right) = 0.9913$$

$$\left(\begin{array}{l}\text{Radiation coefficient for exchange}\\\text{between two 73.5 F surfaces}\end{array}\right) = 1.054$$

The great majority of exchanges will occur between two surfaces at temperatures of approximately 67.5 F and 73.5 F and therefore with a radiation coefficient of 1.02; this value of the coefficient can be used with an accuracy of ± 3 per cent for all room surface exchanges other than those involving glass area. Thus, in summary,

$$1.02 \doteq h_{rif} = h_{rfi} \doteq h_{rwf} = h_{rfw} \doteq h_{rcf} = h_{rfc} \doteq h_{rwi}$$

$$= h_{riw} \doteq h_{rci} = h_{ric} \doteq h_{rcw} = h_{rwc} \tag{7–35}$$

For radiant exchange between inside surfaces and single-glazed window area, a first approximation is obtained by evaluating the inside-glass surface temperature in terms of "standard" values of h_i and U taken as 1.65 and 1.13 Btu/(hr)(sq ft)(°F), respectively. Then

$$\frac{t_a - t_g}{t_a - t_o} = \frac{r_i}{R} = \frac{1/1.65}{1/1.13} = 0.685$$

For inside environment at an arbitrary 73.5 F and outside air at 0 F,

$$t_g = 73.5 - \left(\frac{1}{1.65}\right)(1.13)(73.5 - 0) = 23.2 \text{ F}$$

and

$$h_{rig} = \frac{0.1713[(460 + 73.5)/100]^4 - [(460 + 23.2)/100]^4}{73.5 - 23.2}$$

$$= 0.907 \doteq 0.91$$

whereas for outside air temperature of 30 F,

$$t_g = 73.5 - \left(\frac{1}{1.65}\right)(1.13)(73.5 - 30) = 29.8 \text{ F}$$

and

$$h_{rig} = 0.956 \doteq 0.96$$

Thus an average value of h_{rig} over the usual range of outside design temperatures would be 0.93 Btu/(hr)(sq ft)(°F) for radiant transfer from any inside surface (except window area) to inside window surface; therefore

$$0.93 \doteq h_{rgi} = h_{rig} \doteq h_{rgw} = h_{rwg} \doteq h_{rgf} = h_{rfg} \doteq h_{rgc} = h_{rcg} \quad (7\text{--}36)$$

The outside equivalent radiation coefficient, h_{ro}, is taken (as discussed in Art. 5–3, page 168) as 0.70 Btu/(hr)(sq ft)(°F).

Conductances from Inside Surface to Outside Air. For each different type of surface through which heat is flowing, the conductance will be the reciprocal of the sum of resistances of each homogeneous part of the structure plus the resistances of air spaces plus the combined resistances of the outside film. For a first numerical example the room of Fig. 7–1 will be considered as uninsulated. The structure will be considered to be located in New Haven, Connecticut, and design outside-air temperature will be selected on the probability that a lower average daily temperature will occur, statistically, only once in 13 yr. From Table 3–1 the outside design air temperature will be 0 F, and from Table 5–1 the design wind velocity will be 8.1 mph; the corresponding combined resistance (convection plus radiation) is 0.248 for a smooth (such as painted wood siding) surface.

1. *Wall.* The frame wall consists of 1-in. by 8-in. drop-wood siding, having a resistance (from Table 5–2) of 0.79, placed on ½-in. gypsum board sheathing (resistance of 0.45 from the same table), and with interior finish consisting of metal lath with ¾-in. lightweight aggregate plaster (resistance of 0.47 from Table 5–2). Outside film resistance is 0.248 as noted above.

The convective resistance of the air space located between framing members in the wall will depend on the temperature difference across it and the equivalent radiant resistance will depend on mean temperature of air space, temperature difference across it, and emissivity of the two "seeing" surfaces. To estimate order of magnitude of air-space resistance, take unity as a first approximation to its combined resistance and use the same value for first approximation to the resistance of the combined inside film coefficient. Then

$$\Delta t_{\text{air space}} = \frac{r_{\text{air space}}}{R}(t_a - 0)$$

Substituting numerical values and using 73.5 F as the "equivalent" inside air temperature,

$$\Delta t_{\text{air space}} = \frac{1}{1 + 0.47 + 1 + 0.45 + 0.79 + 0.248}(73.5 - 0)$$

$$\frac{1}{3.958}\,73.5 \doteq 20\ \text{F}$$

The corresponding value of the conductance by convection across the air space is given by Eq. 4–68 as

$$a_c = 0.093(20)^{1/3} = 0.255 \text{ Btu/(hr)(sq ft)(°F)}$$

The approximate mean temperature of the air space is

$$t_{\text{air space, mean}} = 73.5 - \frac{1 + 0.47 + 0.5}{3.958} \, 73.5$$

$$= 73.5 - 36.6 = 36.9 \text{ F}$$

The equivalent radiation coefficient between black surfaces at mean temperature of 36.9 F and temperature difference of 20 F can be approximated as 0.854 by extrapolation from Fig. 4–14. But the emissivity factor for the actual air space, based on low reflective surfaces having emissivities of 0.964, is given by Eq. 4–117:

$$F_e = \frac{(0.964)^2}{0.964 + 0.964 - (0.964)^2} = 0.930$$

Hence the corrected equivalent radiation coefficient is

$$a_r = (0.854)(0.930) = 0.794$$

and the conductance of the air space is

$$a_c + a_r = 0.255 + 0.794 = 1.049 \text{ Btu/(hr)(sq ft)(°F)}$$

and the resistance is $1/1.049$, or 0.953. The resistance of the wall from inside surface to outside air is the reciprocal of its conductance, or

$$\frac{1}{C_w} = 0.47 + 0.953 + 0.45 + 0.79 + 0.248 = 2.911$$

and

$$C_w = 0.344 \text{ Btu/(hr)(sq ft)(°F)}$$

Evaluation of the inside convective film coefficient, h_{cw}, for the wall requires knowledge of the temperature drop across the inside film. Based on assumed film resistance of unity,

$$\Delta t_{\text{film}} = \frac{1}{1 + 2.911} \, 73.5 = 18.8$$

from which (by Eq. 4–53)

$$h_{cw} = 0.274(18.8)^{0.25} = 0.570 \text{ Btu/(hr)(sq ft)(°F)}$$

2. *Glass.* The commonly used over-all coefficient of heat transfer for a single-glazed window is taken as 1.13 Btu/(hr)(sq ft)(°F) based on a combined inside film coefficient of 1.65 Btu/(hr)(sq ft)(°F). Using these values as a first approximation, the temperature drop across the inside film would be

$$\Delta t_{\text{film}} = \frac{1.13}{1.65} \, 73.5 = 50 \text{ F}$$

and the corresponding value of the convective film coefficient for the inside film of the window (by Eq. 4–53) is

$$h_{cg} = 0.274(50)^{0.25} = 0.730 \text{ Btu/(hr)(sq ft)(°F)}$$

The surface-to-surface resistance of an average single-glazed window can be taken as 0.112; hence the resistance from inside surface to outside air is

$$\frac{1}{C_g} = 0.112 + 0.248 = 0.360$$

giving

$$C_g = 2.778 \text{ Btu/(hr)(sq ft)(°F)}$$

3. *Inside Partitions.* The equilibrium surface temperature of a non-transmitting interior partition will be below room air temperature, since the partition will be losing energy by radiation to the colder wall, window, floor, or ceiling surfaces, or to all. As a first approximation the convective film coefficient for non-transmitting partitions will be taken as 0.40 Btu/(hr)(sq ft)(°F). Based on an assumed film temperature drop of slightly less than 5 F, and based on Eq. 4–53, the conductance C_i of a non-transmitting partition is zero.

4. *Roof and Ceiling.* The construction of the flat roof and ceiling consists of $\frac{3}{8}$ in. of built-up roofing on a 1-in. wood deck (combined resistance 1.310 from Table 5–11), separated by an air space from a metal lath and $\frac{3}{4}$-in. lightweight aggregate plaster ceiling (resistance of lath and plaster is 0.47, from Table 5–11). Combined outside film resistance is taken, as for the wall, as 0.248 Btu/(hr)(sq ft)(°F). Based on first approximations, similar to those used in the above analysis of the wall, the inside convective film coefficient can be evaluated (Eq. 4–59) as

$$h_{cc} = 0.689 \text{ Btu/(hr)(sq ft)(°F)}$$

and the conductance (ceiling surface to outside air) as

$$C_c = 0.365 \text{ Btu/(hr)(sq ft)(°F)}$$

5. *Floor.* The floor consists of $\frac{3}{4}$-in. hardwood over felt and a $\frac{25}{32}$-in. wood subfloor (combined resistance of 1.72 from Table 5–8); there is no ceiling and the floor is considered to be over a ventilated crawl space in which the air temperature approximates the outside value. Conservatively (because of lesser air motion in the crawl space) taking the exterior combined coefficient at the same value (0.248) as for the wall, the resistance from inside surface to outside air is $1.72 + 0.248$ or 1.968; hence

$$C_f = \frac{1}{1.968} = 0.508 \text{ Btu/(hr)(sq ft)(°F)}$$

If the inside film resistance is assumed, as a first approximation at unity, then

$$\Delta t_{\text{film}} = \frac{1}{1.968 + 1}\, 73.5 = 24.8 \text{ F}$$

and (by Eq. 4–61)

$$h_{cf} = 0.126(24.8)^{0.25} = 0.282 \text{ Btu/(hr)(sq ft)(°F)}$$

Explicit Form of Simultaneous Equations. The constants for use in the heat-balance equations have now been established. For Eq. 7–30 the following values are to be used:

$$F_{fw} = 0.299 \quad F_{iw} = 0.262 \quad F_{gw} = 0.032 \quad F_{cw} = 0.290 \quad C_w = 0.344$$

$$h_{rfw} = h_{riw} = h_{rcw} = 1.02; \quad h_{rgw} = 0.93; \quad h_{cw} = 0.570; \quad t_o = 0$$

giving[1]

$$t_w = \frac{\begin{aligned}[(0.299)(1.02)t_f] + [(0.262)(1.02)t_i] + [(0.032)(0.93)t_g] \\ + [(0.290)(1.02)t_c] + [0.570t_a + 0]\end{aligned}}{\begin{aligned}(0.299)(1.02) + (0.262)(1.02) + (0.032)(0.93) + (0.290)(1.02) \\ + 0.570 + 0.344\end{aligned}}$$

$$= \frac{0.3050t_f + 0.2672t_i + 0.0298t_g + 0.2958t_c + 0.570t_a}{1.8118}$$

$$= 0.1683t_f + 0.1475t_i + 0.01645t_g + 0.1633t_c + 0.3146t_a \qquad (7\text{–}30a)$$

For Eq. 7–31,

$$F_{if} = 0.300 \quad F_{gf} = 0.086 \quad F_{wf} = 0.214 \quad F_{cf} = 0.410; \quad C_f = 0.508$$

$$h_{rif} = h_{rwf} = h_{rcf} = 1.02; \quad h_{rgf} = 0.93; \quad h_{cf} = 0.282; \quad t_o = 0$$

giving

$$t_f = \frac{\begin{aligned}[(0.300)(1.02)t_i] + [(0.086)(0.93)t_g] + [(0.214)(1.02)t_w] \\ + [(0.410)(1.02)t_c + 0.282t_a + 0]\end{aligned}}{\begin{aligned}(0.300)(1.02) + (0.086)(0.93) + (0.214)(1.02) + (0.410)(1.02) \\ + 0.282 + 0.508\end{aligned}}$$

$$= \frac{0.306t_i + 0.0800t_g + 0.2183t_w + 0.4182t_c + 0.282t_a}{1.8125}$$

$$= 0.1688t_i + 0.0441t_g + 0.1204t_w + 0.2307t_c + 0.1556t_a \qquad (7\text{–}31a)$$

[1] Although the empirical coefficients in the simultaneous equations are not accurate to more than two decimal places, the actual mathematical solution will be carried out to four-place accuracy. This is necessary, numerically, since in many cases three-place differences result from subtractions involving four-place terms.

For Eq. 7–32,

$$F_{wg} = 0.080 \quad F_{fg} = 0.304 \quad F_{ig} = 0.253 \quad F_{cg} = 0.325 \quad C_g = 2.778$$

$$h_{rwg} = h_{rfg} = h_{rig} = h_{rcg} = 0.93; \quad h_{cg} = 0.730; \quad t_o = 0$$

$$t_g = \frac{[(0.080)(0.93)t_w] + [(0.304)(0.93)t_f] + [(0.253)(0.93)t_i] + [(0.325)(0.93)t_c] + [0.730t_a + 0]}{[(0.080)(0.93)] + [(0.304)(0.93)] + [(0.253)(0.93)] + [(0.325)(0.93)] + [0.730 + 2.778]}$$

$$= \frac{0.0744t_w + 0.2827t_f + 0.2353t_i + 0.3023t_c + 0.730t_a}{4.4027}$$

$$= 0.0169t_w + 0.0642t_f + 0.0534t_i + 0.0687t_c + 0.1658t_a \tag{7–32a}$$

For Eq. 7–33,

$$F_{gi} = 0.072 \quad F_{wi} = 0.188 \quad F_{fi} = 0.300 \quad F_{ci} = 0.300 \quad C_i = 0$$

$$h_{rgi} = 0.93; \quad h_{rwi} = h_{rfi} = h_{rci} = 1.02; \quad h_{ci} = 0.400; \quad t_o = 0$$

$$t_i = \frac{[(0.072)(0.93)t_g] + [(0.188)(1.02)t_w] + [(0.300)(1.02)t_f] + [(0.300)(1.02)t_c] + [0.400t_a + 0]}{[(0.072)(0.93)] + [(0.188)(1.02)] + [(0.300)(1.02)] + [(0.300)(1.02)] + [0.400 + 0]}$$

$$= \frac{0.0670t_g + 0.1918t_w + 0.3060t_f + 0.3060t_c + 0.4000t_a}{1.2708}$$

$$= 0.0527t_g + 0.1509t_w + 0.2408t_f + 0.2408t_c + 0.3148t_a \tag{7–33a}$$

For Eq. 7–34,

$$F_{gc} = 0.092 \quad F_{wc} = 0.208 \quad F_{fc} = 0.410 \quad F_{ic} = 0.300 \quad C_c = 0.365$$

$$h_{rgc} = 0.93; \quad h_{rwc} = h_{rfc} = h_{ric} = 1.02; \quad h_{cc} = 0.689; \quad t_o = 0$$

$$t_c = \frac{[(0.092)(0.93)t_g] + [(0.208)(1.02)t_w] + [(0.410)(1.02)t_f] + [(0.300)(1.02)t_i] + [0.689t_a + 0]}{[(0.092)(0.93)] + [(0.208)(1.02)] + [(0.410)(1.02)] + [(0.300)(1.02)] + [0.689 + 0.365]}$$

$$= \frac{0.0856t_g + 0.2122t_w + 0.4182t_f + 0.3060t_i + 0.689t_a}{2.0760}$$

$$= 0.0412t_g + 0.1021t_w + 0.2014t_f + 0.1474t_i + 0.3319t_a \tag{7–34a}$$

The five heat balance equations (Eqs. 7–30a through 7–34a) together with the comfort equation as applied to a standing subject at room center (Eq. 7–20) constitute a set of six equations relating six unknown temperatures.

Solution of Simultaneous Equations. In starting the solution of these simultaneous equations, a first step is the elimination of the surface temperature of the glass. Eliminating t_g between Eqs. 7–31a and 7–32a,[2]

$$t_g = 0.0169t_w + 0.0642t_f + 0.0534t_i + 0.0687t_c + 0.1658t_a$$
$$= 22.6757t_f - 3.8277t_i - 2.7301t_w - 5.2313t_c - 3.5283t_a$$

giving

$$2.7470t_w - 22.6115t_f + 3.8811t_i + 5.3000t_c + 3.6941t_a = 0 \qquad (a)$$

From Eqs. 7–32a and 7–30a,

$$t_g = 0.0169t_w + 0.0642t_f + 0.0534t_i + 0.0687t_c + 0.1658t_a$$
$$= 60.790t_w - 10.231t_f - 8.967t_i - 9.927t_c - 19.125t_a$$

giving

$$10.2952t_f - 60.7731t_w + 9.0204t_i + 9.9957t_c + 19.2908t_a = 0 \qquad (b)$$

From Eqs. 7–32a and 7–33a,

$$t_g = 0.0169t_w + 0.0642t_f + 0.0534t_i + 0.0687t_c + 0.1658t_a$$
$$= 18.9753t_i - 2.8633t_w - 4.5693t_f - 4.5693t_c - 5.9734t_a$$

giving

$$2.8802t_w + 4.6335t_f - 18.9219t_i + 4.6380t_c + 6.1392t_a = 0 \qquad (c)$$

From Eqs. 7–32a and 7–34a,

$$t_g = 0.0169t_w + 0.0642t_f + 0.0534t_i + 0.0687t_c + 0.1658t_a$$
$$= 24.2718t_c - 2.4782t_w - 4.8883t_f - 3.5777t_i - 8.0558t_a$$

giving

$$2.4951t_w + 4.9525t_f + 3.6311t_i - 24.2031t_c + 8.2216t_a = 0 \qquad (d)$$

From Eqs. 7–32a and 7–20,

$$t_g = 0.0169t_w \mid 0.0642t_f \mid 0.0534t_i + 0.0687t_c + 0.1658t_a$$
$$= 1830.6 - 12.4533t_a - 2.8618t_c - 1.9290t_w - 2.9676t_i - 3.6961t_f$$

giving

$$1.9459t_w + 3.7603t_f + 3.0210t_i + 2.9305t_c + 12.6191t_a - 1830.6 = 0 \quad (e)$$

Eliminating t_i between Eqs. (c) and (a) yields

$$t_i = 0.1522t_w + 0.2449t_f + 0.2451t_c + 0.3244t_a$$
$$= 5.8261t_f - 0.7078t_w - 1.3656t_c - 0.9518t_a$$

[2] Mathematical elegance has been sacrificed in this numerical solution in favor of less concise but more obvious (and equally exact) procedures. Thus, in solving the simultaneous linear equations, advantage has not been taken of determinants or other devices for reducing the arithmetical work; the method here used is cumbersome, but the procedure has been given in full in order to provide the designer with an exact prototype that he can readily follow. Engineers familiar with more powerful mathematical methods will readily visualize means of simplifying and condensing the solution.

giving

$$0.8600t_w - 5.5812t_f + 1.6107t_c + 1.2762t_a = 0 \qquad \text{(f)}$$

From Eqs. (c) and (b),

$$t_i = 0.1522t_w + 0.2449t_f + 0.2451t_c + 0.3244t_a$$
$$= 6.7373t_w - 1.1413t_f - 1.1081t_c - 2.1386t_a$$

giving

$$1.3862t_f - 6.5851t_w + 1.3532t_c + 2.4630t_a = 0 \qquad \text{(g)}$$

From Eqs. (c) and (d),

$$t_i = 0.1522t_w + 0.2449t_f + 0.2451t_c + 0.3244t_a$$
$$= 6.6655t_c - 0.6871t_w - 1.3639t_f - 2.2642t_a$$

giving

$$0.8393t_w + 1.6088t_f - 6.4204t_c + 2.5886t_a = 0 \qquad \text{(h)}$$

From Eqs. (c) and (e),

$$t_i = 0.1522t_w + 0.2449t_f + 0.2451t_c + 0.3244t_a$$
$$= 605.96 - 0.6441t_w - 1.2447t_f - 0.9699t_c - 4.177t_a$$

giving

$$0.7963t_w + 1.4896t_f + 1.2150t_c + 4.5014t_a - 605.96 = 0 \qquad \text{(i)}$$

Eliminating t_w between Eqs. (g) and (f) yields

$$t_w - 0.2105t_f + 0.2055t_c + 0.3740t_a = 6.4898t_f - 1.8729t_c - 1.4839t_a$$

giving

$$6.2793t_f - 2.0784t_c - 1.8579t_a = 0 \qquad \text{(j)}$$

From Eqs. (g) and (h),

$$t_w = 0.2105t_f + 0.2055t_c + 0.3740t_a = 7.6497t_c - 1.9168t_f - 3.0842t_a$$

giving

$$2.1273t_f - 7.4442t_c + 3.4582t_a = 0 \qquad \text{(k)}$$

From Eqs. (g) and (i),

$$t_w = 0.2105t_f + 0.2055t_c + 0.3740t_a = 760.97 - 1.8707t_f$$
$$- 1.5258t_c - 5.6529t_a$$

giving

$$2.0812t_f + 1.7313t_c + 6.0269t_a = 760.97 \qquad \text{(l)}$$

Eliminating t_f between Eqs. (j) and (k) yields

$$t_f = 0.3310t_c + 0.2959t_a = 3.4994t_c - 1.6256t_a$$

giving

$$1.9215t_a - 3.1684t_c = 0 \qquad \text{(m)}$$

From Eqs. (j) and (l),

$$t_f = 0.3310t_c + 0.2959t_a = 365.64 - 0.8319t_c - 2.8959t_a$$

giving

$$1.1629t_c + 3.1918t_a = 365.64 \qquad (n)$$

Eliminating t_c between Eqs. (m) and (n) yields

$$t_c = 0.6066t_a = 316.68 - 2.7444t_a$$

giving

$$t_a = 94.5 \text{ F}$$

Note: The air temperature required to prevent excess body-heat loss is so high that comfort could not be realized in a room as poorly insulated as the one in this example. The solution thus demonstrates that inadequate thermal resistance can make it not merely impracticable but actually impossible to comfortably heat a structure.

Then from Eq. (m),

$$t_c = \frac{(1.9207)(94.5)}{3.1665} = 59.32 \text{ F}$$

From Eq. (k),

$$t_f = \frac{[(7.4442)(57.32)] - [(3.4582)(94.50)]}{2.1273} = 44.96 \text{ F}$$

From the left side of the equation above (j),

$$t_w = [(0.2105)(44.96)] + [(0.2055)(57.32)] + [(0.3740)(94.5)] = 56.60 \text{ F}$$

From the left side of the equation above (f),

$$t_i = [(0.1522)(56.60)] + [(0.2449)(44.96)] + [(0.2451)(57.32)]$$
$$+ [(0.3244)(94.5)] = 64.33 \text{ F}$$

From the left side of the equation above (a),

$$t_g = [(0.0169)(56.6)] + [(0.0642)(44.96)] + [(0.0534)(64.33)]$$
$$+ [(0.0687)(57.32)] + [(0.1658)(94.5)] = 26.31 \text{ F}$$

Summarizing: $t_a = 94.5$ F, $t_c = 59.32$ F, $t_f = 44.96$ F, $t_w = 56.60$ F, $t_i = 64.33$ F, $t_g = 26.31$ F, $mrt = 147 - 94.5 = 52.5$ F.

Revised Values of Coefficients. The convective film coefficients, air-space conductances, and equivalent radiation coefficients were all evaluated (Art. 7–3, page 295) from approximate temperature drops based on assumed film or air-space resistances. With room air and surface temperatures now known, it is possible to recalculate the coefficients and then re-do the problem, to realize a more exact solution. Thus each of the equivalent radiant coefficients that are grouped in Eq. 7–35 can now be precisely evaluated:

$$h_{rif} = \frac{0.1713\left[\left(\dfrac{460 + 64.33}{100}\right)^4 - \left(\dfrac{460 + 44.96}{100}\right)^4\right]}{64.33 - 44.96}$$

$$= 0.9230 \text{ Btu/(hr)(sq ft)(°F)}$$

By similar calculation the other coefficients are obtained as

$$h_{rif} = h_{rfi} = 0.9230; \quad h_{riw} = h_{rwi} = 0.9370; \quad h_{ric} = h_{rci} = 0.9291$$

$$h_{rfw} = h_{rwf} = 0.9135; \quad h_{rfc} = h_{rcf} = 0.9208; \quad h_{rwc} = h_{rcw} = 0.9522$$

Similarly, the coefficients for radiant exchange with the glass (grouped in Eq. 7–36) become

$$h_{rgi} = h_{rig} = 0.8797; \quad h_{rgw} = h_{rwg} = 0.8647; \quad h_{rgf} = h_{rfg} = 0.8343;$$

$$h_{rgc} = h_{rcg} = 0.8719$$

The conductance and convective film coefficient for the wall (refer to Art. 7–3, page 296) can be recalculated as follows:

$$h_{cw} = 0.274(t_a - t_w)^{0.25} = (0.274)(94.5 - 56.60)$$

$$= 0.680 \text{ Btu/(hr)(sq ft)(°F)}$$

The revised temperature drop across the air space, based on assumed unit combined resistances of inside film and of air space, is

$$\Delta t_{\text{air space}} = \frac{1}{3.958}(94.5) = 24 \text{ F}$$

giving

$$a_c = 0.093(24)^{1/3} = 0.268 \text{ Btu/(hr)(sq ft)(°F)}$$

The approximate mean temperature of the air space is

$$t_{\text{air space, mean}} = 94.5 - \left(\frac{1.97}{3.958}\right)94.5$$

$$= 94.5 - 47.0 = 47.5 \text{ F}$$

The corresponding equivalent radiation coefficient can then be evaluated (using the procedure of Art. 7–3, page 299) as

$$a_r = 0.833 \text{ Btu/(hr)(sq ft)(°F)}$$

and the revised air space conductance is

$$a = a_c + a_r = 0.268 + 0.833 = 1.101 \text{ Btu/(hr)(sq ft)(°F)}$$

The revised value of conductance from inside wall surface temperature to outside air is

$$C_w = \frac{1}{0.47 + (1/1.101) + 0.45 + 0.79 + 0.248}$$

$$= \frac{1}{2.866} = 0.349 \text{ Btu/(hr)(sq ft)(°F)}$$

The revised inside convective film for the window is

$$h_{cg} = 0.274(94.5 - 26.3)^{0.25} = 0.790 \text{ Btu/(hr)(sq ft)(°F)}$$

and window conductance (inside surface to outside air) remains unchanged.

Corrections to coefficients for inside partitions, roof and ceiling, and floor can be made in the same way, giving

$$h_{ci} = 0.641; \quad h_{cc} = 0.850; \quad h_{cf} = 0.334$$

$$C_i = 0; \quad C_c = 0.3694; \quad C_f = 0.508 \text{ (unchanged)}$$

Revised Solution of Simultaneous Equations. Substitution of the revised coefficients (from Art. 7–3, page 306) into Eqs. 7–30 through 7–34 and Eq. 7–20 and solving simultaneously give

$$t_a = 91.42 \text{ F}; \quad t_c = 59.24 \text{ F}; \quad t_f = 49.29 \text{ F}; \quad t_w = 59.42 \text{ F};$$

$$t_i = 70.44 \text{ F}; \quad t_g = 27.58 \text{ F}$$

The mean radiant temperature is $147 - 91.4 = 55.6$ F

The revised air and surface temperatures differ by so little from the values obtained in Art. 7–3, page 296, that there is no need for a further revision of film coefficients or of air-space conductances.

7–4. Transmission Load Based on Rational Analysis. The basic purpose of the rational heat-balance analysis is to permit precise evaluation of heating load. With inside surface temperatures of transmitting structural sections established (as in the preceding article), the total transmission loss from the structure is

$$q = C_w A_w(t_w - t_o) + C_g A_g(t_g - t_o) + C_f A_f(t_f - t_o) + C_c A_c(t_c - t_o)$$

$$(7\text{–}37)$$

where areas (from Art. 7–2) are

$$A_c = 400; \quad A_w = 286.4; \quad A_g = 113.6; \quad A_i = 400; \quad A_f = 400$$

Recalculated values of conductances are given in Art. 7–3, page 306, and revised air and surface temperatures are also given in Art. 7–3, page 307. Substituting these values in Eq. 7–37,

$$q = [(0.349)(286.4)(59.42)] + [(2.778)(113.6)(27.58)] + [(0.508)(400)(49.29)]$$

$$+ [(0.3694)(400)(59.24)]$$

$$= 5939.3 + 8703.7 + 10{,}015.7 + 8753.3$$

$$= 33{,}412 \text{ Btu/hr}$$

A comparison of the above transmission load with that calculated from the first approximate estimate of the various conductances is instructive. Using conductances for the first approximation and the resultant air and surface temperatures (Art. 7-3, pages 296–305) in Eq. 7–37 gives

$$q = [(0.344)(286.4)(56.60)] + [(2.778)(113.6)(26.32)] + [(0.508)(400)(44.96)]$$
$$+ [(0.365)(400)(59.32)]$$
$$= 5576.2 + 8292.9 + 9135.9 + 8660.8$$
$$= 31,666 \text{ Btu/hr}$$

The first approximation was therefore within $[(33,412 - 31,666)/33,412]100$, or 5.2 per cent of the more exact second approximation.

7–5. Evaluation of Equivalent Air-to-Surface Radiation Film Coefficient. In Art. 7–3, page 297, a group of first-power radiation coefficients was obtained that related transfer by radiation from one room surface to another (thus h_{rig} indicated transfer from inside partition to glass). From the load data now available, it is possible to calculate corresponding equivalent radiation coefficients based on temperature difference from room air to each inside surface. Thus, for establishing a heat balance on the inside surface of the wall,

$$C_w(t_w - t_o) = h_{cw}(t_a - t_w) + h_{rw}(t_a - t_w) \qquad (7–38)$$

where h_{rw} is the equivalent radiation film coefficient from room surfaces to inside wall surface but is expressed in terms of air-to-wall temperature difference. Solving for h_{rw},

$$h_{rw} = \frac{C_w(t_w - t_o) - h_{cw}(t_a - t_w)}{t_a - t_w}$$
$$= \frac{C_w(t_w - t_o)}{t_a - t_w} - h_{cw} \qquad (7–39)$$

and substituting known temperature and coefficients,

$$h_{rw} = \frac{(0.349)(59.42)}{91.42 - 59.42} - 0.680$$
$$= 0.648 - 0.680 = -0.032 \text{ Btu/(hr)(sq ft)(°F)}$$

The negative value of h_{rw} shows that there is a net radiant *loss* from the inside surface of the wall. This result strikingly demonstrates the fallacy in using a so-called standard value of combined inside film coefficient.

A check on h_{rw} can be obtained by summing up the rates of radiant energy reception at the inside of the wall surface (as given by the bracketed term on the right side of Eq. 7–29),

$$h_{rw}(t_a - t_w) = F_{iw}h_{riw}(t_i - t_w) + F_{gw}h_{rgw}(t_g - t_w)$$
$$+ F_{cw}h_{rcw}(t_c - t_w) + F_{fw}h_{rfw}(t_f - t_w) \qquad (7–40)$$

Substituting known shape factors, coefficients, and temperatures,

$$h_{rw} = \frac{\begin{array}{c}[(0.262)(0.9370)(70.44 - 59.42)] + [(0.032)(0.8647)(27.58 - 59.42)] \\ + [(0.290)(0.9522)(59.24 - 59.42)] + [(0.299)(0.9135)(49.29 - 59.42)]\end{array}}{91.42 - 59.42}$$

$$= \frac{2.7050 - 0.8810 - 0.0497 - 2.7669}{32}$$

$$= \frac{-0.9926}{32} = -0.031 \text{ Btu/(hr)(sq ft)(°F)}$$

The equivalent radiation coefficient for the floor (by analogy with Eq. 7–39) is

$$h_{rf} = \frac{C_f(t_f - t_o)}{t_a - t_f} - h_{cf}$$

$$= \frac{(0.508)(49.29)}{91.42 - 49.29} - 0.334$$

$$= 0.594 - 0.334 = +0.260 \text{ Btu/(hr)(sq ft)(°F)} \qquad (7\text{–}41)$$

For the ceiling,

$$h_{rc} = \frac{C_c(t_c - t_o)}{t_a - t_c} - h_{cc}$$

$$= \frac{(0.3694)(59.24)}{91.42 - 59.24} - 0.850$$

$$= 0.680 - 0.850 = -0.170 \text{ Btu/(hr)(sq ft)(°F)} \qquad (7\text{–}42)$$

For the window area,

$$h_{rg} = \frac{C_g(t_g - t_o)}{t_a - t_g} - h_{cg}$$

$$= \frac{(2.778)(27.58)}{91.42 - 27.58} - 0.790$$

$$= +0.410 \text{ Btu/(hr)(sq ft)(°F)} \qquad (7\text{–}43)$$

The net loss by radiation to transmitting surfaces is

$$q = h_{rw}A_w(t_a - t_w) + h_{rf}A_f(t_a - t_f) + h_{rc}A_c(t_a - t_c) + h_{rg}A_g(t_a - t_g)$$

$$= [(-0.032)(286.4)(91.42 - 59.42)] + [(0.260)(400)(91.42 - 49.29)]$$

$$+ [(-0.170)(400)(91.42 - 59.24)] + [(0.410)(113.6)(91.42 - 27.58)]$$

$$= -293 + 4382 - 2188 + 2973 = 4874 \text{ Btu/hr} \qquad (7\text{–}44)$$

The radiant transfer to unit area of transmitting surface is

$$q_{\text{unit area}} = \frac{4874}{1200} = 4.06 \text{ Btu/hr}$$

The weighted average temperature difference from room air to transmitting surface is

$$t_a - t_m = \Sigma\left[\frac{A_x}{A_c + A_f + A_w + A_g}(t_a - t_x)\right]$$

$$= \frac{286.4}{1200}(91.42 - 59.42) + \frac{400}{1200}(91.42 - 49.29)$$

$$+ \frac{400}{1200}(91.42 - 59.24) + \frac{113.6}{1200}(91.42 - 27.58)$$

$$= 7.64 + 14.03 + 10.73 + 6.04 = 38.44 \text{ F} \qquad (7\text{--}45)$$

Based on the mean air-to-surface temperature difference,

$$h_{ras} = \frac{q_{\text{unit area}}}{t_a - t_m}$$

$$= \frac{4.06}{38.44} = 0.106 \text{ Btu/(hr)(sq ft)}(°\text{F}) \qquad (7\text{--}46)$$

The above result shows that the equivalent inside film coefficient for radiant transfer is actually very much less than the value that has conventionally been used in calculating transmission losses. The usual value is based on the incorrect assumption that the inside surface temperature of all surfaces "seen" by a particular transmitting surface is equal to air temperature. Thus radiant transfer to a window is conventionally calculated on the basis that all walls, floor, and ceiling surfaces are at room air temperature and that the equivalent radiation coefficient for the glass is therefore

$$h_{rg} = \frac{0.1713[(T_a/100)^4 - (T_g/100)^4]}{t_a - t_g} \qquad (7\text{--}47)$$

The value of h_r calculated by the above equation and used in the "standard" combined inside film coefficients given in the *ASHRAE Guide*[3] is of the order of 0.7 to 0.9 Btu/(hr)(sq ft)(°F). Thus Table 2 on page 96 of the 1959 edition of the *Guide* gives radiation rates for walls (vertical surfaces) which correspond to an h_r range of from 0.83 to 0.88 Btu/(hr)(sq ft)(°F). The *Guide* value of combined inside film coefficient for a wall is 1.46; hence, approximately,

$$h_{cg\text{stand}} = h_g - h_{rg} = 1.46 - 0.8 = 0.66 \qquad (7\text{--}48)$$

Based on use of $h_{cg\text{stand}}$ but on the recommended value of h_r (from Eq. 7–46), the combined coefficient is

$$h_{g\text{recommend}} = h_{cg} + h_{rg} = 0.66 + 0.11 = 0.77 \text{ Btu/(hr)(sq ft)}(°\text{F}) \qquad (7\text{--}49)$$

[3] Bibliography, item 1.

Thus the effect of using the actual value of h_{rg} (as established for this particular structure) is practically to halve the inside film conductance or to double the resistance. This means that the temperature drop across the inside film will increase and that the optimum inside comfort air temperature will therefore increase.

The room in question has two interior partitions. If there were only one interior partition, the value of h_{ras} would be less than 0.106, whereas if the ceiling or floor, or both, were non-transmitting (in a room with two interior partitions), the value of h_{ras} would exceed 0.106. It is evident, therefore, that the h_{ras} term should be evaluated as a function of the number of inside partitions (or other non-transmitting surfaces). This subject has been covered in Art. 5-3, page 205, and a detailed recommended numerical procedure was established there. The present article relates to Art. 5-3, page 197, in that results of the rational analysis substantiate the assumptions made in developing the recommended procedure.

From an entirely different standpoint a check can be obtained on the assumption made in Art. 5-3, page 200, that all net radiant transfer to transmitting surfaces comes from non-transmitting surfaces. If this is true, the energy gained by convection at non-transmitting surfaces (which must be equal to the net radiant loss from such surfaces) would approximate the net radiant transfer from the room to all transmitting surfaces.

For non-transmitting surfaces,

$$\text{Convection gain} = \text{radiation loss}$$

and for the inside partition of the enclosure which has been analyzed,

$$q = (0.641)(400)(91.42 - 70.44) = 5379 \text{ Btu/hr} \qquad (7\text{-}50)$$

Net loss of radiation to transmitting surfaces has been calculated as 4874 Btu/hr; so, agreement is within 10 per cent. It therefore follows that the inside partition is responsible for approximately 90 per cent of the loss of energy from the room due to net radiation received at inside surfaces of the transmitting sections of the enclosure.

7-6. Comparison of Mean Radiant Temperature and Average Surface Temperature. The mean radiant temperature for the enclosure in question is

$$mrt = 147 - t_a = 147 - 91.4 = 55.6 \text{ F}$$

The corresponding average surface temperature (see Art. 7-2) is

$$ast = [(0.250)(59.24)] + [(0.179)(59.42)] + [(0.071)(27.58)]$$
$$+ [(0.250)(70.44)] + [(0.250)(49.29)] = 57.3 \text{ F}$$

The reasonably close agreement between mrt and ast suggests that the ast can be used in the comfort equation in place of mrt. This simplification makes unnecessary the computation of shape factors of room surfaces with respect to an occupant (as developed in Art. 7–2, page 288); hence it greatly reduces the required work preparatory to solving the simultaneous equations.

7–7. Equivalent Over-all Coefficient of Heat Transfer. Data are now available which permit, for the particular room, evaluation of the true over-all coefficient of heat transfer for each type of transmitting surface. Thus

$$h_w = h_{cw} + h_{rw} = 0.680 - 0.032 = 0.648; \quad r_w = 1.543$$

$$R_w = \frac{1}{C_w} + r_w = \frac{1}{0.349} + 1.543 = 4.408; \quad U_w = 0.227$$

$$h_c = h_{cc} + h_{rc} = 0.850 - 0.170 = 0.680; \quad r_c = 1.471$$

$$R_c = \frac{1}{C_c} + r_c = \frac{1}{0.3694} + 1.471 = 4.178; \quad U_c = 0.239$$

$$h_f = h_{cf} + h_{rf} = 0.334 + 0.260 = 0.594; \quad r_f = 1.684$$

$$R_f = \frac{1}{C_f} + r_f = \frac{1}{0.508} + 1.684 = 3.653; \quad U_f = 0.274$$

$$h_g = h_{cg} + h_{rg} = 0.790 + 0.410 = 1.200; \quad r_g = 0.833$$

$$R_g = \frac{1}{C_g} + r_g = \frac{1}{2.778} + 0.833 = 1.193; \quad U_g = 0.838$$

The equivalent over-all coefficient of heat transfer (as defined in Art. 5–2) is therefore

$$U_e = \frac{A_c}{A_t} U_c + \frac{A_w}{A_t} U_w + \frac{A_f}{A_t} U_f + \frac{A_g}{A_t} U_g + \frac{A_i}{A_t} U_i$$

$$= [(0.250)(0.239)] + [(0.179)(0.227)] + [(0.250)(0.274)]$$

$$+ [(0.071)(0.838)] + 0$$

$$= 0.0598 + 0.0406 + 0.0685 + 0.0595 = 0.2284 \ \text{Btu/(hr)(sq ft)(}^\circ\text{F)}$$

$$(7\text{–}51)$$

7–8. Equivalent Inside Film Coefficient and Equivalent Conductance. The combined inside film coefficient for the homogeneous room having equivalent over-all coefficient of heat transfer of U_e would have a value h_e such that the uniform inside surface temperature, t_{se}, of the equivalent room would equal the mean radiant temperature of the actual room. Thus

$$\frac{t_a - t_{se}}{t_a - t_o} = \frac{1/h_e}{1/U_e}$$

or

$$h_e = \frac{U_e(t_a - t_o)}{t_a - t_{se}}$$

$$= \frac{0.2284(91.42 - 0)}{91.42 - 55.58}$$

$$= 0.5826 \ \text{Btu/(hr)(sq ft)(}^\circ\text{F)} \qquad (7\text{–}52)$$

The equivalent conductance for the homogeneous enclosure is then

$$C_e = \frac{1}{(1/U_e) - (1/h_e)} = \frac{1}{(1/0.2284) - (1/0.5826)}$$

$$= \frac{1}{4.3783 - 1.7164} = \frac{1}{2.6619} = 0.3757 \text{ Btu/(hr)(sq ft)}(°F) \quad (7\text{-}53)$$

7-9. Approximate Load Analysis Based on Equivalent Conductance.

The thermally equivalent homogeneous room having h_e of 0.5826 and C_e of 0.3757 can be used as the basis of an approximate load determination for the actual room. For equilibrium conditions corresponding to optimum thermal comfort, a heat balance on the inside surface and the comfort equation will provide two independent equations relating the unknown inside air temperature and the unknown inside surface temperature.

The heat-balance equation is

$$C_e A_t(t_s - t_o) = h_e A_t(t_a - t_s)$$

giving

$$t_s = \frac{(h_e t_a + C_e t_o)}{C_e + h_e} \quad (7\text{-}54)$$

The comfort equation is in the form

$$t_a = 147 - t_s \quad (7\text{-}55)$$

Eliminating the surface temperature between Eqs. 7-54 and 7-55 and solving for the optimum inside air temperature give

$$t_a = \frac{147 - [C_e t_o/(C_e + h_e)]}{1 + [h_e/(C_e + h_e)]} \quad (7\text{-}56)$$

For the thermally equivalent homogeneous structure,

$$C_e = 0.3757; \quad h_e = 0.5826; \quad t_o = 0$$

so, on substitution,

$$t_a = \frac{147 - 0}{1 + [0.5826/(0.3757 + 0.5826)]}$$

$$= \frac{147}{1.6080} = 91.42 \text{ F} \quad (7\text{-}57)$$

Transmission load is therefore

$$q = U_e A_t(t_a - t_o) = (0.2284)(1600)(91.42)$$

$$= 33,408 \text{ Btu/hr} \quad (7\text{-}58)$$

which is in agreement with the value of 33,412 Btu/hr obtained from the revised rational analysis.

7–10. Rational Analysis of Enclosure with Walls and Ceiling Insulated and Closed Crawl Space at 0 F. The enclosure analyzed in Art. 7–3 by the rational method is the same one analyzed in Example 5–1 by the equivalent-conductance procedure. In Example 5–12 this same enclosure is altered so that walls and ceiling are insulated, the windows double-glazed, and the crawl space beneath the floor is closed but is assumed to have an air temperature of 0 F. A rational analysis of the insulated enclosure would follow the same step-by-step procedure that was used in Art. 7–3, page 303. The shape factors and h_{rxy} terms would have the same values as for the uninsulated structure, but the conductances and inside convective film coefficients would be as follows (refer to solutions of Examples 5–5 and 5–12):

$$C_w = 0.07107; \quad C_c = 0.07899; \quad C_f = 0.3922; \quad C_g = 0.7413$$

$$h_{cw} = 0.38; \quad h_{cc} = 0.39; \quad h_{cf} = 0.21; \quad h_{cg} = 0.45$$

The results of a rational analysis (involving the simultaneous solution of Eq. 7–30 through 7–34 and Eq. 7–20) are

$$t_a = 87.85 \text{ F}; \quad t_c = 62.81 \text{ F}; \quad t_f = 51.04 \text{ F};$$

$$t_w = 64.35 \text{ F}; \quad t_i = 67.14 \text{ F}; \quad t_g = 48.55 \text{ F}$$

The mean radiant temperature is $147 - 87.85 = 59.15$ F and the transmission loss $= q_t = 14{,}538$ Btu/hr.

7–11. Rational Analysis of Enclosure with Walls and Ceiling Insulated and Closed Crawl Space at 40 F. This case corresponds to those analyzed in Example 5–5 by the equivalent-conductance method. Coefficients are as given in Art. 7–10 and the step-by-step rational analysis is the same except that the $C_f t_o$ term in the numerator of Eq. 7–31 is no longer equal to zero. Results are

$$t_a = 83.27 \text{ F}; \quad t_c = 65.31 \text{ F}; \quad t_f = 61.48 \text{ F};$$

$$t_w = 66.39 \text{ F}; \quad t_i = 69.17 \text{ F}; \quad t_g = 45.92 \text{ F}$$

The mean radiant temperature is $147 - 83.27 = 63.73$ F and the transmission loss $= q_t = 10{,}237$ Btu/hr.

7–12. Rational Analysis of Enclosure with Walls, Ceiling, and Floor Insulated. This enclosure is the one analyzed by the equivalent-conductance method in Examples 5–10 and 5–13. All coefficients are as in Art. 7–10 except that

$$C_f = 0.07321 \quad \text{and} \quad h_{cf} = 0.17$$

If the crawl space is assumed closed and at a temperature of 40 F (as in Example 5–13), the results of the rational analysis are

$$t_a = 81.97 \text{ F}; \quad t_c = 67.39 \text{ F}; \quad t_f = 67.54 \text{ F};$$

$$t_w = 68.26 \text{ F}; \quad t_i = 71.06 \text{ F}; \quad t_g = 47.04 \text{ F}$$

The mean radiant temperature is $147 - 81.97 = 65.03$ F and the transmission loss $= q_t = 8579$ Btu/hr.

If the crawl space is open and at a temperature of 0 F (as in Example 5-10), the results of the rational analysis are

$$t_a = 85.19 \text{ F}; \quad t_c = 64.27 \text{ F}; \quad t_f = 57.12 \text{ F};$$
$$t_w = 65.54 \text{ F}; \quad t_i = 68.33 \text{ F}; \quad t_g = 45.48 \text{ F}$$

The mean radiant temperature is $147 - 85.19 = 61.81$ F and the transmission loss $= q_t = 8664$ Btu/hr.

7-13. Comparison of Rational Method and Equivalent-Conductance Method.

Table 7-2 summarizes the results of the rational and equivalent-conductance analyses that have been made on the same enclosure

TABLE 7-2
Comparison of Transmission Losses from Recommended Procedure and from Rational Procedure

	Recommended Procedure	Rational Procedure
Enclosure uninsulated: data from Example 5-1 (second approximation) and from Art. 7-4 with revised coefficients		
q_t · · · · · · ·	32,022 Btu/hr	33,412 Btu/hr
t_a · · · · · · ·	92.4/F	91.4 F
Enclosure insulated in walls and ceiling; floor uninsulated but over closed crawl space at 0 F: data from Example 5-11 and Art. 7-10		
q_t · · · · · · ·	13,705 Btu/hr	14,538 Btu/hr
t_a · · · · · · ·	85.4 F	87.9 F
Enclosure insulated in walls and ceiling; floor uninsulated but over closed crawl space at 40 F: data from Example 5-5, Example 5-8, and Art. 7-11		
q_t · · · · · · ·	9,617 Btu/hr	10,237 Btu/hr
t_a · · · · · · ·	80.9 F	83.3 F
Enclosure insulated in walls, ceiling, and floor but floor over open crawl space at 0 F: data from Example 5-9 and from Art. 7-12		
q_t · · · · · · ·	9,008 Btu/hr	8,664 Btu/hr
t_a · · · · · · ·	80.2 F	85.2 F
Enclosure insulated in walls, ceiling, and floor but floor over closed crawl space at 40 F: data from Example 5-12 and from Art. 7-12)		
q_t · · · · · · ·	7,747 Btu/hr	8,580 Btu/hr
t_a · · · · · · ·	78.6 F	82.0 F

with different insulation conditions and for different crawl-space conditions. For extreme load conditions, as in the first two cases, the two methods agree within 5 per cent, whereas for well-insulated structures, the difference is somewhat greater. In all cases in practice, the simplicity of the equivalent conductance procedure will dictate its use.

PROBLEMS

7–1. Develop an explicit form (similar to Eq. 7–20) of the comfort equation for a subject who is standing on a diagonal of the room of Fig. 7–1 and at a point that is 4 ft out from each of two adjacent interior walls. Using the suface temperatures obtained in Art. 7–3, calculate the mean radiant temperature of the room with respect to the subject, and compare this value with that (52.5 F from the solution in Art. 7–3, page 305) for a subject standing in the center of the room.

7–2. Using the surface temperatures from Art. 7–3 page 305, calculate the mean radiant temperature with respect to a sphere located at the center of the room, and compare it with the *mrt* for a subject standing at room center.

7–3. Develop the *mrt* equation for a sphere 3 ft above the floor and in the same location as the standing subject of problem 7–1. Using data from Art. 7–3, page 295, calculate the *mrt* with respect to the sphere, and compare it with that (from solution of problem 7–1) for a standing subject at the same location.

7–4. In Art. 7–2, page 294, the statement is made that for rooms with ceiling heights less than 12 ft, the shape factors of room surfaces with respect to a centrally located, standing subject are approximated by the ratio of surface area to enclosure area. Investigate the degree of failure of this approximation for a windowless, 20-ft by 20-ft room with a 20-ft ceiling.

7–5. Discuss the significance of the value of A_s obtained in Eq. 7–17.

The following six problems should be undertaken as design projects rather than ordinary problem assignments. Although the solutions to these problems are straightforward and parallel in method, they are nonetheless lengthy and time-consuming.

7–6. A center-line partition is installed in the room shown in Fig. 7–1. The partition establishes two rooms, one with a single 5-ft by 5.68-ft window and the other with two windows, one 10 ft by 5.68 ft and the other 5 ft by 5.68 ft. (a) For the conditions of Example 5–1, calculate *by the rational method* the optimum air and surface temperatures in each of the two rooms. (b) Calculate the total transmission load for the structure (noting that although the exposures of the structure are unchanged, the optimum inside conditions and the value of the transmission load will have changed). (c) Discuss the influence of the partition on load and on thermal comfort.

7–7. Repeat problem 7–6 for the conditions of Example 5–5.

7–8. Repeat problem 7–6 for the conditions of Example 5–10.

7–9. Repeat problem 7–6 for the conditions of Example 5–12.

7–10. Repeat problem 7–6 for the conditions of Example 5–13.

7–11. Using the results of problems 5–19 through 5–23 and of problems 7–6 through 7–10, prepare a table similar to Table 7–2. Discuss the significance of the differences between results for the unpartitioned and for the partitioned structure.

8

PANEL HEATING LOAD ANALYSIS

When large sections of the enclosure surface are used as heating panels, the rational analysis of Chapter 7 and the equivalent-conductance analysis of Chapter 5 require modification. In a panel-heated room, the unheated surfaces frequently reach equilibrium temperatures greater than room air temperature. When this occurs, the simple heat-balance equation (5–10) is no longer applicable, since the inside surface is gaining energy by radiation but losing energy by convection. In this case a combined inside film coefficient cannot be established; hence Eq. 5–10 expands to the form

$$C_u(t_u - t_o) = h_{cu}(t_a - t_u) + h_{rpu}F_{pu}(t_p - t_u) \tag{8–1}$$

with equivalent conductance C_u evaluated by the equation (analogous with Eq. 5–4b)

$$C_u = \frac{C_g A_g}{A_u} + \frac{C_w A_w}{A_u} + \frac{C_c A_c}{A_u} + \frac{C_f A_f}{A_u} \tag{8–2}$$

where C_u = equivalent conductance from inside surface of all unheated room areas (including non-transmitting sections such as inside partitions) to outside air.

A_u = total area of all unheated room surfaces
   $= A_g + A_w + A_c + A_f + A_i = A_e - A_p$.

t_u = uniform surface temperature of unheated room surface in thermally equivalent room having unheated surface conductance C_u.

h_{cu} = inside film coefficient for convective transfer to or from unheated surface of room.

h_{rpu} = equivalent first-power coefficient (defined by Eq. 4–113) for radiant transfer from heating panel to unheated surface of equivalent room.

F_{pu} = shape factor of panel with respect to energy received from the unheated surfaces ($F_{pu}A_u = F_{up}A_p$).

A second modification in method of analysis when using panels arises because, in any panel system, infiltration air is heated to room temperature by the panel; hence panel load and panel surface temperature are determined by combined ventilation and transmission loads. If air is mechanically introduced, the same situation applies unless the air is preheated from a separate heat source to room temperature. Even if no infiltration or ventilation were to occur (or if ventilation air were introduced at room temperature),

317

the presence of the panel as a heat source would require establishing an equation expressing equality between convective loss from the panel and convective gain by the unheated surface.

For the above reasons a modified panel-design procedure is required. In the following article, the rational procedure will be applied to a panel system, whereas in Art. 8–4 the equivalent-conductance procedure will be adapted for use with panel heating.

8–1. Rational Load Analysis for Panel Heating System. For any type of heating system other than one using large panels, the rational analysis as developed in Chapter 7 utilizes a series of heat balances and the comfort equation. In the most common case, heat balances would be established on glass, transmitting wall, non-transmitting wall (as inside partitions), ceiling, and floor. The five heat-balance equations plus the comfort equation then provide six simultaneous equations that can be solved to determine the five unknown inside surface temperatures (t_g, t_w, t_i, t_c, t_f) and the unknown optimum design inside-air temperature.

For the most general case in panel heating, the same five inside surface temperatures and the air temperature are again unknowns, but an additional unknown is the panel surface temperature (if panel area is arbitrarily selected) or the panel area (if design panel surface temperature is arbitrarily selected). Thus need exists for a seventh independent equation to permit simultaneous solution for the seventh unknown. Such an equation can most readily be established by setting up a heat balance on the infiltration or ventilation air passing through the room. The heat gain of the ventilation air, as it is raised from outside air temperature to room air temperature, is equated to the gain by convection from the panel and the loss by convection to the unheated room surfaces (in cases where t_u is found to exceed t_a, the "loss" by convection to the unheated walls will be negative, indicating a gain).

$$0.2411W(t_a - t_o) = h_{cp}(t_p - t_a)A_p - h_{cg}(t_a - t_g)A_g - h_{cw}(t_a - t_w)A_w$$
$$- h_{ci}(t_a - t_i)A_i - h_{cc}(t_a - t_c)A_c - h_{cf}(t_a - t_f)A_f$$
$$(8-3)$$

giving

$$t_a = \frac{h_{cp}t_pA_p + h_{cg}t_gA_g + h_{cw}t_wA_w + h_{ci}t_iA_i + h_{cc}t_cA_c + h_{cf}t_fA_f + 0.2411Wt_o}{h_{cp}A_p + h_{cg}A_g + h_{cw}A_w + h_{ci}A_i + h_{cc}A_c + h_{cf}A_f + 0.2411W}$$
$$(8-4)$$

where $h_{cp}, h_{cg} \cdots$ = film coefficients for convective heat transfer between panel, glass, . . . and room air.

0.2411 = specific heat of air, Btu/(lb)(°F).[1]

W = infiltration rate or ventilation rate (based on "thermal" air changes as discussed in Art. 6–1) in lb/hr.

[1] In a strict sense the humid specific heat, c_H (Eq. 6–12), should be used, but at winter design conditions the specific humidity of the outside air is so low that the increase of c_H over 0.2411 is negligible.

Eq. 8-4 together with Eqs. 7-20, 7-30, 7-31, 7-32, 7-33, and 7-34 provide seven simultaneous equations from which the six unknown surface temperatures and the unknown room air temperature can be established. With temperatures known, the rate of transmission loss can be calculated by Eq. 7-37; the sensible fraction of the ventilation loss is then

$$\text{SHL} = (0.2411)(W)(t_a - t_o) \tag{8-5}$$

If the enclosure is humidified, the latent heat load would be separately calculated and added to known transmission load and to known sensible ventilation load, to determine the total required rate of energy input to the enclosure.

An alternative procedure is to calculate the sum of transmission load and sensible ventilation load as the energy output of the panel:

$$
\begin{aligned}
q_t + \text{SHL} = [&h_{rgp}F_{gp}(t_p - t_g) + h_{rwp}F_{wp}(t_p - t_w) + h_{rip}F_{ip}(t_p - t_i) \\
& + h_{rcp}F_{cp}(t_p - t_c) + h_{rfp}F_{fp}(t_p - t_f) + h_{cp}(t_p - t_a)]A_p
\end{aligned} \tag{8-6}
$$

Load evaluation by means of Eq. 8-6 also serves as an independent check on the accuracy of the numerical solution of the seven simultaneous equations.

In many cases the procedure for the rational panel analysis will be subject to simplification. Thus, if the entire ceiling or floor area is utilized as a panel, the number of unknown surface temperatures reduces by one, and only six simultaneous equations need be solved.

EXAMPLE 8-1. In order to permit direct comparison of heating load for a panel system with load for other systems, reinvestigate the enclosure that was analyzed for convective heating in Arts. 7-3 and 7-4. Assume that any ventilation air introduced into the room is preheated to room air temperature; hence the system is thermally equivalent to one with zero ventilation. Take all areas, shape factors, and thermal coefficients as equal to those used in Art. 7-3, page 295. The entire area of both inside partitions is to constitute the heating panel.

Solution: Eqs. 7-30, 7-31, 7-32, 7-34, and 7-20 apply to this case, but Eq. 7-33 is inapplicable, since there is no longer an unheated non-transmitting surface within the enclosure. Substituting known values in each equation gives Eqs. (a), (b), (d), and (e) in exactly the same form as given in Art. 7-3, page 303,[2]

$$2.7470t_w - 22.6115t_f + 3.8811t_i + 5.3000t_c + 3.6941t_a = 0 \tag{a}$$

$$10.2952t_f - 60.7731t_w + 9.0204t_i + 9.9957t_c + 19.2908t_a = 0 \tag{b}$$

$$2.4951t_w + 4.9525t_f + 3.6311t_i - 24.2031t_c + 8.2216t_a = 0 \tag{d}$$

$$1.9459t_w + 3.7603t_f + 3.0210t_i + 2.9305t_c + 12.6191t_a - 1830.6 = 0 \tag{e}$$

In order to establish a revised Eq. (c), the value of h_{cp} must be determined for use in Eq. 8-4. The panel surface temperature at design load is unknown, but in

---

[2] Although the empirical coefficients in the simultaneous equations are not accurate to more than two decimal places, the actual mathematical solution will be carried out to four-place accuracy. This is necessary, numerically, since in many cases three-place differences result from subtractions involving four-place terms.

order to obtain a first approximation to h_{cp}, the value of t_p will be assumed at 110 F, with t_a assumed as 75 F; then Δt_{film} is 110 − 75, or 35 F, and by Eq. 5–39, (assuming its applicability to heated as well as unheated wall surfaces) the convective coefficient becomes

$$h_{cp} = 0.274(\Delta t_f)^{0.25} = 0.274(35)^{0.25} = 0.67 \text{ Btu/(hr)(sq ft)(°F)}$$

By substituting known values in Eq. 8–4 and noting that W is zero,

$$t_a = \frac{[(0.67)(400)t_p] + [(0.730)(113.6)t_g] + [(0.570)(400)t_w] + [(0.282)(400)t_f] + [(0.689)(400)t_c]}{[(0.67)(400)] + [(0.730)(113.6)] + [(0.570)(400)] + [(0.282)(400)] + [(0.689)(400)]}$$

$$= 0.2771t_p + 0.857t_g + 0.2357t_w + 0.1166t_f + 0.2849t_c \qquad (8\text{–}4a)$$

Eliminating t_g between Eqs. 7–32a and 8–4a gives a revised Eq. (c):

$$t_g = 0.0169t_w + 0.0642t_f + 0.0534t_p + 0.0687t_c + 0.1658t_a \qquad (7\text{–}32a)$$

$$= 11.6686t_a - 3.2334t_p - 2.7503t_w - 1.3606t_f - 3.3244t_c \qquad (8\text{–}4a)$$

giving
$$11.5028t_a - 3.2868t_p - 2.7672t_w - 1.4248t_f - 3.3931t_c = 0 \qquad (c)$$

Eliminating t_p between Eqs. (a) and (b),

$$t_p = 5.8261t_f - 0.7078t_w - 1.3656t_c - 0.9518t_a \qquad (a')$$

$$= 6.7373t_w - 1.1413t_f - 1.1081t_c - 2.1386t_a \qquad (b')$$

giving
$$7.4451t_w - 6.9674t_f + 0.2575t_c - 1.1868t_a = 0 \qquad (f)$$

From Eqs. (a) and (c),

$$t_p = 5.8261t_f - 0.7078t_w - 1.3656t_c - 0.9518t_a \qquad (a')$$

$$= 3.4997t_a - 0.8419t_w - 0.4335t_f - 1.0323t_c \qquad (c')$$

giving
$$4.4515t_a - 0.1341t_w - 6.2596t_f + 0.333t_c = 0 \qquad (g)$$

From Eqs. (a) and (d),

$$t_p = 5.8261t_f - 0.7078t_w - 1.3656t_c - 0.9518t_a \qquad (a')$$

$$= 6.6655t_c - 0.6871t_w - 1.36391t_f - 2.2642t_a \qquad (d')$$

giving
$$8.0311t_c + 0.02070t_w - 7.1900t_f - 1.3124t_a = 0 \qquad (h)$$

From Eqs. (a) and (e),

$$t_p = 5.8261t_f - 0.7078t_w - 1.3656t_c - 0.9518t_a \qquad (a')$$

$$= 605.96 - 0.6441t_w - 1.2447t_f - 0.9699t_c - 4.177t_a \qquad (e')$$

giving
$$605.96 + 0.0637t_w - 7.0708t_f + 0.3957t_c - 3.2252t_a = 0 \qquad (i)$$

Eliminating t_w between Eqs. (f) and (g),

$$t_w = 0.9358t_f - 0.0346t_c + 0.15941t_a \tag{f'}$$

$$= 33.1954t_a - 46.6786t_f + 2.4855t_c \tag{g'}$$

giving

$$33.0360t_a - 47.6144t_f + 2.5201t_c = 0 \tag{j}$$

From Eqs. (f) and (h),

$$t_w = 0.9358t_f - 0.0346t_c + 0.15941t_a \tag{f'}$$

$$= -387.9758t_c + 347.3430t_f + 63.4010t_a \tag{h'}$$

giving

$$63.2416t_a + 346.407t_f - 387.9412t_c = 0 \tag{k}$$

From Eqs. (f) and (i),

$$t_w = 0.9358t_f - 0.0346t_c + 0.15941t_a \tag{f'}$$

$$= 111.0016t_f - 9512.715 - 6.2119t_c + 50.6311t_a \tag{i'}$$

giving

$$50.4717t_a + 110.0802t_f - 6.1773t_c - 9512.715 = 0 \tag{l}$$

Eliminating t_f between Eqs. (k) and (j),

$$t_f = -0.1826t_a + 1.1199t_c \tag{k'}$$

$$= 0.6938t_a + 0.05293t_c \tag{j'}$$

giving

$$0.8764t_a - 1.0670t_c = 0 \tag{m}$$

From Eqs. (k) and (l),

$$t_f = -0.1826t_a + 1.1199t_c \tag{k'}$$

$$= -0.4585t_a + 0.05612t_c + 86.416 \tag{l'}$$

giving

$$-0.2759t_a - 1.0638t_c + 86.416 = 0 \tag{n}$$

Eliminating t_c between Eqs. (m) and (n),

$$t_c = 0.8214 \tag{m'}$$

$$= 81.2333 - 0.2594t_a \tag{n'}$$

giving

$$1.0808t_a = 81.2333$$

$$t_a = 75.16 \text{ F}$$

Then

$$t_c = 61.74 \text{ F} \qquad \text{From Eq. (m')}$$
$$t_f = 55.42 \text{ F} \qquad \text{From Eq. (k')}$$
$$t_w = 61.71 \text{ F} \qquad \text{From Eq. (f')}$$
$$t_p = 123.36 \text{ F} \qquad \text{From Eq. (a')}$$
$$t_g = 27.89 \text{ F} \qquad \text{From Eq. 7–32a}$$

The mean radiant temperature (Eq. 7–15 with numerical values from Eq. 7–20) is

$$mrt = [(0.2298)(61.74)] + [(0.1549)(61.71)] + [(0.0803)(27.89)]$$
$$+ [(0.2383)(123.36)] + [(0.2968)(55.42)]$$
$$= 71.83 \text{ F}$$

Then, as a check,

$$t_a + mrt = 75.16 + 71.83 = 146.99$$

which is in agreement with the selected thermal level of 73.5 F.

The transmission load (in this case equal to the total load) is (by Eq. 7–37)

$$q_t = C_w A_w (t_w - t_o) + C_g A_g (t_g - t_o) + C_f A_f (t_f - t_o) + C_c A_c (t_c - t_o)$$
$$= [(0.344)(286.4)(61.71)] + [(2.778)(113.6)(27.89)] + [(0.508)(400)(55.42)]$$
$$+ [(0.365)(400)(61.74)] \qquad\qquad (8\text{–}7)$$
$$= 8801.5 + 6079.8 + 9043.2 + 11261.2$$
$$= 35{,}186 \text{ Btu/hr}$$

A second approximation could be realized by revising the thermal coefficients in accord with the air and surface temperatures determined above. The revised values of h_{rpg}, h_{rpw}, h_{rpf}, and h_{rpc} would be changed considerably,[3] whereas values of such terms as h_{rwf} and h_{rwc} would change very little. The value of h_{cp} would be based on a Δt_{film} of 123-75, or 48, rather than the assumed Δt_{film} of 35; note, however (from Eq. 5–39) that this change in Δt_{film} would only increase h_{cp} from the assumed value of 0.67 to the revised value of 0.72.

The results of Example 8–1 are of particular interest in that the calculated optimum inside-air temperature of 75 F shows that the structure would be comfortably heated to the selected thermal level of 73.5 F by means of a wall-panel system. This is in contrast with the result of the analysis for convective heating (Art. 7–3), which established that the optimum design inside-air temperature (94.5 F) would be so high that physical comfort would be impossible even though the conditions for thermal comfort (as expressed in the comfort equation) were met.

The increased transmission load of the panel versus the convective heating system (35,186 Btu/hr for the panel and 31,666 Btu/hr for the convection system) suggests that wall-panel heating used in an uninsulated and un-ventilated structure should be considered essentially as a remedial measure for overcoming cold-wall effect. The design load is 11.1 per cent greater, but this premium permits reduction of the air temperature to a livable value.

EXAMPLE 8–2. Reinvestigate the enclosure of Example 8–1, considering that infiltration occurs at a rate of one air change per hour.

Solution: For the 20-ft by 20-ft by 10-ft enclosure, one air change per hour would correspond to 4000 cu ft/hr, or (for standard air) 300 lb/hr. Eq. 8-4 would

---

[3] For example, the new value of h_{rpc} would be obtained from Fig. 4–14 at t_h of 123 F and t_c of 62 F; the value of h_{rpc} is then 1.16 Btu/(hr)(ft sq)(°F).

then be written with all terms as in the solution of Example 8–1 except that there would be an additive term in the denominator of

$$0.2411W = (0.2411)(300) = 72.33$$

giving

$$t_a = 0.2751t_p + 0.0798t_g + 0.2193t_w + 0.1085t_f + 0.2561t_c \qquad (8\text{–}4b)$$

Eliminating t_g between Eqs. 7–32a and 8–4b gives

$$12.3655t_a - 3.5008t_p - 2.7650t_w - 1.4238t_f - 3.3908t_c = 0 \qquad (c')$$

Eqs. (a), (b), (d), and (e) retain the forms of Example 5–1; hence simultaneous solution of these equations together with Eq. (c') can be carried out as before. The results are

$$t_a = 72.89 \text{ F}; \quad t_c = 62.32 \text{ F}; \quad t_f = 56.48 \text{ F}; \quad t_w = 62.3 \text{ F};$$
$$t_p = 130.48 \text{ F}; \quad t_g = 28.01 \text{ F}$$

The mean radiant temperature is $147 - 72.89 = 74.11$ F; the transmission loss is 35280 Btu/hr; the sensible ventilation load $= 0.2411W(t_a - t_o) = (0.2411)(300)(72.89) = 5272$ Btu/hr; and the total sensible load $= 35280 + 5272 = 40,552$ Btu/hr. (If room humidity were controlled, the latent heat load carried by the humidifier would be added to the sensible heat load to *determine the total heat requirements of the system.*)

In Example 8–1 it was found that use of wall panels in the uninsulated, unventilated enclosure gave an 11.1 per cent greater transmission loss than that for convective heating. From Example 8–2 the existence of moderate ventilation increases the excess transmission loss to $[(35.280 - 31,660)/31,660]100$, or 11.4 per cent, but this is more than offset by the reduced ventilation load due to lower inside air temperature. Thus, with convective heating, the sensible ventilation load would be $(0.2411)(300)(94.5)$, or 6835 Btu/hr, and the total sensible load would be $31,660 + 6835$, or 38,500 Btu/hr. The total sensible load for the panel-heated enclosure is therefore $[(40.552 - 38,500)/38,500]100$, or 5 per cent greater than that for the convective heating.

EXAMPLE 8–3. Reinvestigate the enclosure of Example 8–2 for an outside-air mechanical ventilation rate of five air changes per hour.

Solution: The procedure is exactly as before, with W now equal to 1500lb/hr. Results are

$$t_a = 64.33 \text{ F}; \quad t_c = 64.55 \text{ F}; \quad t_f = 56.48 \text{ F}; \quad t_w = 64.67 \text{ F}$$
$$t_p = 157.56 \text{ F}; \quad t_g = 28.50 \text{ F}$$
$$mrt = 147 - 64.33 = 82.67 \text{ F}$$
$$q_t = 37,091 \text{ Btu/hr}$$
$$q_{SVL} = (0.2411)(1500)(64.33) = 23,265 \text{ Btu/hr}$$

The results of Example 8–3 clearly demonstrate that for poorly insulated structures with high ventilation rates, the lower air temperature associated with panel heating as compared with convective heating will provide an economic as well as a comfort advantage. With panel heating, the total sensible load is 37,091 + 23,265, or 60,356 Btu/hr. With convective heating, the transmission load (31,660 Btu/hr) is less by 5431 Btu/hr, but the sensible ventilation load [$q_{SVL} = (0.2411)(1500)(94.5) = 34.175$] is greater by 10,910 Btu/hr. The saving on total sensible load attributable to the panel system is therefore [(31,660 + 34,175 − 60,356)/(31,660 + 34,175)]100, or 8.3 per cent. Note, however, that the required panel-surface temperature, 157.56 F, is impracticably high; hence, if a panel system were to be used, it would be necessary to increase the heated area by utilizing part of the ceiling or floor as well as the interior walls.

EXAMPLE 8–4. Consider that the walls and ceiling of the enclosure being analyzed are insulated as in Example 5–5, the windows are double glass, the floor is insulated as in Example 5–10, and the crawl space below the floor is closed and at a temperature of 40 F. Both interior partitions are to be used as heating panels. Calculate the design value of the inside air temperature, the transmission load, and the total load for (a) no ventilation, (b) infiltration equivalent to one air change per hour, (c) mechanical ventilation equal to five air changes per hour.

Solution: The thermal coefficients for this case, summarized from Arts. 7–10 and 7–12, are

$$C_w = 0.07107; \quad C_c = 0.07899; \quad C_f = 0.07321; \quad C_g = 0.7413;$$
$$h_{cw} = 0.38; \quad h_{cc} = 0.39; \quad h_{cf} = 0.17; \quad h_{cg} = 0.45$$

Then substituting known terms into Eqs. 7–20, 7–30, 7–31, 7–32, 7–34, and 8–4 and solving these equations simultaneously gives

(a) For no ventilation:

$$t_a = 74.83 \text{ F}; \quad t_c = 69.74 \text{ F}; \quad t_f = 71.15 \text{ F}; \quad t_w = 69.44 \text{ F}$$
$$t_p = 85.65 \text{ F}; \quad t_g = 47.98 \text{ F}$$
$$mrt = 147 - 74.83 = 72.17 \text{ F}$$
$$q_t = 8569.5 \text{ Btu/hr} = q_{total}$$

(b) For one air change per hour:

$$t_a = 73.35 \text{ F}; \quad t_c = 72.34 \text{ F}; \quad t_f = 74.30 \text{ F}; \quad t_w = 72.85 \text{ F}$$
$$t_p = 93.13 \text{ F}; \quad t_g = 48.47 \text{ F}$$
$$mrt = 147 - 73.35 = 73.65 \text{ F}$$
$$q_t = 8874.3 \text{ Btu/hr}; \quad q_{SVL} = 5305 \text{ Btu/hr}$$
$$q_{total} = 14,179 \text{ Btu/hr}$$

(c) For five air changes per hour:

$$t_a = 62.11 \text{ F}; \quad t_c = 76.31 \text{ F}; \quad t_f = 80.27 \text{ F}; \quad t_w = 76.40 \text{ F}$$
$$t_p = 115.68 \text{ F}; \quad t_g = 51.12 \text{ F}$$
$$mrt = 147 - 62.11 = 84.89 \text{ F}$$
$$q_t = 9473 \text{ Btu/hr}; \quad q_{SVL} = 22,462 \text{ Btu/hr}$$
$$q_{total\ sensible} = 31,935 \text{ Btu/hr}$$

The structure of Example 8–4 is thermally identical to that which was analyzed rationally for convective heating in Art. 7–12. With convective heating, the transmission loss was found to be 8579 Btu/hr, with required inside air temperature of 82 F. Thus, for the insulated, unventilated enclosure, the difference in transmission load between panel heating and convective heating is so small (8570 versus 8579 Btu/hr) as to be negligible. With one air change, the transmission loss with panel heating increases by 3.6 per cent, but the sensible ventilation load is greater for the convective system; so, the total load with panel heating is slightly less (2.3 per cent) than with convective heating. With ventilation at a rate of five air changes, the lower temperature in the panel heated enclosure (62.1 F versus 82.0 F) greatly reduces the sensible ventilation load and thereby leads to a 16.5 per cent reduction in total load as compared with convective heating.

8–2. Ineffectiveness of Reflective Surfaces in Panel Heating. The rational analysis of Art. 8–1 is based on the assumption that the effective emissivity of all surfaces in an enclosure can be taken as unity. In this article it will be shown that the assumption is valid and that in a room of average size, highly reflective surfaces (such as metal-foil surfacing on the ceiling) have no appreciable effect on comfort conditions within the room or on heat losses from it.

Under idealized but impractical conditions, reflective surfacing would be effective. As an example consider a room in which the thermal level is to be established at 73.5 F. The body-surface temperature of the occupants would then be (by Eq. 1–12)

$$t_b = 0.21t_a + 0.54mrt + 26.9$$
$$= 0.21(147 - mrt) + 0.54mrt + 26.9 \qquad (8\text{–}8)$$
$$= 0.33mrt + 57.77$$

If all room surfaces were at a uniform temperature and if the emissivity were unity, body temperature and mrt would be equal (by Eq. 8–8) when

$$mrt = 0.33mrt + 57.77$$

or

$$mrt = 86.2 \text{ F}$$
$$t_a = 147 - 86.2 = 60.8 \text{ F}$$

Under these circumstances the thermally comfortable occupant would have no net loss of body heat by radiation. It follows, then, that equal thermal comfort would be experienced in any environment in which air temperature was 60.8 F and net radiant loss was zero.

Assume now the existence of a surfacing material having emissivity and transmissivity of zero (100 per cent reflectivity). Replace the 86.2 F enclosure with one having 100 per cent reflective inside surfaces, and assume that loss of radiation by gaseous absorption is negligible (refer to Art. 8–3 for a discussion of the actual significance of gaseous absorption). In this enclosure, *regardless of inside surface temperature*, there could be no net radiant transfer to or from the occupants. The radiant flux within the enclosure would necessarily build up until the radiant energy being returned to the occupants after from 1 to n interreflections at the enclosure would equal that which would be received by the occupant if the enclosure were at a uniform, inside black-body surface temperature of 86.2 F.

Although the comfort characteristics of the black body and idealized reflective enclosures described above would be identical, the heat-load characteristic would be markedly different. Transmission losses from the black-body enclosure would be proportional to $(86.2 - t_o)$, whereas for the perfectly reflective room, the inside surface temperature would reach an equilibrium value lower than the 60.8 F inside air temperature. Thus, for an outside design temperature of 0 F, the reflective room would have less transmission losses by something more than $[(86.2 - 60.8)/(86.2 - 0)]100$, or 29.5 per cent of the transmission losses from the room with non-reflective surfaces. Likewise, the much higher inside-surface temperature of the non-reflective room would be responsible for large losses of heat to the ventilation air (noting that ventilation would be *required* in order to prevent the room air temperature from rising).

Consideration of the advantage of reflective surfaces as indicated by the above idealized analysis has led to serious misconceptions concerning the effectiveness or utility of commercially available metallic foil when applied as inside ceiling or wall surfacing. With perfectly reflecting surfaces or with perfectly absorbing surfaces, the radiant exchange between enclosure and occupant is independent of room size. All real surfaces, however, are partially reflective, having emissivity less than unity but greater than zero; hence they absorb a fraction of the energy emitted by the occupant and reflect the remainder. Of the portion reflected, the fraction reabsorbed by the occupant depends not only on the emissivities of surrounding surfaces but also on the number of re-reflections that take place among enclosing surfaces before the energy is returned to the occupant. As the room size increases, fewer of the infinite number of energy paths through the room will strike the occupant; hence the fraction of energy reabsorbed will decrease. Thus, for a large room, even with highly reflective surfacing, the greater portion of the energy emitted by the occupant will be absorbed as a result of the large number of interreflections among room surfaces. This subject is investigated quantitatively in the next discussion.

DEVELOPMENT OF THE RATIONAL REFLECTION EQUATION. Expressions will now be derived for the energy *received* at a small finite surface, ΔA_2, of that energy initially emitted by a small finite surface, ΔA_1, when radiation occurs through a non-absorbing medium. In addition to seeing ΔA_2, the emitting surface will be assumed to see two other small surfaces (each having an emissivity e_3) and of combined area ΔA_3; all surfaces of the enclosure other than ΔA_1, ΔA_2, and ΔA_3 will be taken as black bodies.

Definition of Radiosity. If ΔA_1 *sees* any surface having an emissivity less than that of a black body, some of the energy from ΔA_1 which strikes that surface will be returned and re-reflected (if $e_1 < 1$) so that the total energy leaving ΔA_1 will exceed the emissive power E_1 (defined by Eq. 4–104). The total energy leaving a surface per unit time per unit area is defined as radiosity R and is equal to the sum of energies leaving by emission, reflection, and transmission. That part of the radiosity due to energy originally emitted by the surface will henceforth be designated as R_S, the *self-radiosity*. The energy leaving ΔA_1 in the direction of ΔA_2 of that originally emitted by ΔA_1 is therefore

$$q'' = R_{S_1} F_{\Delta A_2 \, \Delta A_1} \Delta A_1 \qquad (8\text{–}9)$$

where R_{S_1} includes some energy initially emitted by ΔA_1, which was returned after reflection from ΔA_2 or from any other surface. The evaluation of R_{S_1} requires a knowledge of the emissivities of all surfaces of the system, their shape factors with respect to ΔA_1 and with respect to one another, and the rate at which radiant energy is absorbed by the gaseous medium through which transfer occurs. Maximum self-radiosity (based on energy initially emitted by ΔA_1) would occur when gaseous absorption is zero; the rational analysis that follows is established for this condition.

For ΔA_2 *a Black Body;* ΔA_1 *and* ΔA_3 *Gray Bodies.* This analysis can most effectively be carried out by first evaluating the self-radiosity of ΔA_1 (due only to energy directly emitted by ΔA_1 or re-reflected after being returned from ΔA_3) and then determining the energy received at ΔA_2 either directly from ΔA_1 or after reflections from ΔA_3.

SELF-RADIOSITY OF ΔA_1. Since $e_2 = 1$, there is no reflection of energy from ΔA_2, and so the term R_{S_1} for this problem is the sum of energy initially emitted by ΔA_1 plus that leaving ΔA_1 for a second time after undergoing 1, 2, 3, . . . or n reflections from ΔA_3, plus that leaving ΔA_1 for the third time after 1, 2, 3, . . . or n reflections from ΔA_3, plus that leaving ΔA_1 for the fourth, fifth, . . . and nth times, each after 1, 2, 3, . . . or n reflections from ΔA_3.

From Eq. 4–104, the energy emitted by ΔA_1 and striking ΔA_3 is

$$q'' = E_1 \Delta A_1 F_{\Delta A_3 \, \Delta A_1} \qquad (8\text{–}10)$$

where the double prime on q (as in Eq. 8–9) indicates radiant transfer between two very small areas. But Kirchhoff's law states that the absorptivity is equal to emissivity; hence reflectivity of a non-transmitting body is $(1 - e)$ and the energy emitted by ΔA_1 and reflected from ΔA_3 is therefore

$$q'' = E_1 \Delta A_1 (1 - e_3) F_{\Delta A_3 \, \Delta A_1} \qquad (8\text{–}11)$$

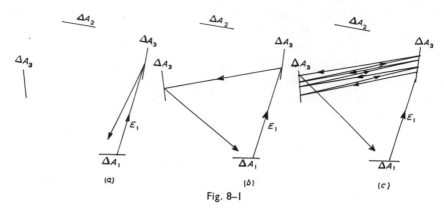

Fig. 8–1

The energy returning to ΔA_1 after one reflection from ΔA_3 (refer to Fig. 8–1a) is then

$$q'' = [E_1\,\Delta A_1(1-e_3)F_{\Delta A_3\,\Delta A_1}]F_{\Delta A_1\,\Delta A_3} \qquad (8\text{–}12)$$

Similarly, the energy returning to ΔA_1 after two reflections from ΔA_3 (Fig. 8–1b) is

$$q'' = [E_1\,\Delta A_1(1-e_3)F_{\Delta A_3\,\Delta A_1}F_{\Delta A_1\,\Delta A_3}][F_{\Delta A_3\,\Delta A_3}(1-e_3)] \qquad (8\text{–}13)$$

and after n reflections from ΔA_3 (refer to Fig. 8–1c), is

$$q'' = [E_1\,\Delta A_1(1-e_3)F_{\Delta A_3\,\Delta A_1}F_{\Delta A_1\,\Delta A_3}][F_{\Delta A_3\,\Delta A_3}(1-e_3)]^{n-1} \qquad (8\text{–}14)$$

Thus the total energy returned to ΔA_1 for the first time is (from Eqs. 8–12, 8–13, and 8–14)

$$q'' = [E_1\,\Delta A_1(1-e_3)F_{\Delta A_3\,\Delta A_1}F_{\Delta A_1\,\Delta A_3}] \cdot \{1 + [(1-e_3)F_{\Delta A_3\,\Delta A_3}]$$
$$+ [(1-e_3)F_{\Delta A_3\,\Delta A_3}]^2 + \cdots + [(1-e_3)F_{\Delta A_3\,\Delta A_3}]^{n-1}\} \qquad (8\text{–}15)$$

The second term of the above equation is an infinite series of the form

$$1 + a + a^2 + a^3 + \cdots + a^n = \frac{1}{1-a}$$

and so Eq. 8–15 becomes

$$q'' = E_1\,\Delta A_1(1-e_3)F_{\Delta A_3\,\Delta A_1}F_{\Delta A_1\,\Delta A_3}S_1 \qquad (8\text{–}16)$$

where

$$S_1 = \frac{1}{1-[F_{\Delta A_3\,\Delta A_3}(1-e_3)]} \qquad (8\text{–}17)$$

From Eq. 8–16 the total energy leaving ΔA_1 for the second time is

$$q'' = E_1\,\Delta A_1(1-e_1)(1-e_3)F_{\Delta A_3\,\Delta A_1}F_{\Delta A_1\,\Delta A_3}S_1 \qquad (8\text{–}18)$$

and for the nth time,

$$q'' = E_1\,\Delta A_1[(1-e_1)(1-e_3)F_{\Delta A_3\,\Delta A_1}F_{\Delta A_1\,\Delta A_3}S_1]^{n-1} \qquad (8\text{–}19)$$

The self-radiosity, R_{S_1}, of ΔA_1 based on energy initially emitted by ΔA_1 is therefore equal to its emissive power E_1, plus a series of terms (of the form of Eq. 8–19), giving the energy re-reflected from ΔA_1 for the first, second, third, ... $(n - 1)$ times:

$$R_{S_1} = E_1\{1 + [(1 - e_1)(1 - e_3) F_{\Delta A_3\ \Delta A_1} F_{\Delta A_1\ \Delta A_3} S_1]$$

$$+ \cdots + [(1 - e_1)(1 - e_3) F_{\Delta A_3\ \Delta A_1} F_{\Delta A_1\ \Delta A_3} S_1]^{n-1}\} \qquad (8\text{--}20)$$

or

$$R_{S_1} = E_1 S_2 \qquad (8\text{--}21)$$

where

$$S_2 = \frac{1}{1 - [(1 - e_1)(1 - e_3) F_{\Delta A_3\ \Delta A_1} F_{\Delta A_1\ \Delta A_3} S_1]} \qquad (8\text{--}22)$$

Energy Received at ΔA_2. The total energy received at ΔA_2 of that initially emitted by ΔA_1 consists of that fraction of the self-radiosity of ΔA_1 that is transferred directly to ΔA_2 plus the fractions received at ΔA_2 after 1, 2, 3, or n reflections from ΔA_3.

By analogy with Eq. 8–14, the energy striking ΔA_2 from ΔA_1 after the nth reflection from ΔA_3 (refer to Fig. 8–2) is

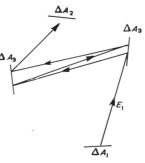

$$q'' = R_{S_1} \Delta A_1 F_{\Delta A_3\ \Delta A_1}(1 - e_3) F_{\Delta A_2\ \Delta A_3}$$

$$\times\ [F_{\Delta A_3\ \Delta A_3}(1 - e_3)]^{n-1} \qquad (8\text{--}23)$$

and the total energy striking ΔA_2 from ΔA_1, directly or indirectly, is

$$q'' = R_{S_1} \Delta A_1 F_{\Delta A_2\ \Delta A_1} + R_{S_1} \Delta A_1 (1 - e_3)$$

$$\times\ F_{\Delta A_3\ \Delta A_1} F_{\Delta A_2\ \Delta A_3} S_1 \qquad (8\text{--}24)$$

Fig. 8-2

where S_1 is given by Eq. 8–17 and R_{S_1} by Eq. 8–21. Since $e_2 = 1$, all energy falling on ΔA_2 is absorbed, and so Eq. 8–24 gives the total transfer of energy from ΔA_1 to ΔA_2.

For ΔA_1, ΔA_2, and ΔA_3 All Gray Bodies. Eq. 8–24 must be modified to account for energy received at ΔA_2 after multiple reflections between ΔA_2 and ΔA_3 and between ΔA_2 and ΔA_1. For the conditions of this case, the term R_{S_1} of Eq. 8–20 is no longer equal to the self-radiosity of ΔA_1, since it does not include the energy returned to and re-reflected from ΔA_1 after reflection from ΔA_2; it remains, however, a useful concept and will be used in the analysis.

Multiple Reflections Between ΔA_2 and ΔA_3. Consider first the correction for multiple reflections between ΔA_2 and ΔA_3, and note that Eq. 8–24 gives the total energy from ΔA_1 striking ΔA_2 *for the first time.* This quantity, multiplied by $(1 - e_2)/\Delta A_1$, is the reflected energy leaving ΔA_2 for the first time, or the radiosity of ΔA_2 (based on area ΔA_1) due to energy once received from ΔA_1 directly or indirectly and then reflected:

$$R_{r_1} = R_{S_1}[F_{\Delta A_2\, \Delta A_1} + (1 - e_3) F_{\Delta A_3\, \Delta A_1} F_{\Delta A_2\, \Delta A_3} S_1](1 - e_2) \quad (8\text{--}25)$$

The radiosity of ΔA_2 (based on area of ΔA_1) due to energy twice received and reflected (after n reflections between ΔA_{3a} and ΔA_{3b}, but energy which has not been returned from ΔA_2 to ΔA_1) is obtained by analogy from Eq. 8–18:

$$R_{r_2} = R_{r_1}(1 - e_2)(1 - e_3) F_{\Delta A_3\, \Delta A_2} F_{\Delta A_2\, \Delta A_3} S_1 \quad (8\text{--}26)$$

or due to energy n times received and reflected (by analogy with Eq. 8–19),

$$R_{r_n} = R_{r_1}[(1 - e_2)(1 - e_3) F_{\Delta A_3\, \Delta A_2} F_{\Delta A_2\, \Delta A_3} S_1]^{n-1} \quad (8\text{--}27)$$

The total radiosity of ΔA_2 (based on area of ΔA_1) due to energy emitted by ΔA_1 (except energy re-reflected between ΔA_1 and ΔA_2) is

$$R_r' = R_{r_1} + R_{r_2} + \cdots + R_{r_n} \quad (8\text{--}28)$$

Then, substituting from Eqs. 8–26 and 8–27,

$$R_r' = R_{r_1}\{1 + [(1 - e_2)(1 - e_3) F_{\Delta A_3\, \Delta A_2} F_{\Delta A_2\, \Delta A_3} S_1] + \cdots + [\cdots]^{n-1}\}$$
$$(8\text{--}29)$$

$$= R_{r_1} S_3 \quad (8\text{--}30)$$

where

$$S_3 = \frac{1}{1 - [(1 - e_2)(1 - e_3) F_{\Delta A_3\, \Delta A_2} F_{\Delta A_2\, \Delta A_3} S_1]} \quad (8\text{--}31)$$

Substituting for R_{r_1} from Eqs. 8–25 and 8–21 gives

$$R_r' = E_1 S_2 S_3 [F_{\Delta A_2\, \Delta A_1} + (1 - e_3) F_{\Delta A_3\, \Delta A_1} F_{\Delta A_2\, \Delta A_3} S_1](1 - e_2) \quad (8\text{--}32)$$

The total energy striking ΔA_2 of that originally emitted by ΔA_1 (except as a result of re-reflections between ΔA_1 and ΔA_2) is then

$$q'' = \left(\frac{1}{1 - e_2}\right) R_r' \, \Delta A_1 \quad (8\text{--}33)$$

MULTIPLE REFLECTIONS BETWEEN ΔA_2 AND ΔA_1. To complete the exact analysis, it is necessary to evaluate the fraction of $R_r' \, \Delta A_1$ which returns to ΔA_2 after one or more reflections from ΔA_1. By analogy with Eq. 8–24 and with substitution of R_r' for R_{S_1}, the total energy returned to ΔA_1 after being once received at ΔA_2 is

$$q'' = R_r' \, \Delta A_1[F_{\Delta A_1\, \Delta A_2} + (1 - e_3) F_{\Delta A_3\, \Delta A_2} F_{\Delta A_1\, \Delta A_3} S_1] \quad (8\text{--}34)$$

The fraction of this energy reflected from ΔA_1 is

$$q'' = R_r' \, \Delta A_1[F_{\Delta A_1\, \Delta A_2} + (1 - e_3) F_{\Delta A_3\, \Delta A_2} F_{\Delta A_1\, \Delta A_3} S_1](1 - e_1) \quad (8\text{--}35)$$

By analogy with Eq. 8–32, the radiosity of ΔA_2 based on area of ΔA_1 and due to energy received a second time from ΔA_1 is then

$$R'_{r_1} = R'_r\{[F_{\Delta A_1\,\Delta A_2} + (1 - e_3)F_{\Delta A_3\,\Delta A_2}F_{\Delta A_1\,\Delta A_3}S_1](1 - e_1) \cdot$$
$$S_2S_3[F_{\Delta A_2\,\Delta A_1} + (1 - e_3)F_{\Delta A_3\,\Delta A_1}F_{\Delta A_2\,\Delta A_3}S_1](1 - e_2)\} \quad (8\text{–}36)$$

The radiosity of ΔA_2 due to energy received an nth time from ΔA_1 is given by Eq. 8–36, with the outside brace raised to the $(n - 1)$ power.

Then total radiosity of ΔA_2 based on area of ΔA_1 and due to energy initially emitted by ΔA_1 is

$$R_T = \frac{R'_r}{1 - (\text{brace of Eq. 8\text{–}36})} = R'_r S_4 \quad (8\text{–}37)$$

and, substituting for R'_r from Eq. 8–32,

$$R_T = E_1 S_2 S_3 S_4 [F_{\Delta A_2\,\Delta A_1} + (1 - e_3)F_{\Delta A_3\,\Delta A_1}F_{\Delta A_2\,\Delta A_3}S_1](1 - e_2)$$
$$(8\text{–}38)$$

The total gross energy transfer from ΔA_1 to ΔA_2 is

$$q'' = e_2 E_1 S_2 S_3 S_4\,\Delta A_1[F_{\Delta A_2\,\Delta A_1} + (1 - e_3)F_{\Delta A_3\,\Delta A_1}F_{\Delta A_2\,\Delta A_3}S_1] \quad (8\text{–}39)$$

Summary. The exact equation expressing gross transfer of energy initially emitted by any infinitesimal gray area, ΔA_1, to any other gray area, ΔA_2 (when the surround consists of gray surface, ΔA_3, which *sees* itself, and of black-body surface), has been established as

$$q'' = \sigma e_1 e_2 T_1^4\,\Delta A_1 S_2 S_3 S_4[F_{\Delta A_2\,\Delta A_1} + (1 - e_3)F_{\Delta A_3\,\Delta A_1}F_{\Delta A_2\,\Delta A_3}S_1]$$
$$(8\text{–}40a)$$

where

$$S_1 = \frac{1}{1 - F_{\Delta A_3\,\Delta A_3}(1 - e_3)} \quad (8\text{–}40b)$$

$$S_2 = \frac{1}{1 - (1 - e_1)(1 - e_3)F_{\Delta A_3\,\Delta A_1}F_{\Delta A_1\,\Delta A_3}S_1} \quad (8\text{–}40c)$$

$$S_3 = \frac{1}{1 - (1 - e_2)(1 - e_3)F_{\Delta A_3\,\Delta A_2}F_{\Delta A_2\,\Delta A_3}S_1} \quad (8\text{–}40d)$$

$$S_4 = \frac{1}{1 - (1 - e_1)(1 - e_2)S_2 S_3[F_{\Delta A_1\,\Delta A_2} + (1 - e_3)F_{\Delta A_3\,\Delta A_2}F_{\Delta A_1\,\Delta A_3}S_1] \cdot [F_{\Delta A_2\,\Delta A_1} + (1 - e_3)F_{\Delta A_3\,\Delta A_1}F_{\Delta A_2\,\Delta A_3}S_1]}$$
$$(8\text{–}40e)$$

EXTENSION OF THE REFLECTION EQUATION (8–40) TO RADIATION BETWEEN LARGE AREAS. For Eq. 8–40a to be applicable to heating problems, ΔA_3 must be expanded to represent all the interior surface, except A_1 and A_2, of the enclosure. Examination of the equation shows that the only terms affected by the size and relative position of the three infinitesimal areas are the seven shape factors $F_{\Delta A_3\,\Delta A_1}$, $F_{\Delta A_3\,\Delta A_2}$, $F_{\Delta A_2\,\Delta A_1}$, $F_{\Delta A_3\,\Delta A_3}$, $F_{\Delta A_1\,\Delta A_3}$, $F_{\Delta A_2\,\Delta A_3}$, $F_{\Delta A_1\,\Delta A_2}$, of which the last three, by the reciprocity theorem, can be expressed in terms of area ratio multiplied by the first three. Then only four independent shape factors remain, and these appear in Eq. 8–40a either individually or as products.

Inequality Between Shape Factors for Large and for Small Areas. Because individual shape factors vary widely over a large area, the four shape factors noted above cannot be extended to large areas merely by writing $F_{A_x A_y}$ in place of $F_{\Delta A_x\,\Delta A_y}$. Consider, for example, the shape factor product $F_{\Delta A_2\,\Delta A_3}F_{\Delta A_3\,\Delta A_1}$ which appears in the bracketed term of Eq. 8–40a, and investigate the error resulting from the substitution of $F_{A_2 A_3}F_{A_3 A_1}$ in place of this term. The exact term to replace $F_{\Delta A_2\,\Delta A_3}F_{\Delta A_3\,\Delta A_1}$ when the surfaces become A_1, A_2, and A_3 must represent the transfer of energy from A_1 after one reflection from A_3 to A_2 and is derived as follows: Energy leaving ΔA_1 and striking ΔA_3,

$$q'' = E_1\,\Delta A_1 F_{\Delta A_3\,\Delta A_1}$$

Energy leaving A_1 and striking ΔA_3,

$$q' = E_1 A_1 F_{\Delta A_3 A_1} \tag{8–41}$$

Energy reflected from ΔA_3 and striking ΔA_2,

$$q'' = E_1(1 - e_3)A_1 F_{\Delta A_3 A_1}F_{\Delta A_2\,\Delta A_3} \tag{8–42}$$

Energy reflected from ΔA_3 and striking A_y,

$$q' = E_1(1 - e_1)A_1 F_{\Delta A_3 A_1}F_{A_2\,\Delta A_3} \tag{8–43}$$

Energy emitted by A_1 and striking A_2 after reflection from A_3,

$$q = E_1(1 - e_3)A_1 \sum_{A_3} F_{\Delta A_3 A_1}F_{A_2\,\Delta A_3} \tag{8–44}$$

Since both shape factors under the summation sign in Eq. 8–44 are variable with respect to position on A_3, it follows that

$$\sum_{A_3} F_{\Delta A_3 A_1}F_{A_2\,\Delta A_3} \neq F_{A_3 A_1}F_{A_2 A_3} \tag{8–45}$$

By evaluating independently the two sides of the above inequality, the magnitude of the error resulting from use of the product $F_{A_3 A_1}F_{A_2 A_3}$ can be determined.

EXAMPLE 8–5. A cubical room is made up entirely of surfaces having an emissivity of 0.93. Neglecting gaseous absorption, calculate the fraction of energy emitted by the floor A_1, which strikes the ceiling A_2, after being once reflected from the wall surface A_3.

Solution: The exact solution is given by Eq. 8–44, in which the summation can be evaluated to any desired degree of accuracy by dividing the wall into narrow bands of length equal to the room perimeter and into width small in comparison with room dimensions. Each such band represents ΔA_3, and the fraction of energy transferred from the ceiling via one wall reflection to the floor is

$$\sum_{A_3} F_{\Delta A_3 A_1} F_{A_2 \Delta A_3} \doteq \sum (F_{\Delta A_{3_1} A_1} F_{A_2 \Delta A_{3_1}} + \cdots + F_{\Delta A_{3_n} A_1} F_{A_2 \Delta A_{3_n}})$$
(8–46)

Select the band width as one-fifth the wall height and adopt the nomenclature of Fig. 8–3. By observation, $F_{A_2 \Delta A_3}$ (for four walls) is four times greater than

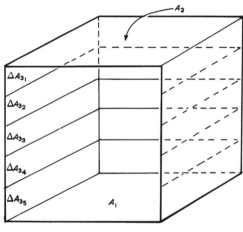

Fig. 8–3

$F_{(A_2)(\Delta A_3/4)}$ (for one wall) and this latter shape factor can be obtained from Fig. 4–20 by the method of Case 1 in Art. 4–7, page 123. By similarly evaluating all other shape factors and substituting numerical values in Eq. 8–46,

$$\begin{aligned}
\sum_{A_3} F_{\Delta A_3 A_1} F_{A_2 \Delta A_3} &\doteq [(0.32)(0.10)] + [(0.20)(0.10)] + [(0.12)(0.15)] \\
&\quad + [(0.08)(0.25)] + [(0.08)(0.40)] \\
&\doteq 0.032 + 0.020 + 0.018 + 0.020 + 0.032 \\
&\doteq 0.122
\end{aligned}$$
(8–47)

The approximate solution is given by the right side of Eq. 8–45, with shape factors determined directly from Fig. 4–20.

$$F_{A_3 A_1} F_{A_2 A_3} = (0.80)(0.20) = 0.160$$
(8–48)

The fraction transferred is $(1 - e_3)$ times the shape factor products, or 0.00854 for the more exact case and 0.01120 for the approximate solution.

Comparison of the results shows that the approximate method indicates over 30 per cent more energy transfer by reflection than the summation method; its use serves to give undue importance to the effect of reflection. The approximation can therefore be used conservatively in arriving at an estimate of the importance of the various terms of Eq. 8–40a, since any term which is negligible when evaluated by the approximate method will necessarily be of even less significance when evaluated accurately.

Influence of Reflection on Gross Transfer. The importance of each term in Eq. 8–40a can be visualized by applying this equation to the room of Example 8–5. The results from such an analysis, as far as they may indicate that parts of the equation can be neglected, will be conservative because:

1. The approximation of over-all shape-factor products overemphasizes the effect of reflection.
2. The room selected, a cube, has an unusually large ratio of wall-to-wall surface, so that the effect of reflection would be greater in this room than in one of usual proportion.

EXAMPLE 8–6. The emissivity (0.93) of surfaces in the room of Example 8–5 is close to that of most interior surfacing materials; hence the results of an analysis of this room should be representative of average practice. Investigate the influence of each reflection term in Eq. 8–40a on the gross radiant transfer from floor to ceiling.

Solution: The first step is to determine all the required shape factors. As noted in Eq. 8–48,

$$F_{A_3 A_1} = 0.8; \quad F_{A_2 A_3} = 0.2$$

By inspection of the room,

$$F_{A_3 A_1} = F_{A_3 A_2} = 0.8 \quad \text{and} \quad F_{A_2 A_3} = F_{A_1 A_3} = 0.2$$

But since A_1 is completely enclosed by A_2 and A_3,

$$F_{A_2 A_1} + F_{A_3 A_1} = 1$$

and therefore

$$F_{A_1 A_2} = F_{A_2 A_1} = 1.0 - 0.8 = 0.2$$

similarly, A_3 sees A_1, A_2, and itself, so that

$$F_{A_3 A_3} = 1 - F_{A_1 A_3} - F_{A_2 A_3} = 1 - 0.2 - 0.2 = 0.6$$

Summarizing:

$$F_{A_1 A_2} = F_{A_2 A_1} = F_{A_1 A_3} = F_{A_2 A_3} = 0.2$$
$$F_{A_3 A_1} = F_{A_3 A_2} = 0.8 \quad \text{and} \quad F_{A_3 A_3} = 0.6$$

Then, by Eqs. 8–40b, 8–40c, 8–40d, and 8–40e,

$$S_1 = \frac{1}{1 - [(0.6)(0.07)]} = \frac{1}{0.958} = 1.044$$

$$S_2 = \frac{1}{1 - [(0.07)(0.07)(0.8)(0.2 S_1)]} = \frac{1}{0.9992} = 1.0008$$

$$S_3 = \frac{1}{1 - [(0.07)(0.07)(0.8)(0.2 S_1)]} = 1.0008$$

$$S_4 = \frac{1}{1 - \{(0.07)(0.07)[0.2 + (0.2)(0.8)(0.07 S_1)] S_2 S_3 [0.2 + (0.2)(0.8)(0.07 S_1)]\}}$$
$$= 1.0000006$$

Substituting for S_2, S_3, and S_4 in Eq. 8–40a,

$$q = e_2E_1A_1(1.0008)(1.0008)(1.0000006)[F_{A_2A_1} + F_{A_2A_3}F_{A_3A_1}(1 - e_3)S_1]$$
$$= 1.0016e_2E_1A_1[F_{A_2A_1} + F_{A_2A_3}F_{A_3A_1}(1 - e_3)S_1] \tag{8–49}$$

If the S_2, S_3, S_4 coefficients are excluded, the resultant error is 16/10,016, or 0.16 per cent, which is negligible. Accordingly, Eq. 8–40a can be simplified to the form

$$q = e_2E_1A_1[F_{A_2A_1} + F_{A_2A_3}F_{A_3A_1}(1 - e_3)S_1] \tag{8–50}$$

for which the accuracy is better than 99.8 per cent. Then, substituting for the terms in the bracket,

$$q = e_2E_1A_1[(0.2) + (0.2)(0.8)(0.07)(1.044)]$$
$$= e_2E_1A_1(0.2 + 0.0117) \tag{8–51a}$$
$$= 0.2117e_2E_1A_1 \tag{8–51b}$$

The first term in the bracket of Eq. 8–51a is the fraction of energy transferred directly to A_2; the second term represents the fraction reaching A_2 after n reflections from A_3. If S_1 were dropped from the reflection term, its value would reduce from 0.0117 to 0.0112, and the coefficient in Eq. 8-51b would become 0.2112, thereby introducing another negligible error (0.2 per cent) into the result. The revised coefficient (0.2112) now consists of the fraction of energy directly transferred, plus the fraction transferred after one reflection from A_3. The reflection term 0.0112 was calculated from $(1 - e_3)F_{A_3A_1}F_{A_2A_3}$ (see Eq. 8-48) and could with greater accuracy be determined by using the summed coefficient from Eq. 8–47, giving

$$(0.122)(0.07) = 0.00854$$

Eq. 8–51b then becomes

$$q = (0.2 + 0.00854)e_2E_1A_1 = 0.2085e_2E_1A_1 \tag{8–51c}$$

instead of the more exact value

$$q = 1.0016e_2E_1A_1[(0.2) + (0.00954)(1.044)] = 0.2093e_2E_1A_1 \tag{8–49a}$$

The first wall reflection is seen, therefore, to be the only one that needs to be accounted for (with resultant accuracy of $99\frac{1}{2}$ per cent), and the effect of neglecting even this reflection would be to introduce an additional error of only 4.2 per cent.

The procedure followed in Example 8–6 is equally applicable to enclosures in which the walls, floor, or ceiling are covered with reflective surfacing. Study of a few typical enclosures by this method will demonstrate that the net loss of body heat by radiation is practically the same in a thermally black room as in one surfaced with the best commercially available reflective material. This subject is covered both experimentally and theoretically in the literature;[4] both studies indicate the ineffectiveness of reflective surfaces as means of reducing body-heat loss in a room of average size.

[4] B. F. Raber and F. W. Hutchinson, "Panel Heating and Cooling Performance Studies," *ASHVE Trans.*, Vol. 48, 1942.

8–3. Gaseous Absorption of Radiation.[5]   The exchange of radiant energy between surfaces is usually evaluated on the assumption that the intervening medium is non-absorbing. Actually, both absorption and emission of radiation occur in room air, owing to the presence of carbon dioxide and of water vapor. The influence of the carbon dioxide is small and that of the water vapor is widely variable, but the combined effect of gaseous radiation in an average room and under average conditions will be shown to be of the order of 10 per cent. This value, in itself, is not insignificant, but when metal-surfaced reflective materials are considered for use in panel heating, the importance of gaseous radiation is enormously magnified, and as will also be shown, becomes the controlling factor of design for reflective systems.

The great practical importance of gaseous radiation in connection with the use of reflective surfaces can be readily visualized by considering that the effect of gaseous radiant absorption in a room surfaced with a perfect reflector (refer to Art. 8–2) would be to dissipate more than 80 per cent of the radiant energy emitted by the occupant. Thus even a perfectly reflecting surrounding (which does not exist) would conserve only 20 per cent of body radiant heat loss; in such a case neglect of gaseous absorption would alter the entire concept and lead to a completely ineffective installation.

From the standpoint of total energy requirements of the average non-reflective panel-heating system, gaseous radiation is relatively unimportant. It is responsible for approximately a 10 per cent decrease in the radiant effect of the panel and a consequent increase in the convective fraction of energy dissipation. For a ceiling panel, the convective increase is of the order of 25 per cent, whereas for wall or floor panels, it is of the order of 14 per cent and 9 per cent respectively. The absolute value of the increase of convection is, of course, the same for all panel locations, but the fractional increase is much greater for ceiling panels which normally have a low absolute convection loss.

In industrial installations, or for any local heating panels that are designed to irradiate the subject at a given rate (refer to Art. 8–5), the average effect of absorption is to necessitate a 10 per cent increase in the design area of the panel. It should be noted particularly that this size of increment applies only to local units. General heating panels sized by the usual methods need not be corrected for size but will have to be corrected for performance differences due to greater air heating effect.

Equivalent Gaseous Radiation Coefficient. Standard references on heat transfer provide data on the emissive power of water vapor and of carbon dioxide as functions of the vapor pressure, the gas temperature, and the mean length of path through the gas.

---

[5] This article is based on or revised from F. W. Hutchinson, "Influence of Gaseous Radiation in Panel Heating," *ASHVE Trans.*, Vol. 53, 1947, by permission from the American Society of Heating, Refrigerating and Air-Conditioning Engineers.

Water Vapor. For water vapor at temperatures such as occur in panel heating, the emissive power can be expressed by the following equation:

$$E = aT_g^{3.54} \tag{8–52}$$

where E = emissive power of water vapor, Btu/(hr)(sq ft).

T_g = absolute temperature of gas, deg.

a = a coefficient that varies as a function of the product $P'L$.

P' = partial pressure of the water vapor expressed as a fraction of atmosphere.

L = beam length, varying from two-thirds of the diameter for a sphere to 1.3 times the ceiling height for a room with dimensions in a ratio of 1:2:6, in which radiation is to one of the large faces.

For rooms of average size and shape, with radiation considered as occurring from a ceiling or a floor panel, the value of L can conveniently and with accuracy be taken as equal to the ceiling height. The partial pressure of water vapor in room air is fixed when the absolute humidity is known; hence it can be expressed as a function of both room air temperature and relative humidity as two conveniently measurable variables.

In evaluating radiant exchange between surfaces separated by a non-absorbing medium, it has been found convenient to use an equivalent film coefficient for radiation h_r, as defined in Eq. 4–113. A similar equivalent coefficient for radiation to or from water vapor is

$$h_w = \frac{a(T_h^{3.54} - T_c^{3.54})}{t_h - t_c} \tag{8–53}$$

where h_w = equivalent film coefficient for radiation to or from water vapor, Btu/(hr)(sq ft)(°F).

T_h = absolute (°F + 460) temperature of either the water vapor or the exchanging surface, whichever is hotter.

T_c = absolute temperature of either the water vapor or exchanging surface, whichever is cooler.

Fig. 8–4 is a graphical solution of Eq. 8–53. Use of the graph can best be explained by means of an example.

EXAMPLE 8–7. In a room with air at 72 F, 50 per cent relative humidity, evaluate the absorption by the water vapor of radiation from a surface at 83 F; ceiling height is 9 ft.

Solution: Enter the upper right quadrant at 72 F and move horizontally left to intersect the 50 per cent RH line (see dashed example on graph), then rise to the curve for 9-ft ceiling height, move horizontally left to the directrix, and drop vertically to the lower left quadrant. Now re-enter the chart in the lower right quadrant at the 83 F surface temperature, rise to 72 F air temperature, and move horizontally left to intersect the previously established vertical at a value of $h_w = 0.086$. Thus the transfer rate to the gas by radiation is $0.086(83 - 72) = 0.95$ Btu/sq ft.

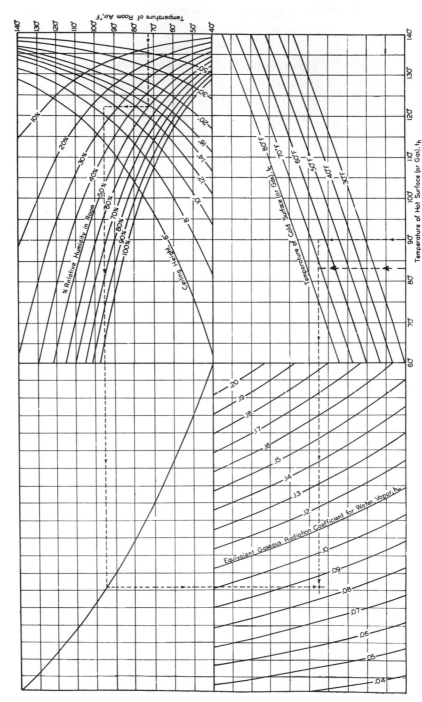

Fig. 8–4. Graphical solution for determining the equivalent coefficient for radiation to or from water vapor. (Courtesy of American Society of Heating, Refrigerating and Air-Conditioning Engineers.)

CARBON DIOXIDE. The emissive power for carbon dioxide is given by an equation similar to that for water vapor but with an exponent of 5.3 and a different functional relationship between the coefficient a and the PL product. The concentration of carbon dioxide in outside air is 0.0003 parts per part (by volume), and in the air of an occupied space its concentration reaches an equilibrium value dependent on the ventilation rate. Taking 0.6 cu ft/hr as the CO_2 output of an occupant and taking 10 cfm/occupant as the minimum outside air for ventilation, the equilibrium CO_2 concentration, X, is given by

$$[(0.0003)(10)(60)] + 0.6 = (60)(10X)$$

where

$$X = 0.0013 \quad \text{(or 0.13 per cent by volume)} \tag{8–54}$$

Taking $L = 10$, a is $(7.6)10^{-15}$, and the value of the equivalent coefficient for exchange between a 120 F panel and 60 F gas is approximately 0.025 Btu/(hr)(sq ft)(°F). Values of this coefficient greater than 0.025 are unlikely to occur in panel-heating practice, and since the coefficient is small with respect to usual values of the water vapor coefficient, it is suggested that a fixed conservative value of 0.02 be used for all average cases.

Total Gaseous Radiation. An equivalent gaseous radiation coefficient, h_g, can now be defined by the equation

$$h_g = h_w + 0.02 \tag{8–55}$$

where h_g = equivalent gaseous radiation coefficient, Btu/(hr)(sq ft)(°F).
       h_w = equivalent water vapor radiation coefficient, Btu/(hr)(sq ft)(°F).

The value of h_w is determined from Fig. 8–4. For many practical problems the coefficient can be further simplified by selecting representative average temperatures and thereafter neglecting the effect on h_g of the temperature. Similarly, *standard* room conditions can be selected, the ceiling height fixed, and a single value of h_g thereby obtained which will be applicable to most problems. For air at 72 F and 50 per cent relative humidity in a room with 9-ft ceiling and with unheated surfaces at 60 F, the value of h_w, from Fig. 8—4, would be 0.080, whereas for the same room with heated panel surface at 100 F, the corresponding value of h_w would be 0.090; the average value of the total gas coefficient is therefore

$$h_g = 0.085 + 0.02 = 0.10$$

When the statement of a problem does not permit exact evaluation of the conditions of gaseous radiant exchange, it is recommended that the above value of the coefficient be used.

In similar manner, a fixed value of the equivalent radiation coefficient for transfer through a non-absorbing medium is frequently used. For the temperature range common in panel heating, the value of this constant is commonly taken as 1.08. Thus, for an *average* room under *average* panel-heating conditions, the effect of gaseous absorption is to reduce the energy exchange by radiation between the heating panel and the surrounds by

$$\frac{0.10}{1.08} = 0.09, \quad \text{or} \quad 9 \text{ per cent}$$

SUMMARY. It is a popular misconception that separation distance (aside from its effect on shape factor) does not affect the rate of radiant exchange between two surfaces. Actually, radiant exchange decreases as distance increases because of absorption by the carbon dioxide and water vapor present in the intervening air space.

Gaseous radiation does not appreciably affect either panel size or panel rating for an ordinary panel-heating system, but it does reduce the effectiveness of local panels (see Art. 8–5) by about 10 per cent. Because of cumulative absorption as associated with multiple reflections, gaseous radiation is responsible for reducing the effectiveness of reflective surfaces (when used as room surfacing in an attempt to reduce radiant body-heat loss) to a negligible value. Thus it can be shown[6] that use of commercial foil for surfacing a room larger than 15 ft by 15 ft by 9 ft would conserve not more than 2 per cent (3 Btu/hr) of body heat.

8–4. Equivalent Conductance Load Analysis for Panel-Heating Systems. The heat balance expressed by Eq. 8–1 is for unit area of unheated surface. If this equation is written for the room as a whole, it takes the form

$$C_u(t_u - t_o)A_u = h_{cu}(t_a - t_u)A_u + h_{rpu}F_{up}(t_p - t_u)A_p \qquad (8\text{–}56)$$

Now dividing all terms by the total enclosure area A_e, and letting u and v represent, respectively, the unheated and heated fractions of room surface,

$$C_u(t_u - t_o)u = h_{cu}(t_a - t_u)u + h_{rpu}F_{up}(t_p - t_u)v \qquad (8\text{–}57)$$

giving

$$t_u = \frac{h_{rpu}F_{up}vt_p + h_{cu}ut_a + C_uut_o}{h_{rpu}F_{up}v + h_{cu}u + C_uu} \qquad (8\text{–}58)$$

which is one of the three equations required for design.

A second design equation is obtained from Eq. 8–4 by writing it in terms of heated and unheated areas and then dividing all terms by A_e and substituting u and v for the area ratios:

$$t_a = \frac{h_{cp}vt_p + h_{cu}ut_u + [0.2411(W/A_e)t_o]}{h_{cp}v + h_{cu}u + [0.2411(W/A_e)]} \qquad (8\text{–}59)$$

The third design equation is obtained by substituting u and v in the comfort equation:

$$t_a = 147 - vt_p - ut_u \qquad (8\text{–}60)$$

When panel area is arbitrarily selected, the values of u and v are known, and Eqs. 8–58, 8–59, and 8–60 can then be solved simultaneously for t_p, t_a, and t_u. When panel temperature is arbitrarily selected, the same three equations can be solved for u, t_a, and t_u.

[6] Refer to reference in footnote 5.

EXAMPLE 8–8. For the room of Example 5–1 calculate the transmission load (using the equivalent conductance design procedure) if panel heating is used, the panel area occupying all the surface of the two inside partitions. Assume zero ventilation rate.

Solution: The thermal coefficients, from the solution of Example 5–1, are:

$$A_w = 286.4 \qquad A_c = 400 \qquad A_f = 400 \qquad A_g = 113.6$$

$$C_w = 0.3488 \qquad C_c = 0.3504 \qquad C_f = 0.5081 \qquad C_g = 2.778$$

$$h_{cw} = 0.535 \qquad h_{cc} = 0.610 \qquad h_{cf} = 0.28 \qquad h_{cg} = 0.72$$

In this case all unheated surfaces of the enclosure are transmitting areas; hence the only radiation to be accounted for is that from the panel to the unheated surfaces:

$$C_u = \frac{[(0.3488)(286.4)] + [(0.3504)(400)] + [(0.5081)(400)] + [(2.778)(113.6)]}{1200}$$

$$= 0.6324$$

$$h_{cu} = \frac{[(0.535)(286.4)] + [(0.610)(400)] + [(0.28)(400)] + [(0.72)(113.6)]}{1200}$$

$$= 0.4925$$

In this room the panel sees itself; so,

$$F_{pp} + F_{up} = 1$$

From Fig. 4–20, $F_{pp} = 0.15$; hence,

$$F_{up} = 0.85 \qquad v = \frac{A_p}{A_e} = \frac{400}{1600} = 0.25 \qquad u = 1 - v = 0.75$$

The value of h_{rpu} will depend on t_p and t_u, but as a first approximation it can conservatively be taken as 1.08 (refer to Fig. 4–14 for the range of t_p and t_u combinations for which 1.08 would be exact). The value of h_{cp} will likewise have to be approximated. The room in question is the same one that was analyzed by the rational method in Example 8–1, so, the same assumptions will be made. For assumed panel temperature of 110 F and assumed air temperature of 75 F, the Δt_{film} is 35 F, and the corresponding value of h_{cp} (from Eq. 5–39) was calculated as 0.67.

By substituting into the three design equations,

$$t_u = \frac{[(1.08)(0.85)(0.25)t_p] + [(0.4925)(0.75)t_a] + 0}{[(1.08)(0.85)(0.25)] + [(0.4925)(0.75)] + [(0.6324)(0.75)]}$$

$$= \frac{0.2295t_p + 0.3694t_a}{1.0732}$$

$$= 0.2138t_p + 0.3442t_a \tag{8–58a}$$

$$t_a = \frac{[(0.67)(0.25)t_p] + [(0.4925)(0.75)t_u] + 0}{[(0.67)(0.25)] + [(0.4925)(0.75)] + 0}$$

$$= \frac{0.1675t_p + 0.3694t_u}{0.5369}$$

$$= 0.3120t_p + 0.6880t_u \tag{8–59a}$$

$$t_a = 147 - 0.25t_p - 0.75t_u \tag{8–60a}$$

Eliminating t_u between Eqs. 8–58a and 8–59a,

$$t_u = 0.2138t_p + 0.3442t_a \tag{8–58a}$$

$$= 1.4535t_a - 0.4535t_p \tag{8–59b}$$

giving

$$1.1093t_a - 0.6673t_p = 0 \tag{a}$$

Eliminating t_u between Eqs. 8–58a and 8–60a,

$$t_u = 0.2138t_p + 0.3442t_a \tag{8–58a}$$

$$= 196 - 0.3333t_p - 1.3333t_a \tag{8–60b}$$

giving

$$196 - 0.5471t_p - 1.6775t_a = 0 \tag{b}$$

Eliminating t_a between Eqs. (a) and (b)

$$t_a = 0.6016t_p \tag{c}$$

$$= 116.84 - 0.3261t_p \tag{d}$$

giving

$$0.9277t_p = 116.84; \quad t_p = 125.95 \text{ F}$$

Then, from Eq. (c),

$$t_a = (0.6016)(125.95) = 75.77 \text{ F}$$

and from Eq. 8–58a,

$$t_u = [(0.2138)(125.95)] + [(0.3442)(75.77)]$$

$$= 26.93 + 26.08 = 53.01 \text{ F}$$

The transmission load is therefore

$$q_t = C_u A_u(t_u - t_o)$$

$$= (0.6324)(1200)(53.01 - 0)$$

$$= 40,228 \text{ Btu/hr}$$

A check on transmission load can be obtained by calculating the energy output of the panel:

$$q_t = h_{rup} F_{up} A_p(t_p - t_u) + h_{cp} A_p(t_p - t_a)$$

$$= [(1.08)(0.85)(400)(125.95 - 53.01)] + [(0.67)(400)(125.95 - 75.77)]$$

$$= 26,784 + 13,448 = 40,232 \text{ Btu/hr}$$

The mean radiant temperature is

$$mrt = 147 - t_a = 147 - 75.77 = 71.23 \text{ F}$$

which checks as

$$mrt = vt_p + ut_u = [(0.25)(125.95)] + [(0.75)(53.01)]$$

$$= 31.49 + 39.76 = 71.25 \text{ F}$$

The results of the Example 8–8 agree closely, as far as temperature relationships are concerned, with results obtained for the same enclosure

conditions by the rational procedure employed in Example 8–1. The transmission load obtained from the equivalent-design procedure is conservatively
high; hence it indicates that the method can be safely used. If additional
accuracy were required, the coefficients used in Example 8–8 would be re-
examined in terms of the results obtained. Usually, however, this extra step
is not considered necessary.

EXAMPLE 8–9. Reinvestigate the enclosure of Example 8–2, using the
equivalent conductance design procedure, for an infiltration rate of one air change
per hour.

Solution: This condition corresponds to the one for which a rational analysis
was presented in Example 8–2. From that solution the ventilation rate is 300
lb/hr. Eqs. 8–58a and 8–60b are unchanged from Example 8–8, but Eq. 8–59
now has an additive ventilation term in the denominator:

$$t_a = \frac{0.1675t_p + 0.3694t_u}{0.5369 + [(0.2411)(300)/1600]}$$

$$= \frac{0.1675t_p + 0.3694t_u}{0.5821}$$

$$= 0.2878t_p + 0.6346t_u \qquad (8\text{–}59\text{a})$$

Eliminating t_u between Eqs. 8–58a and 8–59a,

$$t_u = 0.2138t_p + 0.3442t_a \qquad (8\text{–}58\text{a})$$

$$= 1.5758t_a - 0.4535t_p \qquad (8\text{–}59\text{b})$$

giving

$$1.2316t_a - 0.6673t_p = 0 \qquad (\text{a})$$

Eliminating t_u between Eqs. 8–58a and 8–60a gives Eq. (b) as in Example
8–8.

Eliminating t_a between Eqs. (a) and (b)

$$t_a = 0.5418t_p \qquad (\text{c})$$

$$= 116.84 - 0.3261t_p$$

giving

$$0.8679t_p = 116.84; \quad t_p = 134.62 \text{ F}$$

The remaining steps of the analysis correspond to those of Example 8–8.
The results are

$$t_a = 72.94 \text{ F} \qquad t_u = 53.89 \text{ F}$$

$$q_t = 40,896 \qquad mrt = 74.06 \text{ F}$$

$$\text{Sensible ventilation load} = (0.2411)(300)(72.94)$$

$$= 5276 \text{ Btu/hr}$$

$$\text{Total sensible load} = 40,896 + 5276 = 46,172 \text{ Btu/hr}$$

EXAMPLE 8–10. Reinvestigate the enclosure of Example 8–9, using the
equivalent conductance design procedure, for an outside-air mechanical ventilation rate of five air changes per hour.

Solution: The solution is exactly as in Example 8–9 except that W is now equal to 1500 lb/hr. The results are

$$t_p = 163.69 \text{ F}; \quad t_a = 63.46 \text{ F}; \quad t_u = 56.84 \text{ F}$$

$$q_t = 43{,}135 \text{ Btu/hr}; \quad mrt = 83.54 \text{ F}$$

Sensible ventilation load $= 22{,}950$ Btu/hr

Total load $= 43{,}135 + 22{,}950 = 66{,}085$ Btu/hr

EXAMPLE 8–11. Investigate the insulated structure described in Example 8–4 using the equivalent conductance design procedure, for operation with (a) no ventilation, (b) infiltration equivalent to one air change per hour, (c) mechanical ventilation (using untempered outside air) at a rate of five air changes per hour.

Solution: From Example 8–4 the thermal coefficients are

$$A_w = 286.4 \qquad A_c = 400 \qquad A_f = 400 \qquad A_g = 113.6$$

$$C_w = 0.07107 \qquad C_c = 0.07899 \qquad C_f = 0.07321 \quad C_g = 0.7413$$

$$h_{cw} = 0.38 \qquad h_{cc} = 0.39 \qquad h_{cf} = 0.17 \qquad h_{cg} = 0.45$$

(a) The air temperature in the crawl space below the floor is now at 40 F, so a corrective temperature ratio must be used with the floor term in the equation for equivalent conductance; the correction will be based on assumed t_a of 73.5 F.

$$C_u = \{[(0.07107)(286.4)] + [(0.07899)(400)]$$
$$+ [(0.07321)(400)(73.5 - 40)/(73.5 - 0)] + [(0.7413)(113.6)]\}/1200$$
$$= 0.1246$$

$$h_c = \frac{[(0.38)(286.4)] + [(0.39)(400)] + [(0.17)(400)] + [(0.45)(113.6)]}{1200}$$
$$= 0.2774$$

All other coefficients have the same values as in Example 8–8, and the method of solution is exactly the same. The results are

$$t_p = 86.13 \text{ F}; \quad t_a = 75.40 \text{ F}; \quad t_u = 66.76 \text{ F}$$

$$q_t = 9982 \text{ Btu/hr}; \quad mrt = 71.60 \text{ F}$$

(b) With ventilation rate of one air change per hour, the procedure is similar to that of Example 8–9 except that thermal coefficients are as in part (a) of this example. The results are

$$t_p = 94.48 \text{ F}; \quad t_a = 71.70 \text{ F}; \quad t_u = 68.92 \text{ F}$$

$$q_t = 10{,}305 \text{ Btu/hr}; \quad mrt = 75.30 \text{ F}$$

Sensible ventilation load $= 5186$ Btu/hr

Total sensible load $= 10{,}305 + 5186 = 15{,}491$ Btu/hr

(c) For ventilation rate of five air changes per hour, the results are

$$t_p = 121.03 \text{ F}; \quad t_a = 59.91 \text{ F}; \quad t_u = 75.77 \text{ F}$$

$$q_t = 11{,}329 \text{ Btu/hr}; \quad mrt = 87.09 \text{ F}$$

Sensible ventilation load $= 21{,}666$ Btu/hr

Total sensible load $= 11{,}329 + 21{,}666 = 32{,}995$ Btu/hr

Examples 8–1 and 8–8, 8–2 and 8–9, 8–3 and 8–10, 8–4 and 8–11 demonstrate use of the rational design procedure and the equivalent-conductance design procedure, respectively, as applied to the same structure for the same load conditions. The calculated design value of the inside air temperature and the calculated mean radiant temperature are observed to agree closely for the two design procedures. The load calculated by the equivalent-conductance method is greater than by the rational method; hence it can be considered conservative.

EXAMPLE 8–12. Using data from the solution of Example 8–2, calculate (a) the average surface temperature of the unheated surfaces, (b) the average surface temperature for the room as a whole, (c) the true mean radiant temperature, (d) the accuracy with which the solution meets the conditions imposed by the comfort equation.

Solution: (a) For the unheated surfaces of the room,

$$ast_u = \frac{t_w A_w + t_c A_c + t_f A_f + t_g A_g}{A_u}$$

$$= \frac{[(62.30)(286.4)] + [(62.32)(400)] + [(56.48)(400)] + [(28.01)(113.6)]}{1200}$$

$$= \frac{17{,}843 + 24{,}928 + 22{,}592 + 3182}{1200}$$

$$= \frac{68{,}545}{1200} = 57.12 \text{ F}$$

(b) For the room as a whole,

$$ast = vt_p + u(ast_u)$$
$$= [(0.25)(130.48)] + [(0.75)(57.12)]$$
$$= 32.62 + 42.84 = 75.46 \text{ F}$$

(c) The true mean radiant temperature of the room is obtained from Eq. 7–20:

$$mrt = [(0.2298)(62.32)] + [(0.1549)(62.3)] + [(0.083)(28.01)]$$
$$+ [(0.2383)(130.48)] + [(0.2968)(56.48)]$$
$$= 74.08 \text{ F}$$

(d) Apply the comfort equation:

$$t_a + mrt = 72.89 + 74.08 = 146.97$$

which shows that the thermal level within the room under design load conditions will have the selected (73.5 F) value.

In the examples of the equivalent-conductance method that have been used in this article the panel was considered to be a large plane surface. When smaller panels are used, such as baseboard units, the same design procedure is applicable, provided there is no auxiliary convective heating from the rear of the panel. If air flow does occur through or from behind the panel, the convective heating effect will usually be so great that the warm panel surface will not appreciably alter the mean radiant temperature within the room. For this type of system the authors recommend that the transmission load be determined by the equivalent-conductance method, as used for a convection heating system (this method was developed in Chapter 5).

Some panel-heating installations that utilize large panels also have fractional heating by warm air. When this is the case, and assuming that the greater part of the load is carried by the panel, the analysis can follow the method of this chapter. In this case the convective heating effect is considered to provide tempering of the ventilation air; so, the panel-load analysis is corrected for the convection merely by appropriately reducing the number of thermal air changes.

The usual range of selected panel-surface temperature under conditions of design load is from 90 F to 120 F for ceiling panels, 80 F to 100 F for wall panels, and 80 F to 90 F for floor panels. Because of greater convection from a floor location, panel effectiveness (for increasing the *mrt* of the room) is greatest for ceiling panels and least for floor panels.

8-5. Corrective Panel Heating.
In many cases small heated panels can be used as effective and economical means of establishing local comfort. Corrective heating panels are of two types: (1) spot units intended to establish comfortable conditions in a small region within a large unconditioned area; (2) spot units to supplement inadequate general heating or cooling.

Spot Units: Local. Examples of this type of system are found in industrial plants, warehouses, garages, and other buildings in which the density of occupancy is frequently so low that it is not economically feasible to raise the energy level of the entire environment to a value corresponding to comfort. Local or spot panels can be employed in such cases to transfer energy directly to a workman whose activities are localized within a restricted area. The effectiveness of this type of installation is obviously limited to a very small area, and the system is therefore adaptable only to applications in which the workmen do not require freedom of movement, like machine operators in an assembly line and station operators in process industries.

The performance of a spot panel is similar to that of a simple auxiliary heating unit. The quantity of energy transferred by convection between the panel and its surroundings is usually so small with respect to the needs for ambient-air heating that it can be entirely neglected and regarded solely as a loss due to inability to achieve complete energy dissipation by radiant means. The spot panel is, in theory at least, a 100 per cent radiant unit, and its design and performance can be investigated from considerations of radiant transfer alone. In practice there will, of course, be substantial convective losses, but this fraction of the total energy requirement does not play any part in determining the effectiveness of the panel for the purpose for which it is installed. Thus auxiliary units are somewhat simpler to design than other types, since they need meet only one design criterion: ability to establish a radiant transfer to or from the subject in amount sufficient to re-establish the normal net body-heat loss corresponding to the attainment of comfort.

Paradoxically, although local panel installations require less analytical work to design than any other type, they also require a more exact design and are subject to extreme variations in performance and effectiveness if incorrectly sized or improperly installed. These conditions result from the fact that a spot radiant-heating or cooling unit must be "fitted" to the subject with a degree of precision no less than that required in fitting clothes. The area, temperature, and distance from the subject must be correlated to establish the required exchange rate, while the same factors (and in addition the geometrical relationship between panel and subject) must also be related in such a way that the heating or cooling will be effectively distributed and an adequate sensation of warmth experienced by the subject, not merely as a cumulative over-all response but also with respect to individual parts and areas of the body.

The thermal effectiveness of auxiliary panels is very low; in most installations not more than 2 or 3 per cent. But, wasteful though such a system may seem, it is nonetheless many times more effective thermally than the convective method whose place it takes.

SPOT UNITS: SUPPLEMENTARY. In many installations, the use of 100 per cent local units is impracticable because of the need for providing some appreciable degree of general heating throughout the entire enclosure. On the other hand, the normal working arrangement within the enclosure may be such that a substantial reduction in general air temperature would be permissible if supplementary energy transfer were provided locally at the stations regularly occupied by workmen. For installations of this kind, auxiliary radiant panels afford maximum effectiveness, since the entire energy dissipation rate of the panel goes to reduce the convective load carried by the general system, while the direct radiant transfer between subject and panel becomes a "dividend" which serves to establish local comfort without requiring the expenditure of any more energy than that needed to maintain the ambient air at its "tempered" state.

The design of supplementary panels follows the same procedure as for 100 per cent auxiliary units except that a design error is significant only with respect to the effectiveness of the panel in maintaining conditions of local comfort and not with respect to the over-all energy requirements of the enclosure. Thus a poorly designed supplementary heating panel may operate with very low effectiveness, requiring an unusually large energy input in order to secure adequate net radiant transfer to the subject. The large amount of energy that leaves the panel but is not received by the subject then serves to heat the ambient air and hence to reduce, unit by unit, the energy demand called for by the room thermostat. This type of panel is therefore particularly attractive because it affords a possibility of reducing total energy require-ments for the system as a whole while being unattended by any hazard of excess losses resulting from inadequate or improper panel design.

DESIGN PROCEDURE. The first step in the design of either of the above types of spot panel is to determine the rate at which radiant energy must be supplied directly to the subject. It was shown in Art. 1–4 that in an environ-ment with air and surrounding surfaces at 70 F (a thermal level, t_c, of 70 F) body-heat loss by radiation is approximately 200 Btu/hr and by convection is approximately 100 Btu/hr.

In a factory building with thermal level of 60 F, the clothed surface temperature of an occupant would be (by Eq. 1–12),

$$t_b = [(0.21)(60)] + [(0.54)(60)] + 26.9 = 71.9 \text{ F} \qquad (8\text{–}61)$$

Radiation loss to the 60 F surround (by Eq. 1–1) would amount to

$$q_r = (0.172)(19.5)\left[\left(\frac{460 + 71.9}{100}\right)^4 - \left(\frac{460 + 60}{100}\right)^4\right] \qquad (8\text{–}62)$$
$$= 232 \text{ Btu/hr}$$

and convective loss to the 60 F air (by Eq. 1–2) would be

$$q_c = (0.55)(21.6)(71.9 - 60) = 141 \qquad (8\text{–}63)$$

Thus, if a factory worker in the 60 F thermal level environment were to be warmed by a spot panel to a condition equivalent to a 70 F thermal level, it would be necessary for the panel to irradiate him at a rate of $232 + 141 - 200 - 100$, or 73 Btu/hr. The design problem therefore reduces to one of determining the temperature, size, and location of a spot panel that will irradiate the subject at the 73 Btu/hr rate.

The first part of the problem, temperature, can be solved arbitrarily by fixing a maximum permissible surface temperature in terms of the material of which the panel is to be made. For plaster, concrete, and wood-veneer panels, a maximum value of 120 F is generally used, since this is low enough to ensure adequate distribution, avoidance of uncomfortable intensities, and protection against structurally undesirable thermal stresses in the panel itself. The two remaining problems, which are necessarily related, are those of panel size and location.

The increased emissive power of a 120 F panel over that of the surrounding surfaces at 60 F (by Eq. 4–104) is

$$\Delta E = 0.1713\left[\left(\frac{460 + 120}{100}\right)^4 - \left(\frac{460 + 60}{100}\right)^4\right] \tag{8–64}$$

$$= 68.6 \text{ Btu/(hr)(sq ft)}$$

provided the surface has a radiation characteristic approaching that of a thermal black body. The total irradiation received by the subject will depend on the area of panel and on its average shape factor (which, in turn, depends on the panel location) with respect to himself. Thus

$$q_{\text{irrad}} = 68.6 F_{sp} A_p \tag{8–65}$$

But the required irradiation rate has been established; so, substituting this value into Eq. 8–65 and solving for panel area give

$$A_p = \frac{73/68.6}{F_{sp}} = \frac{1.06}{F_{sp}} \tag{8–66}$$

Although simple in form, Eq. 8–66 does not lend itself to a direct analytical solution, since the term F_{sp}, the shape factor of the subject with respect to radiation leaving the panel, is itself a function of the panel area as well as of the location (as wall, floor, or ceiling), and the distance of the panel from the occupant (as determined, for example, by ceiling height).

Experimentally determined shape factors for standing subjects with respect to elements of panel area located 8 ft, 10 ft, or 12 ft above the floor have been presented in Figs. 4–31, 4–32, and 4–33, respectively. Shape factors for a sitting subject with respect to elements of panel area at 8 ft, 10 ft, or 12 ft above the floor are given in Figs. 4–35, 4–36, and 4–37, respectively. Shape factors for a standing subject with respect to elements of panel area in the floor are given in Fig. 4–34. By using data from these figures, average shape factors for each location and size of panel can be developed and a tabular solution of Eq. 8–66 thereby established.

This procedure will be demonstrated for a particular case. Consider a workman standing directly under the center of a 120 F heating panel embedded in an 8-ft ceiling. In order to determine the panel size, assume an area, determine the shape factor of the subject with respect to a panel of the assumed area, and use this shape factor in the equation to calculate a panel area. Then compare the assumed and calculated areas, and if they differ appreciably, make a corrected assumption and repeat the process.

Assume that a 4-ft by 4-ft square panel will be satisfactory. Fig. 8–5 shows one quadrant of such a panel with the point shape factors, from Fig. 4–31, given for each square foot of area. The average shape factor is then $(0.034 + 0.041 + 0.041 + 0.040)/4 = 0.039$. As the other three quadrants are identical to the one considered, it follows that the shape factor of the subject with respect to the entire 16-sq ft panel will be 0.039. Substituting this value in Eq. 8–66 gives a required area of 27 sq ft (for a 120 F panel), as compared with an assumed area of 16 sq ft. The assumed area must therefore be increased. Assume next that a 6-ft by 6-ft panel will suffice. Refer now

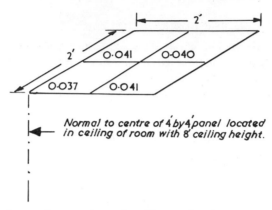

Fig. 8–5. Shape factors of one quadrant of a ceiling panel with respect to standing subject.

to Fig. 8–6 and determine the average-point shape factor for one quadrant as 0.039. In this case the value is unchanged from that for the smaller panel; hence the required panel area remains 27 sq ft and the 6-ft by 6-ft panel would be too large. By interpolation, the required panel area would be given by

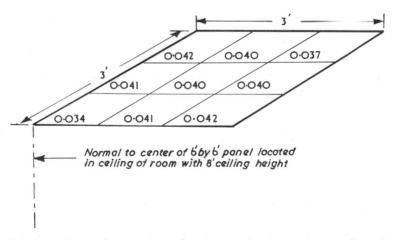

Fig. 8–6. Shape factors of one quadrant of a ceiling panel with respect to standing subject.

a spot unit 5.2 ft by 5.2 ft. Since, however, (Art. 8–3), there is a 9 per cent diminution of radiant transfer due to gaseous absorption, it follows that the panel area should be increased to approximately 5.4 ft by 5.4 ft.

By the method used above, the same problem can be solved for spot panels located at ceiling heights other than 8 ft or for panels located on the floor or in adjacent walls. Ceiling panels need not, of course, be embedded in the actual ceiling structure of the building. For industrial applications the room ceiling may be very high, but local panels can be suspended directly over the head of each operator at the lowest height consistent with maintenance of required clearance space. When panels are suspended, however, a 4-in. downward-oriented lip should be placed around the edge to pocket the warm air and to reduce the tendency for slip to occur across the panel face.

ENERGY REQUIREMENTS. Irrespective of differences in location and in size of any spot-type panel, it will be found that the energy required at the panel will be ten or more times the irradiation rate but will vary greatly among the different panel locations. It is particularly important to recognize, however, that the heat-dissipation rates are not proportional to total heating costs. Irrespective of the quantity of energy dissipated by the supplementary type of panel, this energy is not an added loss, but (as discussed on page 348) serves to reduce, unit for unit, the quantity of heat that must be supplied by the primary heating system.

In some particularly well-insulated structures, or in factory rooms where the density of occupancy is great, the total design dissipation rate of the panels may be in excess of the calculated total energy required to maintain an inside air temperature of 60 F. Where this is true, the panels completely replace the general heating system, and the consequent installation is identical in effect to panel space-heating as used in residences and office buildings. With such a system the design air temperature of 60 F will obviously not be experienced. Convection from the panels will raise the air temperature, and in consequence the amount of direct irradiation required will be reduced so that the panel will operate at a surface temperature lower than the design value.

The magnitude of the saving in heating cost that will be obtained by use of local panels and 60 F general air temperature can be readily evaluated in terms of the average outside air temperature during the heating season. If this average were 20 F, the saving would be approximately $(70 - 60)/(70 - 20)$, or 20 per cent, whereas for an average outside air temperature of 40 F, a saving of 33 per cent would be effected. Note, however, that as the outside temperature increases (that is, as the load on the system decreases), a condition will inevitably arise for which the energy dissipation rate of the local panels will be equal to the total load. For outside air temperatures higher than this value, the inside air temperature will necessarily rise above 60 F, the panel surface temperature will then be reduced to less than 120 F, and the percentage of saving will decrease.

OPTIMUM SHAPE AND LOCATION OF SPOT PANELS. Examination of the shape factor patterns shown in Figs. 4–31 through 4–37 of Art. 4–7 will bring out a number of facts that can be used to optimize spot panel shape, area, and location.

Consider, for example, a design problem in which supplementary radiant energy is to be supplied to a standing worker who remains at a fixed station and is to receive radiation from a heating panel located in a 12-ft ceiling. Reference to Fig. 4–33 shows that the maximum shape factor occurs when the element of panel area is located approximately 5 ft directly in front of, or directly behind, the subject. If, in this problem, the worker were required by the nature of his duties to stand and face a given direction, the best panel arrangement would then be one in which the requisite total area of panel was split in two equal parts and the parts centered on points in the ceiling 5 ft ahead of and behind the worker.

Consideration of the numerical values of shape factors for the above case shows that the recommended panel arrangement would result in a transfer of twice as much energy to the occupant as would be received by him from a panel of the same total size and same surface temperature if it were located directly over his head. This ratio would hold, of course, only if the panel area or areas were sufficiently small to permit the assumption that the point shape factors read from Fig. 4–33 for zero distance in the x-direction and for 5 ft out in the y-direction were substantially constant over the panel surface. If this condition is not met, the *average* shape factor for panels centered 5 ft out can be obtained from the data of Fig. 4–33.

The 100 per cent variation in effectiveness of the two panel arrangements considered above demonstrates how important shape-factor analysis can be in supplementary heating design. For general space-heating problems, the matter of distribution of panel area is important from the standpoint of uniformity of heating effect, but failure to carry out such a distribution analysis accurately will not usually have any serious influence on the first cost of the system, since the total required panel area will probably not be greatly affected. With supplementary systems, on the contrary, the area of required panel, and hence the first cost of the installation, is directly related to the effectiveness of direct radiant transfer from panel to occupant and therefore varies directly with the shape factor of the subject with respect to the panel. Thus a 10 per cent error in determining the shape factor will lead to a 10 per cent variation of actual from design performance, while a 10 per cent variation in shape factor as determined for two different panel locations will be responsible for a 10 per cent difference in the size (assuming operation at the same surface temperature) of two panels, each of which will provide the same direct radiant transfer to the occupant. The shape factor is beyond doubt the most important single variable in determining the first cost, the effectiveness, and the operating cost of supplementary heating or cooling panels.

The panel selection for the case considered above was based on the assumption that the worker faced always in the same direction. If this were not so, the split panel, out 5 ft either in front of or behind the worker, would not be satisfactory, since a 90-deg change in the direction faced by the worker would reduce his reception of radiation by one-third. For this condition a more effective method of distributing the panel area would be to provide a circular band of 10-ft average diameter, the width of the band depending on the required total area. By examination of Fig. 4–33, the variation of shape factor for different points along the average diameter is seen to be from 0.012 for a point in front of the subject to 0.008 for a point at one side. The average shape factor of the subject with respect to this 10-ft circle is thus seen to be approximately 0.010. The area of the circular band panel would therefore have to exceed the total area of the front and back panels by 20 per cent, which indicates that if a change in the job requirements could be made to permit the worker to remain always facing in the same direction, a 20 per cent reduction in supplementary heating costs could be achieved. On the other hand, if limited, general space heating is needed in addition to the direct radiant transfer, ineffectively designed supplementary panels would not necessarily be responsible for increased heating costs, since the fraction of energy that leaves the panels but is not received by the occupants will meet some of the requirement for space-heating load.

One other fact that is evident from examination of Figs. 4–31, 4–32, and 4–33, but is frequently not realized by the designer, is that the direct radiant transfer from panel to occupant is extremely small. For a 12-ft ceiling height (Fig. 4–33), the maximum rate of direct transfer is seen to be only 1.2 per cent of the energy leaving the panel by radiation. Since the panel is also dissipating a substantial quantity of heat by convection, the fraction of total dissipated energy that reaches the occupant as a result of direct radiant transfer is, for this case, something less than 1 per cent. For an average room with a 12-ft ceiling, the percentage of radiant transfer received from a panel would be of the order of 0.75 per cent; the exact percentage could be obtained, for any particular problem, from the data of Fig. 4–33.

For 8-ft and 10-ft ceiling heights, the respective maximum transfer rates are (from Figs. 4–31 and 4–32) 4.7 and 2.2 per cent while the average transfer from a panel would be of the order of 2.5 and 1.5 per cent, respectively. Comparison of the graphs for the three ceiling heights will also show that height is of greatest importance when the occupant is near the finite area in question. As he moves away from it a distance of 10 ft or more, the height becomes less important, and for distances greater than 15 ft, the fraction of energy transferred is practically the same for all three conditions.

PROBLEMS

8–1. The transmission load calculated in Example 8–1 was 35,186 Btu/hr. Check this value by calculating the heat output of the panel.

8–2. A cubical room has a ceiling panel occupying the entire ceiling. The emissivities of the panel and of the floor are both 0.93, but all walls are covered with reflective surfacing, for which the emissivity is 0.10. Calculate the gross transfer by radiation from the panel to the floor.

8–3. Investigate the influence of gaseous radiation on the effectiveness of highly reflective room surfaces. (Hint: Repeat the derivation of Art. 8–2, page 326, but with an added coefficient in each term to account for depletion of radiation due to gaseous absorption.)

8–4. Air at 140 F and 20 per cent RH flows through the 8-ft diameter drum of a rotary dryer. If drum walls are at 80 F, determine the rate of loss by radiation from the water vapor in the drying air to the inside of the drum.

8–5. In Example 8–12(c) the value of the true mean radiant temperature is calculated as 74.08 F (by Eq. 7–20) with respect to a subject standing at the center of the room. Use the *mrt* equation developed in problem 7–1 to investigate the increase of *mrt* as the subject moves from room center along a diagonal toward that corner at which the two non-transmitting walls meet.

The next four problems, 8–6 through 8–9, should be undertaken as design projects rather than ordinary problem assignments. Although the solutions to these problems are straightforward and parallel in method the solutions given in corresponding examples, they are nonetheless lengthy and time-consuming.

8–6. Examples 8–1 through 8–4 and Examples 8–8 through 8–11 are all based on the room illustrated in Fig. 7–1. Consider that a center-line partition is installed in this room, thus establishing one smaller room with a single 5-ft by 5.68-ft window and a second smaller room with two windows, one 10 ft by 5.68 ft and the other 5 ft by 5.68 ft. In the undivided room, panel heating was provided by using all the surface of the two non-transmitting walls. If this same surface is used as panel area in the partitioned rooms, it is evident that the room with one window will have panel area of (1.5) (20) (10), or 300 sq ft, whereas the room with two windows will have only 100 sq ft of panel area.

For the conditions of Example 8–1, (a) calculate *by the rational method* the optimum panel, air, and surface temperatures at design load in the rooms on either side of the partition. (b) Calculate *by the rational method* the total transmission load for the structure. (c) Compare the results for parts (a) and (b) with the results given in the solution of Example 8–1 and discuss the influence of the partition on load and on thermal comfort.

8–7. Repeat problem 8–6 for the conditions of Example 8–2.

8–8. Repeat problem 8–6 for the conditions of Example 8–3.

8–9. Repeat problem 8–6 for the conditions of Example 8–4.

8–10. For the conditions of Example 8–8, (a) calculate *by the equivalent-conductance design procedure* the optimum panel, air, and surface temperatures at design load in the rooms on either side of the partition. (b) Calculate *by the equivalent-conductance design procedure* the total transmission load for the structure. (c) Compare the results for parts (a) and (b) with the results given in the solution of Example 8–8, and discuss the influence of the partition on load and on thermal comfort.

8–11. Repeat problem 8–10 for the conditions of Example 8–9.

8–12. Repeat problem 8–10 for the conditions of Example 8–10.

8–13. Repeat problem 8–10 for the conditions of Example 8–11.

8–14. Tabulate the values of t_p, t_a, q_t, sensible ventilation load, and total sensible heat load from the solutions of Examples 8–1 through 8–4. As a second column in the same table, tabulate the same data from the solutions of Examples

8–8 through 8–11. As a third column, use data from solutions of problems 8–6 through 8–9, and as a fourth column, use data from the solutions of problems 8–10 through 8–13.

8–15. For a subject working in a fixed standing position (but facing in various directions), calculation shows that a 6-ft diameter panel, 10 ft above the floor and centered above the subject, will establish comfortable warmth under design conditions if panel surface (with emissivity of 0.9) is maintained at a uniform temperature of 97 F. Air temperature is 74 F. What would be the required area of (a) a replacing, centered, square panel which would operate at the same temperature, (b) a replacing minimum-area annular-ring panel centered over the subject and operating at the same temperature, (c) a replacing rectangular panel 24 ft long and of unspecified width? (Note: the center line of the panel in part (c) is normal to the direction in which the subject faces and is a horizontal distance of 5 ft out from the subject, 10 ft above the floor, and has the same emissivity and surface temperature as the original circular panel.)

8–16. The four local panels described in problem 8–15 all irradiate the subject at the same rate. Evaluate the energy requirement for each of these panels.

9

SOLAR HEATING DATA AND ANALYSES

The quantity of solar energy received at the earth's surface is almost unimaginable. In 10 minutes on a clear day the earth receives as much heat from the solar source as is released by the combustion of wood, oil, coal, and natural gas—for all purposes and throughout the world—in an entire year. Many methods have been, and are being, attempted to enable man to capture directly and to utilize effectively the thermal energy corresponding to absorbed solar radiation, but as yet the problems of collection and storage have not been satisfactorily solved.

As applied to space heating, solar energy has been partially utilized in many different types of systems. Various kinds of collecting substances, such as two-phase fluids, have been tried, and many methods of storage for off-peak use have been developed. For the purpose of the present chapter, however, the *methods* are not of significance, as interest here is limited to the available rates of irradiation for differently located and oriented surfaces and the magnitude of the expected thermal advantage (or disadvantage) attributable to so-called solar windows. Thus the basic irradiation rates established in subsequent sections of this chapter should be equally useful for analysis of the reception, collection, and energy-loss rates of *any* existing or proposed type of solar-heating device. The same data can be used in performance analyses for estimating the reduction in seasonal heating load that can be expected from the solar contribution of either opaque structural surfaces or windows.

9–1. The Solar Source. A first step in any solar analysis is determination of the solar irradiation intensity, I_0, for unit area located at sea level and so oriented that, at a given distance, it is normal to the sun's rays. The units of intensity are Btu per hour per square foot, and the intensity varies as a function of the instantaneous length of path through the earth's atmosphere, the instantaneous physical and chemical character of the atmosphere, and the variations of intensity at a fixed point outside the earth's atmosphere.

Variation of intensity as a function of atmospheric path length can readily be expressed as a function of solar altitude H, measured in degrees above the horizon. Thus, when the sun is directly overhead ($H = 90$ deg), the path length through the atmosphere is along a radius of the atmospheric sphere and hence is a minimum, whereas for a rising or setting sun ($H \doteq 0$ deg), the

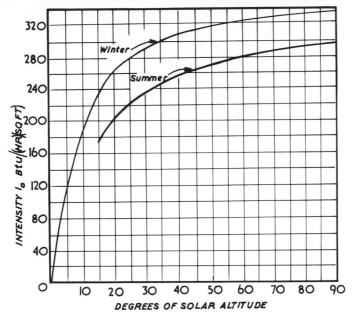

Fig. 9–1. Direct solar irradiation of a plane normal to the sun's rays and at sea level.

rays enter the atmosphere along a slanted course and must travel a maximum distance through the atmosphere before reaching the earth's surface.

Variation of intensity as a function of atmospheric quality (for a given value of the solar altitude) is determined by the absorption characteristics of ozone, water vapor, and carbon dioxide, and the scattering effect of dust and of water droplets. The influences of ozone and of carbon dioxide are relatively unchanging, but it is evident that wide variation, both with respect to time and location, can be expected in the influence of dust and of moisture. For engineering purposes an approximate intensity, at given solar altitude, can be evaluated in terms of average summer or winter dust count and average summer or winter moisture content. Fig. 9–1 presents a curve of I_0 versus H, recommended for use during the winter months and based on a dust count of 300 particles/cu cm (particles assumed 1 μ in diameter) and a vapor content equivalent to that at 33 F dew-point temperature. For the seven-month heating season (October through April), it is recommended that this curve be used in establishing I_0 for all times except during the months of March and April. Fig. 9–1 also presents a curve recommended for the summer months and based on the same dust content as the winter curve but on a higher moisture content. This curve is recommended for use in obtaining heating season values of I_0 for the months of March and April. Both curves of Fig. 9–1 were established by the method proposed by Moon,[1] and the

[1] Perry Moon, "Proposed Standard Radiation Curves for Engineering Use," *J. Franklin Institute*, Vol. 230, No. 5, November, 1940.

summer curve is taken directly from his paper. Aside from the theoretical considerations that entered into development of the recommended curves, their validity as engineering seasonal approximations is substantiated by close agreement with curves obtained experimentally in various localities.

Variation of intensity at a point outside the earth's atmosphere occurs seasonally as a result of the greater distance of the earth from the sun during the summer months. In constructing the winter curve of Fig. 9–1, a base value of solar intensity *outside* the earth's atmosphere was taken as 435 Btu/(hr)(sq ft). The effect of increasing distance between earth and sun is to reduce the January base value by approximately 5 Btu/)(hr)(sq ft)(month on either side of January); thus for February, the base value would be 430 Btu/(hr)(sq ft) and for October it would be 420 Btu/(hr)(sq ft). For any month from October through February the intensity is therefore obtained by reading the value, at known solar altitude, from the winter curve of Fig. 9–1 and then correcting it by a multiplying factor of $(435 - 5x)/435$, where x is the number of months from January to the month in question. Intensities for either March or April can be obtained with adequate accuracy by direct reading (at known value of H) from the summer curve of Fig. 9–1.

Sky Radiation. The daytime visibility of those parts of the sky distant from the sun's location demonstrates that part of the solar energy which is scattered by dust and water droplets must reach the earth indirectly. Unlike direct solar radiation, sky radiation is received at a point on the earth's surface through all angles of the encompassing hemisphere. The intensity of sky radiation, I_s, as received on a vertical surface, is influenced both by the intensity of direct radiation I_0 and by the amount of scattering. As previously stated, I_0 decreases as H decreases, but scattering increases as H decreases; hence the sun's altitude affects the value of I_s in two different ways. Insufficient data do not permit accurate estimation of sky radiation during the winter months, but the relative influence of this irradiation rate on total solar irradiation is small, so that possible inaccuracies in generalizations based on existing data would not be expected seriously to impair the accuracy of the over-all irradiation rates.

Fig. 9–2 is an empirical curve based on examination and partial correlation of available data. This curve gives the ratio R of direct solar intensity on a normal surface I_0, to intensity of sky radiation on a vertical surface I_s, as a function of solar altitude. Thus

$$I_s = \frac{I_0}{R} \qquad (9\text{–}1)$$

where I_0 is obtained from Fig. 9–1 (either directly or by use of the correction coefficient indicated on the figure) and R is obtained from Fig. 9–2. Examination of Fig. 9–2 shows that at small values of H (as at sunrise or sunset), sky radiation is of the order of 50 per cent of direct solar radiation, whereas for a solar position directly overhead, it is of the order of 5 per cent. The value of R from Fig. 9–2 is for days when the sun is not obscured. In misty or cloudy weather the relative importance of sky radiation would obviously be much greater.

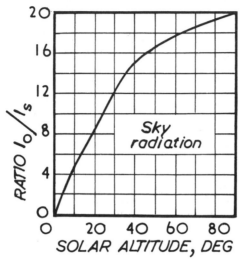

Fig. 9–2. Ratio of intensity of direct solar radiation in a plane normal to the sun's rays to the intensity of sky radiation on a vertical window.

QUANTITY OF SOLAR RADIATION. The terms I_0 and I_s, defined earlier in this chapter, are instantaneous rates of irradiation. In order to obtain the quantity of energy received during any given clear sky period, it would be necessary to assume I_0 and I_s as constant for a selected time interval and then to sum these values over the number of successive time intervals in question. A very commonly used procedure is to evaluate I_0 and I_s for the solar altitude applicable at the beginning of each hour of the day that the sun is above the horizon and then to assume that these values apply with adequate accuracy throughout the hour in question. When this procedure is used, the total quantity of solar energy received on a clear day is equal to the averaged hourly rate for the day, multiplied by the number of hours (plus fraction) of possible sunshine.

Table 9–1 gives maximum hours of possible radiation for vertical surfaces facing in various directions and for flat roofs. The tabular values are given for each of four latitudes and values for other latitudes applicable to the continental United States can be readily obtained either by interpolation or limited extrapolation for other latitudes applicable to the continental United States. Examination of the table will show that maximum hours are the same for the months of November and January and for October and February; values are specifically for the twenty-first day of each month but can be used as though constant throughout the month. If the total quantity of direct irradiation received on a plane always normal (and therefore necessarily moving) to the sun's rays were desired, it would be obtained by taking the average hourly value of I_0 and multiplying it by the maximum number of hours (and fraction thereof) of sunshine received on a flat roof. Note particularly, however, that this quantity would *not* equal the quantity of direct solar

TABLE 9–I
Maximum Hours of Possible Irradiation

	South-facing	Southeast- or Southwest-facing	East- or West-facing	Flat Roofs
		Vertical Walls		
30° *Latitude*				
October	11.3	7.9	5.7	11.4
November	10.5	8.1	5.3	10.6
December	9.7	8.0	5.0	10.0
January	10.5	8.1	5.3	10.6
February	11.3	7.9	5.7	11.4
March	12.0	7.8	6.0	12.0
April	9.0	7.6	6.5	13.0
35° *Latitude*				
October	11.1	8.0	5.6	11.2
November	10.0	8.9	5.0	10.0
December	9.7	9.1	4.9	9.8
January	10.0	8.9	5.0	10.0
February	11.1	8.0	5.6	11.2
March	12.0	7.8	6.0	12.0
April	9.5	8.4	6.5	13.0
40° *Latitude*				
October	10.7	8.0	5.4	10.8
November	9.6	7.9	4.8	9.6
December	9.2	7.8	4.6	9.2
January	9.6	7.9	4.8	9.6
February	10.7	8.0	5.4	10.8
March	12.0	8.2	6.0	12.0
April	10.0	8.4	6.7	13.4
45° *Latitude*				
October	10.8	8.2	5.4	10.8
November	9.4	7.8	4.7	9.4
December	9.2	7.8	4.6	9.2
January	9.4	7.8	4.7	9.4
February	10.8	8.2	5.4	10.8
March	12.0	8.4	6.0	12.0
April	10.3	8.8	6.9	13.8

energy irradiating 1 sq ft of flat roof because (though hours of irradiation are the same in the horizontal plane of the roof as on a unit area plane moving to maintain a normal to the sun's rays) the latter plane would be irradiated at a greater rate.

9–2. Irradiation Rates. The solar intensity I_0 has been defined for unit area of surface normal to the sun's rays. For any surface that is not in a plane at 90 deg with the direction of the sun's rays, the irradiation rate I will be less than I_0 by enough to compensate for the greater inclined plane area that is irradiated through unit normal area. If the angle between a perpendicular to the actual plane and a perpendicular to the normal plane is i, then the area A_a of the actual plane that receives direct solar energy at a rate equal to unit area of the normal plane is

$$A_a \cos i = 1$$

giving

$$A_a = \frac{1}{\cos i} \tag{9–2}$$

Since the irradiation of area A_a of the actual plane in Btu/hr is equal to I_0, it follows that the actual direct solar intensity I at the actual plane is

$$IA_a = \frac{I}{\cos i} = I_0$$

giving

$$I = I_0 \cos i \tag{9–3}$$

ANGLE OF INCIDENCE. Although i was defined as the angle between normals to the two planes, its major significance is based on the fact that it is also the angle between the direction of the sun's rays and the normal to the actual plane: the *angle of incidence* of the solar energy on the actual plane. Evaluation of i is a first step in determining the rate of reception of solar energy on any surface.

Vertical Surfaces. By trigonometry the cosine of the angle of incidence must be equal to the product of the cosines of its vertical and horizontal component angles. Thus, for vertical surfaces,

$$\cos i = \cos H \cos B \tag{9–4}$$

where H = solar altitude above the true horizon.
         B = horizontal angle between the direction of the sun's rays and a
              normal to the irradiated vertical surface.

Values of B are usually expressed in terms of the orientation of the surface and the solar azimuth A. Azimuth is a fundamental solar angle and is expressed in degrees east or west of north (up to 180 deg for due south at solar noon). Thus, for various orientations of vertical surfaces, the values[2] of B are

1. South-facing: $B = 180 - A$ (9–5)
2. East-facing, morning hours only:
                              $B = 90 - A$ (9–6)
   West-facing, afternoon hours only:
                              $B = 90 - A$ (9–7)

[2] The numerical value of B is always positive regardless of the sign of the difference of angles.

3. Southeast-facing:
   Morning hours only: $B = 135 - A$ (9–8a)
   Afternoon hours only:[3]

$$B = 225 - A \qquad (9\text{–}8b)$$

Southwest-facing:
   Afternoon hours only: $B = 135 - A$ (9–9a)
   Morning hours only:[3] $B = 225 - A$ (9–9b)

From the solar standpoint it is evident from the above equations that an east or southeast vertical surface during the morning hours (based on *solar* noon) is identical to a west or southwest, respectively, vertical surface during the afternoon hours.

Horizontal Surfaces.   The angle of incidence for a horizontal surface is obtained directly from the solar altitude, since

$$i = 90 - H \qquad (9\text{–}10)$$

Inclined Surfaces.[4]   When applied to a wall or roof or skylight that inclines away from the sun, the basic equation for angle of incidence (Eq. 9–4) takes the revised form

$$\cos i = \cos H' \cos B' \qquad (9\text{–}11)$$

where H' and B' are equivalent values of H and B and are related to the inclined wall in exactly the same way that angles H' and B' are related to a vertical wall.   Thus, for a wall inclined D degrees backward from normal, the equivalent values of the horizontal angle H' are measured in a plane running through the base of the wall and inclined upward from the horizontal by an amount equal to the backward inclination of the actual wall; the equivalent solar altitude H' is measured in degrees above the plane in which B' is measured.   Fig. 9–3 shows the geometrical relationships involved in establishing the trigonometric expressions for the equivalent angles B' and H'.   Fig. 9–3a is a plan view of the system for a wall facing southeast but inclined D degrees backward from the vertical.   Considering a point O on such a wall, the line OP is the horizontal projection of the line from O to the position of the sun, and B is the actual horizontal angle.   Distances x and y are lengths of sides of an arbitrarily selected rectangle based on OP as the hypotenuse. Fig. 9–3b is an elevation of the system in a vertical plane which runs in a southeasterly direction.   The line ON is a normal to the wall; hence it is at an angle D with the horizontal.   Note that the same angle D also appears between b and c of the smaller triangle in Fig. 9–3b.   Fig. 9–3c is an elevation of the system of Fig. 9–3a, taken in a direction normal to line OP.   Fig. 9–3d is a plan in a plane through OP, whereas Fig. 9–3e is an elevation taken from Fig. 9–3d.

---

[3] Up to a maximum B-value of 90°, hence for A values greater than 135°.

[4] Fig. 9–3, in this article, and the accompanying derivation are (with permission) from: "Solar Irradiation of Inclined Surfaces: Southeast or Southwest-Facing," F. W. Hutchinson and M. O. Cotter, *Heating, Piping Air Conditioning*, October, 1955.

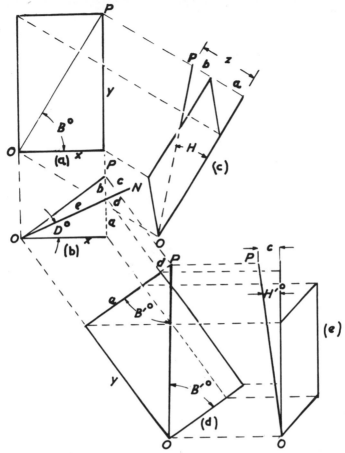

Fig. 9–3. Solar geometry for irradiation of inclined surfaces. (Adapted, by permission, from *Heating, Piping & Ventilating*.)

To determine H' let the distance x, as shown in Fig. 9–3a, equal unity. Then

$$y = \tan B \qquad (9\text{--}12)$$

and from Fig. 9–3b it is evident that

$$a = \tan D \qquad (9\text{--}13)$$

From Figs. 9–3a and 9–3c it then follows that

$$z = (z^2 + y^2)^{1/2}(\tan H)$$
$$= (1 + \tan^2 B)^{1/2}(\tan H) \qquad (9\text{--}14)$$

and

$$b = z - a = (\tan H)(x^2 + y^2)^{1/2} - \tan D$$
$$= (\tan H)(1 + \tan^2 B)^{1/2} - \tan D \qquad (9\text{--}15)$$

From Fig. 9–3b,

$$c = b(\cos D) = [(\tan H)(1 + \tan^2 B)^{1/2} - \tan D](\cos D) \qquad (9\text{–}16)$$

But the distance OP is the sum of the squares of the distances x, y, and z, or

$$OP = [1 + \tan^2 B + (1 + \tan^2 B)(\tan^2 H)]^{1/2}$$
$$= [(1 + \tan^2 B)(1 + \tan^2 H)]^{1/2} \qquad (9\text{–}17)$$

From Fig. 9–3b the sine of H' is c/OP; hence,

$$\sin H' = \frac{[(\tan H)(1 + \tan^2 B)^{1/2} - (\tan D)](\cos D)}{[(1 + \tan^2 B)(1 + \tan^2 H)]^{1/2}} \qquad (9\text{–}18)$$

Knowing $\sin H'$, the actual value in degrees of the equivalent solar altitude can be readily determined from any table of trigonometric functions.

To determine the equivalent horizontal angle B', note (from Figs. 9–3a, 9–3b, and 9–3d) that

$$\tan B' = \frac{y}{d + e} = \frac{\tan B}{b \cos (90 - D) + (1/\cos D)}$$
$$= \frac{\tan B}{[\tan H(1 + \tan^2 B)^{1/2} - \tan D] \cos (90 - D) + (1/\cos D)} \qquad (9\text{–}19)$$

Knowing $\tan B'$, the degree value of the equivalent horizontal angle can be readily determined from any table of trigonometric functions.

In cases where the user is concerned only with the angle of incidence and with the rate of irradiation, the above derivation of equivalent solar angles can be by-passed, and the cosine of the actual angle of incidence can be calculated from the following equation:

$$\cos i = \frac{1 + (1 + \tan^2 B)^{1/2}(\tan H)(\tan D)}{[(1 + \tan^2 B)(1 + \tan^2 H)(1 + \tan^2 D)]^{1/2}} \qquad (9\text{–}20)$$

IRRADIATION OF PLANES. With I_0 determined by the method of Art. 9–1 and the angle of incidence determined by the method of Art. 9–2, page 361 it is now possible to use Eq. 9–3 to evaluate the instantaneous irradiation rate for a plane surface having any orientation. The step-by-step procedure is as follows:

1. Determine the latitude at which the irradiated surface is located.
2. Determine the correction for the locality in question to be applied to standard time in order to convert it to solar time.
3. For known latitude and solar time refer to any set of standard solar tables to determine the azimuth A and solar altitude H.
4. With known H, go to Fig. 9–1 and read the I_0 value for January.
5. Correct the January I_0 by use of the coefficient, shown on Fig. 9–1, for the month in question (except that I_0 values for March and April are taken from the summer curve of Fig. 9–1 and used without correction).

6. With A known, determine angle B, or angles B' and H', by the methods of Art. 9-2, page 362.

7. With B and H, or B' and H', known, calculate the angle of incidence i from Eq. 9–4 or Eq. 9–11.

8. With I_0 and i known, calculate the intensity of irradiation I for the particular plane by means of Eq. 9–3.

Tables 9–2 through 9–9 present in direct-reading form the values of angle of incidence and of irradiation rates as functions of time of day, month of the year, latitude at which the structure is located, and orientation of the wall, window, roof skylight, or other irradiated surface. Tables 9–2 through 9–5 are for surfaces that are south-facing, and Tables 9–6 through 9–9 are for surfaces that are either east-facing or west-facing. Interpolation between the two sets of tables will permit obtaining irradiation rates on surfaces that face in any direction from east through south of east to south of west to west. Interpolation between monthly values of irradiation rate will permit determination of the direct irradiation rate at any daylight hour of the year. Each set of four tables is for latitudes of 30°, 35°, 40°, and 45° and hence cover all continental United States.

Each table presents data for October 1 through April 30, a seven-month period which in many localities is identified as the heating season. The hourly data in each table are based on exact conditions for the twenty-first day of the month in question, but for usual engineering computations they can be used with adequate accuracy for any other day of the same month. In terms of solar relationships (as contrasted with weather and with dry-bulb temperature) conditions for January and November are so close (angles of incidence being exactly the same and I_0 values differing by only 1 per cent) that they can be taken as the same; likewise, solar values for February and October can be taken as the same.

Table 9–2, for south-facing surfaces at latitude 30°, is representative of the form of all the tables. The first column gives the month and the *solar* hour of the day. Conditions given in the other columns are those existing at the start of the stated solar hour.

The second column gives the intensity I_0 on a surface normal to the sun's rays. All irradiation rates given in the table are for direct solar energy *only* and hence do not include sky radiation. If corresponding rates of sky radiation are desired, they can readily be obtained from Fig. 9–2 for the known values of I_0 and H (noting that H is obtainable from the table by subtracting the angle of incidence for a horizontal surface, column 3, from 90°), as obtained from the table. The reason for not including sky radiation with the I-values given in the table is that analysis of transmission, reflection, and absorption of the impinging radiation is carried out differently (see Art. 9–3) for the two types of energy.

Tabular irradiation values are for clear days; during periods of partially obscured or intermittent sunshine, the actual rate of irradiation will be less

TABLE 9–2
South-facing Wall, Roof, or Skylight: Latitude 30°

Solar Time	Normal Intensity	Horizontal		30-deg Backward Slope		60-deg Backward Slope		Vertical		Effective Altitude
	I_0	i	I_H	i	$I_{30°}$	i	$I_{60°}$	i	I_V	H''
October										
8A.M., 4P.M...	253.0	72	78.2	57	138.9	61	123.5	64	109.2	36°
9A.M., 3P.M...	285.7	61	139.5	46	198.0	48	193.0	58	150.4	43
10A.M., 2P.M...	302.5	51	190.2	33	253.0	32	256.1	53	182.7	46
11A.M., 1P.M...	312.4	44	224.8	23	286.8	19	295.2	50	201.2	48
12 Noon	314.3	41	237.4	19	297.5	11	308.9	49	206.2	49
November										
8A.M., 4P.M...	220.0	77	49.5	55	125.9	63	101.2	58	116.7	23
9A.M., 3P.M...	276.0	66	112.2	42	205.0	48	183.2	51	171.9	33
10A.M., 2P.M...	295.0	58	156.3	28	259.9	35	240.4	45	209.8	37
11A.M., 1P.M...	305.0	52	187.8	16	292.5	24	277.5	41	228.6	39
12 Noon	308.0	50	198.0	10	303.6	20	289.5	40	235.9	40
December										
8A.M., 4P.M...	192.7	79	36.8	54	112.7	64	86.0	56	108.5	19
9A.M., 3P.M...	264.9	69	95.2	40	202.0	50	171.8	48	177.9	28
10A.M., 2P.M...	285.7	61	138.4	28	251.7	38	224.8	42	211.8	33
11A.M., 1P.M...	296.5	55	170.0	15	286.1	27	263.5	38	232.2	36
12 Noon	299.5	53	180.2	7	297.1	23	275.5	37	239.2	37
January										
8A.M., 4P.M...	220.0	77	49.5	55	125.9	63	101.2	58	116.7	23
9A.M., 3P.M...	276.0	66	112.2	42	205.0	48	183.2	51	171.9	33
10A.M., 2P.M...	295.0	58	156.3	28	259.9	35	240.4	45	209.8	37
11A.M., 1P.M...	305.0	52	187.8	16	292.5	24	277.5	41	228.6	39
12 Noon	308.0	50	198.0	10	303.6	20	289.5	40	235.9	40
February										
8A.M., 4P.M...	253.0	72	78.2	57	138.9	61	123.5	64	109.2	36
9A.M., 3P.M...	285.7	61	139.5	46	198.0	48	193.0	58	150.4	43
10A.M., 2P.M...	302.5	51	190.2	33	253.0	32	256.1	53	182.7	46
11A.M., 1P.M...	312.4	44	224.8	23	286.8	19	295.2	50	201.2	48
12 Noon	314.3	41	237.4	19	297.5	11	308.9	49	206.2	49
March										
7A.M., 5P.M...	157.0	76	37.8	77	35.1	71	52.3	83	17.4	56
8A.M., 4P.M...	223.0	64	97.8	65	93.7	60	110.6	76	51.9	58
9A.M., 3P.M...	258.9	51	163.0	52	158.2	45	184.3	70	88.2	58
10A.M., 2P.M...	274.6	41	207.2	42	203.8	30	237.1	65	116.0	59
11A.M., 1P.M...	283.3	32	240.2	34	233.8	15	273.5	62	131.3	59
12 Noon	285.5	29	249.8	31	244.6	8	282.5	61	138.4	59
April										
8A.M., 4P.M...	241.0	58	127.7	72	76.4	60	121.5	87	14.7	81
9A.M., 3P.M...	270.4	44	194.5	60	133.8	46	189.5	81	42.3	75
10A.M., 2P.M...	282.5	33	236.9	51	177.3	32	238.8	76	67.5	72
11A.M., 1P.M...	289.4	22	268.2	45	205.2	19	273.2	74	81.8	71
12 Noon	290.7	18	276.4	42	216.0	13	283.5	72	89.3	71

TABLE 9–3
South-facing Wall, Roof, or Skylight: Latitude 35°

Solar Time	Normal Intensity	Horizontal		30-deg Backward Slope		60-deg Backward Slope		Vertical		Effective Altitude
	I_0	i	I_H	i	$I_{30°}$	i	$I_{60°}$	i	I_V	H''
October										
8A.M., 4P.M...	245.1	73	71.7	58	131.0	61	117.2	63	110.1	33°
9A.M., 3P.M...	281.7	63	127.8	45	197.5	48	187.4	57	154.5	40
10A.M., 2P.M...	298.5	54	175.4	31	254.9	34	248.5	50	192.9	42
11A.M., 1P.M...	306.4	49	201.0	17	292.5	22	283.0	45	217.3	43
12 Noon	310.4	46	215.7	14	301.0	16	298.1	44	223.3	44
November										
8A.M., 4P.M...	195.0	79	37.2	55	111.3	64	85.7	57	107.0	19
9A.M., 3P.M...	268.0	69	96.1	41	202.0	51	170.0	49	176.9	29
10A.M., 2P.M...	288.0	62	135.3	28	255.0	39	224.6	42	215.6	32
11A.M., 1P.M...	295.0	58	156.2	15	285.7	30	255.2	36	239.2	33
12 Noon	300.0	55	172.0	5	298.9	25	272.0	35	245.7	35
December										
8A.M., 4P.M...	185.8	80	32.3	54	109.5	64	81.7	55	107.6	17
9A.M., 3P.M...	245.1	73	71.7	41	184.5	53	147.9	46	171.4	23
10A.M., 2P.M...	272.8	66	111.0	28	240.2	42	202.5	38	213.6	27
11A.M., 1P.M...	285.7	61	138.5	14	277.2	33	240.0	33	240.2	30
12 Noon	291.6	59	150.2	0	291.6	29	255.1	31	250.0	31
January										
8A.M., 4P.M...	195.0	79	37.2	55	111.3	64	85.7	57	107.0	19
9A.M., 3P.M...	268.0	69	96.1	41	202.0	51	170.0	49	176.9	29
10A.M., 2P.M...	288.0	62	135.3	28	255.0	39	224.6	42	215.6	32
11A.M., 1P.M...	295.0	58	156.2	15	285.7	30	255.2	36	239.2	33
12 Noon	300.0	55	172.0	5	298.9	25	272.0	35	245.7	35
February										
8A.M., 4P.M...	245.1	73	71.7	58	131.0	61	117.2	63	110.1	33
9A.M., 3P.M...	281.7	63	127.8	45	197.5	48	187.4	57	154.5	40
10A.M., 2P.M...	298.5	54	175.4	31	254.9	34	248.5	50	192.9	42
11A.M., 1P.M...	306.4	49	201.0	17	292.5	22	283.0	45	217.3	43
12 Noon	310.4	46	215.7	14	301.0	16	298.1	44	223.3	44
March										
7A.M., 5P.M...	157.0	76	37.6	76	38.2	74	44.2	82	21.2	52
8A.M., 4P.M...	223.0	64	96.8	64	99.6	59	113.9	74	58.6	53
9A.M., 3P.M...	258.9	51	162.0	50	165.7	43	189.9	68	97.6	54
10A.M., 2P.M...	273.4	42	203.2	39	211.6	29	239.4	62	127.1	54
11A.M., 1P.M...	280.8	35	230.0	31	240.0	15	271.5	59	144.8	54
12 Noon	283.3	32	240.3	28	247.0	4	282.0	58	150.1	55
April										
8A.M., 4P.M...	241.0	58	124.0	69	82.8	59	119.2	84	24.9	77
9A.M., 3P.M...	267.7	46	186.0	57	144.5	45	187.5	77	59.5	71
10A.M., 2P.M...	281.6	34	233.2	47	190.8	30	245.0	72	85.8	69
11A.M., 1P.M...	287.2	26	258.0	41	218.3	17	275.0	69	103.1	66
12 Noon	289.3	22	268.2	38	227.7	8	286.3	68	108.4	66

TABLE 9–4
South-facing Wall, Roof, or Skylight: Latitude 40°

Solar Time	Normal Intensity	Horizontal		30-deg Backward Slope		60-deg Backward Slope		Vertical		Effective Altitude
	I_0	i	I_H	i	$I_{30°}$	i	$I_{60°}$	i	I_V	H''
October										
8A.M., 4P.M...	230.3	75	58.9	59	119.2	63	104.0	63	104.4	30°
9A.M., 3P.M...	272.8	66	111.0	44	197.0	49	178.2	53	163.5	34
10A.M., 2P.M...	291.6	58	154.5	30	251.0	36	235.0	46	202.5	37
11A.M., 1P.M...	299.5	53	180.2	17	287.0	25	271.9	41	227.5	38
12 Noon	302.5	51	190.2	6	301.0	22	280.9	39	235.1	39
November										
8A.M., 4P.M...	180.0	81	28.2	56	100.0	66	74.1	56	99.4	16
9A.M., 3P.M...	240.0	74	65.5	43	174.2	55	138.3	46	166.0	22
10A.M., 2P.M...	276.0	66	113.6	28	243.5	42	205.1	38	216.1	27
11A.M., 1P.M...	288.0	62	135.2	15	278.0	34	238.4	32	243.1	29
12 Noon	289.0	61	140.0	5	287.6	31	247.3	29	252.7	29
December										
8A.M., 4P.M...	177.9	81	27.8	55	103.3	65	75.6	55	103.3	15
9A.M., 3P.M...	221.4	76	53.4	42	165.0	55	126.2	44	159.6	19
10A.M., 2P.M...	260.0	70	88.9	28	229.5	45	183.5	35	213.7	23
11A.M., 1P.M...	272.8	66	112.4	15	263.9	38	216.4	28	240.7	25
12 Noon	276.8	65	117.0	5	275.5	35	226.5	25	250.9	25
January										
8A.M., 4P.M...	180.0	81	28.2	56	100.0	66	74.1	56	99.4	16
9A.M., 3P.M...	240.0	74	65.5	43	174.2	55	138.3	46	166.0	22
10A.M., 2P.M...	276.0	66	113.6	28	243.5	42	205.1	38	216.1	27
11A.M., 1P.M...	288.0	62	135.2	15	278.0	34	238.4	32	243.1	29
12 Noon	289.0	61	140.0	5	287.6	31	247.3	29	252.7	29
February										
8A.M., 4P.M...	230.3	75	58.9	59	119.2	63	104.0	63	104.4	30
9A.M., 3P.M...	272.8	66	111.0	44	197.0	49	178.2	53	163.5	34
10A.M., 2P.M...	291.6	58	154.5	30	251.0	36	235.0	46	202.5	37
11A.M., 1P.M...	299.5	53	180.2	17	287.0	25	271.9	41	227.5	38
12 Noon	302.5	51	190.2	6	301.0	22	280.9	39	235.1	39
March										
7A.M., 5P.M...	133.5	78	27.8	76	31.8	75	34.2	81	20.4	47
8A.M., 4P.M...	215.6	66	87.6	62	102.3	59	109.7	72	67.4	48
9A.M., 3P.M...	247.0	56	138.2	49	163.1	45	174.1	64	108.5	48
10A.M., 2P.M...	264.5	48	170.4	36	213.0	32	216.5	57	143.8	49
11A.M., 1P.M...	274.6	41	207.3	26	247.4	17	262.0	53	165.8	50
12 Noon	276.9	39	215.1	21	258.5	13	270.0	51	174.3	50
April										
8A.M., 4P.M...	237.9	59	122.5	67	91.7	59	123.9	81	35.4	72
9A.M., 3P.M...	264.4	48	176.9	55	152.0	44	190.0	74	73.6	67
10A.M., 2P.M...	278.9	38	219.8	45	198.5	29	243.0	68	105.7	64
11A.M., 1P.M...	284.1	31	243.5	35	232.6	15	275.0	63	128.0	62
12 Noon	286.7	27	255.3	31	246.1	10	282.1	63	130.2	61

TABLE 9–5
South-facing Wall, Roof, or Skylight: Latitude 45°

Solar Time	Normal Intensity I_0	i	Horizontal I_H	i	30-deg Backward Slope $I_{30°}$	i	60-deg Backward Slope $I_{60°}$	i	Vertical I_V	Effective Altitude H''
October										
8A.M., 4P.M...	217.5	77	48.7	59	113.3	64	93.1	62	102.7	25°
9A.M., 3P.M...	266.9	68	100.0	43	193.7	52	165.0	52	165.6	31
10A.M., 2P.M...	281.7	63	127.7	30	243.5	40	214.3	42	208.1	32
11A.M., 1P.M...	291.6	58	154.5	15	282.4	30	252.2	36	236.4	33
12 Noon	294.6	56	164.9	10	291.0	24	269.0	34	244.2	34
November										
8A.M., 4P.M...	164.0	82	22.9	56	90.9	66	66.4	55	93.1	10
9A.M., 3P.M...	220.0	77	49.5	43	160.5	57	121.3	45	156.8	18
10A.M., 2P.M...	248.0	73	72.0	30	214.0	48	166.0	34	205.4	19
11A.M., 1P.M...	270.0	68	101.3	17	258.5	40	208.0	27	240.6	23
12 Noon	276.0	66	112.2	6	274.3	36	222.7	24	252.1	24
December										
8A.M., 4P.M...	177.9	87	9.0	57	94.4	70	60.0	54	105.7	5
9A.M., 3P.M...	192.7	79	36.8	41	145.0	58	103.2	42	142.7	14
10A.M., 2P.M...	217.5	77	49.0	31	186.5	51	137.0	31	187.1	15
11A.M., 1P.M...	253.0	72	78.2	18	240.0	43	184.3	23	232.4	19
12 Noon	266.9	68	100.0	8	264.0	38	211.0	22	247.5	22
January										
8A.M., 4P.M...	164.0	82	22.9	56	90.9	66	66.4	55	93.1	10
9A.M., 3P.M...	220.0	77	49.5	43	160.5	57	121.3	45	156.8	18
10A.M., 2P.M...	248.0	73	72.0	30	214.0	48	166.0	34	205.4	19
11A.M., 1P.M...	270.0	68	101.3	17	258.5	40	208.0	27	240.6	23
12 Noon	276.0	66	112.2	6	274.3	36	222.7	24	252.1	24
February										
8A.M., 4P.M...	217.5	77	48.7	59	113.3	64	93.1	62	102.7	25
9A.M., 3P.M...	266.9	68	100.0	43	193.7	52	165.0	52	165.6	31
10A.M., 2P.M...	281.7	63	127.7	30	243.5	40	214.3	42	208.1	32
11A.M., 1P.M...	291.6	58	154.5	15	282.4	30	252.2	36	236.4	33
12 Noon	294.6	56	164.9	10	291.0	24	269.0	34	244.2	34
March										
7A.M., 5P.M...	117.0	79	15.7	79	22.5	81	131.0	80	20.0	41
8A.M., 4P.M...	207.2	68	77.3	62	95.3	60	103.2	70	72.0	44
9A.M., 3P.M...	237.9	59	122.6	47	162.5	46	165.0	61	140.8	44
10A.M., 2P.M...	258.9	51	163.0	34	215.5	33	218.3	53	154.3	44
11A.M., 1P.M...	267.7	46	186.2	22	249.0	20	251.5	49	179.8	44
12 Noon	270.7	44	195.0	16	260.4	14	262.6	46	188.1	45
April										
8A.M., 4P.M...	235.1	60	117.5	65	96.5	58	124.5	79	45.8	69
9A.M., 3P.M...	260.4	50	167.4	52	159.7	43	189.0	70	87.4	61
10A.M., 2P.M...	274.6	41	207.5	37	218.5	29	241.1	63	122.9	58
11A.M., 1P.M...	280.8	35	230.0	31	240.5	15	271.6	59	144.8	57
12 Noon	283.3	32	240.5	26	255.0	8	281.0	58	150.1	56

TABLE 9–6
East- or West-facing Wall, Roof, or Skylight: Latitude 30°

Solar Time	Normal Intensity	Horizontal		30-deg Backward Slope		60-deg Backward Slope		Vertical		Effective Altitude
East, West	I_0	i	I_H	i	$I_{30°}$	i	$I_{60°}$	i	I_V	H''
October										
7A.M., 5P.M...	152.0	82	21.2	27	135.4	54	90.4	19	143.9	8°
8A.M., 4P.M...	251.0	72	77.6	27	223.0	46	173.5	32	212.7	20
9A.M., 3P.M...	286.0	61	138.7	31	244.0	40	220.3	46	199.7	35
10A.M., 2P.M...	301.0	51	189.3	42	222.3	38	237.4	61	147.2	52
11A.M., 1P.M...	308.0	44	221.3	54	180.3	41	232.2	75	80.1	70
12 Noon	313.5	40	240.2	68	119.5	49	206.5	90		
1P.M., 11A.M..	308.0	44	221.3	82	41.5	60	152.0			
2P.M., 10A.M..	301.0	51	189.3			73	90.4			
3P.M., 9A.M...	286.0	61	138.7			86	20.3			
November										
7A.M., 5P.M...	80.0	87	4.2	35	65.8	60	40.4	23	73.6	
8A.M., 4P.M...	218.0	77	49.1	33	182.0	45	158.6	35	178.1	15
9A.M., 3P.M...	277.0	66	112.7	39	216.7	46	191.0	48	185.0	31
10A.M., 2P.M...	294.0	58	155.8	48	195.7	46	203.0	63	135.8	49
11A.M., 1P.M...	304.0	52	187.2	59	157.8	48	203.0	76	74.0	68
12 Noon	308.0	50	198.0	71	99.2	56	171.5	90		
1P.M., 11A.M..	304.0	52	187.2	84	29.5	65	128.8			
2P.M., 10A.M..	294.0	58	155.8			77	67.0			
3P.M., 9A.M...	277.0	66	112.7			89	5.1			
December										
8A.M., 4P.M...	194.0	79	37.0	38	153.7	55	110.1	36	156.0	13
9A.M., 3P.M...	265.0	69	95.0	42	196.3	51	167.7	50	171.9	29
10A.M., 2P.M...	286.0	61	138.5	50	184.3	49	186.3	62	132.5	46
11A.M., 1P.M...	296.0	55	169.7	60	146.4	52	182.3	76	70.9	67
12 Noon	298.7	53	179.7	73	89.8	59	155.5	90		
1P.M., 11A.M..	296.0	55	169.7	85	23.5	68	111.3			
2P.M., 10A.M..	286.0	61	138.5			79	53.8			
January										
7A.M., 5P.M...	80.0	87	4.2	35	65.8	60	40.4	23	73.6	
8A.M., 4P.M...	218.0	77	49.1	33	182.0	45	158.6	35	178.1	15
9A.M., 3P.M...	277.0	66	112.7	39	216.7	46	191.0	48	185.0	31
10A.M., 2P.M...	294.0	58	155.8	48	195.7	46	203.0	63	135.8	49
11A.M., 1P.M...	304.0	52	187.2	59	157.8	48	203.0	76	74.0	68
12 Noon	308.0	50	198.0	71	99.2	56	171.5	90		
1P.M., 11A.M..	304.0	52	187.2	84	29.5	65	128.8			
2P.M., 10A.M..	294.0	58	155.8			77	67.0			
3P.M., 9A.M...	277.0	66	112.7			89	5.1			
February										
7A.M., 5P.M...	152.0	82	21.2	27	135.4	54	90.4	19	143.9	8
8A.M., 4P.M...	251.0	72	77.6	27	223.0	46	173.5	32	212.7	20
9A.M., 3P.M...	286.0	61	138.7	31	244.0	40	220.3	46	199.7	35
10A.M., 2P.M...	301.0	51	189.3	42	222.3	38	237.4	61	147.2	52
11A.M., 1P.M...	308.0	44	221.3	54	180.3	41	232.2	75	80.1	70
12 Noon	313.5	40	240.2	68	119.5	49	206.5	90		
1P.M., 11A.M..	308.0	44	221.3	82	41.5	60	152.0			
2P.M., 10A.M..	301.0	51	189.3			73	90.4			
3P.M., 9A.M...	286.0	61	138.7			86	20.3			

TABLE 9–6 (continued)

Solar Time	Normal Intensity	Horizontal		30-deg Backward Slope		60-deg Backward Slope		Vertical		Effective Altitude
East, West	I_0	i	I_H	i	$I_{30°}$	i	$I_{60°}$	i	I_V	H''
March										
6A.M., 6P.M...	56.0	85	4.9	25	50.8	55	32.1	5	55.8	5°
7A.M., 5P.M...	157.0	76	38.0	16	151.0	46	108.5	16	151.2	14
8A.M., 4P.M...	223.0	64	97.8	14	216.5	36	181.4	30	193.6	27
9A.M., 3P.M...	258.9	53	155.6	23	238.9	28	227.8	46	180.8	42
10A.M., 2P.M...	274.6	41	207.2	36	223.5	25	248.9	64	118.9	56
11A.M., 1P.M...	283.3	32	239.4	50	183.3	31	243.2	75	72.8	73
12 Noon	286.5	29	250.8	64	125.4	42	214.3	90		
1P.M., 11A.M..	283.3	32	239.4	78	57.1	53	170.4			
2P.M., 10A.M..	274.6	41	207.2			66	110.8			
3P.M., 9A.M...	258.9	53	155.6			81	42.0			
April										
6A.M., 6P.M...	69.0	83	8.4	18	65.6	54	40.9	13	67.0	7
7A.M., 5P.M...	202.8	69	72.8	10	199.7	39	157.5	21	189.1	21
8A.M., 4P.M...	241.0	58	127.7	4	240.5	28	212.8	32	203.9	32
9A.M., 3P.M...	270.4	44	194.5	19	255.6	16	260.0	47	183.0	47
10A.M., 2P.M...	282.5	33	237.0	33	238.0	14	274.0	61	138.3	60
11A.M., 1P.M...	289.4	22	268.3	47	195.6	22	268.0	76	71.1	75
12 Noon	290.0	18	276.0	62	138.0	35	239.0	90		
1P.M., 11A.M..	289.4	22	268.3	75	72.5	47	196.5			
2P.M., 10A.M..	282.5	33	237.0			61	136.0			
3P.M., 9A.M...	270.4	44	194.5			88	8.9			

than the tabular value. For problems involving summer cooling, the clear weather data would be conservative, but when used for solar heating computations, such data are obviously non-conservative and should be adjusted by the designer in terms of experience and of weather bureau records for the locality in question. If more accurate data are lacking, it is suggested that the clear weather values be multiplied by the percentage of maximum possible sunshine (given in column 2 of Table 9–15) and then reduced to 60 per cent of this value as an arbitrary and conservative correction for reduced normal intensity during times of light cloudiness.

In using the I values from the tables, it must be remembered that "irradiation" refers to energy impinging on the surface and is not necessarily indicative either of energy entering the structure through a window or of energy actually absorbed by an opaque wall. The irradiation rate is, however, the basic term needed for analysis of either transmission or absorption. Transmissivity, absorptivity, and reflectivity (each expressed as a fraction of total impinging radiation) are functions of the material in question and the angle of incidence; the first two usually increase markedly as the angle of incidence decreases. When these values are known for the particular surface, they can be multiplied by the tabulated direct irradiation rates (at each angle of

TABLE 9–7
East- or West-facing Wall, Roof, or Skylight: Latitude 35°

Solar Time	Normal Intensity	Horizontal		30-deg Backward Slope		60-deg Backward Slope		Vertical		Effective Altitude
East, West	I_0	i	I_H	i	$I_{30°}$	i	$I_{60°}$	i	I_V	H''
October										
8A.M., 4P.M...	245.0	73	71.7	29	215.0	47	165.5	32	216.3	19°
9A.M., 3P.M...	282.0	63	128.0	33	235.2	42	209.9	45	222.2	33
10A.M., 2P.M...	297.0	54	174.5	44	212.8	41	224.0	61	178.7	50
11A.M., 1P.M...	303.0	49	198.8	56	167.3	46	211.0	75	103.6	69
12 Noon	308.9	45	218.2	69	109.1	52	189.2	90		
1P.M., 11A.M..	303.0	49	198.8	84	31.5	64	132.6			
2P.M., 10A.M..	297.0	54	174.5			75	79.0			
3P.M., 9A.M...	282.0	63	128.0			88	11.9			
November										
8A.M., 4P.M...	196.0	79	37.4	37	156.7	55	112.2	14	190.5	11
9A.M., 3P.M...	268.0	69	96.1	41	201.2	50	171.5	49	176.9	28
10A.M., 2P.M...	287.0	62	134.8	50	184.0	50	184.0	62	134.2	45
11A.M., 1P.M...	294.0	58	155.9	61	141.0	54	171.4	76	73.6	65
12 Noon	300.0	55	172.0	73	86.0	60	149.0	90		
1P.M., 11A.M..	294.0	58	155.9	87	14.8	70	98.0			
2P.M., 10A.M..	287.0	62	134.8			80	49.6			
December										
8A.M., 4P.M...	179.0	80	31.1	39	138.9	47	123.0	37	144.8	12
9A.M., 3P.M...	239.0	73	69.9	45	170.0	54	138.5	49	163.0	24
10A.M., 2P.M...	267.0	66	108.6	52	163.2	55	157.0	62	137.5	41
11A.M., 1P.M...	279.0	61	135.2	62	128.9	57	151.0	76	76.9	64
12 Noon	287.6	58	152.4	75	76.2	63	131.9	90		
1P.M., 11A.M..	279.0	61	135.2	88	9.8	73	83.8			
2P.M., 10A.M..	267.0	66	108.6			83	31.4			
January										
8A.M., 4P.M...	196.0	79	37.4	37	156.7	55	112.2	14	190.5	11
9A.M., 3P.M...	268.0	69	96.1	41	201.2	50	171.5	49	176.9	28
10A.M., 2P.M...	287.0	62	134.8	50	184.0	50	184.0	62	134.2	45
11A.M., 1P.M...	294.0	58	155.9	61	141.0	54	171.4	76	73.6	65
12 Noon	300.0	55	172.0	73	86.0	60	149.0	90		
1P.M., 11A.M..	294.0	58	155.9	87	14.8	70	98.0			
2P.M., 10A.M..	287.0	62	134.8			80	49.6			
February										
8A.M., 4P.M...	245.0	73	71.7	29	215.0	47	165.5	32	216.3	19
9A.M., 3P.M...	282.0	63	128.0	33	235.2	42	209.9	45	222.2	33
10A.M., 2P.M...	297.0	54	174.5	44	212.8	41	224.0	61	178.7	50
11A.M., 1P.M...	303.0	49	198.8	56	167.3	46	211.0	75	103.6	69
12 Noon	308.9	45	218.2	69	109.1	52	189.2	90		
1P.M., 11A.M..	303.0	49	198.8	84	31.5	64	132.6			
2P.M., 10A.M..	297.0	54	174.5			75	79.0			
3P.M., 9A.M...	282.0	63	128.0			88	11.9			

TABLE 9–7 (continued)

Solar Time	Normal Intensity	Horizontal		30-deg Backward Slope		60-deg Backward Slope		Vertical		Effective Altitude
East, West	I_0	i	I_H	i	$I_{30°}$	i	$I_{60°}$	i	I_V	H''
March										
6A.M., 6P.M...	56.0	85	4.9	26	50.4	55	32.1	5	55.8	5°
7A.M., 5P.M...	157.0	76	38.0	17	149.8	46	108.4	16	150.8	14
8A.M., 4P.M...	223.0	64	97.8	15	215.0	36	180.7	31	191.7	27
9A.M., 3P.M...	258.9	55	148.4	25	235.0	31	231.0	47	176.0	43
10A.M., 2P.M...	273.4	42	203.2	38	214.3	28	241.7	61	131.6	57
11A.M., 1P.M...	280.8	35	230.0	51	176.4	35	231.2	75	70.6	73
12 Noon	283.5	32	240.3	65	119.1	43	208.5	90		
1P.M., 11A.M..	280.8	35	230.0	79	54.0	55	160.5			
2P.M., 10A.M..	273.4	42	203.2			66	110.2			
3P.M., 9A.M...	258.9	55	148.4			82	36.1			
April										
6A.M., 6P.M...	83.5	82	11.6	24	76.4	53	50.8	13	81.4	8
7A.M., 5P.M...	189.8	71	61.8	11	186.2	41	143.2	19	179.3	19
8A.M., 4P.M...	241.0	58	127.7	6	239.5	28	211.9	32	202.8	32
9A.M., 3P.M...	267.7	46	186.1	20	251.5	19	253.0	47	183.1	45
10A.M., 2P.M...	281.6	34	233.4	35	231.3	18	268.0	62	132.1	61
11A.M., 1P.M...	287.2	26	258.0	48	192.0	25	260.2	75	72.2	74
12 Noon	289.1	22	268.0	62	134.0	37	232.0	90		
1P.M., 11A.M..	287.2	26	258.0	77	66.8	46	200.4			
2P.M., 10A.M..	281.6	34	233.4	89	2.4	61	136.0			
3P.M., 9A.M...	267.7	46	186.1			75	69.4			
4P.M., 8A.M...	241.0	58	127.7			88	9.1			

incidence) to obtain the actual rate of solar energy transmitted, absorbed, or reflected.

The third and fourth columns of Table 9–2 give the angle of incidence and the solar intensity I_H for a horizontal surface such as a flat roof.

The fifth and sixth columns and the seventh and eighth columns give incidence angle and solar intensity for south-facing walls, roofs, or skylights that are inclined 30° and 60°, respectively, backward from the vertical and away from the sun.

The ninth and tenth columns of Table 9–2 are for vertical south-facing walls or windows.

The last column of the table gives an "effective" solar altitude which is useful in evaluating the extent to which a given amount of roof overhang serves to shade a window in summer or to impede solar gain in winter. The derivation and use of H'' is discussed in Art. 9–4.

Tables 9–3, 9–4, and 9–5 are the same as Table 9–2 except that they are applicable to latitudes 35°, 40°, and 45°. Examination of these tables will show that for a given month and hour, I_0 decreases with increasing latitude and i increases with increasing latitude; both these relationships cause I_H, $I_{30°}$, $I_{60°}$, and I_V to decrease as latitude increases.

TABLE 9–8
East- or West-facing Wall, Roof, or Skylight: Latitude 40°

Solar Time	Normal Intensity	Horizontal		30-deg Backward Slope		60-deg Backward Slope		Vertical		Effective Altitude
East, West	I_0	i	I_H	i	$I_{30°}$	i	$I_{60°}$	i	I_V	H''
October										
7A.M., 5P.M...	152.0	82	21.2	28	134.7	54	90.0	20	143.2	8°
8A.M., 4P.M...	232.0	75	60.0	30	201.9	49	150.9	31	197.8	17
9A.M., 3P.M...	274.0	66	111.5	37	219.7	46	191.2	46	188.9	31
10A.M., 2P.M...	291.0	58	154.1	47	199.7	45	204.7	61	141.5	47
11A.M., 1P.M...	298.0	53	179.5	59	153.5	50	192.3	76	73.6	68
12 Noon	304.5	51	191.7	72	95.2	57	165.8	90		
1P.M., 11A.M..	298.0	53	179.5	85	26.1	67	118.6			
2P.M., 10A.M..	291.0	58	154.1			77	63.0			
3P.M., 9A.M...	274.0	66	111.5			89	2.2			
November										
8A.M., 4P.M...	170.0	81	26.6	38	134.0	57	92.7	35	139.2	11
9A.M., 3P.M...	240.0	74	66.2	44	172.0	55	136.7	48	160.3	22
10A.M., 2P.M...	277.0	66	112.7	52	169.4	54	163.0	62	130.3	41
11A.M., 1P.M...	287.0	62	134.9	63	131.5	58	153.7	75	74.1	61
12 Noon	288.0	61	139.7	76	69.8	65	121.0	90		
1P.M., 11A.M..	287.0	62	134.9	89	3.2	74	79.6			
2P.M., 10A.M..	277.0	66	112.7			83	32.6			
December										
8A.M., 4P.M...	168.0	81	26.3	40	129.3	58	89.8	37	134.2	11
9A.M., 3P.M...	223.0	76	54.0	47	152.2	58	118.7	50	144.8	20
10A.M., 2P.M...	261.0	70	89.2	56	147.5	58	136.9	63	118.9	37
11A.M., 1P.M...	274.0	66	111.5	66	112.0	62	129.1	76	64.8	60
12 Noon	276.8	65	117.0	78	58.5	69	101.1	90		
1P.M., 11A.M..	274.0	66	111.5			76	64.2			
2P.M., 10A.M..	261.0	70	89.2			86	18.0			
January										
8A.M., 4P.M...	170.0	81	26.6	38	134.0	57	92.7	35	139.2	11
9A.M., 3P.M...	240.0	74	66.2	44	172.0	55	136.7	48	160.3	22
10A.M., 2P.M...	277.0	66	112.7	52	169.4	54	163.0	62	130.3	41
11A.M., 1P.M...	287.0	62	134.9	63	131.5	58	153.7	75	74.1	61
12 Noon	288.0	61	139.7	76	69.8	65	121.0	90		
1P.M., 11A.M..	287.0	62	134.9	89	3.2	74	79.6			
2P.M., 10A.M..	277.0	66	112.7			83	32.6			
February										
7A.M., 5P.M...	152.0	82	21.2	28	134.7	54	90.0	20	143.2	8
8A.M., 4P.M...	232.0	75	60.0	30	201.9	49	150.9	31	197.8	17
9A.M., 3P.M...	274.0	66	111.5	37	219.7	46	191.2	46	188.9	31
10A.M., 2P.M...	291.0	58	154.1	47	199.7	45	204.7	61	141.5	47
11A.M., 1P.M...	298.0	53	179.5	59	153.5	50	192.3	76	73.6	68
12 Noon	304.5	51	191.7	72	95.2	57	165.8	90		
1P.M., 11A.M..	298.0	53	179.5	85	26.1	67	118.6			
2P.M., 10A.M..	291.0	58	154.1			77	63.0			
3P.M., 9A.M...	274.0	66	111.5			89	2.2			

TABLE 9–8 (continued)

Solar Time	Normal Intensity	Horizontal		30-deg Backward Slope		60-deg Backward Slope		Vertical		Effective Altitude
East, West	I_0	i	I_H	i	$I_{30°}$	i	$I_{60°}$	i	I_V	H''
March										
6A.M., 6P.M...	56.0	85	4.9	25	50.8	55	32.1	5	55.8	5°
7A.M., 5P.M...	133.5	78	27.8	20	125.5	48	88.5	15	129.0	12
8A.M., 4P.M...	215.6	66	87.8	19	204.3	39	168.5	23	198.2	25
9A.M., 3P.M...	247.0	56	138.1	27	219.5	33	206.5	45	173.7	38
10A.M., 2P.M...	264.5	48	177.0	39	204.7	33	221.0	60	134.1	53
11A.M., 1P.M..	274.6	41	207.4	53	165.0	38	215.0	75	70.4	71
12 Noon	277.0	39	215.2	67	107.5	48	186.1	90		
1P.M., 11A.M..	274.6	41	207.4	81	43.1	58	144.7			
2P.M., 10A.M..	264.5	48	177.0			71	66.0			
3P.M., 9A.M...	247.0	56	138.1			82	32.9			
April										
6A.M., 6P.M...	98.0	81	15.3	23	90.4	51	61.0	13	95.6	9
7A.M., 5P.M...	196.3	70	67.1	10	193.1	40	150.0	20	184.5	20
8A.M., 4P.M...	237.9	59	122.5	8	235.2	30	206.5	32	200.8	31
9A.M., 3P.M...	264.4	48	177.0	21	246.3	22	244.4	46	182.2	44
10A.M., 2P.M...	278.9	38	220.0	36	227.0	22	257.8	61	135.3	58
11A.M., 1P.M..	284.1	31	243.5	50	183.3	30	246.0	76	70.8	74
12 Noon	286.8	27	255.7	63	131.0	38	226.8	90		
1P.M., 11A.M..	284.1	31	243.5	78	60.4	52	175.3			
2P.M., 10A.M..	278.9	38	220.0			64	122.5			
3P.M., 9A.M...	264.4	48	177.0			69	94.6			
4P.M., 8A.M...	237.9	59	122.5			89	58.2			

The set of Tables 9–6 through 9–9 contain the same information as Tables 9–2 through 9–5 except that they are for east- or west-facing surfaces rather than south-facing. It will be noted that east-facing vertical walls are irradiated from sunrise until solar noon, but that east-facing walls with a backward slope continue to receive direct sunshine during the early afternoon hours. Similarly, west-facing vertical walls are first irradiated at solar noon, whereas backward-sloped, west-facing walls start receiving radiation during the morning hours.

In comparing tabular data for a south-facing wall with those for an east-facing wall at the same latitude, it will be noticed that for some months there is one additional hour of morning sunshine on the east wall. This condition results from the fact that during some months, sunrise is north of east. Hence a wall facing south does not receive direct solar irradiation until the sun has been above the horizon sufficiently long to have moved south of east; in the same way a wall facing west will, during some months, receive more hours of afternoon sunshine than one facing south, since sunset will occur north of east during these months.

Aside from the direct-reading characteristics of Tables 9–2 through 9–9, they also provide indirect information sufficient to permit exact calculation

TABLE 9–9
East- or West-facing Wall, Roof, or Skylight: Latitude 45°

Solar Time	Normal Intensity	Horizontal		30-deg Backward Slope		60-deg Backward Slope		Vertical		Effective Altitude
East, West	I_0	i	I_H	i	$I_{30°}$	i	$I_{60°}$	i	I_V	H''
October										
8A.M., 4P.M...	215.0	77	48.4	32	182.9	52	133.5	32	183.2	15°
9A.M., 3P.M...	268.0	68	100.5	38	210.0	48	179.5	46	184.6	29
10A.M., 2P.M...	282.0	63	128.2	49	185.6	50	181.3	60	140.5	42
11A.M., 1P.M...	291.0	58	154.2	61	139.7	54	169.5	76	72.1	65
12 Noon	296.7	55	170.0	73	85.0	60	147.5	90		
1P.M., 11A.M..	291.0	58	154.2	87	14.7	70	97.0			
2P.M., 10A.M..	282.0	63	128.2			82	40.8			
November										
8A.M., 4P.M...	154.0	82	21.4	39	118.9	58	81.1	36	124.9	10
9A.M., 3P.M...	218.0	77	49.1	47	150.0	58	115.1	48	144.9	19
10A.M., 2P.M...	248.0	73	72.6	56	139.1	61	122.1	61	118.6	31
11A.M., 1P.M...	271.0	68	101.5	66	110.8	63	122.7	75	69.2	56
12 Noon	280.0	65	118.4	78	59.2	68	102.8	90		
1P.M., 11A.M..	271.0	68	101.5			79	53.4			
2P.M., 10A.M..	248.0	73	72.6			89	35.5			
December										
8A.M., 4P.M...	168.0	81	16.3	38	131.5	58	89.0	38	132.5	11
9A.M., 3P.M...	194.0	79	37.0	49	127.0	61	94.6	50	124.9	17
10A.M., 2P.M...	215.0	77	48.4	59	109.5	63	97.0	63	98.4	26
11A.M., 1P.M...	251.0	72	77.6	68	92.4	67	98.2	76	61.8	51
12 Noon	260.0	69	93.3	80	46.6	72	80.7	90		
1P.M., 11A.M..	251.0	72	77.6			82	36.3			
January										
8A.M., 4P.M...	154.0	82	21.4	39	118.9	58	81.1	36	124.9	10
9A.M., 3P.M...	218.0	77	49.1	47	150.0	58	115.1	48	144.9	19
10A.M., 2P.M...	248.0	73	72.6	56	139.1	61	122.1	61	118.6	31
11A.M., 1P.M...	271.0	68	101.5	66	110.8	63	122.7	75	69.2	56
12 Noon	280.0	65	118.4	78	59.2	68	102.8	90		
1P.M., 11A.M..	271.0	68	101.5			79	53.4			
2P.M., 10A.M..	248.0	73	72.6			89	35.5			
February										
8A.M., 4P.M...	215.0	77	48.4	32	182.9	52	133.5	32	183.2	15
9A.M., 3P.M...	268.0	68	100.5	38	210.0	48	179.5	46	184.6	29
10A.M., 2P.M...	282.0	63	128.2	49	185.6	50	181.3	60	140.5	42
11A.M., 1P.M...	291.0	58	154.2	61	139.7	54	169.5	76	72.1	65
12 Noon	296.7	55	170.0	73	85.0	60	147.5	90		
1P.M., 11A.M..	291.0	58	154.2	87	14.7	70	97.0			
2P.M., 10A.M..	282.0	63	128.2			82	40.8			

TABLE 9–9 (continued)

Solar Time	Normal Intensity	Horizontal		30-deg Backward Slope		60-deg Backward Slope		Vertical		Effective Altitude
East, West	I_0	i	I_H	i	$I_{30°}$	i	$I_{60°}$	i	I_V	H''
March										
6A.M., 6P.M...	56.0	85	4.9	25	50.7	55	32.1	5	55.8	5°
7A.M., 5P.M...	117.0	79	22.3	21	109.1	50	75.8	15	113.1	11
8A.M., 4P.M...	207.2	68	77.7	21	193.1	41	155.3	31	178.1	24
9A.M., 3P.M...	237.9	59	122.5	30	205.9	37	189.5	45	167.1	36
10A.M., 2P.M...	258.9	51	162.8	42	193.5	37	205.9	60	129.4	51
11A.M., 1P.M...	267.7	46	186.2	55	152.7	43	195.1	75	69.0	70
12 Noon	270.6	44	194.8	69	96.8	52	167.0	90		
1P.M., 11A.M..	267.7	46	186.2	83	33.2	62	126.1			
2P.M., 10A.M..	258.9	51	162.8			73	76.4			
3P.M., 9A.M...	237.9	59	122.5			85	22.4			
April										
6A.M., 6P.M...	98.0	81	15.3	22	90.6	55	96.3	13	95.6	9
7A.M., 5P.M...	196.3	70	67.2	10	193.0	45	139.0	20	184.3	20
8A.M., 4P.M...	235.1	60	117.5	11	230.4	31	201.0	32	198.4	31
9A.M., 3P.M...	260.4	50	167.5	23	239.1	25	248.0	46	179.3	43
10A.M., 2P.M...	274.6	41	207.3	38	218.0	24	251.2	61	131.8	58
11A.M., 1P.M...	280.8	35	230.0	51	176.2	33	234.0	77	70.6	73
12 Noon	283.5	32	240.5	65	120.2	43	208.0	90		
1P.M., 11A.M..	280.8	35	230.0	79	53.9	54	163.5			
2P.M., 10A.M..	274.6	41	207.3			66	113.5			
3P.M., 9A.M...	260.4	50	167.5			78	55.7			
4P.M., 8A.M...	235.1	60	117.5			89	2.7			

of irradiation rate for a surface having any orientation whatsoever. In order to conserve space, the basic solar angles (elevation and azimuth) have not been given explicitly in the tables. Each of these angles can, however, be obtained from the tabular data. Thus, at any given latitude, month, and hour, the solar altitude is obtained by subtracting the angle of incidence for a horizontal surface from 90 deg. Then, taking the tabular i value for a south-facing vertical wall (at same latitude, month, and hour), the angle B is obtained from Eq. 9–4 as

$$\cos B = \frac{\cos i}{\cos H}$$

giving

$$B = \cos^{-1} \frac{\cos i}{\cos H} \tag{9–21}$$

The azimuth is then obtained from Eq. 9–5 as

$$A = 180 - B \tag{9–22}$$

EXAMPLE 9–1. Determine the total, direct solar energy received on a vertical east-facing wall at latitude 30° during an average clear day in February.

Solution: Column 10 of Table 9–6 gives east-wall irradiation rates during February for each hour from 7 A.M. through 11 A.M. Adding these five values and dividing to obtain an average give

$$I_{V(\text{avg})} = \frac{143.9 + 212.7 + 199.7 + 147.2 + 80.1}{5}$$

$$= 156.7 \text{ Btu/(hr) sq ft}$$

Table 9–1 gives 5.7 as the maximum possible February hours of sunshine on an east-facing wall at latitude 30°. The daily energy reception is therefore

$$Q = (5.7)(156.7) = 893.3 \text{ Btu/sq ft}$$

EXAMPLE 9–2. Determine the solar energy received on the wall of Example 9–1 by sky radiation.

Solution: The values of H for the hours from 7 A.M. to solar noon are obtained from the angle of incidence on a horizontal surface, and the corresponding values of R are obtained from Fig. 9–2.

7 A.M. and 5 P.M.:	$H = 90 - 82 = 8°$;	$R = 4$
8 A.M. and 4 P.M.:	$H = 90 - 72 = 18°$;	$R = 8$
9 A.M. and 3 P.M.:	$H = 90 - 61 = 29°$;	$R = 12$
10 A.M. and 2 P.M.:	$H = 90 - 51 = 39°$;	$R = 15$
11 A.M. and 1 P.M.:	$H = 90 - 44 = 46°$;	$R = 16$
12 noon:	$H = 90 - 40 = 50°$;	$R = 17$

The average hourly intensity of sky radiation, noting that sky radiation is received for *all* sunshine hours of the day, is

$$I_s = \sum \frac{I_0}{R}$$

$$= 2\left(\frac{152.0}{4} + \frac{251.0}{8} + \frac{286.0}{12} + \frac{301.0}{15} + \frac{308.0}{16} + \frac{313.5}{17}\right)$$

$$= 283.5 \text{ Btu/(hr) sq ft}$$

The quantity of sky radiation received throughout the day (11.3 hr of sunshine from Table 9–1) is

$$Q = (11.3)(283.5) = 3203.6 \text{ Btu/sq ft}$$

9–3. Performance of Solar Windows.

Many factors may indicate, or justify, the use of large window areas in residences. In most cases, however, the ultimate decision will be made by the homeowner and will be evaluated, not in terms of possible technical advantages or technical disadvantages but rather by the dictates of his individual traits and personal preferences. Large windows are important physiologically because of their influence on internal lighting; hence they deserve consideration in terms of the science of illumination and as aids to the art of seeing. From the economic standpoint, large windows permit the collection of substantial amounts of solar energy that can be used in place of oil, or gas, or coal as a source of heat for maintaining required comfort conditions within the house; hence, with proper design, large windows serve to reduce heating costs during the winter months.

Basically, however, the average homeowner will make the decision to use extensive glass areas in terms of such psychological factors as the desire to avoid the feeling of being "shut-in" by opaque walls and with the positive objective of bringing the effect of outdoor space and beauty within the indoor environment. Whether a "picture window" frames a distant vista of particular delight or serves to integrate the living space with the adjacent garden, in either case it justifies itself in terms of aesthetic advantage. Thus the substantial reduction in heating costs that is normally associated with the use of solar windows can best be regarded as a "dividend" returned on the homeowner's investment in greater comfort and in more beautiful surroundings. A well-designed "picture window" is a luxury, but it is a unique luxury in that it often returns an interest on the original investment, in fuel dollars saved, that makes it more than self-supporting.

Technically, effective performance of a solar window requires careful and exact engineering design. The intent of this section is to provide simple and direct design procedures that will enable the engineer to evaluate rapidly the possible thermal advantage associated with large windows.

The concept of a window facing south as a receiver of solar energy useful for home heating is as old as man's search for shelter. Even in the days of cave and cliff dwellers (as an examination of such sights will disclose), man favored openings on the south side of his habitation to enable solar energy to come in during the winter months. Although glazing was not then known, solar radiation was admitted through uncovered openings and "trapped" within the occupied space by interreflection and absorption in the walls and floor. Rather surprisingly, the thermal capacity of some caves was such that substantial heating effect could be obtained, over the entire 24 hr, from solar energy captured and stored during the intervals in which the sun shone.

With the advent of glass, and more particularly with the recent commercial development of a double-pane, sealed, thermally resistant window, the possibility of effectively utilizing solar energy for home heating has tremendously increased. The large number of solar houses now in use precludes any need of explaining the effectiveness of south-wall solar heating, but less well understood is the fact that in many localities a double-glazed window in *any* wall facing from east through south to west will also serve to reduce the seasonal heating cost for the structure. There are, of course, special advantages in locating such windows in the optimum position (that is, facing south), but when this is impossible, some partial economic advantage may still remain irrespective of the required direction, provided only that it is south rather than north of east or west. Even in some localities, windows facing north of east or west will pay for themselves in decreased operating cost of the heating system, but these cases are relatively unusual, and in general any window designed for thermal gain should be oriented away from the north.

INFLUENCE OF THERMAL CAPACITY. Complete utilization of solar energy requires that it reduce, unit-for-unit, the energy output of the supplementary heating system. During periods of cold weather no difficulty is experienced in attaining this condition, since the demand for heat will in general be in excess of the solar supply, and such solar gain as is experienced will therefore be used immediately in making up losses from the structure. For winter conditions the only factor tending to reduce unit-for-unit utilization of the solar gain is the possibility of excess heat loss through those floor areas that are exposed to direct sunshine. Irradiated floor sections rise in temperature and hence, for fixed inside air temperature, conduct more heat out of the room than would otherwise be necessary. Fortunately, however, this condition is usually not serious, since for rooms of the second floor, or those over unventilated basements, or those directly on the ground, a large fraction of the excess energy conducted through the floor will either be utilized in making up losses of other heated spaces or (as in the case of a floor slab placed directly on the ground) will go into storage for later return and regenerative use within the house. The one case involving direct and complete loss of energy is that represented by a floor directly over an open, cross-ventilated "creep" space.

During the spring and fall, or during warm periods in midwinter, complete utilization of solar energy is somewhat more difficult to attain, although a high utilization factor can normally be realized in any house having a moderate thermal capacity. Concrete floor slabs, for example, serve as effective reservoirs for receiving solar energy (when directly irradiated) and partially storing it for release at some subsequent time. By judicious arrangement of thermally heavy parts of the structure, it is usually possible to reduce the instantaneous delivery of solar heat to the air of the occupied space and to conserve it for use during the later hours when direct solar energy is not available. In effect, such regenerative storage distributes the solar energy received during a relatively small number of hours over a much longer period of time, thereby reducing the periodicity of load on the supplementary heating system and assuring more complete utilization of the solar heat that enters the house during afternoon hours or at other times when the heating load may not be great.

Architecturally the distribution of thermally heavy parts of the structure requires careful design, since under some circumstances the need is for avoidance of storage and assurance of immediate release of the solar input. Rooms served by east windows, for example, receive solar energy during the morning hours when, more than any other time of day, the heating load is large. For such rooms heavy floor slabs should be avoided, since the objective is not to store the solar heating effect but to utilize it immediately in raising or in maintaining the room air temperature. The contrary effect occurs with respect to west windows, since they receive heat during the warmest part of the day. In this case the design objective is to keep as much as possible of the solar gain from appearing as an air heating effect, and rather to store the solar energy (as in a concrete floor slab) for later release. The storage characteristics of any structure should be carefully integrated with the method of automatic control that is used for the supplementary heating system.

Solar mechanics assist in providing one interesting solution of the seasonal storage problem which can be used to occasional advantage: The solar altitude in spring and fall exceeds that of midwinter; hence the irradiated section of the floor will be farther back in the room during the winter months than during the other seasons. This fact can be utilized by increasing the thermal density of the floor in the front part of the room, thereby building into the structure a storage characteristic such that solar energy will be rapidly utilized during cold weather but partially stored for regenerative use during the spring and fall.

STEADY-STATE SOLAR EQUATION.[5] The possible thermal advantage of a so-called solar window depends at any given time on the net reduction (over that for a corresponding area of opaque wall) in the net rate of heat flow from the heating system to the inside surface of the window. Assuming that all the solar energy transmitted through the window eventually appears as an internal energy increase of the inside air, it is then evident that for steady-state conditions, the equivalent transmission loss through the window will be equal to the algebraic sum of the solar transmission gain and the net energy supplied from the heating plant. In equation form,

$$q_i = q_t + q_h \qquad (9\text{--}23)$$

where q_i = steady-state transmission of heat (by convection and radiation) from the interior of the room to the inside surface of the window, Btu/(hr)(sq ft of irradiated glass).

q_t = steady-state transmission of solar energy into the room through the window, Btu/(hr)(sq ft of irradiated glass).

q_h = steady-state make-up of energy from the heating plant to the window at that rate required to maintain the inside thermal level at its predetermined value.

The major assumption underlying Eq. 9–23 is that solar transmission gains serve to reduce, unit-for-unit, the actual transmission losses from the room. In order for this to be true, all solar energy transmitted through the window would have to be absorbed within the room and subsequently released by convection to room air or reradiated as longer wave thermal radiation from the absorbing surfaces. The first condition implies no direct loss through the window of solar energy reflected from an interior surface of the room. This requirement obviously does not exactly hold, since if it did, an observer outside a structure would not be able to see through the windows unless there were artificial inside illumination. The second condition implies zero exposure

[5] The derivation and discussion, but not the tables, in this article are based on F. W. Hutchinson and W. P. Chapman, "A Rational Basis for Solar Heating Analysis," *ASHVE Trans.*, Vol. 52, pp. 305–325, 1946.

(or perfect insulation) of the interim surface at which the solar radiation is absorbed; since by far the greater fraction of solar energy is received at the floor, it follows that the floor is considered as though it were a non-transmitting surface. Note that for this case the thermal capacity of the floor is not an influencing factor because steady state has been assumed; hence there cannot be energy flow to or from storage. (This condition is in contrast to the transient influence of thermal capacity as discussed earlier in this article.)

Solution of Eq. 9–23 for q_h requires prior evaluation of the other two terms. Heat transfer by the combined mechanisms of convection and radiation from the room interior to the window surface is given by

$$q_i = \frac{t_i - t_{gi}}{r_i} \tag{9–24}$$

where r_i = combined thermal resistance of inside film.
t_i = inside air temperature, °F.
t_{gi} = inside surface temperature of irradiated window, °F.

Eq. 9–24 contains t_{gi} as an unknown, since this surface temperature depends not only on conductive transfer through the window but also on the rate at which solar radiation is being absorbed by the glass.

As a typical type of solar window, for demonstration of the method of analysis, consider that the window consists of two identical thicknesses of glass separated by an air space (refer to Fig. 9–4). The instantaneous rate of solar energy absorption at the outer sheet is defined as q_{a1}, and that at the inner sheet is q_{a2}, Btu/(hr)(sq ft of irradiated glass). The over-all coefficient of heat transfer of the window is

$$U_e = \frac{1}{r_o + r_g + r_a + r_g + r_i} \tag{9–25}$$

where r_o = combined thermal resistance of outside film.
r_g = thermal resistance of each of the two identical panes of glass.
r_a = thermal resistance of the air space.
r_i = combined thermal resistance of the inside film.

Absorption of solar radiation by the inner window occurs at rate q_{a2} and can be considered as equivalent to a plane heat source of strength q_{a2} located at the midplane of the inner glass. The temperature gradient from inside surface to the midplane would therefore be a straight line (neglecting the very small variation of thermal conductivity with temperature), based on steady-state transmission at rate q_i. The temperature gradient from the midplane to the outer surface of the inner glass would then necessarily be a steeper straight line corresponding to transmission at a rate of $q_i + q_{a2}$ Btu/(hr)(sq ft of irradiated glass).

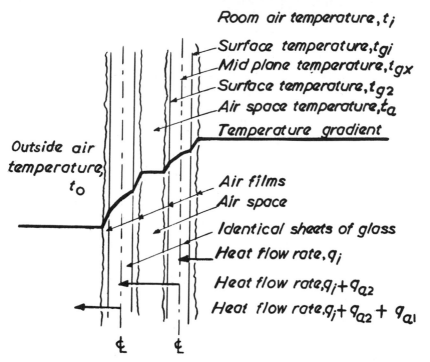

Room air temperature, t_i

Surface temperature, t_{gi}

Mid plane temperature, t_{gx}

Surface temperature, t_{g2}

Air space temperature, t_a

Temperature gradient

Outside air temperature, t_o

Air films

Air space

Identical sheets of glass

Heat flow rate, q_i

Heat flow rate, $q_i + q_{a2}$

Heat flow rate, $q_i + q_{a2} + q_{a1}$

Fig. 9–4. Heat balance on a double-glass window for winter conditions when window is receiving solar radiation.

The rate of conduction through the inner half of the inner glass is

$$q_i = \frac{t_{gi} - t_{gx}}{r_g/2}$$

$$= \frac{2(t_{gi} - t_{gx})}{r_g} \qquad (9\text{–}26)$$

where t_{gx} is the midplane temperature of the inner sheet of glass (°F).

The rate of conduction through the outer half of the inner glass is

$$q_i + q_{a2} = \frac{t_{gx} - t_{g2}}{r_g/2}$$

$$= \frac{2(t_{gx} - t_{g2})}{r_g} \qquad (9\text{–}27)$$

where t_{g2} is the outside surface temperature of the inner glass (°F).

Eqs. 9–26 and 9–27 contain t_{gi}, t_{gx}, and t_{g2} as unknowns. By adding the equations to eliminate t_{gx},

$$2q_i + q_{a2} = \frac{2(t_{gi} - t_{g2})}{r_g} \qquad (9\text{–}28)$$

The rate of heat loss from the outside surface of the inner glass to the air space is

$$q_i + q_{a2} = \frac{t_{g2} - t_a}{r_a/2}$$

$$= \frac{2(t_{g2} - t_a)}{r_a} \tag{9-29}$$

where t_a is the air space temperature (°F).

Eqs. 9–24, 9–28, and 9–29 can now be solved simultaneously to eliminate the unknown surface temperatures t_{gi} and t_{g2}. Solving Eqs. 9–28 and 9–24 for t_{gi} and equating give

$$\left(2q_i + q_{a2} + \frac{2t_{g2}}{r_g}\right)\frac{r_g}{2} = \left(\frac{t_i}{r_i} - q_i\right)r_i$$

from which

$$t_{g2} = t_i - q_i(r_i + r_g) - \frac{r_g}{2}q_{a2} \tag{9-30}$$

Solving Eq. 9–29 for t_{g2} and equating to the right side of Eq. 9–30 give

$$t_{g2} = (q_i + q_{a2})\frac{r_a}{2} + t_a$$

$$= t_i - q_i(r_i + r_g) - \frac{r_g}{2}q_{a2}$$

giving

$$q_i = \frac{(t_i - t_a) - [(r_g/2) + (r_a/2)]q_{a2}}{r_i + r_g + (r_a/2)} \tag{9-31}$$

But the reciprocal of the denominator of Eq. 9–31 is equal to the conductance from room air to window air space; therefore

$$C_{g2} = \frac{1}{r_i + r_g + (r_a/2)}$$

and on substitution in Eq. 9–31,

$$q_i = C_{g2}(t_i - t_a) - C_{g2}\left(\frac{r_g}{2} + \frac{r_a}{2}\right)q_{a2} \tag{9-32}$$

The first term on the right side of Eq. 9–32 is equal to the steady-state transmission loss for the window under conditions when there is no absorption of solar radiation; the second term on the right accounts for the effect of the equivalent source of strength q_{a2}.

Eq. 9–32 cannot be used for direct solution of q_i because it contains the window air-space temperature t_a as an unknown. This term can be eliminated by writing an equation (analogous in form to Eq. 9–32) for rate of heat transfer through the outer of the two sheets of glass:

$$q_i + q_{a2} = C_{g1}(t_a - t_o) - C_{g1}\left(\frac{r_g}{2} + r_o\right)q_{a1} \tag{9-33}$$

where

$$C_{g1} = \frac{1}{(r_a/2) + r_g + r_o}$$

Solving both Eqs. 9–32 and 9–33 for t_a and equating give

$$\frac{C_{g2}t_i - C_{g2}[(r_g/2) + (r_a/2)]q_{a2} - q_i}{C_{g2}}$$

$$= \frac{C_{g1}t_o + C_{g1}[(r_g/2) + r_o]q_{a1} + q_i + q_{a2}}{C_{g1}}$$

from which

$$q_i = \left[t_i - \left(\frac{r_g}{2} + \frac{r_a}{2} \right) q_{a2} - \frac{q_{a2}}{C_{g1}} \right.$$

$$\left. - \left(\frac{r_g}{2} + r_o \right) q_{a1} - t_o \right] \frac{1}{(1/C_{g1}) + (1/C_{g2})} \qquad (9\text{–}34)$$

But

$$\frac{1}{(1/C_{g1}) + (1/C_{g2})} = U_e$$

and on substitution into Eq. 9–34 and simplification,

$$q_i = U_e(t_i - t_o) - U_e \left[\left(\frac{r_g}{2} + \frac{r_a}{2} + \frac{1}{C_{g1}} \right) q_{a2} + \left(\frac{r_g}{2} + r_o \right) q_{a1} \right] \qquad (9\text{–}35)$$

The first bracketed term on the right side of Eq. 9–35 can be simplified by eliminating C_{g1}:

$$\frac{r_g}{2} + \frac{r_a}{2} + \frac{1}{C_{g1}} = \frac{r_g}{2} + \frac{r_a}{2} + \frac{r_a}{2} + r_g + r_o$$

$$= r_o + 1.5r_g + r_a$$

giving

$$q_i = U_e(t_i - t_o) - U_e[(r_o + 1.5r_g + r_a)q_{a2} + (0.5r_g + r_o)q_{a1}] \qquad (9\text{–}36)$$

Then, substituting into Eq. 9–23 for q_i from Eq. 9–36 and solving for q_h,

$$q_h = U_e(t_i - t_o) - \{U_e[(r_o + 1.5r_g + r_a)q_{a2} + (0.5r_g + r_o)q_{a1}] + q_t\} \qquad (9\text{–}37)$$

The first term of Eq. 9–37 is equal to the rate of steady-state heat transmission that would occur if no solar effect were experienced; the second term of the equation must therefore be an evaluation of the entire solar effect; thus

$$q_h = U_e(t_i - t_o) - V_h \qquad (9\text{–}38)$$

where $V_h = U_e[(r_o + 1.5r_g + r_a)q_{a2} + (0.5r_g + r_o)q_{a1}] + q_t \qquad (9\text{–}39)$

= instantaneous steady-state solar effect expressed in Btu/(hr)(sq ft of irradiated glass).

The explicit form of the expression for V_h that is given in Eq. 9–39 has been derived for two identical panes of glass; for any other type of window, such as one with three identical panes or one with two or more panes which differ from one another, a similar equation can be readily derived.

In order to evaluate the saving (or loss) of energy due to use of 1 sq ft of irradiated window in place of an equal area of opaque wall (neglecting winter heating effect due to absorption of solar energy by the opaque wall), subtract the excess transmission loss through the window from the ∇_h term, which represents gross solar advantage. Thus

$$\Delta q = \nabla_h - (U_e - U_w)(t_i - t_o) \qquad (9\text{--}40)$$

where Δq = steady-state thermal advantage, Btu/(hr)(sq ft).

$\qquad\quad U_w$ = over-all coefficient of heat transfer of the opaque wall which is replaced by the solar window, Btu/(hr)(sq ft)(°F).

Since the solar term ∇_h is independent of the outside air temperature t_o, it follows that the magnitude of the solar heat gain is the same (other conditions being unchanged), irrespective of the value of the outside air temperature. Note, therefore, that if a window is used for which the over-all coefficient is identical with that of the replaced wall area, the instantaneous rate of steady-state saving in heat load (for the same solar conditions) would be the same in very warm weather as in very cold weather.

EVALUATION OF THE SOLAR TERM. The solar term, defined in Eq. 9–39, relates two characteristics of the system: (1) the solar transmission and absorption rates q_t, q_{a1}, q_{a2}; (2) the non-solar heat-transmission characteristics of the system as given by the terms

$$K_1 = U_e(0.5r_g + r_o) \qquad (9\text{--}41)$$

$$K_2 = U_e(r_o + 1.5r_g + r_a) \qquad (9\text{--}42)$$

or

$$\nabla_h = K_2 q_{a2} + K_1 q_{a1} + q_t \qquad (9\text{--}43)$$

For a given type of window, K_1 and K_2 have fixed values; so, ∇_h is then a function only of the three solar energy rates. Each of these rates depends on the physical characteristics of the glass, the angle of incidence, and the solar irradiation.

Glass Characteristics. When a sheet of glass is irradiated, some of the energy is reflected, some absorbed, and some transmitted. The characteristics of the glass that determine the distribution between these three forms of energy disposal are the thickness and the absorption coefficient, their product KL being the determining factor. Using equations available in the literature, the absorptivity, reflectivity, and transmissivity of a single pane can be readily determined as a function of KL and of the angle of incidence. Likewise, the transmissivity can be determined for windows made up of two identical sheets of glass, and the absorptivity determined for both the inner sheet and the outer sheet of these windows. Equations used for the double-glass window characteristics are modified forms of the equations derived in the reference,[6]

$$T_{1,2} = \frac{T_1^2}{1 - R_1^2} \tag{9–44}$$

$$A_{1 \text{ of } 2} = (1 - R_1^2 + R_1 T_1)\left(\frac{A_1}{1 - R_1^2}\right) \tag{9–45}$$

$$A_{2 \text{ of } 2} = \frac{T_1 A_1}{1 - R_1^2} \tag{9–46}$$

where $T_{1,2}$ = transmissivity for *direct* solar radiation at a given time and day of a double-glass window consisting of identical sheets of glass.

$A_{1 \text{ of } 2}$ = absorptivity for direct solar radiation of the outside sheet of two identical sheets of glass.

$A_{2 \text{ of } 2}$ = absorptivity for direct solar radiation of the inside sheet of two identical sheets of glass.

A_1, T_1, R_1 = absorptivity, transmissivity, and reflectivity for direct solar radiation of a single sheet of glass; each of these properties varies with the KL value for the glass and with the angle of incidence of the solar radiation.

The influence of non-direct radiation on the characteristics of the glass requires special consideration. Based on a graphical integration for sky radiation, it has been shown that the integrated values of A_s and T_s can be considered equivalent to the specular values based on an incidence angle of 60 deg. Then, for double-glass windows, the absorptivity with respect to sky radiation is

$$A_{s(1 \text{ of } 2)} = A_{1 \text{ of } 2} \qquad \text{(for 60 deg)} \tag{9–47}$$

and

$$A_{s(2 \text{ of } 2)} = A_{2 \text{ of } 2} \qquad \text{(for 60 deg)} \tag{9–48}$$

while the transmissivity of the combined two sheets of glass is

$$T_{s1,2} = T_{1,2} \qquad \text{(for 60 deg)} \tag{9–49}$$

The rate of direct solar energy absorption at the outer sheet is

$$q_{a1 \text{ direct}} = I_o \cos i A_{1 \text{ of } 2} = I_V A_{1 \text{ of } 2} \tag{9–50}$$

and the rate of absorption of sky radiation at the outer sheet is

$$q_{a1_{\text{sky}}} = I_s A_{s(1 \text{ of } 2)} = \frac{I_o}{R} A_{s(1 \text{ of } 2)}$$

$$= \frac{I_V}{R \cos i} A_{s(1 \text{ of } 2)} \tag{9–51}$$

[6] George V. Parmelee, "The Transmission of Solar Radiation Through Flat Glass Under Summer Conditions," ASHVE Journal Section, *Heating, Piping and Air Conditioning*, October–November, 1945.

Total absorption rate at the outer sheet is therefore given by the sum of Eqs. 9–50 and 9–51,

$$q_{a1} = I_V \left(\frac{A_{1 \text{ of } 2} + A_{s(1 \text{ of } 2)}}{R \cos i} \right) \tag{9–52}$$

The total absorption rate at the inner of the two sheets of glass, by analogy with Eq. 9–52, is

$$q_{a2} = I_V \left(\frac{A_{2 \text{ of } 2} + A_{s(2 \text{ of } 2)}}{R \cos i} \right) \tag{9–53}$$

Total transmission through the double window is

$$q_t = I_V \frac{T_{1,2} + T_{s1,2}}{R \cos i} \tag{9–54}$$

Substituting from Eqs. 9–53, 9–54, and 9–55 into Eq. 9–43 gives

$$\nabla_h = I_V \left[K_2 \left(A_{2 \text{ of } 2} + \frac{A_{s(2 \text{ of } 2)}}{R \cos i} \right) \right.$$
$$\left. + K_1 \left(A_{1 \text{ of } 2} + \frac{A_{s(1 \text{ of } 2)}}{R \cos i} \right) + T_{1,2} + \frac{T_{s1,2}}{R \cos i} \right] \tag{9–55}$$

Eq. 9–55 is difficult to work with. Calculation of numerical values of ∇_h over a wide range of i shows that *for the heating season*, neglect of the absorption fraction of sky radiation (but retaining the T_s term) will introduce an error in ∇_h of approximately $\frac{1}{2}$ of 1 per cent. This value is too small to be of practical significance; hence Eq. 9–55 can, with accuracy, be simplified to the form

$$\nabla_h = I_V \left(K_1 A_{1 \text{ of } 2} + K_2 A_{2 \text{ of } 2} + T_{1,2} + \frac{T_{s1,2}}{R \cos i} \right) \tag{9–56}$$

$$= (I_o \cos i)\phi = I_V \phi \tag{9–57}$$

where

$$\phi = K_1 A_{1 \text{ of } 2} + K_2 A_{2 \text{ of } 2} + T_{1,2} + \frac{T_{s1,2}}{R \cos i} \tag{9–58}$$

Seasonal Integration. Eq. 9–40 provides the instantaneous rate of thermal saving of an irradiated window corresponding to any given set of steady-state conditions. Practical application of this equation requires that it be adapted for determination of the actual quantitative saving expressed in Btu per heating season. Thus

$$\Delta Q_{\max} = \sum [\nabla_h \, \Delta\theta - (U_e - U_w)(t_i - t_o) \, \Delta\theta]$$
$$= \sum \nabla_h \, \Delta\theta - (U_e - U_w) \sum (t_i - t_o) \, \Delta\theta \tag{9–59}$$

where $\Delta\theta$ is a small selected time increment (such as 1 hr) during which ∇_h is considered to remain constant.

The summation of Eq. 9–59 must be carried out over the entire heating season; the resultant value of $\Delta Q_{\max}$ will then be the seasonal saving on a window that is unshaded and in a locality where the sun is never obscured.

If $\Delta \theta$ is taken as 1 hr and if the heating season is considered to extend from October 1 to May 1, the number of $\Delta \theta$ intervals would be 5088, and Eq. 9–59 would become

$$\Delta Q_{\max} = \sum_{n=1}^{n=5088} \nabla_h - (U_e - U_w) \sum_{n=1}^{n=5088} (t_i - t_{o_n}) \qquad (9\text{--}60)$$

The term t_n can now be defined by the equation

$$t_i - t_n = \sum_{n=1}^{n=5088} \frac{t_i - t_{o_n}}{5088} \qquad (9\text{--}61)$$

giving

$$t_n = \sum_{n=1}^{n=5088} \frac{t_{o_n}}{5088} \qquad (9\text{--}62)$$

Thus t_n is the *average* outside air temperature during the heating season, and its approximate value for any locality can be obtained from Table 9–15. Eq. 9–60 therefore simplifies to the form

$$\Delta Q_{\max} = \sum_{n=1}^{n=5088} \nabla_h - 5088(U_e - U_w)(t_i - t_n) \qquad (9\text{--}63)$$

In its present form Eq. 9–63 expresses the seasonal saving, in Btu, that would be attributable to 1 sq ft of unshaded glass if the sun were to shine for 100 per cent of the possible sunshine hours of the heating season. During the selected seven-month heating period, the maximum possible hours of sunshine (determined from data on the time of sunrise and sunset) are 2278 hr for latitude 40° and 2360 hr for latitude 35°. For many localities the weather bureau can provide information on the average number of actual hours of sunshine to be expected during a particular month, and from this one can readily calculate for any locality the fraction of maximum possible time that the sun will be expected to shine. Table 9–15 (column 2) gives fractions for a large number of American cities. Values in the table were computed by dividing the average number of sunshine hours during a seven-month heating season by the maximum possible hours, as stated above. The sunshine fraction is customarily referred to as the *usage ratio* and is identified by the symbol F. With this substitution, Eq. 9–63 can now be written in a form that will give the *actual* seasonal saving in any locality:

$$\Delta Q = F \sum_{n=1}^{n=5088} \nabla_h - 5088(U_e - U_w)(t_i - t_n) \qquad (9\text{--}64)$$

If complete data were available on the distribution of actual sunshine hours through the day (for a given locality), Eq. 9–64 could be given added accuracy by placing F under the summation sign and letting it represent the statistical fraction for a given hour rather than for the entire heating season. As the equation is now written, the fraction of sunshine is necessarily treated as though it were the same for each hour of the day. Although such a uniform distribution does not actually occur, it is probable that for most localities, the error introduced from this cause is not great.

All required terms for evaluating solar heating effect can now be evaluated, and Eq. 9–64 can therefore be solved by calculating the 5088 values of ∇_h which are needed to permit a seasonal summation. Formidable as this task may seem, it is not unduly difficult, since more than half of the ∇_h terms will necessarily be equal to zero. The number of terms requiring evaluation is therefore reduced to something under 2500, the exact number varying with latitude and being numerically equal to the maximum possible hours of sunshine during the seven-month heating season (refer to Table 9–1).

A further reduction can be attained by selecting one date as representative of average conditions during an entire month and by noting further that the average solar days of October and February are identical, as are the average solar days of November and January (refer to Art. 9–2, page 365). Thus a solar analysis of five days of the heating season, each day having approximately ten possible hours of sunshine, will give data sufficient for a solution. Even so, the task of calculating 50 values of ∇_h for each type of window at each latitude is no small one.

EXAMPLE 9–3. Calculate the maximum rate of hourly solar gain through unit area of a south-facing window at latitude 35° and for 11 A.M. in January. The window consists of two $\frac{1}{4}$ in. panes separated by a $\frac{1}{4}$ in. air space and has the following thermal characteristics:

$$r_0 = 0.1970; \quad r_g = 0.0625; \quad r_a = 0.7107; \quad r_i = 0.5768;$$

$$R = 0.1970 + 0.0625 + 0.7107 + 0.0625 + 0.5768 = 1.6095;$$

$$U_e = 0.6213$$

The KL value is 0.145, and the index of refraction of the glass, μ, is 1.5626.

Solution: From Table 9 -3, for latitude 35°, the angle of incidence on a south-facing vertical surface at 11 A.M. in January is 36 deg. By the method given in the reference in Art. 9–3, page 387 (for known μ and known i), the values of T_1, R_1, and A_1 can be computed. The corresponding values of $T_{1,2}$, $A_{1 \text{ of } 2}$, and $A_{2 \text{ of } 2}$ are then calculated from Eqs. 9–44, 9–45, and 9–46:

$$T_{1,2} = 0.60845; \quad A_{1 \text{ of } 2} = 0.15312; \quad A_{2 \text{ of } 2} = 0.11291$$

A similar set of calculations for angle of incidence of 60 deg gives the equivalent sky-radiation terms as

$$T_{s1,2} = 0.49148; \quad A_{s(1 \text{ of } 2)} = 0.17549; \quad A_{s(2 \text{ of } 2)} = 0.11260$$

From Fig. 9–2 for H of 32 deg, R is 13; so, $R \cos i$ is equal to (13)(0.8109), or 10.540.

Evaluation of ϕ requires prior evaluation of the thermal coefficients K_1 and K_2. By Eq. 9-41,

$$K_1 = U_e(0.5r_g + r_o)$$
$$= 0.6213\,[(0.5)(0.0625) + 0.1970]$$
$$= 0.1418$$

By Eq. 9-42

$$K_2 = U_e(r_o + 1.5r_g + r_a)$$
$$= 0.6213\,[0.1970 + (1.5)(0.0625) + 0.7107]$$
$$= 0.6228$$

Then, solving for ϕ by means of Eq. 9-58,

$$\phi = K_1 A_{1\ of\ 2} + K_2 A_{2\ of\ 2} + T_{1,2} + \frac{T_{s1,2}}{R \cos i}$$

$$= \frac{[(0.1418)(0.15312)] + [(0.6228)(0.11291)] + 0.60845 + 0.49148}{10.540}$$

$$= 0.7471$$

If the absorption terms are included (refer to Eq. 9-55), the value of ϕ increases by

$$\Delta\phi = \frac{K_1 A_{s(1\ of\ 2)} + K_2 A_{s(2\ of\ 2)}}{R \cos i}$$

$$= \frac{[(0.1418)(0.17549)] + [(0.6228)(0.11260)]}{10.540}$$

$$= 0.0090$$

and the exact value of the solar term (as it appears in Eq. 9-55) is

$$\nabla_h = I_V(0.7471 + 0.0090)$$

$$= 0.7561 I_V$$

From column 10 of Table 9-3 the intensity on a south-facing wall, latitude 35°, at 11 A.M. in January is 239.2 Btu/(hr) sq ft of irradiated surface); thus

$$\nabla_h = (0.7561)(239.2) = 180.86 \text{ Btu}$$

(*Note:* The example shows the procedure for numerical evaluation of ∇_h; the answer could have been obtained directly from column 4 of Table 9-12.)

TABULAR PERFORMANCE DATA FOR SOLAR WINDOWS. By the method of Example 9-3, hourly solar gain can be determined for any type of window at any time and latitude and for any orientation. To assist the designer in estimating seasonal effects, computations have been made hourly, monthly, and seasonally for four types of commonly used double-glazed windows: (1) two $\frac{1}{8}$-in. panes of plate glass (KL of 0.072) separated by $\frac{1}{4}$ in.; (2) two $\frac{1}{8}$-in. panes separated by $\frac{1}{2}$ in.; (3) two $\frac{1}{4}$-in. panes of plate glass (KL of 0.145) separated by $\frac{1}{4}$ in.; (4) two $\frac{1}{4}$-in. panes separated by $\frac{1}{2}$ in.

Table 9–10 summarizes values of the maximum possible solar energy gain (∇_s expressed in Btu per season) on a seasonal basis for an unshaded window of $\frac{1}{8}$-in. or $\frac{1}{4}$-in. double-glass (the two panes being identical) with $\frac{1}{4}$-in. or $\frac{1}{2}$-in. spacing. The table covers a range of latitudes from 30° through 45° and is for orientations from east-facing through south-facing to west-facing.

TABLE 9–10

Seasonal Values of the Solar Term, ∇_s, for Double-glazed Windows

Distance Between Panes	$\frac{1}{8}$-in. Glass		$\frac{1}{4}$-in. Glass	
	$\frac{1}{4}$ in.	$\frac{1}{2}$ in.	$\frac{1}{4}$ in.	$\frac{1}{2}$ in.
South-facing:				
30° latitude . . .	275,076	275,351	239,801	240,062
35° latitude . . .	296,424	296,714	260,116	260,383
40° latitude . . .	302,129	302,434	265,827	266,082
45° latitude . . .	307,824	308,126	271,482	271,751
Southeast-facing or southwest-facing:				
30° latitude . . .	219,775	219,982	193,807	193,960
35° latitude . . .	260,532	260,781	233,726	233,969
40° latitude . . .	225,675	225,879	199,444	199,623
45° latitude . . .	238,210	238,442	210,117	210,304
East-facing or west-facing:				
30° latitude . . .	150,727	150,872	133,063	133,149
35° latitude . . .	161,719	161,878	149,166	149,294
40° latitude . . .	139,952	140,085	122,821	122,902
45° latitude . . .	134,170	134,296	118,301	118,377

Table 9–11 is for a south-facing window located at latitude 30°. Values of the hourly solar gain, ∇_h in Btu/(hr)(sq ft of irradiated glass), are given for each daylight hour of each month of the heating season and for each of the four indicated types of double-glazed windows. The last column gives a shading factor E (refer to Art. 9–4, page 405, for derivation and discussion) which is equal to the fraction of the window area that is irradiated at a particular time if the window is designed with roof overhang (see Art. 9–4, page 404) such that the window is fully irradiated at solar noon on December 21 only and fully shaded at solar noon on June 21 only. Thus, for a window with this type of overhang, the product of E and ∇_h would give the Btu/(hr)(sq ft) of solar gain based on total window area. For types of overhang designed on a basis other than December 21–June 21, the shading factor at any hour can be computed by the method of Art. 9–4, page 406, using values of the effective altitude H'', obtained from the last column of Tables 9–2 through 9–9.

Tables 9–12 through 9–14 are of the same form as Table 9–11 but are, respectively, for latitudes 35°, 40°, and 45°.

TABLE 9–11
Values of the Solar Term, ∇_h, for Double-glazed Vertical South-facing Windows: Latitude 30°

Distance Between Panes	$\frac{1}{8}$-in. Glass		$\frac{1}{4}$-in. Glass		Shading Factor
	$\frac{1}{4}$ in.	$\frac{1}{2}$ in.	$\frac{1}{4}$ in.	$\frac{1}{2}$ in.	E
October					
8A.M., 4P.M........	85.861	85.958	74.301	74.295	1.00
9A.M., 3P.M........	116.236	116.368	101.618	101.713	0.98
10A.M., 2P.M........	143.648	143.790	125.913	126.082	0.96
11A.M., 1P.M........	159.813	159.971	140.499	140.708	0.95
12 Noon	163.940	164.121	144.293	144.511	0.95
November					
8A.M., 4P.M........	101.574	101.688	88.432	88.449	1.00
9A.M., 3P.M........	141.204	141.338	123.861	124.251	1.00
10A.M., 2P.M........	172.303	172.487	152.176	152.393	1.00
11A.M., 1P.M........	186.366	186.522	165.197	165.456	0.99
12 Noon	192.343	192.528	171.225	171.493	0.99
December					
8A.M., 4P.M........	103.325	103.433	89.801	89.802	1.00
9A.M., 3P.M........	153.492	153.634	135.594	135.745	1.00
10A.M., 2P.M........	179.162	179.352	158.973	159.202	1.00
11A.M., 1P.M........	196.464	196.650	173.792	174.043	1.00
12 Noon	200.617	200.761	179.187	179.469	1.00
January					
8A.M., 4P.M........	103.980	104.096	90.527	90.544	1.00
9A.M., 3P.M........	144.482	144.619	126.737	127.136	1.00
10A.M., 2P.M........	176.337	176.526	155.739	155.961	1.00
11A.M., 1P.M........	190.790	190.950	169.118	169.383	0.99
12 Noon	196.764	196.953	175.160	175.434	0.99
February					
8A.M., 4P.M........	87.873	87.972	76.041	76.036	1.00
9A.M., 3P.M........	119.087	119.222	104.110	104.208	0.98
10A.M., 2P.M........	147.110	147.256	128.948	129.121	0.96
11A.M., 1P.M........	163.636	163.797	143.860	144.073	0.95
12 Noon	167.847	168.032	147.732	147.955	0.95
March					
7A.M., 5P.M........	29.418	29.445	25.252	25.101	0.91
8A.M., 4P.M........	39.338	39.370	34.512	34.420	0.87
9A.M., 3P.M........	68.935	69.008	59.093	59.083	0.88
10A.M., 2P.M........	92.984	93.076	79.757	79.810	0.87
11A.M., 1P.M........	114.684	114.806	99.426	99.536	0.88
12 Noon	118.350	118.460	102.821	102.938	0.87
April					
8A.M., 4P.M........	18.250	18.260	15.311	15.209	0.33
9A.M., 3P.M........	28.307	28.330	24.879	24.791	0.62
10A.M., 2P.M........	44.399	44.431	38.873	38.821	0.69
11A.M., 1P.M........	60.346	60.396	50.493	50.471	0.72
12 Noon	64.159	64.221	54.309	54.298	0.72

TABLE 9-12
Values of the Solar Term, ∇_h, for Double-glazed Vertical South-facing Windows: Latitude 35°

Distance Between Panes	$\frac{1}{8}$-in. Glass		$\frac{1}{4}$-in. Glass		Shading Factor
	$\frac{1}{4}$ in.	$\frac{1}{2}$ in.	$\frac{1}{4}$ in.	$\frac{1}{2}$ in.	E
October					
8A.M., 4P.M........	88.368	88.454	76.124	76.127	0.99
9A.M., 3P.M........	122.995	123.101	106.533	106.641	0.91
10A.M., 2P.M........	155.204	155.373	136.245	136.437	0.93
11A.M., 1P.M........	175.539	175.730	155.449	155.688	0.92
12 Noon	180.136	180.289	159.735	159.984	0.91
November					
8A.M., 4P.M........	99.092	99.196	85.896	85.894	1.00
9A.M., 3P.M........	149.239	149.394	131.190	131.320	1.00
10A.M., 2P.M........	178.846	179.015	158.657	158.880	0.99
11A.M., 1P.M........	198.131	198.318	176.694	176.958	0.99
12 Noon	202.604	202.796	180.591	180.874	0.98
December					
8A.M., 4P.M........	103.774	103.892	90.595	90.595	1.00
9A.M., 3P.M........	151.518	151.655	133.503	133.642	1.00
10A.M., 2P.M........	183.739	183.910	163.415	163.637	1.00
11A.M., 1P.M........	204.306	204.498	182.679	182.950	1.00
12 Noon	212.866	213.041	190.047	190.335	1.00
January					
8A.M., 4P.M........	101.688	101.796	87.925	87.923	1.00
9A.M., 3P.M........	152.779	152.939	134.303	134.436	1.00
10A.M., 2P.M........	183.040	183.212	162.377	162.606	0.99
11A.M., 1P.M........	202.802	202.994	180.860	181.130	0.99
12 Noon	207.372	207.568	184.841	185.131	0.98
February					
8A.M., 4P.M........	90.472	90.560	77.937	77.940	0.99
9A.M., 3P.M........	125.904	126.012	109.053	109.162	0.91
10A.M., 2P.M........	158.878	159.052	139.471	139.667	0.93
11A.M., 1P.M........	179.707	179.903	159.140	159.385	0.92
12 Noon	184.470	184.622	163.574	163.829	0.91
March					
8A.M., 4P.M........	51.549	51.603	43.262	43.190	0.80
9A.M., 3P.M........	86.736	86.832	73.956	73.984	0.81
10A.M., 2P.M........	114.247	114.368	98.775	98.876	0.80
11A.M., 1P.M........	135.529	135.668	117.288	117.442	0.81
12 Noon	137.816	137.974	119.780	119.941	0.79
April					
8A.M., 4P.M........	21.710	21.723	18.125	18.018	0.12
9A.M., 3P.M........	37.501	37.528	32.234	32.161	0.45
10A.M., 2P.M........	59.771	59.829	50.060	50.035	0.53
11A.M., 1P.M........	82.442	82.503	70.472	70.505	0.61
12 Noon	88.859	88.949	75.826	75.875	0.61

TABLE 9–13

Values of the Solar Term, ∇_h, for Double-glazed Vertical South-facing Windows: Latitude 40°

Distance Between Panes	$\frac{1}{8}$-in. Glass		$\frac{1}{4}$-in. Glass		Shading Factor
	$\frac{1}{4}$ in.	$\frac{1}{2}$ in.	$\frac{1}{4}$ in.	$\frac{1}{2}$ in.	E
October					
8A.M., 4P.M........	97.763	97.855	84.645	84.634	0.96
9A.M., 3P.M........	133.270	133.397	116.712	116.838	0.93
10A.M., 2P.M........	165.756	165.915	146.238	146.443	0.90
11A.M., 1P.M........	186.031	186.209	165.245	165.502	0.89
12 Noon	192.321	192.528	170.890	171.159	0.88
November					
8A.M., 4P.M........	94.304	94.401	81.926	81.914	1.00
9A.M., 3P.M........	145.550	145.695	128.416	128.526	1.00
10A.M., 2P.M........	181.440	181.609	161.367	161.587	0.98
11A.M., 1P.M........	203.314	203.504	181.194	181.460	0.97
12 Noon	211.050	211.248	188.271	188.555	0.97
December					
8A.M., 4P.M........	100.263	100.366	87.489	87.487	1.00
9A.M., 3P.M........	144.821	144.965	128.001	128.114	1.00
10A.M., 2P.M........	187.201	187.607	166.628	166.842	1.00
11A.M., 1P.M........	207.796	207.989	185.510	185.775	1.00
12 Noon	216.201	216.401	193.271	193.549	1.00
January					
8A.M., 4P.M........	96.537	96.637	83.867	83.854	1.00
9A.M., 3P.M........	149.051	149.201	131.505	131.618	1.00
10A.M., 2P.M........	185.738	185.911	165.189	165.414	0.98
11A.M., 1P.M........	208.021	208.215	185.388	185.660	0.97
12 Noon	216.008	216.210	192.694	192.984	0.97
February					
8A.M., 4P.M........	88.291	88.375	76.444	76.434	0.96
9A.M., 3P.M........	136.441	136.572	119.489	119.618	0.93
10A.M., 2P.M........	169.695	169.857	149.712	149.923	0.90
11A.M., 1P.M........	190.554	190.736	169.262	169.526	0.89
12 Noon	195.338	195.548	173.571	173.844	0.88
March					
7A.M., 5P.M........	7.915	7.917	6.434	6.405	0.77
8A.M., 4P.M........	59.323	59.389	50.448	50.389	0.75
9A.M., 3P.M........	100.837	100.930	87.198	87.256	0.76
10A.M., 2P.M........	132.121	132.255	114.738	114.878	0.75
11A.M., 1P.M........	156.063	156.237	136.989	137.186	0.76
12 Noon	161.450	161.629	141.867	142.078	0.75
April					
8A.M., 4P.M........	26.995	27.013	22.978	22.875	0.11
9A.M., 3P.M........	49.906	49.948	43.173	43.126	0.35
10A.M., 2P.M........	81.622	81.705	69.357	69.385	0.46
11A.M., 1P.M........	101.978	102.077	88.408	88.490	0.51
12 Noon	112.478	112.584	97.052	97.157	0.53

TABLE 9–14

Values of the Solar Term, ∇_h, for Double-glazed Vertical South-facing Windows: Latitude 45°

Distance Between Panes	$\frac{1}{8}$-in. Glass		$\frac{1}{4}$-in. Glass		Shading Factor
	$\frac{1}{4}$ in.	$\frac{1}{2}$ in.	$\frac{1}{4}$ in.	$\frac{1}{2}$ in.	E
October					
8A.M., 4P.M.	89.198	89.290	76.913	76.901	0.97
9A.M., 3P.M.	139.129	139.260	121.866	121.996	0.91
10A.M., 2P.M.	175.027	175.212	155.119	155.335	0.90
11A.M., 1P.M.	198.201	198.388	176.500	176.766	0.88
12 Noon	204.092	204.285	181.863	182.148	0.87
November					
8A.M., 4P.M.	93.639	93.748	79.860	79.835	1.00
9A.M., 3P.M.	139.872	140.010	123.526	123.630	1.00
10A.M., 2P.M.	178.454	178.614	158.787	158.976	1.00
11A.M., 1P.M.	204.702	204.890	182.536	182.788	0.99
12 Noon	213.296	213.468	190.831	191.126	0.98
December					
8A.M., 4P.M.	102.814	102.931	89.707	89.711	1.00
9A.M., 3P.M.	135.808	135.950	120.230	120.276	1.00
10A.M., 2P.M.	170.635	170.785	151.940	152.095	1.00
11A.M., 1P.M.	204.977	205.163	183.405	183.638	1.00
12 Noon	215.152	215.350	192.320	192.585	1.00
January					
8A.M., 4P.M.	95.800	95.912	81.703	81.678	1.00
9A.M., 3P.M.	143.252	143.394	126.511	126.618	1.00
10A.M., 2P.M.	182.724	182.888	162.586	162.780	1.00
11A.M., 1P.M.	209.490	209.683	186.807	187.064	0.99
12 Noon	218.319	218.495	195.325	195.627	0.98
February					
8A.M., 4P.M.	90.253	90.345	77.822	77.811	0.97
9A.M., 3P.M.	140.743	140.876	123.281	123.412	0.91
10A.M., 2P.M.	177.156	177.343	157.005	157.224	0.90
11A.M., 1P.M.	200.491	200.680	178.539	178.808	0.88
12 Noon	206.544	206.740	184.049	184.337	0.87
March					
7A.M., 5P.M.	35.266	35.303	30.504	30.352	0.84
8A.M., 4P.M.	63.578	63.647	54.524	54.470	0.71
9A.M., 3P.M.	107.373	107.483	93.103	93.173	0.72
10A.M., 2P.M.	145.467	145.629	127.054	127.225	0.71
11A.M., 1P.M.	170.685	170.872	150.500	150.731	0.70
12 Noon	179.814	179.988	159.363	159.610	0.72
April					
8A.M., 4P.M.	31.081	31.103	26.970	26.875	0.00
9A.M., 3P.M.	69.220	69.283	59.265	59.259	0.35
10A.M., 2P.M.	103.887	103.986	90.192	90.273	0.45
11A.M., 1P.M.	124.717	124.848	108.965	109.101	0.47
12 Noon	136.120	136.277	118.307	118.466	0.49

EXAMPLE 9–4. The computation in Example 9–3 checked the value of ∇_h, for 11 A.M. in January, given in column 4 of Table 9–12. Assuming that the other values in column 4 of Table 9–12 are correct, use them to calculate the daily solar gain ∇_d for January and the monthly solar gain ∇_m for January ($\frac{1}{4}$-in. glass with $\frac{1}{4}$-in. air space).

Solution: From Table 9–1, a south-facing, unshaded vertical window at latitude 35° receives 10.0 hr of maximum irradiation during a January day. Then, summing up the nine hourly irradiation rates from column 4 of Table 9–12 and multiplying by 10/9,

$$\nabla_d = \frac{10}{9}[2(87.925 + 134.303 + 162.377 + 180.860) + 184.841]$$

$$= \frac{10}{9}(1315.77) = 1462 \text{ Btu/day}$$

The month of January has 31 days; hence,

$$\nabla_m = (31)(1462) = 45{,}322 \text{ Btu/month}$$

EXAMPLE 9–5. Repeat Example 9–4 for the other six months of the heating season and thereby check the value of ∇_s that is given in Table 9–10 for a $\frac{1}{4}$-in. by $\frac{1}{4}$-in. by $\frac{1}{4}$-in. window, south-facing at latitude 35°.

Solution: The ∇_m values for October, November, December, February, March, and April are calculated as in Example 9–4. Then, adding the seven ∇_m values for October through April, respectively, gives

$$\nabla_s = 42{,}365 + 42{,}960 + 44{,}575 + 45{,}322 + 39{,}172 + 32{,}492 + 13{,}230$$

$$= 260{,}116 \text{ Btu/season}$$

This value agrees with the ∇_s for the south-facing window at latitude 35°, as given in column 4 of Table 9–10.

In calculating the seasonal thermal advantage (or disadvantage) attributable to a solar window, Table 9–15 will be useful in providing data for a particular locality for both average expectancy of sunshine, F, and for normal outside air temperature, t_n (as defined in Eq. 9–62).

If more specific data are lacking for a particular window and its exposure conditions, the following average values of the over-all coefficient of heat transfer are recommended:

Type of Window, in.	U_e
$\frac{1}{8}, \frac{1}{4}, \frac{1}{8}$	0.65
$\frac{1}{8}, \frac{1}{2}, \frac{1}{8}$	0.58
$\frac{1}{4}, \frac{1}{4}, \frac{1}{4}$	0.62
$\frac{1}{4}, \frac{1}{2}, \frac{1}{4}$	0.56

EXAMPLE 9–6. A 6-ft by 4-ft window consisting of two identical sheets of $\frac{1}{8}$-in. clear plate glass separated by a $\frac{1}{4}$-in. sealed air space is to be used in a south wall which has an over-all coefficient of heat transfer of 0.165 Btu/(hr)(sq ft)(°F). The over-all coefficient for the window is 0.65 Btu/(hr)(sq ft)(°F). Estimate the maximum seasonal saving due to the unshaded window. The house is located in Lincoln, Nebraska (latitude 42°), and inside-air design temperature is 75 F.

TABLE 9–15
Average Expectancy of Sunshine and Normal Outside
Temperature for Selected Localities

City	Fraction, F, of Maximum Possible Sunshine	Normal Temperature During 7-month Heating Season, t_n
Albany, N.Y.	0.463	35.2
Albuquerque, N.M.	0.770	47.0
Atlanta, Ga.	0.522	51.5
Baltimore, Md.	0.553	43.8
Birmingham, Ala.	0.510	53.8
Bismarck, N.D.	0.546	24.6
Boise, Id.	0.540	45.2
Boston, Mass.	0.540	38.1
Burlington, Va.	0.419	31.5
Chattanooga, Tenn.	0.503	49.8
Cheyenne, Wyo.	0.666	41.3
Cleveland, Ohio	0.408	37.2
Columbia, S.C.	0.511	54.0
Concord, N.H.	0.515	33.3
Dallas, Texas	0.470	52.5
Davenport, Iowa	0.539	40.0
Denver, Colo.	0.705	38.9
Detroit, Mich.	0.429	35.8
Eugene, Ore.	0.439	50.2
Harrisburg, Pa.	0.495	43.6
Hartford, Conn.	0.532	42.8
Helena, Mont.	0.521	40.7
Huron, S.D.	0.579	28.2
Indianapolis, Ind.	0.507	40.3
Jacksonville, Fla.	0.400	62.0
Joliet, Ill.	0.530	40.8
Lincoln, Neb.	0.614	37.0
Little Rock, Ark.	0.513	51.6
Louisville, Ky.	0.514	45.3
Madison, Wis.	0.504	37.8
Minneapolis, Minn.	0.527	29.4
Newark, N.J.	0.550	43.4
New Orleans, La.	0.370	61.6
Phoenix, Ariz.	0.590	59.5
Portland, Me.	0.525	33.8
Providence, R.I.	0.542	37.2
Raleigh, N.C.	0.570	50.0
Reno, Nev.	0.637	45.4
Richmond, Va.	0.594	47.0
St. Louis, Mo.	0.567	43.6
Salt Lake City, Utah	0.592	40.0
San Francisco, Cal.	0.615	54.2
Seattle, Wash.	0.340	46.3
Topeka, Kan.	0.613	42.3
Tulsa, Okla.	0.560	48.2
Vicksburg, Miss.	0.447	56.8
Wheeling, W. Va.	0.408	46.1
Wilmington, Del.	0.558	45.0

Solution: From Table 9–10, the seasonal solar term ∇_s, for a $\frac{1}{8}$-, $\frac{1}{4}$-, or $\frac{1}{8}$-in. south-facing window at latitude 42° is, by interpolation between 40° and 45°,

$$\nabla_s = 302{,}129 + \frac{2}{5}\,(307{,}824 - 302{,}129)$$

$$= 304{,}407 \text{ Btu/(season)(sq ft)}$$

The seasonal saving is given by Eq. 9–64 as

$$\Delta Q_{\text{season}} = (F)(\nabla_s) - 5088\,(U_e - U_w)(t_i - t_n)$$

with F and t_n to be obtained from Table 9–15 (for Lincoln, Nebraska) as 0.614 and 37.0 F, respectively. Thus

$$\Delta Q_{\text{season}} = [(0.614)(304{,}407)] - [(5088)(0.65 - 0.165)(75 - 37)]$$

$$= 186{,}906 - 93{,}772$$

$$= 93{,}134 \text{ Btu/(sq ft)(season)}$$

The window has an area of 24 sq ft, so the maximum seasonal saving would be (24)(93134), or 2,239,536 Btu. If the cost of energy for heating is assumed to be $0.01 per 4000 Btu, the maximum seasonal saving in dollars would be

$$\text{Seasonal saving}_{(\text{max possible})} = \frac{2{,}239{,}536}{(4000)(100)}$$

$$= \$5.60$$

In considering the result of the above example, it must be remembered that it is based on an assumed ability to utilize effectively every possible Btu that enters the structure through the window. Actually, two important factors will inevitably serve to invalidate the assumed condition for at least a fraction of the heating season: (1) During periods when the outside temperature is in the sixties and the sun is shining, it is almost certain that the solar gain will sometimes exceed the heating requirements; hence the inside air temperature will tend to rise above the design value, and in this case the excess solar gain will not serve to reduce the heating load. (2) In many cases during the heating season, aesthetic conditions, or desire for privacy, or glare will cause the occupants to cover the window partially or wholly, thus preventing admission to the structure of maximum possible solar energy.

When a solar window replaces a section of opaque wall having lower over-all coefficient of heat transfer, the result is to increase the maximum design transmission load and consequently increase the size and first cost of the heating plant.

9–4. The Design of Protective Solar Window Overhang.

The function of a solar window is to admit heat and light during the winter months and to admit light but exclude heat during the summer months. This objective requires that the window be exposed to direct sunshine for a large fraction of the time during the winter but shaded from direct sunshine for as large a fraction as possible of summer hours. Shading can, of course, be attained through manual operation of blinds, drapes, louvers, adjustable drops, or variable types of roof overhang, but in many cases such special devices are unnecessary because of the fortunate circumstance that solar geometry assists the designer in providing automatic seasonal control of shading for south-wall windows.

In midwinter the sun rises south of the east-west line and describes an arc that brings it to a maximum elevation (within the latitude range of the United States) of from 20 deg to approximately 40 deg, the value of the maximum varying with latitude. In midsummer the sun rises north of the east-west line and describes an arc that brings it to a maximum elevation (again for the range of latitude of the United States) of from, roughly, 65 deg to 85 deg. The ratio of maximum summer elevation to maximum winter elevation varies with latitude but is the order of from 2 to 3. Therefore it is evident that by designing an overhanging roof in conjunction with a south-wall solar window, it is possible to exclude the high midday summer sun while admitting the much lower midday winter sun.

Control of shading during the morning and afternoon hours is less complete but does retain a high degree of effectiveness, owing to the fact that from April 21 to August 21 the sunrise and sunset are north of the east-west line, and therefore throughout this warm season the sun does not irradiate a south window until some time after it has crossed the horizon. In mid-June, for example, sunrise on the fortieth parallel of latitude (corresponding roughly to the location of Denver, Columbus, and Philadelphia) is before 5 A.M., yet the sun does not shine on a south wall until after 8 A.M., and by that time it is already at an elevation of nearly 40 deg. In this case the *minimum* elevation for midsummer is higher than the *maximum* for midwinter. This factor becomes of even greater significance when it is realized that (again at latitude 40°) throughout the greater part of May, June, and July, the minimum elevation at which irradiation of a south wall occurs is always greater than the elevation at solar noon throughout November, December, and January.

THEORY OF OVERHANG DESIGN. The limiting cases of roof overhang obviously correspond to the extremes of excluding all summer sun or admitting all winter sun. Thus, at latitude 40°, the sun could be excluded from mid-April through mid-August if a sufficient length of overhang were provided to shade the window when the solar altitude is 20 deg, but if complete irradiation is desired from mid-September through mid-March, the overhang would have to be short enough to admit sunlight for all elevations below 50 deg; obviously these two conditions are mutually incompatible. Thus some type of compromise is necessary if fixed-length roof overhang is to be used. The basis for such a compromise is arbitrary and must therefore remain largely a matter of judgment.

In localities where the summers are particularly hot, greater amounts of overhang will often be used with resultant partial sacrifice of winter heating effect, whereas in localities characterized by cold winters and moderate summers, the overhang may be designed to provide a greater thermal gain in winter at the expense of some undesirable heat gain in summer. The latter difficulty often is not of appreciable practical importance, since it is probable that the undesirable summer irradiation will be avoided by manual adjustment of shading. In this respect it is well to note that where doubt or uncertainty exist as to the amount of overhang to provide, it is always preferable to use too little rather than too much. Correction for insufficient overhang is relatively simple and can be accomplished by many types of seasonal or manual adjustments, such as awnings or drops, but correction for excess overhang would necessarily involve a major alteration of the structure.

In establishing a basis for design of roof overhang, two relatively independent decisions must be made. The first is to select the solar elevation corresponding to which the entire window is to be irradiated, and the second is to select the elevation at which the window is to be entirely in the shade. A common selection for complete irradiation is the solar elevation, at the latitude of the particular installation, which occurs at solar noon on the shortest day of the year, December 21. On this basis the window would be partially shaded at noon on all other days of the year. A common alternative is to select the solar elevation at noon on the twenty-first day of either October or November; on either of these bases the window would be completely irradiated for all sunshine hours from October 21 through February 21, or from November 21 through January 21, but would be partially shaded at noon throughout the remainder of the year.

The decision with respect to complete shading may be based on the solar elevation at noon on the longest day of the year, June 21. In this event the entire window would be in the shade at solar noon only on this one day. If shading is based on the noon elevation for some later day, such as July 21 or August 21, the window would then be completely shaded at noon from May 21 to July 21, or from April 21 to August 21. For times when the window is partially shaded, the fraction receiving direct sunshine will depend on the full-radiation design condition as well as the full-shade condition, since for a fixed basis of full-shading, the height of the window will vary with the condition for complete irradiation.

GEOMETRY OF OVERHANG DESIGN. If the criterion of complete shading is taken as a solar elevation of H_s, corresponding to the number of degrees for whatever summer condition is selected, and if H_w is the number of degrees of elevation for the winter condition that determines complete irradiation, the geometrical limitation on positioning of the solar window and on development of roof overhang will be as shown in Fig. 9–5. From this figure it is evident that for a window of height W, there is one and only one position with respect to the edge of the roof overhang (indicated by point E on the figure) at which the window will meet the specified conditions. If the overhang is less than the amount shown as O, the window will be too large (as shown in Fig. 9–5a) with respect to the angular difference $H_s - H_w$, whereas if the overhang is of greater length than O, the window will be too small to

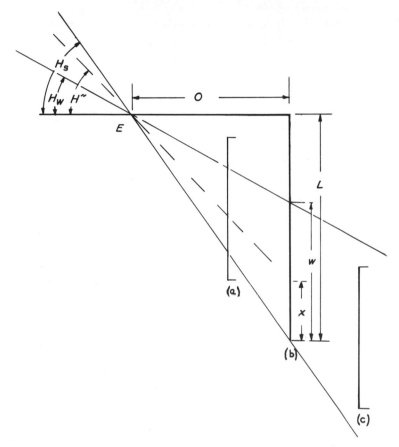

Fig. 9–5. Solar geometry of window overhang design for summer shading and winter irradiation. (a) Insufficient overhang for window height; (b) correct overhang; (c) excessive overhang.

fill the $H_s - H_w$ angular difference. Further, even when the overhang is of the correct length for the selected window height, the system will not function correctly unless the window is located vertically in such a way that the distance from the underside of the overhang to the top of the window is equal to A, as shown on Fig. 9–5.

The above considerations indicate that for effective solar design, a fixed relationship must be established between the dimensions O, A, and W of

Fig. 9–5. Any one of these dimensions can, of course, be fixed arbitrarily, but when this is done, the other two will necessarily have values determined from geometry alone. It is interesting to note that the ceiling height of a room in which solar windows are installed does not have any theoretical influence on either the vertical position of the windows or on the optimum length of roof overhang. If architectural requirements dictate that the window sill be some specified distance from the floor, then (for correct solar design) the window will necessarily be of a height that will allow the ratio of dimensions A and O to have a specified value. The great practical importance of this fact resides in the rigid limitation that it places on the vertical positioning of a solar window. It is impossible to meet specific shading conditions for a window that is of arbitrary height and is located an arbitrary distance above the floor. Unfortunately this fact has not always been recognized by designers, some of whom incorrectly believe that the shading characteristic of a solar window is determined by roof overhang alone.

Evaluation of O and A in terms of window height can be readily accomplished for any specified set of shading conditions. Thus, referring to Fig. 9–5,

$$A = (O)(\tan H_w) \tag{9–65}$$

and

$$W + A = (O)(\tan H_s) \tag{9–66}$$

Then, by subtracting the first equation from the second,

$$W = O(\tan H_s - \tan H_w) \tag{9–67}$$

or

$$O = \frac{W}{\tan H_s - \tan H_w} \tag{9–68}$$

and substituting this value of O in the original equation for A,

$$A = \frac{W(\tan H_w)}{\tan H_s - \tan H_w} \tag{9–69}$$

The last two equations can be written in the form

$$O = O'W \quad \text{and} \quad A = A'W \tag{9–70}$$

where O' and A' are simple multiplying coefficients that can be numerically evaluated for any specified set of shading conditions. Thus, with shading specified and with window height W arbitrarily selected, the required vertical distance from the underside of the roof overhang to the top of the window and the required length of roof overhang can both be readily calculated.

Table 9–16 summarizes values of the coefficients O' and A' for nine sets of shading conditions that cover a wide range of practical applications. For any combination of conditions within the limits of those used in the table, values of O' and A' can be obtained readily by interpolation. Similarly, values of the coefficients for latitudes other than those shown can be determined by interpolation or, approximately and over a small range, by extrapolation. In using the table, recall that the solar positions in July and August are almost the same as in May and April; similarly, the positions in October and November are practically the same as in February and January;

TABLE 9–16

Required Roof Overhang Coefficient* O', and Required Vertical Distance Coefficient† from Top of Window to Underside of Overhang, A', To Provide Complete Irradiation of South Windows at Solar Noon on the Twenty-first Day of October, or November, or December, and Complete Shading at Solar Noon on the Twenty-first Day of June, or July, or August

Latitude	December and June		December and July		December and August	
	O'	A'	O'	A'	O'	A'
30°	0.124	0.094	0.152	0.115	0.413	0.315
35	0.232	0.139	0.293	0.176	0.552	0.331
40	0.349	0.178	0.424	0.198	0.729	0.373
45	0.468	0.189	0.558	0.225	0.881	0.356

Latitude	November and June		November and July		November and August	
	O'	A'	O'	A'	O'	A'
30°	0.126	0.106	0.174	0.146	0.429	0.360
35	0.237	0.166	0.302	0.213	0.583	0.408
40	0.257	0.206	0.445	0.257	0.767	0.443
45	0.482	0.225	0.582	0.271	0.931	0.434

Latitude	October and June		October and July		October and August	
	O'	A'	O'	A'	O'	A'
30°	0.132	0.157	0.195	0.232	0.505	0.602
35	0.255	0.255	0.332	0.332	0.707	0.707
40	0.394	0.332	0.504	0.423	0.962	0.807
45	0.544	0.381	0.669	0.468	1.192	0.834

* Satisfying the equation $O = O'W$, where O is the overhang distance and W is the window height.

† Satisfying the equation $A = A'W$, where A is the vertical distance and W is the window height.

thus the columns headed October–August could just as well be changed to February–April, and the same is true of other column headings.

In some cases it may be architecturally desirable to arbitrarily fix the distance from the underside of the roof overhang to the bottom of the window. In this case the requisite length of overhang can be calculated from the equation

$$L = (O)(\tan H_s) \qquad (9\text{–}71)$$

$$O = L'L \qquad (9\text{–}72)$$

where L is the vertical distance in question (shown as $W + A$ on Fig. 9–2) and L' is a coefficient that has a fixed value for a specified condition of complete window shading. For a value of O, calculated from the above equation, there will necessarily be only one window height for any subsequently selected basis of fixing the condition of complete shading. Thus, if L has a fixed value and O is calculated for the condition of 100 per cent shading on June 21, the single acceptable value of the window height for 100 per cent irradiation on December 21 could be determined by solution of the equation

$$W = \frac{O}{O'} \tag{9–73}$$

where O is known and O' is taken from Table 9–16 for December–June conditions.

Values for L' for three shading conditions over a wide range of latitudes are given in Table 9–17.

TABLE 9–17

Required Roof Overhang Coefficient, L', To Shade South Windows Fully at Noon on the Twenty-first Day of June, or July, or August, When Vertical Distance L from Underside of Overhang to Bottom of Window Is Known (Coefficient to satisfy the equation: Overhang $= L'L$)

Latitude	Coefficient, L'		
	June	July	August
30°	0.1139	0.1673	0.3153
32	0.1495	0.2035	0.3541
34	0.1853	0.2401	0.3939
36	0.2217	0.2773	0.4348
38	0.2586	0.3153	0.4770
40	0.2962	0.3541	0.4206
42	0.3346	0.3939	0.5658
44	0.3739	0.4348	0.6128
46	0.4142	0.4770	0.6619
48	0.4557	0.5206	0.7133

THE SHADING FACTOR E. Irrespective of what design basis is used for determining the overhang, all solar windows will be partially shaded during some hours of the heating season. Since the shaded portion of the window does not contribute to the solar heating effect (neglecting possible gain through sky radiation), it is evident that exact evaluation of the percentage of shaded glass is essential to determination of the window's effectiveness. Further, if the seasonal saving attributable to a solar window is to be expressed in terms of unit area, then the unit of area must be so selected that it will experience the same decrement of gain due to shading as is experienced by the window as a whole; this means that the unit is necessarily a vertical strip of glass equal in length to the height of the window and of uniform width sufficient to include 1 sq ft.

For any solar altitude at solar noon, less than that on which 100 per cent irradiation is based, the shading factor will be unity. Thus, if H_w is selected for December 21, the value of the shading factor E will be unity for all hours during the month of December and for approximately two-thirds of all hours during November and January; during February and October, E would approach unity for approximately 50 per cent of the time. It therefore follows that, with reasonable overhang design, the fraction of window that is prevented from receiving direct sunshine during the winter months is not very great.

When evaluating the performance of a solar window, the "average" shading factor is a meaningless term, since the loss of energy associated with a given value of E depends in large measure on the time of day and on the time of season. Thus, if a south-facing window were 50 per cent in the shade at 9 A.M., the loss of solar heating effect would be substantially less than if the same shade factor occurred at solar noon. Because of this inability to use an average seasonal value of E, it is not possible to apply a simple correction to the performance analysis to account for use of overhang. The difficulty is not an important one, however, since for usual design bases the loss of winter sun due to shading is very slight.

Qualitatively, any change from solar noon of December 21 as a basis for 100 per cent irradiation will *increase* the amount of solar energy received by the window; with respect to the December term, the seasonal saving indicated by such a change is therefore conservative. Any departure from the June 21 basis of complete shading will decrease the value of E for some hours and hence will decrease the seasonal reception of energy. The results are therefore non-conservative when the actual window is designed for complete shading at solar noon of any day except June 21, but the difference is not likely to be of practical importance.

A departure from standard design that is of greater significance is the use of glass areas lower in the wall than will meet the requirements of June 21 shading; such areas will be irradiated at all times throughout the year, and hence their effect is to increase the equivalent E value for the window and correspondingly raise the seasonal energy gain; in this case the performance analysis based on standard-design E values is again conservative. An opposite condition occurs when windows are allowed to project beyond the height corresponding to December 21 irradiation.

Effective Solar Altitude H″. The selection of the boundary shading values, as discussed in Art. 9–4, page 401, is a very simple matter, since the actual elevation of the sun at solar noon is equal to its elevation measured in a vertical plane normal to a south-facing window. For any time of day other than solar noon, however, the *effective* solar altitude H'' differs from the actual value and can be obtained only by trigonometric computation. Thus, at solar noon on December 21 at latitude 30°, the actual elevation is 37 deg and this is also equal to the effective elevation. At 9 A.M., 10 A.M., and 11 A.M.

(correspondingly at 3 P.M., 2 P.M., and 1 P.M.) on this same day, the actual solar altitudes are 21 deg, 29 deg, and 35 deg, respectively, whereas the corresponding effective solar altitudes are 28 deg, 33 deg, and 36 deg, respectively (refer to the last column of Table 9–2). Thus, not only do the effective solar altitudes differ from the actual, but also the variation increases non-linearly as a function of the number of hours on either side of solar noon.

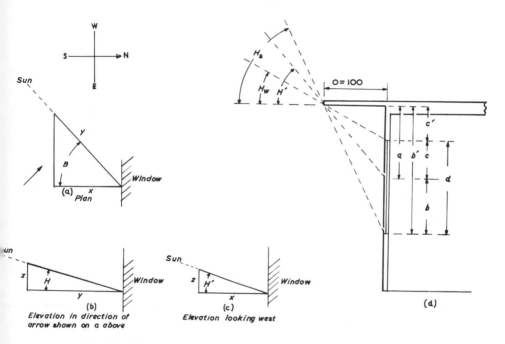

Fig. 9–6. Solar geometry for determination of effective solar altitude.

Figs. 9–6a,b,c provides a graphical visualization of the method used for evaluating the effective solar altitude H''. At any time of any day of the year, the sun's altitude H and its horizontal angle B are known. The horizontal angle B is shown in the plan view of Fig. 9–6a, where the arbitrarily selected distance out from the window, along the normal to the window, is identified as x and the corresponding hypotenuse of the indicated right triangle is then y. By observation,

$$x = y \cos B \qquad (9\text{–}74)$$

or

$$y = \frac{x}{\cos B} \qquad (9\text{–}75)$$

Now taking an elevation in a direction normal to y gives Fig. 9–6b, where the distance out from the window along the normal is y and the angle H is the true solar elevation. The vertical leg of the right triangle of Fig. 9–6b is then

$$z = y \tan H \qquad (9\text{–}76)$$

The effective solar altitude H'' is the sun's apparent elevation when projected on a vertical plane through the normal to the window. Refer to Fig. 9–6c; the horizontal distance out along the normal is x (as evident from Fig. 9–6a), and the vertical distance is z (as evident from Fig. 9–6b); hence the unknown angle H'' is that angle for which the tangent is z/x:

$$H'' = \tan^{-1}\frac{z}{x} \tag{9-77}$$

By substituting from Eqs. 9–75 and 9–76,

$$H'' = \tan^{-1}\frac{y\tan H}{x}$$

$$= \tan^{-1}\frac{x\tan H}{x\cos B}$$

$$= \tan^{-1}\frac{\tan H}{\cos B} \tag{9-78}$$

Values of H'' for south-facing windows at latitudes 30°, 35°, 40°, and 45° are given, respectively, in Tables 9–2 through 9–5; the corresponding values of east- or west-facing windows are given in Tables 9–6 through 9–9. For window orientations between south and east or west, interpolation is possible between the values of Tables 9–2 and 9–6, or 9–3 and 9–7, or 9–4 and 9–8, or 9–5 and 9–9.

Equation for Shading Factor E. With the effective solar elevation known, it is now possible to determine the extent of either shading or irradiation for any selected solar overhang at any time of any day. The shading factor E is defined as the fraction of unit window area (unit area as defined in Art. 9–4, page 405) that is receiving direct sunshine. Refer to Fig. 9–5;

$$E = \frac{X}{W} \tag{9-79}$$

where X is the vertical length of the irradiated section of the window at a time when the effective solar altitude is H''. From Fig. 9–5,

$$X = (O)(\tan H_s) - (O)(\tan H'') \tag{9-80}$$

and

$$W = (O)(\tan H_s) - (O)(\tan H_w) \tag{9-81}$$

giving

$$E = \frac{\tan H_s - \tan H''}{\tan H_s - \tan H_w} \tag{9-82}$$

By means of Eq. 9–82, the shading factor can be readily evaluated at any time in any latitude and for any specified boundary conditions of shading design. Hourly values of H'' are given for the seven months of the heating season for four latitudes, and for south and east or west orientations in Tables 9–2 through 9–9; values of H_s and H_w can be obtained from the same tables for solar noon of the month in question (recalling that H is equal to the i value of the third column subtracted from 90 deg).

EXAMPLE 9–7. Roof overhang for a south-facing 36 in. high vertical window at 40° latitude is designed for full shading at solar noon only on June 21 and for full irradiation at solar noon only on December 21. The window consists of two $\frac{1}{4}$ in. clear plate-glass sheets separated by a $\frac{1}{2}$ in air space. It is 72 in. wide and is located in a 9-ft high wall having an over-all coefficient of heat transfer of 0.25 Btu/(hr)(sq ft)(°F). Determine (a) the length of roof overhang; (b) the distance from floor to bottom of the window; (c) the shading factor at 10 A.M. on a day in February; (d) the irradiation rate for the unshaded portion of the window; (e) the solar term ∇_h at 10 A.M. on February 21; (f) the ratio of effective solar-heating energy on the unshaded portion of the window to irradiation rate; (g) the ratio of effective solar heating energy on the entire window to maximum possible irradiation of an equal-area unshaded window.

Solution: (a) From Table 9–16 for latitude 40° and a June–December shading basis, the overhang coefficient O is obtained as 0.424; thus

$$\text{Overhang length} = O'W = (0.424)(36) = 15.3 \text{ in.}$$

(b) From Table 9–16 for latitude 40° and a June–December shading basis, the vertical placement coefficient A' is 0.178; thus

Vertical distance from floor
to bottom of window)
$= (9)(12) - 36 - A'W = 108 - 36 - (0.178)(36) = 65.6 \text{ in.}$

(This result, the window sill being $5\frac{1}{2}$ ft above the floor, shows that the proposed shading condition would not be satisfactory; the subject should be investigated further and a different shading basis used.)

(c) From Table 9–4 for 10 A.M. on a day in February, the value of H'' is 37 deg. From the same table, H_w (based on solar noon in December) is 25 deg. The value of H_s for solar noon in June is not given in the tables of this chapter but can be found from solar data references to be 74 deg. Then, obtaining tangents of these angles and substituting in Eq. 9–82,

$$E = \frac{\tan H_s - \tan H''}{\tan H_s - \tan H_w} = \frac{3.4874 - 0.7536}{3.4874 - 0.4663} = 0.905$$

(which agrees with the value given in Table 9–13).

(d) From Table 9–4 the irradiation rate for the unshaded portion of the window, I_V, is 202.5 Btu/(hr)(sq ft).

(e) From Table 9–13, for a $\frac{1}{4}$- $\frac{1}{2}$-, $\frac{1}{4}$-in. window, the value of ∇_h at 10 A.M. in February is 149.9 Btu/hr.

(f) The ratio of effective solar-heating energy on the unshaded portion of the window to irradiation rate is [from parts (d) and (e)]

$$\frac{\nabla_h}{I_V} = \frac{149.9}{202.5} = 0.74 \quad \text{or} \quad 74 \text{ per cent}$$

(g) The ratio of effective solar-heating energy on the entire window to maximum possible irradiation of an equal area of unshaded window [from parts (c) and (f)] is

$$\frac{E\nabla_h}{I_V} = (0.905)(0.74) = 0.67, \quad \text{or} \quad 67 \text{ per cent}$$

PROBLEMS

9–1. Calculate the percentage diminution of direct solar energy due to passage through the earth's atmosphere at 2 P.M. and at latitude 30° on a clear day in February.

9–2. Determine, for the shortest day of the year (assumed clear weather), the quantity of solar energy received by unit area of a perfectly absorbing, vertical, south-facing wall at latitude 35°, and compare this with the quantity received at the March equinox.

9–3. Repeat problem 9–2 for unit area of a horizontal roof.

9–4. Determine the rate of reception of sky radiation on unit area of a backward-sloping, southeast-facing roof at latitude 40° for 3 P.M. on a clear day in March.

9–5. What is the sun's elevation and azimuth at 11 A.M. in January at latitude 45°?

9–6. *Calculate* the rate of direct solar irradiation at 2 P.M. on an April day at latitude 40° for a roof that is inclined backward 45 deg and faces south-southeast. Compare the calculated rate with the rate obtainable by interpolation from the tables.

9–7. Write the equation for ∇_h for a triple window in which the inner and outer panes each have a thermal resistance of r_{g_1}, whereas the middle pane has a resistance of r_{g_2}.

9–8. For a residence located in San Francisco, determine the seasonal gain (or loss) of thermal energy from three south-facing $\frac{1}{4}$-in. by $\frac{1}{2}$-in. by $\frac{1}{4}$-in. windows, each 6 ft wide and 5 ft high. There is no roof overhang. The windows are located in a wall having an over-all coefficient of heat transfer of 0.32 Btu/(hr)(sq ft)(°F).

9–9. A residence located at latitude 30° has a south-facing window that is 6 ft wide by 4 ft high. The bottom of the window is 3 ft above the floor, and the roof is equipped with overhang that extends 4 ft out and is $8\frac{1}{2}$ ft above the floor. Determine the shading factor at solar noon on (a) December 21, (b) April 21.

10

HEATING LOAD ASSOCIATED WITH HUMIDITY CONTROL

One of the most striking paradoxes that faces the heating engineer is the fact that any attempt to control humidity within a heated enclosure necessarily results in an *increase* in heating load. If the uncontrolled humidity is too low, it can be raised only by the introduction of water vapor, with its associated large, latent heat load. If the uncontrolled humidity is too high, the only practical method of reduction (during the heating season) is by increasing the rate at which low-temperature, low-humidity outside air is admitted to the enclosure. Thus, whether the problem is one of correcting the drying effect that is experienced in winter in an average residence, or conversely, of correcting the condensation problem that may occur in a tightly built modern house, the solution in each case requires an increase in the output of the heating system.

10–1. Evaluation of the Humidification Load. The total heating load attributable to either increasing or decreasing the uncontrolled value of the humidity within an enclosure is a function of the net weight of water vapor that must be supplied or rejected in unit time. It follows, therefore, that a first step in humidification analysis is to determine the rates at which water vapor would enter and leave the conditioned space at a time when inside and outside temperatures and humidities were at their design values. With this mass balance established, the weight rate of controlled vapor admission (or rejection) can then be readily obtained. The steady-state moisture gains and losses discussed subsequently should be considered in evaluating design load.

MOISTURE GAIN FROM OCCUPANTS. For lightly clothed, sedentary adults in an environment with thermal level of 73.5 F, the total rate of moisture loss (see Art. 1–4) by lung evaporation and by skin evaporation is approximately $\frac{1}{10}$ lb/hr, with corresponding latent heat loss of approximately 1000 Btu/lb, or 100 Btu/hr. The practical significance of moisture gain from occupants can be recognized most readily by examination of particular cases.

EXAMPLE 10–1. In Example 6–9 it was found that 1540 gal/day of water had to be supplied to the humidifier of an unoccupied 500-seat auditorium, to maintain inside conditions at 75 F dbt with specific humidity of 62 grains/lb during a period in which the outside state remained at 30 F dbt and 20 per cent RH; the rate of mechanical ventilation was 15,000 cfm. What percentage reduction would occur in the rate of water supply to the humidifier if all seats were filled?

Solution: The rate of release of water vapor from the occupants would be

$$\text{Gal/day} = \frac{(\text{occupants})(\text{hours})(\text{lb/hr})}{8.345} \qquad (10\text{--}1)$$

$$= \frac{(500)(24)(0.1)}{8.345}$$

$$= 144$$

$$\text{Reduction} = \frac{144}{1540}\,100 = 9.4 \text{ per cent}$$

EXAMPLE 10–2. A residence 20 ft by 25 ft by $8\frac{1}{2}$ ft is to have the inside air state maintained at 73.5 F dbt with minimum relative humidity of 50 per cent. If infiltration of saturated outside air amounted to one-half air change per hour and if there were four occupants, at what values of outside air temperature would humidification be required (neglect possible moisture sources other than moisture loss of occupants)?

Solution: Ventilation rate amounts to $(20)(25)(8.5)(\frac{1}{2})$, or 2125 cu ft/hr. Based on standard air with specific volume of 13.33 cu ft/lb, the ventilation rate is 2125/13.33, or 159 lb/hr. Moisture release from the occupants amounts to $(4)(0.1)(7000)$, or 2800 grains/hr, which therefore supplies 2800/159, or 17.6 grains/lb, to the infiltration air. Specific humidity within the enclosure (from Fig. 6–5) is not to be allowed to drop below 61 grains/lb; hence the minimum humidity of outside air would be $61 - 17.6$, or 43.4 grains/lb, which corresponds to saturated air at 45 F. Thus the occupants would provide sufficient moisture so that no humidification heat load would occur at outside temperatures (for saturated conditions) above 45 F.

MOISTURE GAIN FROM PROCESSES AND APPLIANCES. The humidification load due to processes and appliances is often ignored for design purposes, since the intermittent carrying-out of the processes (such as cooking and bathing) or use of the appliances (such as washers and dryers) does not permit their contribution to be used to reduce a maximum design load. With respect to critical non-design conditions, however, or in design cases where the problem is one of reducing the inside humidity, such moisture sources should be taken into account.

Tables giving the recommended values of latent heat gains for various appliances are available in standard references. In a restaurant, for example, the moisture gain due to operation of a 1.2-sq ft electric fry kettle amounts to nearly 6 lb/hr, and in a beauty shop the use of a gas-burning five-helmet hair dryer will increase humidity at a rate of 4 lb/hr.

The moisture release in residences is difficult to estimate and varies widely with the working and washing habits of the occupants. In a residence with four occupants, daily moisture release from all sources, including the occupants, is said to be of the order of 25 lb/day or more. As a first approximation it is suggested that residential internal humidification sources be taken as equal in output to that of one and one-half occupants; on this basis total humidification (including that due to occupants) in a residence would be at a rate of 0.1 + 0.15, or 0.25 lb/(hr)(occupant).

MOISTURE LOSS DUE TO INFILTRATION OR MECHANICAL VENTILATION. This moisture loss is usually of much larger magnitude than all others combined. Evaluation of infiltration rates and of latent heat losses associated with ventilation has been covered in Chapter 6; hence this subject need not be here considered until that step in which all losses are to be algebraically summed.

MOISTURE LOSS DUE TO VISIBLE CONDENSATION. Condensation on the inside surface of a window is usually thought of in terms of its nuisance effect or, when the condensate wets the sill and the wall below, its danger to the decoration and structural life of the wetted wall. Thermally, however, window condensation is a form of dehumidification, and the latent heat liberated during such condensation must be replaced (if inside humidity is to be maintained at the design value), thus constituting an added load on the heating system. Analysis is necessary to determine the magnitude and significance of this source of moisture loss.

In Chapter 6 a relationship was established between heat transfer and vapor transfer for the case of evaporation from a wetted surface. Corresponding data are not available for the converse situation of condensation, but an order-of-magnitude estimate of condensation rate can be obtained by assuming that the relationship of Eq. 6–18 is applicable.

EXAMPLE 10–3. For inside state at 73.5 dbt and 50 per cent RH when outside state is at 0 F with a 10-mph wind, estimate the rate of condensation in pounds per hour per 100 sq ft of glass area for single-pane windows in a single-room structure with walls, floor, and ceiling equally exposed.

Solution: The surface-to-surface resistance of the single-pane glass (from Art. 5–3, page 182) is 0.112. The outside film resistance at a wind velocity of 10 mph is obtainable from Table 5–1 (by interpolation, for example, between 10.2 mph at Atlanta and 8.9 mph at Baltimore) as 0.240. The first approximation to the inside film resistance is obtained from Table 5–20 by entering the 0 F column, moving down to $1/C_w = r_g + r_o = 0.112 + 0.240 = 0.352$, and reading h_{cg} as 0.72 based on a film temperature drop of approximately 49 F. Since all room surfaces are exposed (no non-transmitting surfaces), the radiant contribution to the inside film coefficient h_r can be considered negligible. The over-all coefficient of resistance, $1/U_g$ for the window is then

$$R_g = 0.352 + \frac{1}{0.72} = 1.741$$

and the corresponding temperature drop through the film is

$$\frac{t_i - t_g}{t_i - t_o} = \frac{r_g}{R}$$

giving

$$(\Delta t)_{\text{film}} = \frac{(73.5 - 0)(1/0.72)}{1.741}$$

$$= 58.6 \text{ F}$$

As a second approximation return to Table 5–20 and extrapolate (at 0 F) to a Δt of 59 F to obtain a revised h_{cg} of 0.75. Then

$$R_g = 0.352 + \frac{1}{0.75} = 1.685$$

giving

$$(\Delta t)_{\text{film}} = \frac{(73.5 - 0)(1/0.75)}{1.685}$$

$$= 58.1 \text{ F}$$

The new Δt of 58.1 F is so close to the first approximation (58.6 F) that it can be accepted as sufficiently accurate. The inside surface temperature of the window is therefore $73.5 - 58.1 = 15.4$ F.

The specific humidity in the saturated 15.4 F vapor film adjacent to the inside surface of the window is (from Fig. 6–5, by extrapolation) 14 grains/lb, whereas the specific humidity within the room (at 73.5 F dbt and 50 per cent RH) is 61 grains/lb. The latent heat loss (by Eq. 6–17) is then

$$\text{LHL} = h_{fg_g} K'(W'_i - W'_g) \tag{10–2}$$

and the condensation rate per 100 sq ft of glass is (dividing both sides of Eq. 10–2 by h_{fg_g} and by 7000 grains/lb),

$$W_g = \frac{K'(W'_i - W'_g)}{7000} \quad \text{lb/(sq ft)(hr)} \tag{10–3}$$

Then, for a 100-sq ft glass area subject to the specified difference in specific humidity,

$$\text{Window condensation} = \frac{100}{7000}(61 - 14)K'$$

$$= 0.671 K'$$

By Eq. 6–18,

$$K' = \frac{h}{c_H} \tag{10–4}$$

where h is for this case equal to h_{cg} (0.75) and the humid specific heat c_H is (by Eq. 6–12)

$$c_H = c_{pa} + W'_g c_{ps} \tag{10–5}$$

$$= 0.2411 + \frac{14}{7000}(0.5) = 0.2411 + 0.007$$

$$= 0.2481$$

Substituting into Eq. 10–3 gives

$$K' = \frac{0.75}{0.2481} = 3.02$$

and substituting into the equation for condensation gives

$$\text{Window condensation} = (0.671)(3.02) = 2.03 \text{ lb/hr}$$

The significance of the condensation rate in Example 10–3 is evident when one considers that $(0.1/2.03)100$, or 4.9 sq ft of single-glass area (at the stated conditions) will provide dehumidification at a rate exactly equal to the humidification provided by one occupant.

In re-examination of the method followed in establishing the above condensation rate, it should be noted that the dew-point temperature of the room air is 53.5 F, which is much higher than the inside surface temperature of the glass. This means that condensation would commence at 53.5 F and that the condensate would then be subcooled to inside surface temperature. Exact analysis of these series processes of condensation and subcooling leads to thermodynamic difficulty beyond the scope of the present treatment. The above results should therefore be interpreted as indicative only of the order of magnitude of the visible condensation problem.

MOISTURE LOSS DUE TO VAPOR TRANSMISSION. When a total pressure difference exists between inside air and outside air, there may be a flow of air through solid walls by infiltration or exfiltration. The magnitude of this flow has already been investigated (Art. 6–7, page 262), and it is evident that the loss or gain of the water vapor associated with the transmitted air is therefore included as part of the infiltration load.

For many types of wall construction, however, the rate of air flow may be negligible, yet dehumidifying effect due to direct transmission of vapor may still be of significance. Evaluation of moisture loss due to vapor transmission can best be accomplished in two steps: (1) calculation of the transmission rate on the assumption that steady and continuous flow is occurring from inside air to outside air; (2) investigation of the possibility that steady flow may not be occurring and that some of the vapor leaving the enclosure may be condensing within the wall; if this is found to be the case, remedial measures must be taken to prevent or minimize condensation.

Steady-State Vapor Transmission. The equation for the transfer of water vapor through a homogeneous material from a plane of higher vapor pressure to one of lower is comparable to the Fourier equation (4–2 or 4–3) for the transfer of heat from a plane of higher temperature to one of lower. When integrated, the vapor transmission equation in its most widely used form is

$$w' = \frac{\bar{\mu} A (p_i'' - p_o'')}{L} \tag{10–6}$$

where w' = weight of water vapor transmitted, grains/hr.

A = area of cross-section of homogeneous material through which transmission occurs, sq ft.

L = length of path, in.

p_i'' = vapor pressure on the inside surface of the transmitting material, inches of mercury.

p_o'' = vapor pressure on the outside surface of the transmitting material, inches of mercury.

$\bar{\mu}$ = average permeability of the material through which transmission occurs, grains/(hr)(sq ft)(Δ'' Hg/in.)

An obvious objection to Eq. 10–6 is that the vapor pressure units are not those commonly used by the heating engineer. This inconvenience can be readily corrected, however, by noting that 1 in. of mercury is equivalent to 0.4912 psia. By recalling also that there are 7000 grains in 1 lb, Eq. 10–6 can be revised to the more convenient form

$$w = \frac{\bar{\mu}(1/0.4912)A(p_i - p_o)}{7000L}$$

$$= \frac{0.000291\bar{\mu}A(p_i - p_o)}{L} \tag{10–7}$$

where w = weight of water vapor transmitted, lb/hr.
p_i and p_o = vapor pressures on inside and outside surfaces of the transmitting material, psia.

and the units of A, L, and $\bar{\mu}$ are as defined under Eq. 10–6. The units of $\bar{\mu}$, as used in Eq. 10–7, seem incongruous, but the reason for retaining them is that practically all published data on permeability appear in these units.

Just as permeability $\bar{\mu}$ is analogous to thermal conductivity k, so also are permeance M analogous to thermal conductance C, and over-all permeance $\bar{M}$ analogous to over-all coefficient of heat transfer U. Thus

$$\bar{M} = \frac{1}{(1/M_i) + (L_1/\bar{\mu}_1) + (L_2/\bar{\mu}_2) + \cdots + (1/M_o)}$$

$$= \frac{1}{(1/M_i) \mid (1/M_1) + (1/M_2) + \cdots + (1/M_o)} \tag{10–8}$$

where $\bar{M}$ = air-to-air permeance expressed in *perms* and having units of grains/(hr)(sq ft)(Δ'' Hg).
M_i and M_o = permeance, in *perms*, of inside and outside films, respectively.
M_1, M_2, $\cdots$ = permeance, in *perms*, of each of the homogeneous materials that constitute the path along which transmission occurs.
$\bar{\mu}_1$, $\bar{\mu}_2$, $\cdots$ = average permeability, expressed in *perm-inches*, of each homogeneous section of path; units are grains/(hr)(sq ft)(Δ'' Hg/in.).

From Eq. 10–8 it is evident that

$$M_x = \frac{\bar{\mu}_x}{L}$$

Hence the permeability $\bar{\mu}$ is also the permeance of unit thickness. When written in terms of over-all permeance, Eq. 10–7 becomes

$$w = 0.000291\bar{M}A(p_i - p_o) \tag{10–9}$$

Table 10–1 gives values of permeability for a few representative materials. The wide range of values is due to conflicting results obtained by different investigators. If more accurate data are lacking, the designer would do well to use the higher of the indicated values.

TABLE 10–1*
Permeability of Various Materials

Material	Applicable Range of RH, %	Permeability, perm-in.
Air (still)	73–92	120
Insulation:		
Cellular glass	—	0
Corkboard	0–100	9.5–2.1†
Structural uncoated vegetable insulating board	x–40	50–20
Mineral wool (unprotected)	30–100	116
Wood (sugar pine)	x	5.4–0.4
Masonry (1 : 2 : 4 mix)	45–100	3.2

* Data from *ASHAE Guide*, 1959, p. 131.
† The decreasing order of the stated permeabilities indicates that greater permeability is associated with lower relative humidity.

Table 10–2 provides values of the permeance of typical structural and building materials.

EXAMPLE 10–4. On the assumption of steady-state vapor transmission, calculate the rate of moisture loss through two exterior walls (each 20 ft by 10 ft and without windows) of the following construction: Interior finish is unpainted plaster on plain gypsum lath with studs. No insulation is used in the stud spaces. Exterior is $\frac{1}{4}$-in. three-ply DF plywood painted with three coats of white lead-zinc oxide and linseed oil. Inside air is at 73.5 F and 50 per cent RH, whereas outside air is at 40 F and saturation.

Solution: From Table 10–2 the plaster has a permeance of 20 perms; the plywood, 0.72 perms; and the paint, 0.9 perms. The vapor pressures at inner and outer surfaces will be taken as equal to the values in the ambient air, since air movement near the surfaces will have a greater influence on surface vapor pressure than will the vapor-transmission relationships. The air-to-air permeance is then

$$\overline{M} = \frac{1}{(1/20) + (1/0.72) + (1/0.9)}$$

$$= \frac{1}{0.050 + 1.389 + 1.111}$$

$$= \frac{1}{2.550} = 0.392$$

At 73.5 F and 50 per cent RH,

$$p_i = 0.20 \qquad \text{(from Fig. 6–5)}$$

TABLE 10–2*
Permeance of Various Materials

Material	Applicable Range of RH, %	Permeance, perms
Interior finish:		
Plaster on wood lath	30–100	11
Plaster on metal lath, ¾ in.	x–40	15
Plaster on plain gypsum lath, with studs . .	40–85	20
Gypsum wall board, plain, ⅜ in.	20–50	50
Insulating wall board, uncoated, ½ in.	x–40	90–50
Paint (interior, 2 coats):		
Enamels brushed on smooth plaster	0–92	1.5–0.5
Various primers plus 1 coat flat paint on		
plaster	x–40	3–1.6
Flat paint (alone) on insulating board . . .	x–40	4
Water emulsion on insulating board . . .	x–40	85–30
Wood:		
Exterior type, 3-ply DF plywood, ¼ in.. . . .	x–50	0.72
Interior type, 3-ply DF plywood, ¼ in.	x–50	1.86
Masonry:		
Concrete, 8-in. cored block wall,		
limestone aggregate	68–99	2.4
Brick wall with mortar, 4 in.	x–50	0.8
Tile wall with mortar, 4 in.	x–50	0.12
Paint (exterior) 3 coats:		
White lead and oil, prepared paint on		
wood siding	0–50	1.0–0.3
White lead-zinc oxide and linseed oil		
oil on wood	0–95	0.9
Vapor barriers†		
Duplex sheet, asphalt laminae, aluminum		
foil on one side (43 lb/500 sq. ft)	—	0.09
Saturated and coated felt, heavy roll		
roofing (326 lb/500 sq ft)	—	0.15
Asphalt-saturated and coated sheathing		
paper (43 lb/500 sq ft)	—	0.45
Asphalt-saturated sheathing paper		
(22 lb/sq ft)	—	11.8
15-lb asphalt felt (70 lb/sq ft)	—	3.3
15-lb tar felt	—	11.1
Single-sheet Kraft, double-infused		
(16 lb/500 sq ft)	—	36.4

* Data from *ASHAE Guide*, 1959, p.131.

† The permeance given for each vapor barrier is an approximate average of values determined by the "dry-cup" and "wet-cup" test procedure.

At 40 F and 100 per cent RH,

$$p_o = 0.12 \qquad \text{(from Fig. 6–6)}$$

$$\text{Area} = (2)(20)(10) = 400 \text{ sq ft}$$

Substituting in Eq. 10–9,

$$w = (0.000291)(0.392)(400)(0.20 - 0.12)$$

$$= 0.004 \text{ lb/hr}$$

The construction of the wall in Example 10–4 is very poor as far as vapor transmission is concerned, yet the actual rate of vapor loss through 400 sq ft of wall area is only about one-third the rate of loss from one occupant. In thermal terms the loss is of the order of (0.031)(1000)/400, or less than 0.1 Btu/(hr)(sq ft). Thus, for all practical purposes, the influence of steady-state vapor transmission on humidification load is negligible. As discussed in the paragraph which immediately follows this one, however, application of the technique for analysis of vapor transmission is often essential in checking on the possibility that condensation may be occurring within the walls. It should also be noted that the actual rate of transfer of vapor into the wall under unsteady-state conditions may be many times greater than that calculated for steady state.

Unsteady-State Vapor Transmission: Invisible Condensation. Although not a direct part of the problem of load evaluation, invisible condensation is a special condition that requires investigation at the time the design transmission and ventilation loads are calculated. In the absolute sense the rate at which invisible condensation occurs is very small, but the transmitting wall areas are large and the time available for transfer is long (the many months of the heating season), so that even with a "tight" wall construction there will be ample opportunity for relatively large weights of water vapor to flow from the room into the walls. The presence of condensation within the walls increases the conductivity of building materials and may increase the wall conductance to a point such that the load on the heating system will greatly exceed the design value. Thus it is essential that the designer check the invisible condensation characteristics of the particular structure and assure himself that under no foreseeable operating conditions will there be a possibility of serious interwall condensation.

MECHANISM OF INTERWALL CONDENSATION. The only circumstance under which condensation can take place within a wall is when water vapor comes in contact with a surface, or enters a region, where the temperature is below the saturation value corresponding to the pressure of the vapor. For a structure in which both inside and outside wall surfaces are at temperatures greater than the dew points of the inside and outside air, one might mistakenly assume that there would not be a wall condensation problem. Actually, however, frequent cases arise in which vapor is condensing within a wall even though both surfaces are perfectly dry. Analysis of conditions of this kind requires consideration of three factors: (1) the temperature gradient through the wall; (2) the vapor pressure gradient through the wall; (3) the curve showing saturation vapor pressure at each point in the wall.

As a simplest example (the procedure being the same for more complex cases), consider a wall consisting of a width of one homogeneous material. As shown in Fig. 10–1, there would be a temperature drop through the resistance represented by the inside air film, a drop through the wall itself, and a drop through the outside air film. Assuming that condensation is not occurring in the wall, the vapor-pressure gradient (dash-dotted line on Fig. 10–1) will also be a straight line from the inside surface to the outside surface, provided the permeability is a constant. The dashed line in Fig. 10–1 is a plotting of saturation pressure at each plane of the wall as a function of the temperature at any section, as determined from the temperature gradient. It is evident that if the "sag" in saturation-pressure gradient is sufficient to

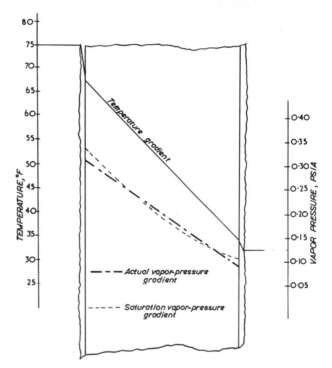

Fig. 10–1. Vapor-pressure gradient leading to internal condensation.

permit this line to cross the straight-line vapor-pressure gradient, as is the case in Fig. 10–1, condensation will necessarily occur in the region where the anticipated actual gradient shows a pressure greater than the saturation value.

Once condensation starts, the thermal conductivity of the wall in the wet region will greatly increase and thereby change the temperature gradient, with corresponding changes in saturation pressure and in actual vapor pressure gradient. Conditions in a wet wall cannot be accurately described, but this difficulty is of no practical importance because the fact that the wall is wet is in itself evidence of the need for remedial measures.

Examination of Fig. 10–1 suggests that condensation could be avoided if the temperature throughout the wall were kept sufficiently high to maintain the saturation vapor pressure at a greater value (at all points in the wall) than the actual vapor pressure. Such a solution would, of course, be an undesirable and uneconomical one, since high wall temperature would mean large energy storage in the wall and would also mean high rate of transmission through the wall. The alternative is to provide lower actual vapor pressures. If the actual vapor-pressure gradient could be caused to sag below the saturation gradient, it is evident that the overlap region of Fig. 10–1 could be eliminated and the "wet" section of wall thereby avoided.

PROCEDURES FOR CONTROL OF INVISIBLE CONDENSATION. The problem stated above is one of reducing the vapor pressure at any plane of the wall to a value less than that of the saturation vapor pressure corresponding to the temperature at the plane in question. This can be accomplished by a number of different methods. Basically, however, all such methods fall in three classes:

1. Altering the vapor pressures acting on wall surfaces.
2. Altering the vapor-pressure gradient by changing the ratio of resistances.
3. Altering the gradient by extraction of vapor along its path of transmission.

The first of these three methods is of limited application, since the humidity effective on the outside surface of the wall is not within control of the designer and that on the inside surface should, for comfort and health, be maintained close to the selected design values. Further, a reduction of inside relative humidity to below the uncontrolled value would result in increased heating load, as discussed in the introduction to this chapter.

The second method of control involves a change in the ratio of vapor resistances such that a new and lower vapor-pressure gradient will be set up in the wall. The end points of any gradient through a given wall will necessarily be fixed by inside and outside conditions, but the shape of the line connecting these end points is subject to control by variation of resistance. In this connection it is important to recognize that the gradient, whether of temperature or of vapor pressure, is an indication of conditions at all planes of the wall, but it says nothing whatever about the rate at which either heat or vapor is flowing through the wall. Thus, by relative adjustment of resistances, it would be possible to alter the shape of a gradient while leaving the flow rate unchanged. Usually, however, an intentional change of gradient is brought about by adding resistance and thus reducing the vapor-flow rate at the same time that the shape of the gradient is changed.

Since gradient is proportional to resistance, the desired reduction in vapor pressure within the wall can be attained by placing some type of vapor-resistant barrier on or near the inside surface of the wall. This type of system is shown in Fig. 10–2, where it is evident that marked reduction in vapor pressure at all points between the end conditions has been realized. Thus a

very effective means of securing protection against interwall condensation is
to provide a vapor barrier on the warm side of the wall.

In many localities common building practice is to place some type of
treated building paper on the *outside*, between the sheathing and the siding
in the case of frame construction. This is done to prevent free moisture from
being driven into the wall during a storm or from seeping in during periods

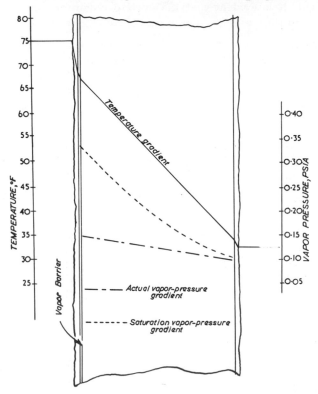

Fig. 10–2. Influence of inside vapor barrier on vapor-pressure gradient.

when the outside surface remains wet. Although effective for its purpose,
this type of construction may have serious effects on interwall condensation,
since, as shown in Fig. 10–3, the exterior barrier leads to a marked rise of
vapor pressure throughout the wall. An exterior barrier prevents free moisture from entering the wall from the outside, but it also prevents vapor from
leaving the wall after it has entered from the inside; hence the end effect may
still be a wet wall. The ideal type of exterior-wall barrier for winter service
would be one that would not allow inward passage of free water but would
offer very low resistance to the outward passage of vapor.

The third method of vapor control is through use of interwall ventilation.
The problem of maintaining low vapor pressure within the wall is one of

removing the vapor that flows in from the room. For fixed room-side conditions, the alternatives are to reduce the vapor resistance on the outside or to extract vapor from the interwall space. Reduction of external resistance is not feasible, but vapor extraction by means of interwall ventilation can sometimes be accomplished. This method is particularly suitable for attic spaces where the vapor pressure may build up as a result of low resistance

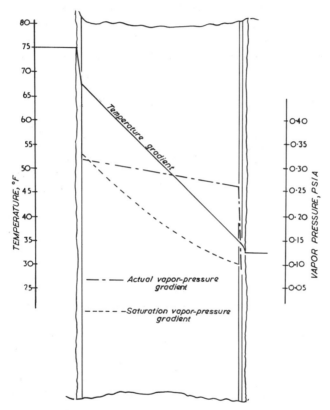

Fig. 10–3. Influence of outside vapor barrier on vapor-pressure gradient.

between room and attic but of high resistance through the roofing. In this event there will be a hazard of condensation occurring on the underside of the roof. By providing ventilation at a rate of approximately 3 cu ft/(hr)(sq ft) ceiling area, condensation in the attic will be avoided for most types of construction, and the resultant increase in heat loss (represented by the heating of ventilation air from outside to attic temperature) will not be unduly large. Attic ventilation can be accomplished either by provision of openings for free circulation or by use of positive mechanical ventilation. The latter method is the more certain and, seasonally speaking, may be the least expensive, since it permits control of ventilation volume at a rate not greater than the actual needs.

REVERSE DIFFUSION. The above discussion of vapor transmission has been with respect to non-hygroscopic materials. Many building materials that are commonly used, such as wood, are hygroscopic; that is, they take up vapor from the surrounding air until the concentration of bound moisture in the material reaches an equilibrium value which is fixed in terms of the *relative humidity* of the air. In cases of this kind the moisture transfer does not occur as vapor, since condensation takes place as soon as the vapor is received at the solid surface. Equilibrium conditions at a surface are determined by *relative* rather than *specific* humidity, and therefore it is evident that there may be more moisture present in the wall near the outside (where temperature and specific humidity are low but relative humidity in winter is likely to be high) than near the inside (where temperature and specific humidity are higher but relative humidity is lower).

EXAMPLE 10–5. Re-examine the wall of Example 10–4 to determine whether or not invisible condensation is occurring. If it is taking place, calculate: (a) the rate at which room dehumidification is occurring, owing to vapor transfer into the wall; (b) the rate of vapor transfer through the wall. Base calculation on outside wind velocity of 11 mph and assume two interior walls and transmitting floor and ceiling.

Solution: The thermal resistance of the plaster on gypsum studs (assuming 3/8-in. gypsum and $\frac{1}{2}$-in. lightweight aggregate plaster) is from Table 5–2, 0.64. Thermal resistance of the plywood exterior is 0.47; outside combined film resistance on a smooth, painted surface with an 11-mph wind (from Table 5–1, as for Springfield, Missouri) is 0.223. Then $r_w + r_o$ is equal to 0.64 +0.47 +0.223, or 1.33, and from Table 5–14 the resistance of the air space, extrapolating to 40 F, is approximately 0.22. The value of $1/C_w$ is therefore 1.33 + 0.22, or 1.55, and from Table 5–20 the corresponding value of the convective fraction of inside film coefficient, by extrapolation to 40 F, is 0.51 with a corresponding temperature drop of 13 F. The equivalent radiation film coefficient is obtained from Table 5–23 for Δt of 13 F and two non-transmitting surfaces as 0.13. The combined inside film coefficient is therefore 0.51 + 0.13, or 0.64, and the corresponding value of r_i is 1.56. Total wall resistance is therefore 1.55 + 1.56, or 3.11.

The temperature at the inside surface of the exterior finish is obtained from

$$\frac{73.5 - t_x}{73.5 - 40} = \frac{3.11 - 0.22 - 0.47}{3.11} = 0.778$$

giving

$$73.5 - t_x = 26.1; \quad t_x = 47.4 \text{ F}$$

The maximum actual vapor pressure that could exist at this surface without causing condensation is therefore the saturation pressure at 47.4 F, or (from Fig. 6–5) 0.16 psia.

Based on the assumption that the laws of vapor transmission parallel those of heat transmission, the anticipated vapor pressure at this surface would be (assuming that vapor-transfer resistance in the inside and outside air film is negligible)

$$\frac{vp_i - vp_x}{vp_i - vp_o} = \frac{1/M_x}{1/\overline{M}}$$

$$\frac{0.20 - vp_x}{0.20 - 0.12} = \frac{1/M_x}{1/\overline{M}} = \frac{1/20}{1 \Big/ \left[\dfrac{1}{(1/20) + (1/0.72) + (1/0.9)}\right]}$$

giving

$$0.20 - vp_x = 0.01024$$

$$vp_x = 0.19$$

This value exceeds the saturation pressure (0.16 psia) at this surface, so that condensation is taking place.

(a) The rate of vapor transfer from the room to the surface on which condensation occurs is

$$w = (0.000291)(20)(400)(0.20 - 0.16)$$
$$= 0.093 \text{ lb/hr}$$

(b) The rate of vapor transfer to the outside is

$$w = (0.000291) \frac{1}{(1/0.72) + (1/0.9)} (400)(0.16 - 0.12)$$

$$= 0.002 \text{ lb/hr}$$

Thus the effect of condensation has been to increase the rate of moisture loss from the room by 0.093/0.004, or 23 times, while simultaneously reducing by one-half the rate at which moisture is being transmitted through the exterior section of the wall.

10–2. Influence of Humidification Load on Total Sensible Load.

By summation of the moisture losses and gains as determined by the methods of Art. 10–1, the designer establishes the required humidification load, expressed as pounds per hour of water vapor, which must be added to the room air. The load on the heating system due to required humidification is therefore (based on an approximate latent heat of 1000 Btu/lb for low-pressure water vapor)

$$q_H = 1000 w_H \tag{10–10}$$

where q_H = load attributable to required humidification, Btu/hr.

w_H = rate of supply of humidifying vapor to the enclosure, lb/hr.

The total load on the heating system is the sum of the transmission load, the sensible ventilation load, and the total humidification load. Transmission and sensible-ventilation loads always (unless tempering is used) appear as sensible loads on the heat-distributing equipment (such as radiators, convectors, heating coils, or panels), but the humidification load may be separately handled or may be either partially or wholly converted to added sensible load that must be carried by the heating units. These three conditions are discussed in the subsequent text.

No Influence of Humidification on Sensible Load. In order for this to be the case, each pound of vapor added to the room air for the purpose of humidification would have to have the same enthalpy as the vapor already in the room. Refer to Fig. 10–4; consider any room state as r. At state r the vapor within the room has a pressure vp_r; hence its saturation temperature is t_s; the vapor therefore possesses $t_r - t_s$ degrees of superheat.

But low-pressure vapor behaves as a perfect gas; hence its enthalpy is a function of temperature only. This means that if water vapor is admitted to the room at any state along the constant temperature line oy, its entering enthalpy will equal its final enthalpy and the energy which it introduces will

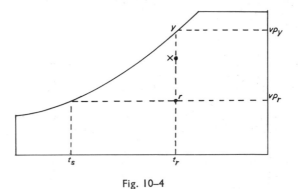

Fig. 10–4

be exactly equal to that needed for humidification (evaporation plus super-heating). If introduced at any temperature less than t_r, the entering vapor will not possess enough energy to provide the humidification load, and the difference will then appear as an increase in sensible heating load. If introduced at a temperature higher than t_r, the energy added with the vapor will exceed the humidification load and will therefore tend to reduce sensible load. The line oy is therefore the locus of all states of entering vapor for which the humidification process will have no influence on the sensible load.

Practical means of supplying air along line oy are limited essentially to evaporation from a wetted surface held at constant temperature t_r. Thus, if a pan of water were heated (if not heated it would tend to cool toward the wet-bulb temperature of room air) to t_r, the vapor pressure in the saturated film adjacent to the water surface would be vp_y and the pressure difference $vp_y - vp_r$ would drive water molecules out into the room. This process would occur at such a very low rate (refer to Example 6–4) that it could not supply adequate vapor for an actual room having even minimal humidification requirements.

The principle discussed in the above paragraph can be used in practice if some means is provided of greatly increasing the evaporating surface. This is sometimes done by utilizing an air washer with high ratio of water flow rate to air flow rate. The recirculating water is heated to t_r, and its temperature drop through the washer is kept to such a low value (by maintaining the indicated high water-air weight ratio) that the thermodynamic process followed by entering recirculated room air at state r occurs along the line oy, with discharge state at some point (such as x of Fig. 10–4) between r and y.

COMPLETE CONVERSION OF HUMIDIFICATION LOAD TO SENSIBLE LOAD. In an ordinary air washer with recirculated spray water (neither heated nor cooled externally), the process approaches an adiabatic (refer to Art. 6–4, page 247, for discussion and to Example 6–7 for a numerical case) and can be approximately represented by a constant-enthalpy line. Thus, referring to Fig. 10–5, if recirculated room air enters the washer at r, it will leave at some

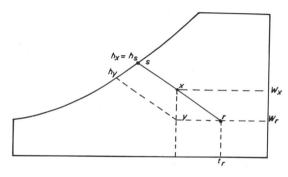

Fig. 10–5

state, such as x, along the constant-enthalpy line rs after having undergone humidification from W_r to W_x. The latent heat gain of $h_x - h_y$ is equal to the sensible heat loss of $h_r - h_y$; hence it follows that the humidification load has been fully converted to a sensible load on the room heating equipment.

In many cases humidification is realized by the direct injection of water into the conditioned space. Usually this is accomplished by passing the water through a nozzle or discharging a small, high-velocity stream against a hard surface to break it up into a fine spray or mist. With injection systems the need is for complete and rapid evaporation of all liquid entering the room, and since evaporation occurs from the liquid surface, the process is hastened if the transfer area is increased. The purpose of creating a spray is to increase the surface-volume ratio. Although the effectiveness of a given humidifier in achieving complete evaporation of the injected water is largely determined by the surface-volume ratio, the final state (for complete evaporation of a given weight of water into a given weight of air) is always the same and is independent of the effectiveness of the atomizing equipment.

Consider an atmosphere at outside state o (refer Fig. 10–6), the specific humidity of which is to be increased by direct water injection, from W_o to W_m. It is necessary to add $(W_m - W_o)/7000$ lb water for each pound of dry air in the conditioned space. The state of the air after humidification, s, can be determined by application of the laws of conservation of mass and of energy. This state must be on the horizontal line through W_m and must also be on the line for which the enthalpy is h_o plus $[(W_m - W_o)(t_w - 32)]/7000$, where t_w is the temperature of the injected water.

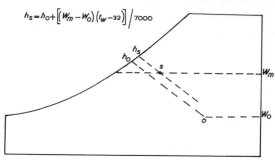

$$h_s = h_o + \left[(W_m - W_o)(t_w - 32)\right]/7000$$

Fig. 10-6

EXAMPLE 10-6. Water at 182 F is sprayed into air at 90 F dbt and 70 F wbt at a rate just sufficient to saturate the air and completely evaporate the water. Calculate the resultant air temperature.

Solution: Basing calculations on 1 lb of air at 90 F dbt and 70 F wbt with enthalpy h_1, an energy balance gives

$$h_1 + \Delta W' h_f = (1 + \Delta W')h_2$$

where $\Delta W'$ = weight of spray water added/lb of air; hence the term is equal to the increase in specific humidity, lb/lb.

h_f = heat of the liquid of the spray water, Btu/lb.

h_2 = enthalpy of the saturated air.

From Fig. 6–5, h_1 is equal to 34 Btu/lb; the heat of the liquid for spray water at 182 is $182 - 32$, or 150 Btu/lb. Then, substituting,

$$34 + 150\Delta W' = (1 + \Delta W')h_2$$

The above equation contains two unknowns, but they are dependent; hence a trial-and-error solution is possible.

As a first attempt, assume that the saturated air temperature is 75 F. In this event h_2 is 38.6 Btu/lb (from Fig. 6–5) and $\Delta W'$ is $(130 - 78)/7000$, or 0.0074 lb/lb. Now, substituting,

$$34 + (150)(0.0074) \approx (1.0074)(38.6)$$
$$35.11 \neq 38.89$$

As a second approximation, assume 71 F and read h_2 as 35.0 and $\Delta W'$ as $(114 - 78)/7000$, or 0.0051, giving

$$34 + (150)(0.0051) \approx (1.0051)(35.0)$$
$$34.8 \neq 35.2$$

Thus it is evident that the initial temperature of the spray water has had no appreciable effect, and the saturated air temperature is within less than a degree of the initial wet-bulb temperature.

From the results of Example 10–6 it follows that for any practical spray-humidification system, in which all the spray water is evaporated, the final state of the conditioned air can (approximately) be considered as falling on a constant-enthalpy line through the initial state. If an exact final state is required, it can be obtained by the trial-and-error method of Example 10–6.

PARTIAL CONVERSION OF HUMIDIFICATION LOAD TO SENSIBLE LOAD. Between the zero conversion process discussed on page 426 and the complete

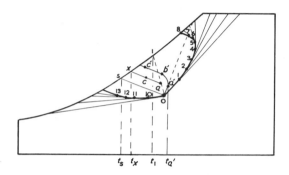

Fig. 10–7. Spray processes of humidification.

conversion process, on page 427, there are an infinite number of possible thermodynamic air-vapor paths along which partial conversion of latent load to sensible load can occur. The principles of humidification with spray water, whether by direct injection or through use of a recirculating air washer, are essentially the same.

From the thermodynamic standpoint, the paths followed by humidification processes in air washers are largely dependent, in the early stages, on the initial water temperature, but the final section of the process is usually one of adiabatic saturation. Refer to Fig. 10–7 and consider, as a first case, that water is supplied at any temperature, t_1, greater than the wet-bulb temperature of the air but less than its dry-bulb temperature. When the water first enters the air stream, the rate of heat transfer to the drop is less than for equilibrium, while the rate of mass transfer from drop to air stream is greater. The latent heat needed to sustain evaporation must therefore come in part from the sensible heat of the liquid, and the liquid temperature will drop until it reaches the equilibrium value corresponding to the final wet-bulb temperature t_x of the air stream. During this transient period the air stream will be gaining latent heat in excess of its loss of sensible heat and therefore its enthalpy will increase. The complete psychrometric path consists of a brief transient process, oa, followed by the equilibrium process of adiabatic partial saturation, ac.

The extreme example of the above case occurs when water is supplied at a temperature *greater* than the dry-bulb temperature of entering air. In that event the transient process is itself divided into two parts: (1) Initially, heat as well as vapor flows from the droplet to the air (line oa', Fig. 10–7); (2) the cooling rate is very great, so that the droplet and air are soon reduced to a common temperature $t_{a'}$. At this point there is no heat transfer either to or from the drop, but vapor is still being transferred to the passing air, and its latent heat must be supplied by sensible cooling of the unevaporated water. The drop temperature falls below the dry-bulb temperature of the air, and the remaining part of the transient period $a'b'$ is the same as in the previous case. Curve o, 1, 2, 3, 4, 5, 6, 7, 8 shows a typical process path.

A second case occurs when water enters at a temperature lower than the wet-bulb temperature of the air. The analysis is essentially the same as for the preceding case but includes preheating of the droplets during the transient period. If the initial water temperature is above the dew point, heat flows to the droplet at a rate greater than that corresponding to equilibrium, while vapor enters the air stream but at a lower rate than for equilibrium. There is thus a gain in total heat at the droplet (since sensible heat gain exceeds latent heat loss) and a resultant temperature rise until equilibrium conditions have been established. The extreme example of this case occurs when water is supplied below the dew point of the air. Under such conditions there is an initial transfer of both heat and vapor *to* the drop, so that the initial period of the process is actually one of dehumidification rather than humidification. During this period the drop temperature rapidly rises while the drop is gaining both sensible and latent heat. When the dew-point temperature is reached, the flow of vapor ceases, but the drop continues to gain sensible heat, its temperature rises, and the vapor flow now starts in the opposite direction. Fig. 10–7, curve 10, 11, 12, 13, shows a typical path for this extreme case.

The obvious disadvantage of evaporating water as a method of humidification is that, as has been shown, the process inevitably becomes one approaching adiabatic humidification, with a consequent temperature reduction of the conditioned air. This disadvantage can be overcome by injecting steam rather than water into the conditioned space. For many industrial humidification problems, steam injection is the simplest and the most economical method (both in first and in operating costs) of raising humidity.

The thermodynamic processes followed by injection steam are shown on the temperature entropy diagram of Fig. 10–8a. Moist steam at state l passes through a throttling valve, undergoing a constant-enthalpy pressure reduction to b, where it is saturated, and beyond to atmospheric pressure; a further irreversible expansion then occurs as the vapor pressure drops to the value at state c, corresponding to the desired vapor pressure in the conditioned space. From state c the highly superheated vapor follows a constant-pressure line, while losing heat to the air, and ends at d, corresponding to the state of vapor in the humidified space. The difference in enthalpy between states c and d is the energy, in Btu/lb steam added, which appears as a sensible heat gain in the conditioned space. On the psychrometric chart of Fig. 10–8b, point d corresponds to the same point on the temperature entropy diagram. Thus the energy available for sensible heating is the difference in enthalpy between line steam and saturated steam at state y.

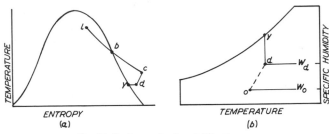

Fig. 10–8. Steam jet humidification.

If the known initial state of the air into which steam is injected is at o (Fig. 10–8b), the temperature after steam injection can be determined as follows: The specific humidity of air at o is

$$c_H = c_{pa} + c_{ps}W'_o = 0.2411 + 0.50W'_o$$

Then, establishing an energy balance on the system,

$$c_H(t_d - t_o) = (h_{s_1} - h_{s_y})(W'_d - W'_o)$$

giving

$$t_d = t_o + \frac{(h_{s_1} - h_{s_y})(W'_d - W'_o)}{0.2411 + 0.50W'_o} \qquad (10\text{--}11)$$

where h_{s_1} = enthalpy of steam at line state, Btu/lb.

  h_{s_y} = enthalpy of saturated steam at the final temperature of the humidified atmosphere.

Eq. 10–11 contains two unknowns, t_d and h_{s_y}, but they are dependent and therefore a trial-and-error solution is possible. The procedure is to assume t_d, obtain the corresponding value of h_{s_y} from the steam tables, and substitute into Eq. 10–11 to test for an equality. The sensible heating effect associated with humidification by steam injection is usually not negligible and should in every case be investigated.

PROBLEMS

10–1. When outside air is at 30 F and 100 per cent RH, an industrial work room (30 ft by 40 ft by 12 ft) is heated to 75 F dbt with associated uncontrolled relative humidity of 50 per cent. Mechanical ventilation is supplied at a minimum permissible rate of one air change per hour and the ventilation air is not tempered. For one type of industrial process, the room state (at fixed dry-bulb temperature) must be changed so that the relative humidity will be 70 per cent, whereas for a different process, the relative humidity must be reduced to 30 per cent. (a) Calculate the increased heating load due to maintenance of the higher relative humidity. (b) Calculate the increased heating load due to maintenance of the lower relative humidity. (c) Is it possible to generalize, from the results of parts (a) and (b) concerning the relative cost in energy requirements of increasing the uncontrolled relative humidity versus decreasing the uncontrolled relative humidity?

10–2. A 75-ft by 30-ft swimming pool is heated to 75 F and is located in a room that is held at 60 F dbt and 50 per cent relative humidity when the outside state is 40 F dbt at 80 per cent RH. The thermal characteristics of the room are such that the transmitting wall having least resistance has an equilibrium inside-surface temperature that is a fraction of a degree above the inside dew-point temperature for given inside and outside states. The convective film coefficient for heat transfer from the pool surface to the room air is 0.65 Btu/(hr)(sq ft)(°F). Calculate the required minimum ventilation rate (using untempered outside air), in cfm, to prevent condensation on the inside surface of the wall. (Assume that the only internal source of water vapor is evaporation from the undisturbed surface of the pool.)

10–3. Humidification requirements for an office building under conditions of design load are such that 150 gal/day of make-up water must be supplied to an adiabatic air washer. Make-up is from the city supply system, with water at 55 F. Inside air temperature is held at 74 F. Calculate the load on the heating system, in Btu/hr, due to the humidification requirements.

10–4. The state in a classroom is automatically maintained at 72 F dbt and 50 per cent RH, regardless of occupancy, when outside air is at 62 F dbt and 54 F wbt. Humidification needs are met by a humidifier, and heating-season dehumidification needs are met by increasing the ventilation rate. Ventilation air is supplied at a minimum rate of 400 cfm of outside air, which is heated (at constant specific humidity) to room temperature before introduction into the room. When the classroom is unoccupied and unlighted, the total heat load is 36,000 Btu/hr. (a) Calculate the transmission load. (b) Calculate the sensible load due to ventilation. (c) Calculate the latent load due to ventilation.

10–5. When the classroom of problem 10–4 is occupied, the lighting needs of the 35 students and 1 teacher are satisfied by an electrical input of 500 w. Under these conditions (a) calculate the latent heat load due to ventilation; (b) calculate the required ventilation rate, in cfm; (c) calculate the total heating load; (d) calculate the required rate of make-up of 55 F city water to the humidifier.

10–6. The windowless walls of a 20-ft by 30-ft by 10-ft building are made of 8-in. cored lightweight-aggregate concrete blocks. On the inside, $\frac{1}{2}$-in. uncoated insulating wall board is directly attached (no air space) to the concrete. Inside air is at 82 F dbt and 75 F wbt, and for design conditions, outside air is saturated at 20 F. Assuming steady-state conditions, calculate the rate of vapor loss through the walls, in lb/24 hr.

10–7. For the conditions of problem 10–6, determine whether or not the assumption of steady-state vapor transmission is valid. If not, calculate the distance in from the inside surface at which condensation would be expected to start.

10–8. Repeat problem 10–7 for a wall having 2 in. of insulation rather than $\frac{1}{2}$ in.

10–9. A wall consists of 8-in. cored lightweight-aggregate concrete blocks with 2 in. of insulation on the inside. A vapor barrier consisting of a duplex sheet of asphalt aluminae (43 lb/500 sq ft) with aluminum foil on one side is placed on the inside surface of the insulation; the barrier is painted with two coats of a flat paint which has a permeance of 4. The thermal resistance of the painted barrier is 3.0 Btu/(hr) (sq ft) (°F). Inside state is at 82 F dbt with 75 F wbt, and outside air is saturated at 20 F. (a) Investigate the likelihood of steady-state vapor transmission. (b) Aside from the painted vapor barrier, this wall is the same as that of problem 10–8; compare the results of these two problems.

10–10. Repeat problem 10–9 for the same wall, but with the insulation removed and the vapor barrier placed directly on the inside surface of the concrete.

10–11. In an industrial room, air is at 90 F dbt and 55 F wbt. Water at 150 F is sprayed into the room air (evaporation being complete) until the specific humidity has been raised to 60 grains/lb. (a) Determine the resultant dry-bulb temperature. (b) By how many degrees would the final dry-bulb temperature be in error if it were assumed that the process were one of adiabatic saturation?

10–12. Air at 70 F dbt and 10 per cent RH flows through an air washer where parallel flow occurs with spray water that enters at 100 F. The ratio of flow rates of water to air is 0.5 lb/lb. Determine the temperature of the leaving air if its relative humidity is 80 per cent.

10–13. The specific humidity in a room at 70 F dbt with 10 per cent RH is to be increased to 100 grains/lb by the direct injection of superheated steam at 20 psia and 300 F. Determine the resultant room temperature.

Part IV

LOAD EVALUATION FOR UNSTEADY STATE

11

INFLUENCE OF DIURNAL PERIODICITY
ON DESIGN LOAD

In preceding chapters, the evaluation of design load has in every case been based on the assumption that the structure is in thermal equilibrium under steady-state conditions. For the great majority of cases this assumption is a valid one, since the heating system must be designed to perform over extended time periods during which the outside temperature remains practically constant at the design value. Even in localities where marked diurnal temperature change is usually associated with cold weather, the steady-state assumption has the advantage of being conservative, since the effect of periodic load change will be to reduce partially the load associated with the lowest outside air temperature that occurs in any 24-hr period.

For the above reasons, departures from steady state can be ignored when designing heating systems for residences or for structurally light commercial buildings. When the structure is large and thermally "heavy," however, the influence of periodic temperature change can be of genuine significance. In such cases the effect of periodic flow of heat to or from storage in the walls, roof, and floor of the building will lead to a displacement, with respect to time, of the maximum heating load and a reduction in the magnitude of that maximum as compared with the value that would be obtained from a steady-state analysis.

The average building is structurally so complex that it becomes difficult to analyze its thermal behavior by means of the rational equations for periodic heat flow. A much simpler procedure, and one that will be used throughout this chapter, is to use approximate methods which permit of graphical solution. Although not exact, such methods can be set up to provide any desired degree of accuracy.

11-1. The Schmidt Method of Finite Differences. The method presented in this article is based on an equation developed by E. Schmidt[1] and extended by Nessi and Nisolle.[2] Consider a finite section of homogeneous wall, Δx, of Fig. 11-1a, across which the temperature gradient at a particular time is given by the dashed line. At that time, the gradient at the left

---

[1] E. Schmidt, *Foppls Festschrift*, Springer, Berlin, 1924, p. 179.
[2] A. Nessi and L. Nisolle, *Méthodes graphiques pour l'étude des installations de chauffage et de réfrigération en régime discontinu*, Dunod, Paris, 1929.

boundary is tangent to the dashed line and the gradient at the right boundary is likewise tangent to the true section-temperature gradient. Draw these tangent lines, establish a pair of construction lines (Fig. 11–1b) at distance $p = K \Delta x$ on either side of the midplane of the Δx section, and label the intersections a, b, and c as shown in the figure. Then extend ab to intersect the right construction line at point e, and connect a and c with a straight line that intersects the midplane of the finite area at point d.

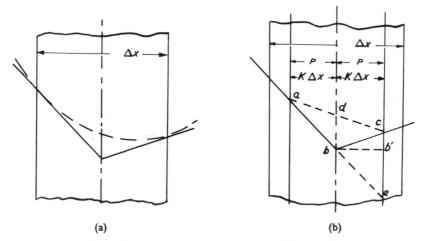

(a)   (b)

Fig. 11–1. Geometry for analysis by method of finite differences.

The instantaneous rate of heat flow into the finite element from the left (considering it to be of unit depth) is

$$q = \frac{\Delta Q_1}{\Delta \theta} = -kA \frac{\Delta t}{\Delta x} = -kA(\text{slope } ab) = +kA \frac{b'e}{p} \qquad (11\text{–}1)$$

and the corresponding rate of heat flow in from the right is

$$q = \frac{\Delta Q_r}{\Delta \theta} = -kA \frac{\Delta t}{\Delta x} = -kA(\text{slope } bc) = +kA \frac{b'c}{p} \qquad (11\text{–}2)$$

The net heat gain by the element during the finite time interval $\Delta \theta$ is equal to the sum of the heat entering from left and right. It can also be expressed in terms of the change in mean temperature, Δt, which must occur during the same time interval in the homogeneous wall section of area A, thickness Δx, density ρ, and specific heat c:

$$\Delta Q_1 + \Delta Q_r = kA(\Delta \theta)\left(\frac{b'e}{p} + \frac{b'c}{p}\right) = \rho c(\Delta t)(\Delta x)A \qquad (11\text{–}3)$$

or

$$\frac{b'e}{p} + \frac{b'c}{p} = \frac{\rho c(\Delta t)(\Delta x)}{k(\Delta \theta)} = \frac{b'e + b'c}{p} = \frac{ce}{p} \qquad (11\text{–}4)$$

By similar triangles, $bd = \frac{1}{2}ce$, giving $ce/p = 2(bd)/p$, which on substitution into Eq. 11-4 [noting that $p = K(\Delta x)$] gives

$$\frac{\rho c(\Delta t)(\Delta x)}{k(\Delta \theta)} = \frac{2(bd)}{K(\Delta x)}$$

or

$$bd = \frac{1}{2}\frac{\rho c}{k}(\Delta t)\left(\frac{\Delta x^2}{\Delta \theta}\right)K = \Delta t\left[\frac{1}{2\alpha}\frac{K(\Delta x)^2}{(\Delta \theta)}\right]$$

where α is the thermal diffusivity (equal to $k/\rho c$) of the wall.

Now, if a relationship is established among Δx, $\Delta \theta$, and K such that

$$\frac{1}{2\alpha}\frac{K(\Delta x)^2}{(\Delta \theta)} = 1 \tag{11-5}$$

then the mean temperature change of the element during the time interval $\Delta \theta$ would be represented by the distance bd. Knowing the temperature gradient abc at a particular time, the temperature at the midplane of the element, $\Delta \theta$ hours later, would be directly determined by drawing line ac and noting the intersection at point d on the midplane; d would give the midplane temperature at the end of the $\Delta \theta$ interval.

In the relationship of Eq. 11-5, the element of wall width, Δx, *must* have a numerical value such that it will be equally divisible into the actual width of wall. The time interval, $\Delta \theta$, should have a numerical value that will be equally divisible into the period for which the analysis is to be conducted; this latter condition is essential when the problem is one involving periodic variation. When both the width and time intervals are arbitrarily selected, the necessary value of K must be determined by solution of Eq. 11-5. Experience shows, however, that accurate results cannot be expected if K is very much greater than unity, since this requires extrapolation of the temperature gradient beyond the boundaries of the finite section. For any particular problem there is an optimum value of K, usually between $\frac{1}{4}$ and 1, for which the greatest accuracy will be realized, but this value cannot be determined except by trial and error, and the process is usually too time consuming to be justified. The error involved in using a value of K other than the optimum (provided it is within the range $\frac{1}{4} < K < 1$) is usually negligible.

An alternative method of realizing any required degree of accuracy, and at the same time simplifying the graphical work, is arbitrarily to fix $K = 1$, select a value of Δx sufficiently small so that change in rate of change of temperature gradient across the section will not be great, and calculate the required value of $\Delta \theta$ needed to satisfy Eq. 11-5. This method has the enormous advantage of eliminating all the construction lines on either side of the finite-section center lines, since p is now equal to Δx (see Fig. 11-2). The temperature at the midplane of a finite section, $\Delta \theta$ hours after a known temperature gradient abc, is fixed by drawing a straight line connecting the intersections of the original temperature gradient at the midplanes of sections to the left and right of the one for which the temperature is to be determined. The desired temperature is given at the intersection of this straight line with the dashed midplane line of the section being investigated. Thus a solution is obtained in terms only of the finite-section center lines and the temperature gradient at the start of the time interval $\Delta\theta$.

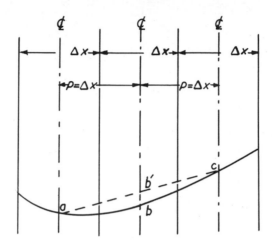

Fig. 11–2. Typical construction for method of finite differences with $K = 1$.

EXAMPLE 11–1. A 12-in. slab of large area has a thermal diffusivity of 0.3 sq ft/hr and is initially at a uniform temperature of 70 F. If the temperature of one surface is suddenly dropped to 10 F and held at that value, determine the temperature 22 min later at a plane 6 in. in from that surface.

Solution: If the slab is divided into four Δx sections of 4 in. thickness (refer to Fig. 11–3a), the corresponding time interval, by Eq. 7–5, would be

$$\Delta\theta = \frac{(\Delta x)^2}{2\alpha} = \frac{(0.25)^2}{(2)(0.3)} = 0.104 \text{ hr}$$

$$= 6\tfrac{1}{4} \text{ min}$$

At time zero, the temperature gradient is given by the horizontal line $abcde$. At the end of the first $\Delta\theta$ time interval, the temperature 3 in. from the cooled surface corresponds to d' and is obtained by drawing a straight line from o to c. The gradient at $1\Delta\theta$ is then $a'b'c'd'o$. At the end of the second $\Delta\theta$ interval, the temperature 3 in. from the cold surface corresponds to d'', which is the same point as d'; the temperature 6 in. from the surface now corresponds to point c'', which is obtained by connecting points d' and b'; the gradient at $2\Delta\theta$ is $a''b''c''d''o$. After the third time interval, d''' is obtained by connecting o with c'', c''' by connecting d'' with b''; and b''' by connecting c'' with a''. The gradient at time $3\Delta\theta$ is then $a''b'''c'''d'''o$. By similar construction (assuming that the warm side of the wall is held at 70 F), the gradient at time $4\Delta\theta$ is obtained as $a''''b''''c''''d''''o$.

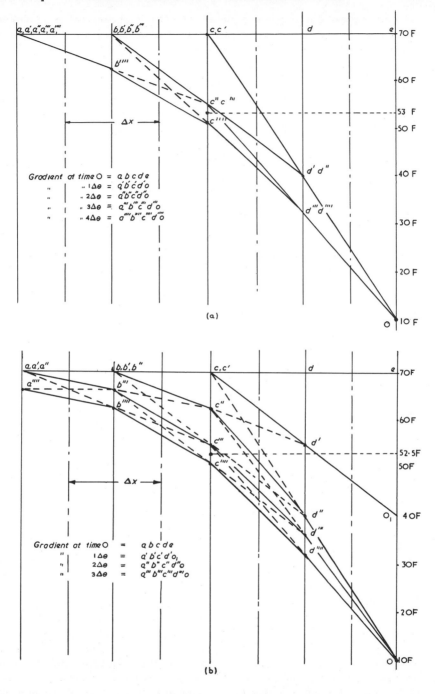

Fig. 11-3. Graphical transient analysis by Schmidt method (Example 11-1).

The temperature 6 in. from the surface after 22 min is between the values for $3\Delta\theta$ ($18\frac{3}{4}$ min) and $4\Delta\theta$ (25 min), and so it is obtained by interpolation between points c''' and c''''. The dotted horizontal line on Fig. 11–3 intersects the temperature scale to give 53 F as the answer.

Note: An obvious disadvantage in this solution is that temperatures at given points are shown as varying only during alternate time intervals; this requires, for accuracy, that $\Delta\theta$ be taken as a very small value. An alternative method of correcting the difficulty is to treat the cooled surface as though it were only partially cooled (in this case, to 40 F) at the end of the first $\Delta\theta$ time interval; the effect of this device is to eliminate the alternate changes. The surface temperature at the end of the second and subsequent $\Delta\theta$ intervals is held constant at 10 F as before; the effect of this correction is to provide a more rapid approach to the true temperatures. Fig. 11–3b shows such a solution as applied to the above Example and indicates a revised and more accurate resultant midplane temperature after 22 min as 52.5 F.

11–2. Extension To Include Surface Films or Radiation Effects.
Before setting up a procedure for applying the Schmidt method to actual problems, it is necessary to provide some means of treating the surface films so that there will not be a discontinuity in the graphical construction at the wall boundaries. If the film transferred heat entirely by conduction and had a thermal conductivity equal to that of the adjacent wall, there would be no discontinuity in the temperature gradient at the wall surface. Such a condition can be readily obtained by establishing an imaginary film having the same conductance as the actual film but having a thermal conductivity equal to that of the wall; the thickness of the equivalent film is then $L = k/h$. By establishing a film of this type on each side of the wall, the entire system can be set up as an equivalent homogeneous wall. The equivalent film thickness is a function of the actual film coefficient, which may vary with respect to time; in that event, the equivalent thickness would likewise vary, but the continuity of gradient at the wall surface would still be realized at all times.

EXAMPLE 11–2. If the slab of Example 11–1 were a wall with inside and outside convective film coefficients (no radiation effects present) of $h_{ci} = 2$ and $h_{co} = 4$, and if inside air temperature were held at 70 F after a sudden drop of outside air temperature from 70 F to 10 F, determine the temperature at the midplane of the wall after 22 min; wall conductivity is 4 Btu/(hr)(sq ft)(°F/ft).

Solution: Fig. 11–4 shows the graphical solution. In this case equivalent inside and outside films of 2-ft and 1-ft thickness, respectively, are constructed adjacent to the wall surfaces, construction is based on the center line of each Δx section, and equivalent center lines set up a distance $\Delta x/2$ on each side of the wall.

The initial horizontal 70 F gradient through the slab and the continuing sharp gradient through the outside $\Delta x/2$ film layer is given by line *abcdef*. At time $1\Delta\theta$, point f' is found by drawing *oe* and point e' by drawing *df*; the gradient at $1\Delta\theta$ is then $a'b'c'd'e'f'$. At time $2\Delta\theta$, point f'' is found by drawing $e'o$, point e''

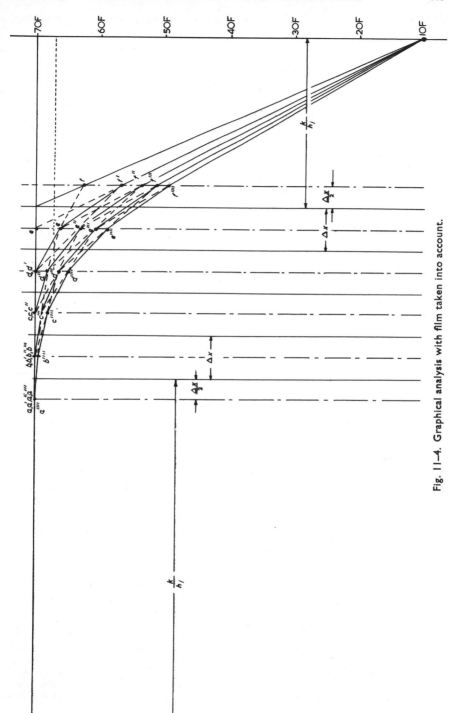

Fig. 11–4. Graphical analysis with film taken into account.

by drawing $d'f'$ and point d'' by drawing $c'e'$; the gradient at $2\Delta\theta$ is then $a''b''c''d''e''f''$. At time $3\Delta\theta$, point f''' is found by drawing $e''o$, point e'' by drawing $d''f''$, point d''' by drawing $c''e''$, and c''' by drawing $b''d''$; the gradient is then $a'''b''c''d''e''f'''$. By similar construction the gradient at the end of the fourth time interval is $a''''b'''c''''d'''e''''f''''$, and the temperature at the midplane is obtained by interpolation (refer to the dotted horizontal line on Fig. 11–4) as 67 F.

Possible radiation effects can be accounted for by using a combined film coefficient, but in doing so, it must be noted that the actual radiation rate must be converted for expression in terms of the temperature drop between air and surface. Thus, if radiation were occurring from an outside surface to a clear night sky at a rate of q_r Btu/(hr)(sq ft), the value of h_r, for use in the combined film coefficient, would be $q_r/(\Delta t)$ where Δt is the temperature difference between outside air and outside surface.

11–3. Periodic Variation. The method of carrying out a graphical analysis of the temperature gradient for a structure subject to periodic daily variation of inside and outside air temperatures will be established for the general case. The data from such a solution can be used to calculate the heating at any hour of the day and to determine the time lag between the incidence of extreme conditions exterior to the structure and the subsequent appearance, within the structure, of the actual load. In many problems involving variable inside temperature (such as intermittent heating of buildings), the time-temperature curve may not be available, but later articles will develop methods whereby this curve can be approximated and the accuracy of the approximation checked. The graphical method will be outlined for two cases: (1) that of a single-section, homogeneous wall with K taken as unity; (2) a composite wall made up of a number of homogeneous sections, for each of which K will have a different value.

CASE 1: PERIODIC FLOW THROUGH A HOMOGENEOUS WALL. Consider a homogeneous wall with inside air at fixed temperature t_i and outside air varying periodically over a known diurnal time-temperature curve. The inside film coefficient h_i will be considered constant, while the outside coefficient h_o varies as a function of periodic diurnal changes in the wind velocity.[3] The graphical construction leading to a complete solution for the temperature-time relationship at all points in this wall is given in Fig. 11–5a, b, c, d, e, each part of which will be explained.

Figure 11–5a. Draw a vertical line S_oS_o'' and on it, starting at some point such as S_o'', establish a 24-hr linear scale of time, $S_o''S_o'$, beginning at the hour for which maximum outside temperature occurs. (The solution does not require that the scale begin and end at the time of maximum temperature,

---

[3] Changes in h_o would also occur due to solar radiation and to nocturnal radiation. Solar radiation is not considered in heating calculations since it cannot be depended on to occur under conditions of maximum heating load. Nocturnal radiation also is neglected on the assumption that design load is most likely to occur on cold cloudy days which will have accompanying cloudy nights (noting that nocturnal radiation is significant only when there is a clear night sky).

but this is a convenient starting point and assists in estimating the first approximation to the temperature gradient.) Normal to $S_o'S_o'''$ and through S_o', draw a line BS_o'; starting with zero at S_o', lay off to the left along this line a linear scale covering the range of values of k_w/h_o that exist throughout the 24-hr period. At any point such as B, far to the left of BS_o', draw a vertical BB', and with point B as any convenient value less than the minimum outside air temperature, establish a linear temperature scale along this line. From B, along BS_o' establish a linear time scale similar to $S_o''S_o'$.

From weather bureau records, direct observation, or other source, obtain data on the outside air temperature as a function of time and plot the time-temperature curve as shown in Fig. 11–5a.[4] A vertical line from any point on the horizontal time scale to intersection with the curve, which is then transferred horizontally to the left, fixes the outside air temperature for that particular time. Since the time-temperature curve is periodic, each temperature between the maximum and minimum must be realized at least twice during the 24 hr, so that any horizontal line gives the temperature at two particular times during the day.

From the weather bureau, or other sources, obtain data on the variation of wind velocity with time. The value of the film coefficient at a given time can then be calculated, and the curve plotted for k_w/h_o as a function of time. Any line from the vertical time scale to intersection with this curve, which is then transferred vertically upward, represents the value of k_w/h_o for that particular hour of the day. For a given time, the intersection of the proper temperature and k_w/h_o lines (such as x and y) establishes the position of a reference point p. Reference points are established at intervals of $\Delta\theta$ hours throughout the day; each such point fixes the outside air temperature and the equivalent outside film thickness at a particular time.

Figure 11–5b. Allow the line S_oS_o' to represent the outside surface of the wall, and establish the requisite reference points with respect to S_oS_o' by the method of Fig. 11–5a. Then move to the right from S_oS_o' a distance equal to the wall width in feet and measured to the same scale as that used for k_w/h_o (the units of which are also feet). This establishes the position of the inside surface of the wall S_iS_o'. For the example illustrated, neither t_i nor h_i vary with time and therefore a single inside reference point, RP_i will suffice; this can be fixed by moving to the right from the inside wall surface a distance k_w/h_i and locating on this vertical the point RP_i, corresponding to the inside air temperature t_i. If either t_i or h_i varied with time, additional inside reference points would be established by the method of Fig. 11–5a.

Figure 11–5c. The sections Δx, of width satisfying Eq. 11–5 for the assumed condition of $K = 1$ and for $\Delta\theta$ having the value selected in

---

[4] Both the time-temperature and the time-film curves shown in Fig. 11–5a are sinusoidal; note, however, that neither a sine curve nor any other symmetrical curve is an implicit requirement for the solution, the only requirement being that the curve repeat itself every 24 hours.

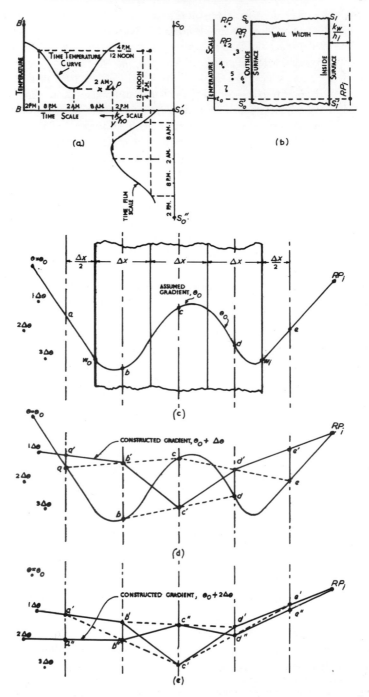

Fig. 11–5. Graphical construction for periodic analysis of homogeneous wall.

establishing the reference points, are now marked off on the wall. Note that care must be exercised to assure that Δx has a value equally divisible into the actual wall width; before fixing reference points, the investigation of this condition should be made to verify the possibility of using the desired value of $\Delta \theta$.

In many cases the Δx corresponding to a desired $\Delta \theta$ is too large (in comparison with the total wall width) to permit an accurate solution, whereas in other cases (notably diurnal periodicity) selection of a small Δx may give a $\Delta \theta$ so small that an impractical number of steps would have to be followed in completing the 24-hr cycle. This basic inflexibility of the (Δx, $\Delta \theta$) relationship is the most serious fault of the graphical method. Whenever accuracy requires a Δx less than that corresponding to a time interval of $\frac{1}{2}$ hr, the graphical method for diurnal periodicity will require so many steps that it will be cumbersome in construction. Fortunately this difficulty does not often exist in structures having a thermal capacity great enough to require analysis of diurnal periodic variation.

Dashed center lines are now drawn through each Δx section, and similar lines are established a distance $\Delta x/2$ out from each wall surface. If the temperature gradient through the wall at any particular time is known, this gradient is established on Fig. 11–5c; if no such gradient is known, one is estimated or assumed for an arbitrarily selected starting time. The need for an assumed initial gradient does not introduce any error into the final result, for regardless of how poor the estimate may be, a correct result, accurate to within the limits of the chosen Δx, is unavoidable, provided directions for the graphical construction are carefully followed. Even if the estimator were so lacking in judgment as to assume that heat flow occurs from low to high temperature, the construction would automatically lead to a correct solution; skill in estimating the initial gradient is repaid, however, with a more rapid solution.

Having fixed an initial temperature gradient, its intersections with center lines of the Δx sections are marked (b, c, d of Fig. 11–5c) and straight lines are drawn from w_o to the outside reference point for the time of the initial gradient and from w_i to the inside reference point. These lines intersect the film construction lines at points a and e, giving as the initial gradient through the system of wall and two equivalent films the line $abcde$. If $abcde$ were the true gradient at the initial time, the first step in the construction would give the correct gradient $\Delta \theta$ hours later, and subsequent steps would give the correct gradients at the initial time plus multiples of $\Delta \theta$; continuing in this way, the constructed temperature gradient after 24 hr would superimpose on the known gradient with which the construction had started.

Since the initial gradient is usually assumed, and therefore not correct, subsequent gradients determined in the process of analysis will likewise be in error, and at the end of the 24-hr period the indicated gradient will differ from the one that was originally assumed. It can be shown that the new gradient is a better approximation to the true value than was the assumed one. The procedure is then to repeat the periodic analysis, using as an initial gradient the result obtained from the first construction. The result for the second 24-hr analysis will be a third approximation, and this can be used as the starting point for a third repetition of the construction. In this way the analysis proceeds until close superposition of the initial and final gradients indicates that a solution has been realized. In most practical problems, a reasonably good estimate of the general location and curvature of the initial temperature gradient will permit realizing an accurate solution in not more than three cycles, and frequently in two. The process of correcting the initial assumption can be accelerated somewhat by carefully scrutinizing the difference in shape and position of the assumed gradient and the first constructed approximation. From the direction and magnitude of the changes, it is often possible to anticipate the need for further correction and to estimate such corrections when drawing the initial gradient at the start of the second cycle.

Figure 11–5d. The only parts of Fig. 11–5c that are used in the actual construction are the section center lines, the two dashed lines located beyond the wall surfaces, the inside and outside reference points, and the assumed initial temperature gradient. This material is shown in Fig. 11–5d with the accompanying construction lines for determination of the gradient at time interval $\Delta\theta$ after the start. To determine the new temperature gradient, connect points a and c to establish b'; connect b and d to establish c'; c and e, for d'. Then connect b' with the outside reference point corresponding to a time $1\Delta\theta$ after that at the start, thereby fixing a'; similarly connect d' with the inside reference point to fix e'. The line $a'b'c'd'e'$ then represents the temperature gradient $1\Delta\theta$ hours after the time for which $abcde$ was drawn.

Figure 11–5e. The gradient $a'b'c'd'e'$ is used for establishing the gradient $2\Delta\theta$ hours after the starting time. Connecting alternately primed points gives the new double-primed points $b''c''d''$. A line connecting b'' with the outside reference point for $2\Delta\theta$ plus the initial starting time fixes a'', and a similar construction determines e''. The new gradient is then $a''b''c''d''e''$. The same construction is repeated for subsequent intervals until at the end of 24 hr a gradient is available for comparison with the one originally assumed. If agreement is close, a solution has been obtained; if not, the cycle is repeated, starting with the gradient determined from the first cycle.

EXAMPLE 11–3. An 8-in. masonry wall is subject to 24-hr periodic variation of outside air temperature. The temperature-time curve is sinusoidal, with a maximum of 70 F at 2 P.M. and a minimum of 30 F at 2 A.M. Inside air temperature is maintained at a constant value of 70 F, and inside and outside combined film coefficients are 1.65 and 6.00 Btu/(hr)(sq ft)(°F), respectively. The thermal diffusivity is 0.049 sq ft/hr. (a) Calculate the rate of heat loss per unit wall area from room air at 4 A.M. (b) Calculate the maximum heating load per unit area. (c) Compare maximum heating loads for steady-state and for periodic conditions.

Solution: If Δx is arbitrarily selected as one-third of the wall thickness, then

$$\Delta \theta = \frac{(\Delta x)^2}{2\alpha} = \frac{[8/(12)(3)]^2}{(2)(0.49)} = 0.5 \text{ hr}$$

The graphical solution is then set up in the usual way, an initial gradient at time zero (2 P.M.) is assumed, and the construction carried out over a sufficient number of 24-hr periods to achieve superposition of temperature gradients.

Fig. 11–6 gives the results for this example. Construction lines used in passing from one gradient to another are not shown in this figure, on which appear only the 48 temperature gradients (since $\Delta \theta$ was taken as $\frac{1}{2}$ hr) resulting from the last cycle of the analysis. From such a solution it is immediately possible to read the temperature at any point in the wall for any time.

(a) To determine the load at 4 A.M., note that this is 14 hr after the time of maximum outside air temperature; hence the wall temperature gradient will correspond to the twenty-eighth time interval. The gradient marked 28 on Fig. 11–6 intersects the inside surface to show a temperature of 55 F; hence the load is

$$q = h(t_a - t_s) = 1.65(70 - 55) = 24.8 \text{ Btu/(hr)(sq ft)}$$

(b) Minimum inside surface temperature (from Fig. 11–6) is shown by the $31\Delta \theta$ temperature gradient; this temperature is approximately 54.5 F and occurs at 2 P.M. plus $15\frac{1}{2}$ hr or at 5:30 A.M. The maximum load is therefore

$$q_{max} = 1.65(70 - 54.5) = 25.6 \text{ Btu/(hr)(sq ft)}$$

(c) Taking the thermal conductivity of the wall as 1.0 Btu/(hr)(sq ft)(°F/ft), the wall resistance would be (8/12)/1.0, or 0.670. The corresponding minimum steady-state inside surface temperature is

$$t_{si} = 70 - \frac{r_i}{R}(70 - 30)$$

$$= 70 - \frac{(1/1.65)}{[(1/1.65) + 0.670 + (1/6.00)]}(40)$$

$$= 70 - \frac{0.606}{1.44}(40) = 53.2 \text{ F}$$

Maximum steady-state heating load is therefore

$$q_{\text{steady-state max}} = 1.65(70 - 53.2) = 27.7 \text{ Btu/(hr)(sq ft)}$$

For the particular conditions of this example the influence of periodic change in outside air temperature is to reduce the design value of transmission load by

$$\frac{27.7 - 25.6}{27.7} = 0.076, \quad \text{or} \quad 7.6 \text{ per cent}$$

Since the graphical analysis for periodic transfer is based on relative rather than absolute values, one solution is valid for an infinite number of cases. Consider the following extensions of the solution for Example 11–3, shown in Fig. 11–6:

1. If the time of the maximum temperature were to change, other conditions remaining the same, the solution would remain valid, and the only

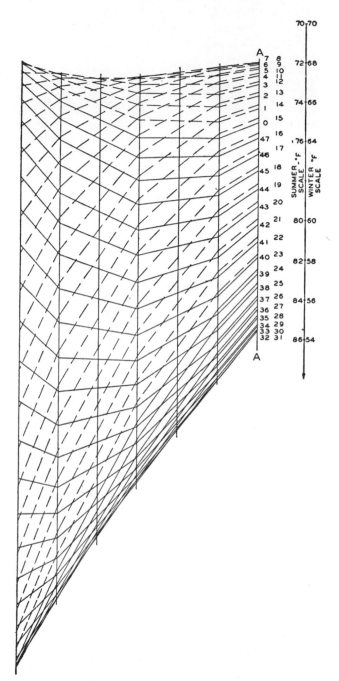

Fig. 11–6. Solution of problem for periodic variation of temperature in homogeneous wall.

needed change in the figure would be to displace the time scale and note that the numbers on the temperature gradients are for the number of $\Delta\theta$ time intervals that have passed since the time of the maximum outside temperature.

2. If other conditions remain the same but the range of outside temperature increases or decreases (with fixed maximum of 70 F), the solution is valid, subject only to numerical adjustment of the temperature scale. If any change occurs in the maximum temperature, the solution still holds, provided the inside temperature remains constant at a value equal to the maximum outside temperature.

3. For summer conditions the same solution applies, subject to the single limitation that the inside air temperature must be constant at a value equal to the minimum outside temperature and the outside temperature variation must follow the same *shape* temperature-time curve as that which applied for winter.

4. The solution is likewise valid for any wall of the same width, whatever its material or physical properties, provided its thermal diffusivity $(k/\rho c)$ has the same value as for the wall of Fig. 11–6 and the equivalent film widths, k/h_i and k/h_o, are the same.

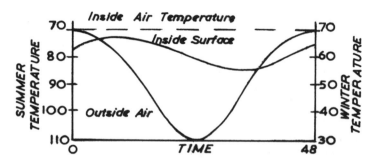

Fig. 11–7. Time-temperature curve for inside-air and inside-wall surface temperature when change is periodic.

Fig. 11–7 groups the temperature-time curves of the outside air, the inside air, and the inside wall surface; the latter curve is plotted from data read directly from Fig. 11–6. Similar curves could readily be established for the temperature-time variation at any selected planes in the wall. From Fig. 11–7 it is evident that the periodic temperature variation becomes less, and the time at which the maximum temperature occurs comes later, as the inside surface is approached. This time lag between incidence of extreme conditions outside and appearance of the maximum inside surface temperature is of great practical importance because it permits determination of the load-time curve for the structure. Assuming constancy of the inside film coefficient, the rate of heat transfer from room air to the wall is directly proportional to the air-to-wall surface temperature difference; thus the vertical distance between the curves for inside air and inside wall surface temperature (Fig. 11–7) is directly proportional to load. Since the inside air temperature does not vary, a load scale could be established beside the temperature scale; zero load occurs at 70 F on the winter temperature scale and maximum load at the point on the scale corresponding to the minimum inside-wall surface temperature.

CASE 2: PERIODIC FLOW THROUGH A COMPOSITE WALL. Application of the graphical analysis to a non-homogeneous wall requires slight modification of the fundamental equation and some increase in the work of construction. To avoid abrupt changes in the slope of the temperature gradient at interfaces between sections of different materials, the artifice is adopted of setting up an equivalent wall having uniform conductivity throughout. This necessitates modification of Eq. 11–5, relating Δx and $\Delta \theta$,

$$\Delta \theta = \frac{K(\Delta x)^2}{2\alpha}$$

The total equivalent width of each homogeneous section of the composite wall will be $k_e w_a / k_a$, where k_e is the uniform conductivity of the fictitious wall, and k_a is the true conductivity of section a, which has width w_a. The term k_e can be selected arbitrarily and may therefore be taken as unity. Then the equivalent total width of section a becomes w_a / k_a, and the equivalent width $\Delta x'$ of the finite element Δx of section a is

$$\Delta x' = \frac{\Delta x}{k_a} \quad \text{or} \quad \Delta x = k_a \, \Delta x' \qquad (11-6)$$

By substituting in Eq. 11–5 for k and for Δx,

$$\Delta \theta = \frac{K(k_a \Delta x')^2}{(2k_a/\rho c)} = \frac{1}{2} \rho c k_a K (\Delta x')^2 \qquad (11-7)$$

Eq. 11–7 must be satisfied for graphical analysis of composite walls.

The procedure for solution of a composite wall problem will be illustrated by setting up the construction for a typical case. Consider the wall of Fig. 11–8a made up of an inside layer of $\frac{1}{2}$-in. plaster on $\frac{3}{8}$-in. plaster board, followed by $3\frac{5}{8}$ in. of rock wool and $1\frac{3}{4}$-in. pine.

For this problem both the inside and outside film coefficients are taken as constant with respect to time, and the inside temperature is also considered to hold a fixed value. The outside temperature varies as shown in Fig. 11–8b; by the usual method, inside and outside reference points are established with respect to the two wall surfaces. Fig. 11–8c shows the set-up for the equivalent wall of unit conductivity.

The next step in the procedure is to establish $\Delta x'$ for each of the three materials and set up the corresponding construction lines. Starting with the plaster, select a value of $\Delta x_p'$, which is equally divisible into the equivalent width of the plaster wall. Since this width is not great, $\Delta x_p'$ was taken, in the example, as equal to the section width, that is, only one $\Delta x'$ was used for the plaster. The value of $\Delta x_p'$ is therefore 0.29 ft (Fig. 11–8d). A time interval of $\frac{1}{2}$ hr was arbitrarily selected and therefore the value of the constant K_p for the plaster is calculated from Eq. 11–7 as $K_p = (2)(0.5)/(78)(0.20)(0.25)(0.29)^2 = 3.05$. As already discussed, values of K greater than unity are to be avoided, since they require extrapolation of the temperature gradient to such an extent that substantial loss of accuracy may result. In the present case, however, the difficulties attendant on a reduction in K are so great and the plaster such a small part of the entire wall structure that a change does not seem justified. Fig. 11–8e shows the center line for the plaster section, with construction lines established a distance $K_p \Delta x_p'$ out on either side.

Similarly a value of $\Delta x_r'$ for the rock wool is chosen (in this case $\Delta x_r'$ was taken as one-half the equivalent section width) and K_r is calculated in the usual way:

$$K_r = \frac{(2)(0.5)}{(12.5)(0.157)(0.022)(6.85)^2} = 0.52 = 0.5 \text{ (approx.)}$$

The center lines of each of the $\Delta x_r'$ sections are shown in Fig. 11–8e with construction lines located a distance $K_r \Delta x_r' = (0.5)(6.85) = 3.42$ on either side. The wood is likewise split into two $\Delta x_w'$ sections of width 0.81, for which the calculated value of K_w is $(2)(0.5)/(34.1)(0.65)(0.09)(0.81)^2 = 0.773$. Both center lines and all four construction lines for the wood are shown in Fig. 11–8e.

The next step is to record the known or assumed temperature gradient at the time for which the construction is to be started. This is done in Fig. 11–8f, which also shows the construction leading to the temperature gradient $\Delta\theta$ hours after the start of the analysis. The assumed gradient intersects the center lines at points a, b, c, d, e, which give the mean temperature of each $\Delta x'$ section at the starting time. The same gradient also intersects the construction lines located to the right and left of each center line. A straight line connecting the latter intersections crosses the corresponding center line at a point that represents the temperature of this $\Delta x'$ section during one $\Delta\theta$ time interval after the time of the original gradient.

In the same way temperatures at the center of all $\Delta x'$ sections are established. Connecting the resultant series of points $a'b'c'd'e'$, and joining a' and e' with the respective reference points for time $\Delta\theta$, gives the temperature gradient $\Delta\theta$ hours after the start, provided the original gradient was correct. If, as is practically certain, the assumed initial gradient is in error, the constructed gradient is also in error, and the entire cyclic construction must be repeated a sufficient number of times, as explained in case 1, to obtain the correct initial gradient. Fig. 11–8g shows the graphical procedure for fixing the gradient $2\Delta\theta$ hours after the start; the construction duplicates that described for Fig. 11–8f except that the starting line is the constructed gradient for $\Delta\theta$ hours rather than the assumed initial gradient. In a similar manner the procedure is repeated as many times as may be required.

For the particular problem of Fig. 11–8, the construction lines at the extreme right and left are located outside the reference lines. This condition frequently occurs and calls merely for extrapolation of the gradients from points a and e through the proper reference points to intersection with the construction lines.

The complete solution of the problem of Fig. 11–8 is presented in Fig. 11–9a, while Fig. 11–9b gives a comparison of temperature-time curves for the outside and inside air and wall surface temperatures.

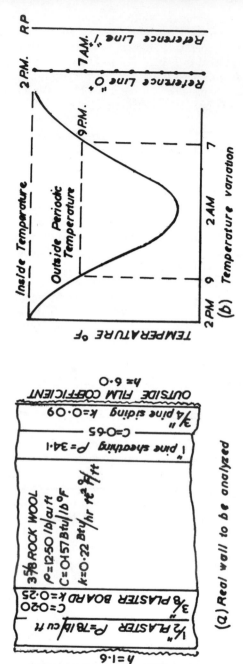

Fig. 11-8. Graphical construction for periodic analysis of composite wall.

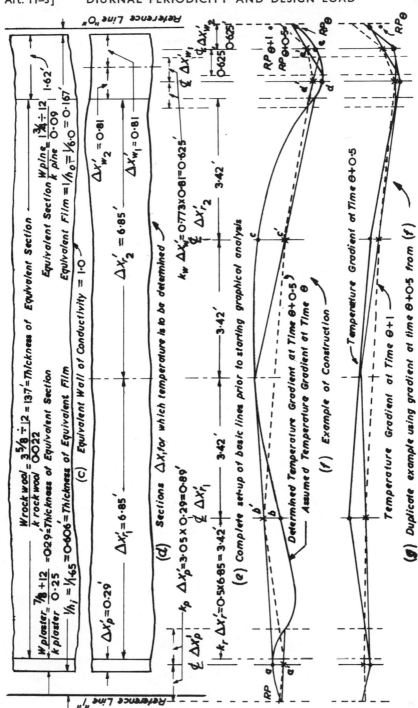

Fig. 11–8 (continued)

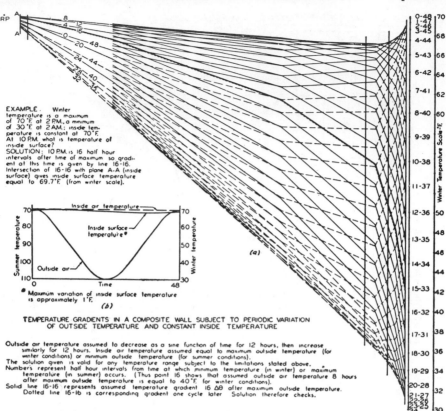

EXAMPLE. Winter temperature is a maximum of 70 °F at 2 P.M., a minimum of 30 °F at 2 A.M.; inside temperature is constant at 70 °F. At 10 P.M. what is temperature of inside surface?
SOLUTION: 10 P.M. is 16 half hour intervals after time of maximum so gradient at this time is given by line 16-16. Intersection of 16-16 with plane A-A (inside surface) gives inside surface temperature equal to 69.7 °F (from winter scale).

(b) Maximum variation of inside surface temperature is approximately 1 °F.

TEMPERATURE GRADIENTS IN A COMPOSITE WALL SUBJECT TO PERIODIC VARIATION OF OUTSIDE TEMPERATURE AND CONSTANT INSIDE TEMPERATURE

Outside air temperature assumed to decrease as a sine function of time for 12 hours, then increase similarly for 12 hours. Inside air temperature assumed equal to maximum outside temperature (for winter conditions) or minimum outside temperature (for summer conditions).
The solution given is valid for any temperature range subject to the limitations stated above. Numbers represent half hour intervals from time at which minimum temperature (in winter) or maximum temperature (in summer) occurs. (Thus point 16 shows that assumed outside air temperature 8 hours after maximum outside temperature is equal to 40 °F for winter conditions).
Solid line 16-16 represents assumed temperature gradient 16 Δθ after maximum outside temperature.
Dotted line 16-16 is corresponding gradient one cycle later. Solution therefore checks.

Fig. 11–9. Graphical solution for periodic analysis of composite wall.

11–4. Graphical Treatment of Air Spaces.

The presence of an air space between sections of a homogeneous wall does not require that the wall be treated as composite; if air spaces occur in a composite wall, the additional complication is less than that represented by a section of solid material. The method of graphical solution for air spaces will be illustrated for a particular case, but the procedure is the same for all types of walls.

Fig. 11–10a is a scale drawing of two sections of homogeneous wall with included air space. The usual construction is used in setting up equivalent films on inside and outside surfaces (Fig. 11–10b), and an equivalent air space, of conductivity equal to that of the wall, is established between wall sections. The assumed temperature gradient is then drawn in (Fig. 11–10c), noting, however, that the air space has a thermal capacity so low that the gradient through it can be taken as a straight line. By the usual method of construction the temperature at the midpoint of each section of the wall is established (giving points b', c', d' and g', h', i'). Since the gradient through the equivalent air space is a straight line and there is no change in gradient at the wall surface on either side, it follows that a straight line joining d' and g' will represent the temperature gradient between these points and will determine points e' and f' (Fig. 11–10d). Repetition of the same procedure determines gradients at subsequent times.

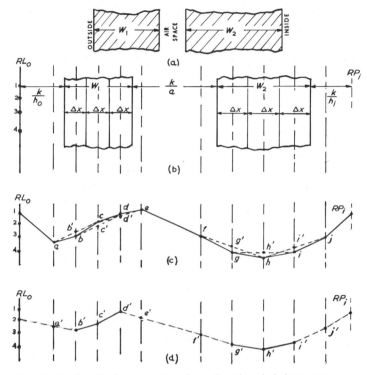

Fig. 11–10. Graphical construction for wall with included air space.

11–5. Periodic Load Analysis for Complete Enclosures. The

Schmidt analysis presented in Art. 11–3 is applicable to one transmitting section of an enclosure. Any actual room will consist of a number of different transmitting surfaces; hence analysis of such a room for periodic load variation will require application of the graphical method to each type of transmitting structure. For a typical room, analyses would be made leading to time–inside-surface temperature curves for walls, floor, and ceiling; total load at a given time would then be

$$q_{\theta_x} = h_{iw}A_w(t_a - t_w)_{\theta_x} + h_{if}A_f(t_a - t_f)_{\theta_x} + h_{ic}A_c(t_a - t_c)_{\theta_x} + h_{ig}A_g(t_a - t_g)_{\theta_x}$$
$$(11\text{–}8)$$

where q_{θ_x} = rate of heat loss from room by transmission, in (Btu/hr), at a particular time θ_x, during the 24-hr period of load variation.

$(t_a - t_w)_{\theta_x}$ = temperature drop across the inside film (wall film in this case) at time θ_x as determined from a time-temperature curve for inside surface temperature.

In using Eq. 11–8, it must be noted that the maximum value of each type of transmission load will probably occur at a different time. In most cases, observation (based on recognition of the type of surface that is responsible for greatest fraction of the load) will permit close selection of the time at which the total transmission load is a maximum. When this is not possible, the maximum transmission load can be precisely determined by plotting time-load curves for each transmitting section and adding the ordinates of all curves, at a particular time, to find the total load at that time. A plot of time versus total transmission load will then fix the maximum load and establish the time at which it occurs.

PROBLEMS

11–1. A 15-in. thick slab of a homogeneous material is so large that heat transfer across the insulated edges can be neglected. Density of the material is 160 lb/cu ft, specific heat is 0.17 Btu/(lb)(°F), and thermal conductivity is 1.15 Btu/(hr)(sq ft)(°F/ft). The slab is slowly heated until it is at a uniform temperature of t_u degrees Fahrenheit throughout. By means of high-velocity jets of cold water, one face of the slab is suddenly reduced to a uniform temperature t_s, and this tempera-ture is held constant for a subsequent period of 2 hr. (a) If it is necessary to determine accurately the temperature in parallel planes 1 in. apart at time inter-vals of 4 min, what would be the required distance, p of Fig. 11–1b, from the center of each 1-in. Δx section to the adjacent construction lines? (b) If the value of p were arbitrarily taken as unity, what would then be the time interval, $\Delta \theta$, between successive evaluations of temperature in planes through the 1-in. Δx center line? (c) If p were taken as unity and the time interval remained at 4 min, what would be the corresponding value of Δx; is this value satisfactory?

11–2. For the conditions of part (a) of problem 11–1: (a) Carry out a graphical solution to determine the temperature gradient through the slab 40 min after the one face is reduced to t_s. (b) If the slab temperature is initially 87 F and its one surface temperature is reduced to 45 F, determine, from the graphical solution of part (a), the temperature 4 in. in from the cold surface 30 min after cooling starts. (c) If the initial slab temperature is 45 F and if the surface temperature is raised to 87 F, determine the temperature 4 in. in from the heated surface 30 min after heating starts.

11–3. Repeat problem 11–2(a) for the conditions of part (b) of problem 11–1. Superimpose the resultant temperature gradient on the gradient obtained in problem 11–2(a) and discuss the observed differences between them.

11–4. For the conditions of problem 11–1b, how long would it be before the influence of the cold surface would be experienced at the warm surface?

11–5. For the slab of problem 11–1, select Δx as 3 in. and K as unity. (a) What would be the corresponding value of $\Delta \theta$? (b) On the basis of this selection, how long would it be before the influence of the cold surface would be experienced at the warm surface? (c) Compare the answer from part (b) with that from problem 11–4 and explain the difference; which is the more nearly correct?

11–6. For the conditions of problem 11–5, (a) determine by interpolation the temperature gradient 40 min after cooling starts, and superimpose this gradient on the one obtained in part (a) of problem 11–2; discuss the differences; (b) determine the time required for the slab gradient to approach within 5 per cent of being a straight line (assuming that the surface temperatures t_u and t_s are held constant).

11–7. The *results* of applying the graphical method to the solution of a typical periodic heat-flow problem are shown in Fig. 11–6. With data as given in the statement of the problem and with an assumed linear temperature gradient from 70 F inside air to 30 F outside air (at 2 A.M. in winter), go through a complete graphical analysis and compare your results with Fig. 11–6.

11–8. From the results of problem 11–7 (or by scaling from Fig. 11–6), plot the temperature-time curves for each of the five Δx midplanes. Draw a line connecting the minimum point of each of the five curves and discuss its shape.

11–9. A structure having the same construction and film coefficients as the one of Fig. 11–6 is maintained at an inside air temperature of 80 F during a cooling season in which the outside air temperature varies from 120 F maximum at 4 P.M. to 80 F at 4 A.M.; the outside time-temperature curve has the same shape as that of Fig. 11–6. From the solution as given, determine the temperature at midpoint of this wall at 6 P.M. and at 10 A.M.

11–10. Go through the detailed construction leading to the graphical solution of the heterogeneous-wall periodic heat-transfer problem that is given in Fig. 11–9.

11–11. From Fig. 11–9 discuss the relative importance, as determining factors in the solution, of each of the homogeneous sections of the heterogeneous wall.

11–12. Obtain a graphical solution for the wall (and the temperature conditions) of Fig. 11–6, but with the assumption that the wall is divided into two sections, one of which is twice as thick as the other; the two sections are separated by an air space having a conductance of 2 Btu/(hr)(sq ft)(°F).

12

INFLUENCE OF INTERMITTENT
OPERATION ON HEATING LOAD

The steady-state load analysis employed in Chapters 5 through 9 and the periodic load analysis developed in Chapter 11 both presuppose constancy of inside air temperature. In many cases occupancy conditions may be such that the inside air temperature can be "set back" a specified number of degrees during the night hours and in some structures the heat may be turned off for part of the night. When "set-back" occurs, the Schmidt method (see Art. 11–1) can still be used, since in this case the heating system maintains the inside temperature at predetermined values for all of the 24-hr period except the relatively short intervals during which the structure cools to the fixed night temperature or is heated to the fixed day temperature. As a first approximation the inside air time-temperature curve can then be drawn as two horizontal (constant temperature) lines connected with straight-line cooling and heating sections for 1-hr duration each, thus approximating the actual (but unknown) true cooling and heating curves.

With intermittent heating a different situation exists and a different method of analysis is required. When the heat is turned off during the night hours, the inside air temperature is uncontrolled. The transient section of the inside air time-temperature curve then extends without discontinuity from the time of turn-off until the heating system is again turned on; at the time a discontinuity occurs, the subsequent section of the time-temperature curve will show a continually rising inside air temperature until the time at which this temperature regains its daytime comfort value. Thus with intermittent heating there will be long time intervals during which the structure is undergoing cooling or heating. Exact analysis of the heating requirements necessitate knowledge of the shape of both the heating and the cooling curves, and determination of these shapes is a problem of transient rather than periodic heat transfer.

For application to heating load problems, the periodic and transient heat-flow analyses are therefore used for opposite purposes. The periodic analysis leads to a determination of the actual load as a function of time. Frequently it makes possible a *reduction* in the size of the equipment over that which would be required if maximum load were assumed to have steady-state value and to occur at the time of most extreme outside conditions. A requirement in carrying out the periodic analysis is knowledge of the time-temperature curves of both inside and outside air.

The transient analysis, on the contrary, is most often used in cases where the time-temperature curve for the inside air is not known. Thus, when intermittent heating is used, the transient analysis assists in determining the rate at which inside air temperature will decrease when the heating system is turned off. Conversely, the transient analysis is used to determine the necessary *increase* in capacity of the heating plant to bring the structure to the desired inside temperature in a reasonable heating-up time. The transient analysis also assists in relating the operating saving, due to intermittent heating, with the added fixed charges resulting from the larger heating plant.

When the heating system in a particular structure is shut off, transmission and ventilation losses lead to a reduction in inside air temperature at a rate dependent on the thermal capacity and the heat-transfer characteristics of the structure and its contents. The cooling curve for the structure depends on wall temperature gradients, but the gradients are in turn dependent on the shape of the cooling curve. Thus the problem of intermittent heating is one in which neither the cooling curve nor the wall gradients are at first known.

A simple but time-consuming method of trial-and-error solution is to assume a cooling curve and apply the Schmidt graphical method (Chapter 11) to a determination of the temperature gradients corresponding to it. With the gradients established, the time-temperature curve at the inside surface can be drawn; the inside-air to inside-surface temperature difference is thereby fixed; hence the heat-transfer rate from room air to inside surface is fixed as a function of time. But the only source of energy is from storage in room air and room furnishings (including interior partitions), so that for each of two small time intervals, the ratio of average loads for one interval to inside air temperature drop during that interval must equal the same ratio for the second interval. In order to adjust inequalities among these ratios, a revised cooling curve can be estimated and used as a second approximation. This procedure is repeated until agreement is reached between the curve used as a basis for the gradient determination and the curve calculated from the gradients so determined.

12–1. The Hölme Method of Successive Steady States.

An approximate method of establishing heating and cooling curves has been proposed by Hölme,[1] and is much more rapid than the construction described above. Even in cases where exact results are essential, the Hölme procedure can be advantageously used to determine an approximate heating or cooling curve, which may then be taken as a starting assumption for the Schmidt trial-and-error method of solution. The Hölme method is based on visualization of

[1] H. Hölme, *Wärme*, October, 1931.

the transient thermal situation within a wall as being equivalent to a series of successive steady states. On this basis, departure of the wall-temperature gradient from a straight line is neglected, and the gradient is assumed, at a given time, to correspond to that for equilibrium.

This condition is closely approached in a structure for which the thermal capacity of the furnishings is large in comparison with the thermal capacity of the walls (or other transmitting surfaces), but it becomes increasingly inaccurate as this ratio decreases. For a thermally very light wall subjected to a very slow change in air temperature on one side, the Hölme approximate solution would differ inappreciably from the exact solution, whereas for a thermally heavy wall that is subject to sudden change in air temperature on one side, the approximation would lead to a large error.

In the subsequent articles the straight-line gradient approximation is used in the development of equations for expressing the heating and cooling curves of a structure.

12–2. Equation for the Cooling Curve. Arbitrarily selecting 0 F as the temperature from which stored heat (actually *internal energy*) will be measured, the total heat stored within the furnishings, air, and inside partitions (assumed at inside air temperature) of a room is

$$Q_t = (V_F \rho_F c_F + V_a \rho_a c_a + V_i \rho_i c_i) t_a \qquad (12\text{–}1)$$

where V is the volume; ρ, the density; c, the specific heat; and the subscripts F, a, and i refer to furnishings, air, and inside partitions, respectively, of a room with inside air temperature at t_a. Since Q_t is a linear function of t_a, the heat entering or leaving storage per degree Fahrenheit change in t_a is independent of the absolute value of t_a; so, we can write

$$Q'_t = V_F \rho_F c_F + V_a \rho_a c_a + V_i \rho_i c_i \qquad (12\text{–}2)$$

where Q'_t is the total heat leaving storage in the room furnishings, air, and inside partitions for each 1 F change in inside air temperature.

As the inside air temperature drops, assuming either constancy of outside air temperature during the time the cooling occurs or variation in outside air temperature according to a known time-temperature curve, the temperature gradient through the wall will become either steeper or flatter. Thus the mean temperature of each homogeneous series section of the wall will change as a function of t_a of the outside air temperature t_o, or of both.

CASE 1: HOMOGENEOUS WALL WITH CONSTANT OUTSIDE AIR TEMPERATURE. In this case the total energy stored within the wall will vary directly with the midplane wall temperature:

$$t_m = t_a - r_m U(t_a - t_o) = t_o + r'_m U(t_a - t_o) \qquad (12\text{–}3)$$

where r_m is the resistance from inside air to wall midplane and r'_m is the resistance from midplane to outside air.

For each 1 F change in t_a, at constant t_o, the mean wall temperature changes by $r_m' U$, and the heat that leaves storage in the wall per 1 F reduction in t_a is then

$$Q_w' = V_w \rho_w c_w r_m' U = \rho_w c_w A_w \frac{x_w}{12} r_m' U \qquad (12\text{-}4)$$

where x is the wall thickness in inches.

The total flow of heat from the outside surface of the wall Q' (assuming for this case that the walls are the only transmitting surfaces of the structure) is equal to the sum of the quantities leaving storage within the structure and its contents:

$$Q' = Q_t' + Q_w' \qquad (12\text{-}5)$$

where Q_t' and Q_w' are from Eqs. 12-2 and 12-4.

The rate of heat transfer through the wall will vary with the air-to-air temperature difference. During the interval in which the inside air temperature drops from t_{a_1} to t_{a_2}, the log mean air-to-air temperature difference is

$$\Delta t_m = \frac{(t_{a_1} - t_o) - (t_{a_2} - t_o)}{\log_e (t_{a_1} - t_o)/(t_{a_2} - t_o)} \qquad (12\text{-}6)$$

As the inside temperature changes from t_{a_1} to t_{a_2}, the total quantity of heat that must leave storage is $Q'(t_{a_1} - t_{a_2})$. The average rate of heat loss during this interval is $q = q' \Delta t_m$, where q' is the unit rate of loss for the structure in Btu/(hr)(°F). The number of hours required for cooling to t_{a_2} is therefore given by

$$\Delta\theta_c = \frac{Q'(t_{a_1} - t_{a_2})}{q' \Delta t_m}$$

$$\Delta\theta_c = \frac{Q'}{q'} \log_e \frac{t_{a_1} - t_o}{t_{a_2} - t_o} \qquad (12\text{-}7)$$

Eq. 12-7 is the cooling equation and gives the number of hours, $\Delta\theta_c$, required for the inside temperature to drop from t_{a_1} to t_{a_2} when the outside temperature is constant at t_o and the heat-transfer and heat-storage characteristics of the structure are as given by terms q' and Q'.

In cases where the outside air temperature changes from t_{o_1} to t_{o_2} while the inside air temperature is changing from t_{a_1} to t_{a_2}, Eq. 12-4 must be rewritten as

$$Q_w'' = \frac{\rho_w c_w A_w (x/12)[t_{o_1} + r_m' U(t_{a_1} - t_{o_1}) - t_{o_2} - r_m' U(t_{a_2} - t_{o_2})]}{t_{a_1} - t_{a_2}} \qquad (12\text{-}8)$$

This value of Q_w'' then replaces Q_w'' in Eq. 12-5 to give

$$Q'' = Q_t' + Q_w'' \qquad (12\text{-}9)$$

and Eq. 12-7 becomes

$$\Delta\theta_c = \frac{Q''(t_{a_1} - t_{a_2})}{q' \Delta t_m}$$

or

$$\Delta\theta_c = \frac{Q''}{q'} \frac{t_{a_1} - t_{a_2}}{(t_{a_1} - t_{o_1}) - (t_{a_2} - t_{o_2})} \log_e \frac{t_{a_1} - t_{o_1}}{t_{a_2} - t_{o_2}} \qquad (12\text{-}10)$$

In most structures there will be more than one kind of transmitting surface. When this is the case, Eq. 12-9 becomes

$$Q'' = Q_t' + \sum^n Q_w'' \qquad (12\text{-}11)$$

where $\sum\limits^{n}$ indicates a summation of Q_w'' values for each of the n types of transmitting surface (such as floor, roof, glass, and exterior wall). For structures of this kind the cooling curve is given by Eq. 12–10 with Q'' evaluated by Eq. 12–11 and with q' now equal to $\sum\limits^{n} U_w A_w$.

CASE 2: COMPOSITE WALLS. For a wall consisting of y different homogeneous sections in series, the mean temperatures $t_{m_1}, t_{m_2} \cdots t_{m_y}$ would each be computed by Eq. 12–3, and Q_{w_y}'' for each section would be calculated by Eq. 12–8. Then

$$Q_w''' = \sum Q_{w_y}'' \tag{12–12}$$

and Eq. 12–9 becomes

$$Q''' = Q_t' + \sum\limits^{n}\left(\sum\limits^{y} Q_{w_y}\right) = Q_t' + \sum Q_w''' \tag{12–13}$$

The average rate of unit heat loss, in Btu/(hr)(°F), is now

$$q' = \sum\limits^{n} U_w A_w \tag{12–14}$$

and so, the cooling equation becomes

$$\Delta\theta_c = \frac{Q'''}{q'} = \left[\frac{t_{a_1} - t_{a_2}}{(t_{a_1} - t_{o_1}) - (t_{a_2} - t_{o_2})}\right]\log_e \frac{t_{a_1} - t_{o_1}}{t_{a_2} - t_{o_2}} \tag{12–15}$$

12–3. Equation for the Heating Curve.

The rapidity with which a structure can be heated depends on the rate of energy input over that required to supply instantaneous equilibrium heat losses. Consider that the heating plant operates at full capacity throughout the heat-up period and let R represent this capacity in Btu/hr; the energy available for raising the temperature level is at any time equal to $(R - q)$, where q is the rate of heat loss from the structure for equilibrium conditions at that time. When heating starts from an inside air temperature equal to that of the outside air temperature $(t_{a_1} = t_{o_1})$, the initial transmission rate is zero, and the entire output of the plant R goes to storage. At a later time when t_{a_1} has risen to t_{a_2}, the transmission loss is $q'(t_{a_2} - t_o)$, for constant outside air temperature at t_o, and the rate of heat flow to storage has been reduced to $R - q'(t_{a_2} - t_o)$. The logarithmic mean rate of heat flow to storage for the time interval during which the inside temperature increases from t_o to t_{a_2} is

$$q_{\text{avg to storage}} = \frac{(R) - [R - q'(t_{a_2} - t_o)]}{\log_e\left[\dfrac{R}{R - q'(t_{a_2} - t_o)}\right]} \tag{12–16}$$

and the number of hours needed to raise the inside temperature from t_o to t_{a_2} is

$$\Delta\theta_h = \frac{Q'}{q'}\log_e\left[\frac{R}{R - q'(t_{a_2} - t_o)}\right] \tag{12–17}$$

Eq. 12–17 is the heating equation (for t_o constant) and permits direct calculation of the number of hours required to raise the inside temperature from an original value of t_o. If heating does not start from $t_a = t_o$, Eq. 12–17 cannot be used directly, but it can be used to determine the time of heating to the original t_{a_1} from t_o and to the final t_{a_2} from t_o; the difference between these two times is then the heating period required to go from t_{a_1} to t_{a_2} for conditions of constant t_o.

By the methods of Art. 12–2, the heating equation for a more complex structure can be written as

$$\Delta\theta_h = \frac{Q'''}{q''} \log_e \left[\frac{R}{R - q''(t_{a_2} - t_o)} \right] \tag{12–18}$$

where Q''' and q' are as defined in Eqs. 12–13 and 12–14, respectively, and $\Delta\theta_h$ is the time to heat from $t_{a_1} = t_o$ to $t_{a_2} = t_{a_2}$ when t_o remains constant.

12–4. Analysis of Intermittent Heating.[2] The principal heating application of the transient heat-flow equations is in the design and performance analysis intermittently operated heating and cooling systems. In the order of their practical importance, as well as simplicity of application, the basic equations (12–7 and 12–17) will be considered as starting points for graphical methods of analyzing such systems.

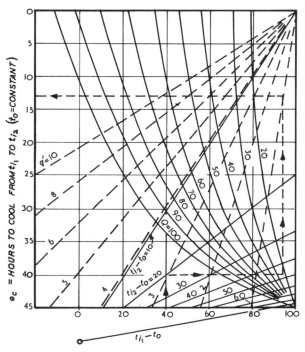

Fig. 12–1. Graphical solution of cooling equation.

GRAPHICAL SOLUTION USING HEATING AND COOLING EQUATIONS. Both Eq. 12–7 and Eq. 12–17 are subject to direct graphical solution. Fig. 12–1

---

[2] The illustrative material in this article is based on, and the numerical example in Art. 12–4 is taken from F. W. Hutchinson, "Graphical Analysis of Intermittent Heating," *Proc. National District Heating Association*, Vol. 32, pp. 102–115, 1941.

presents such a solution for the cooling equation, and Fig. 12–2 does the same for the heating equation. Use of either graph requires knowledge of the heat transfer and heat storage constants q' and Q' of the particular structure. These can be determined by calculation or by graphical solution. Fig. 12–3 illustrates a graphical method of determining both q' and Q' for walls finished

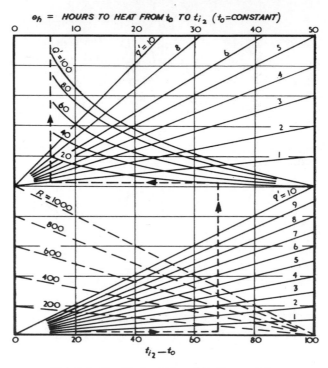

Fig. 12–2. Graphical solution of heating equation.

inside and out in any one of five specific ways;[3] similar curves could be readily established for any other type of wall construction. The method of using Figs. 12–1, 12–2, and 12–3 is shown by the dashed path drawn on each figure.

Having established the heating and cooling curves for a structure, their use in determining the optimum start-up time for intermittent operation and the amount of the saving to be realized by intermittent operation is illustrated in Fig. 12–4. For the case shown, the heating plant is shut down at 4:30 P.M., and cooling proceeds along the cooling curve as indicated. The structure is required to be up to temperature by 9:00 A.M. the following morning; so, heating must be started at such time as will assure the desired inside temperature—in this case 70 F—at 9:00 A.M. but preferably no earlier than this. If

[3] The graph is based on arbitrarily assigned "standard" values of the inside and outside combined film coefficients as 1.65 and 6.00 Btu/(hr)(sq ft)(°F), respectively.

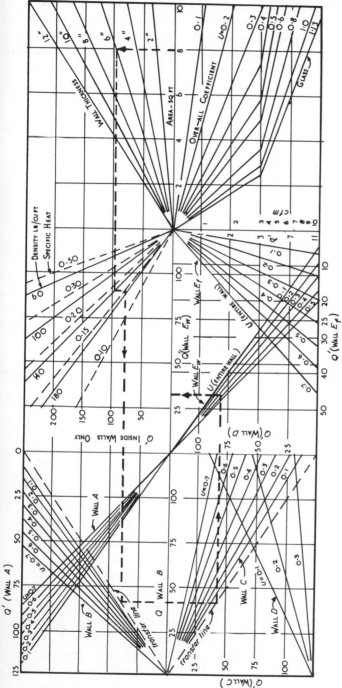

Fig. 12-3. Graphical evaluation of heat-storage and heat-transfer terms.

Wall A   Plain; unfinished surface inside and outside.
Wall B   Plain outside; $\frac{1}{2}$-in. plaster on inside.
Wall C   Plain outside; $\frac{3}{4}$-in. plaster on metal lath (furred) inside.
Wall D   Plain outside; $\frac{3}{4}$-in. plaster (furred) inside, with $\frac{1}{2}$-in. insulation in furred space.
Wall E_w Same wall as C but with 4-in. cut-stone veneer. Q' is for wall exclusive of veneer.
Wall E_f Same as E_w but Q' is for veneer only.

the heating curve is now placed on the graph in such a manner that the 70 F point corresponds to 9:00 A.M., the curve will show the temperature at all previous times during the heating-up period. The intersection of the heating and cooling curves gives the optimum time for starting the heating plant. If started earlier, the inside temperature would reach occupancy level before the required time, with consequent increased loss of heat, but if started later, the desired temperature would not be attained until after 9:00 A.M.

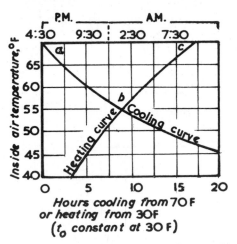

Fig. 12–4. Typical heating and cooling curves for periodic variation.

Coordinates of the heating and cooling curves are degrees and hours, therefore unit area under either of these curves represents one degree-hour, and the total area under the 24-hr time-temperature curve can be readily shown to be proportional to the total heating load. The area abc of Fig. 12–4 is therefore proportional to the saving represented by intermittent rather than continuous heating. Anything that increases abc increases the saving, and vice versa. Note that selection of a larger heating plant makes the heating curve steeper and thereby effects a greater operating saving, owing to intermittent heating. Whether or not the saving is sufficient to justify the added first cost is a problem in economics; obviously, however, there will be an optimum size of heating plant for any particular system. A poorly insulated structure would cool more rapidly, thereby increasing the area above curve ab, but the heating-up rate would be less rapid (for the same size heating plant), so that the area above curve bc would be reduced. The net effect of heat-transmission losses on the economy of intermittent heating would therefore have to be investigated for each case.

Fig. 12–5 shows the curve of heat input plotted against time. During the hours when equilibrium conditions exist, the output of the heating plant remains constant at the value needed to supply energy losses. During cooling, there is, of course, no energy input to the structure, while during the heating-up period the plant operates at constant maximum capacity. The saving due to intermittent heating can be determined from this graph (since unit area is equal to Btu) by subtracting the area *cefg* from area *abcd*.

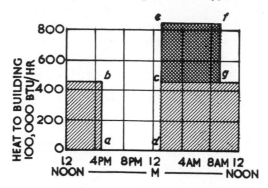

Fig. 12–5. Typical time-load relationship.

GRAPHICAL SOLUTION FOR COMPLEX HEATING AND COOLING CONDITIONS. In many problems the variation of outside temperature with time necessitates determination of the heating and cooling curves from equations other than Eqs. 12–7 and 12–17. Once these curves have been determined, however, the method of analysis for intermittent operation of the heating plant is exactly as outlined in the preceding discussion on page 465.

A more serious difficulty arises in those problems for which the thermal capacity of the outside walls is great in comparison with that of the contents of the structure. Fortunately, such problems are unusual, but when they do occur, a special method of solution is needed because the assumption of instantaneous equilibrium is no longer tenable. For special cases of this kind, the heating and cooling equations can be used only as a means of obtaining a first approximation to the respective curves.

These approximate heating and cooling curves are then used in establishing the inside reference points for the periodic analysis (Chapter 11). Result of such an analysis is the complete set of temperature-gradient curves that would have to exist in the wall if the approximate heating and cooling curves were correct. From the gradients, the inside wall-surface temperature can be determined as a function of time. The mean wall temperature during any time interval can then be estimated with considerable accuracy, and a cooling curve consistent with the temperature gradients can then be determined for a homogeneous walled enclosure from the equation

$$\Delta\theta = \frac{(V_F\rho_F c_F + V_a\rho_a c_a + V_i\rho_i c_i)(t_{a_1} - t_{a_2}) + \rho_w c_w A_w(x_w/12)\Delta t_m}{\dfrac{h_i A_w[(t_{a_1} - t_{s_1}) - (t_{a_2} - t_{s_2})]}{\log_e [(t_{a_1} - t_{s_1})/(t_{a_2} - t_{s_2})]}}$$

$$(12\text{–}19)$$

where t_s is the inside surface temperature of the wall through which heat is flowing, h_i is the inside film coefficient, and the subscripts 1 and 2 correspond to the beginning and end of the cooling time interval $\Delta\theta$. A similar heating equation can be readily set up, as can heating and cooling equations, for more complex structures.

In solving Eq. 12–19, values of t_{a_1}, t_{s_1}, t_{s_2}, and t_m are taken from the periodic solution for a selected time interval $\Delta\theta$; the only unknown is then t_{a_2}, which can be determined by trial and error. In this way a number of values of t_{a_2}, corresponding to various values of $\Delta\theta$, are determined, and a cooling curve is constructed; if it agrees with the curve obtained from Eq. 12–7, a solution has been realized, but if not, the constructed curve is used as the basis of a second approximation and the periodic analysis is then repeated.

In problems where the outside temperature does not appreciably change during that part of the day for which the inside air temperature is maintained at a fixed value, the wall is very likely to reach equilibrium before the cooling period begins. For such cases the analysis of the cooling and heating sections of the 24-hr curve can be carried out as a problem in transient rather than periodic heat flow. In this case the gradient through the wall at the start of cooling is known to be a straight line and the graphical method does not involve an initial assumption. One construction therefore gives the solution.

The establishment of heating and cooling curves for a given structure is helpful, not merely in determining the most economical maximum capacity of the heating plant but also in setting up an operating schedule to permit realizing the greatest possible saving as a result of intermittent heating. Noting that the operating saving varies directly with the overcapacity of the heating plant, it is evident that continuous heating is required to carry design load if the plant selected has no capacity in excess of that needed to carry maximum equilibrium load.

EXAMPLE 12–1. The intermittent heating analysis (assuming instantaneous equilibrium) is to be applied to a large industrial building constructed as follows:

1. Exterior surfaces
    a. Exterior wall (exclusive of glass), 8000 sq ft. The wall is of 6-in. concrete with 4-in. cut stone facing outside and is finished inside with $\frac{3}{4}$-in. plaster on metal lath, furred.

    Concrete: Density $= 140$ lb/cu ft
    Specific heat $= 0.15$ Btu/(lb)(°F)
    Facing: Density $= 160$ lb/cu ft
    Specific heat $= 0.20$ Btu/(lb)(°F)

    Over-all coefficient of heat transfer $= 0.36$
    b. Roof consists of 2500 sq ft of 4-in. concrete slab unfinished on both sides ($U = 0.9$). Storage and transmission characteristics of basement are neglected.
    c. Window area ($U = 1.13$), 2000 sq ft.

2. Interior surfaces
   a. Interior (non-transmitting surface) floors consisting of 4-in. concrete slab, 10,000 sq ft.
   b. Interior partitions consist of 4-in. clay tile plastered ($\frac{1}{2}$ in.) on both sides, 12,500 sq ft.

Density: 130 lb/cu ft
Specific heat = 0.22.

Note: Storage characteristics of furniture are not taken into account in this example, but the methods of including a term for this effect should already be clear.

3. Ventilation requirement of 4000 cfm of outside air.
4. The heating system has a maximum output of 820,000 Btu/hr.

Operating Procedure. To assist in establishing an operating procedure for the heating system, the following information is required:

1. The thermal storage constant Q' of the structure.
2. The heat-transfer constant q' of the structure.
3. Time required to cool from 70 F to 50 F inside air temperature when outside temperature remains constant at 30 F.
4. Time required to raise inside air temperature from 50 F to 70 F when outside temperature is constant at 30 F.
5. The cooling curve.
6. The optimum time for starting to heat if occupancy is such that temperature must be held at 70 F from 9:00 A.M. to 4:30 P.M. but can vary in any way during the night hours. (Based on $t_o = 30$ F.)
7. The heat required when operating as in (6) above, compared with requirements for continuous heating.

Solution: (In this solution the methods of using the graphs are explained, but the numerical results are actually obtained from the equations. The graphs, as drawn, are for illustrative purposes only, but a similar set sufficiently accurate for engineering computations can be constructed readily.)

1. Determination of thermal storage coefficient Q'.
   a. Q'_w for exterior wall consists of two parts: Q'_c for the concrete and plaster, Q'_f for the stone facing. To obtain Q'_c, enter Fig. 12–3 at 8 sq ft, rise to 6-in. wall thickness, move horizontally left to intersect density line for 140 lb/cu ft, drop to intersect specific heat = 0.15, then move to left (see dotted line as example) to transfer line, drop to transfer line in lower left quadrant, move right to intersection with $U = 0.36$ for wall E_w, and then rise to read $Q'_c = 32.5$. Since the actual area is 8000 sq ft rather than 8 sq ft, it follows that $Q'_c = (32.5)(10^3)$.
      Similarly for Q'_f, enter at 8, rise to 4 in., cross to 160, rise to 0.2, cross to transfer line, drop to transfer line, cross to $U = 0.36$ for E_f, and drop to read $Q'_f = 8.13$, or (corrected for 8000 sq ft), $Q'_f = (8.13)(10^3)$.
      Then $Q'_w = Q'_c + Q'_f = (32.5 + 8.13)10^3 = (40.6)(10^3)$.
   b. Q'_r for roof is obtained by entering at 2.5 sq ft, rising to 4 in., crossing to 140, dropping to 0.15, crossing to $U = 0.9$ for wall A, then rising to read $Q'_r = 5$, or (corrected for 2500 sq ft) $Q'_f = (5)(10^3)$.
   c. Q'_g for window area: negligible.

d. Q'_{if} for interior, floors: Enter at 10, rise to 4 in., cross to 160, drop to 0.15, cross to scale for inside walls where read $Q'_{if} = 70$ or (corrected for 10,000 sq ft) $Q'_{if} = (70)(10^3)$.

e. Q'_{ip} for interior partitions: Enter at 1.25, rise to 4 in., cross to 130, rise to 0.22, cross to scale for inside walls where read $Q'_{ip} = 11$, or (corrected for 12,500 sq ft), $Q'_{ip} = (110)(10^3)$.

f. Total thermal storage coefficient for the structure,

$$Q' = Q'_w + Q'_r + Q'_{if} + Q'_{ip}$$
$$= (40.6 + 5.0 + 70.0 + 110.0)10^3 = (226)(10^3)$$

2. Determination of heat-transfer coefficient (q'):

a. To obtain Q'_w for exterior wall, enter at 8, drop to $U = 0.36$, move left to read $q' = 2.9$, or (for 8000 sq ft) $q'_w = (2.9)(10^3)$.

b. For q'_g of glass, enter at 2, drop to 1.13, cross to read $q' = 2.3$, or $q'_g = (2.3)(10^3)$.

c. For q'_r of roof, enter at 2.5, drop to 0.9, cross to read $q' = 2.3$, or $q'_r = (2.3)(10^3)$.

d. For q'_{air}, opposite 4 on cfm scale (Fig. 12–3), read $q' = 4.2$, or (corrected for 4000 cfm) $q'_{air} = (4.2)(10^3)$.

e. Total transmission coefficients:

$$q' = q'_w + q'_g + q'_r + q'_{air}$$
$$= (2.9 + 2.3 + 2.3 + 4.2)10^3 = (11.7)(10^3)$$

3. Determination of time required to cool from 70 F to 50 F when outside temperature is constant at 30 F. Enter Fig. 12–1 at $(t_{a_1} - t_o) = 70 - 30 = 40$ F, rise to $(t_{a_2} - t_o) = 50 - 30 = 20$ F, cross to right to intersect $Q' = 22.5$, rise to $q' = 1.17$, cross to left and read cooling time as 13.3 hr.

4. Determination of time required to heat from 50 F to 70 F with outside temperature constant at 30 F:

a. The time to heat from 30 F to 50 F.

   Note that the constants q', Q', R, having actual values of $(11.7)(10^3)$, $(226)(10^3)$, and $(820)(10^3)$, can be conveniently rearranged to the relative values of 1, 19.3, and 70.

   Enter Fig. 12–2 at $(t_{a_2} - t_o) = 50 - 30 = 20$, rise to $q' = 1$, cross right to $R = 70$, rise to $Q' = 19.3$, cross left to $q' = 1$, rise to read time as 6.5 hr.

b. Similarly, the time to heat from 30 F to 70 F is found to be 16.5 hr.

c. Thus required heating time from 50 F to 70 F is $16.5 - 6.5 = 10$ hr.

5. Cooling curve for the structure. By the method of part (3) above, points on the cooling curve can be determined and the curve drawn. This is done in Fig. 12–4.

6. Heating curve for the structure. Using the method of part (4) above, any required number of points on the heating curve can be determined (for constant t_o and given R) and the curve plotted. This, also, is done on Fig. 12–4.

7. Optimum time to start heating. The inside temperature need not be maintained at 70 F after 4:30 P.M., so at that time heat will be turned off and the structure allowed to cool; thus the time zero (Fig. 12–4) will now be

called 4:30 P.M. At 9 A.M., $16\frac{1}{2}$ hours after the heat is turned off, the temperature must again be 70 F; thus the heating curve must be so placed that it crosses the 70 F line $16\frac{1}{2}$ hr after cooling begins. By pure coincidence the position of the heating curve in Fig. 12–4 already meets this condition and is therefore ready for use. A time scale is now placed across the top of the figure (12–4), and from this the temperature at any time during the night hours can be determined; examination of the figure reveals that the optimum time for starting the heating system is 1:30 A.M. If heating were started later than 1:30 A.M., the building would not be at 70 F by 9 A.M., while if heating were started before 1:30 A.M., the temperature would reach 70 F before 9 A.M., and consequently unnecessary energy would be dissipated.

8. Energy requirements for intermittent and continuous heating. Fig. 12–5 shows the rate of heat supply to the structure as a function of time for an operating schedule in accordance with Fig. 12–4. From 9 A.M. to 4:30 P.M. the structure is assumed at steady state, and heat is required at a rate of $(70 - 30)(11.7)(10^3) = 468,000$ Btu/hr. At 4:30 P.M. heating ceases and no further energy is supplied until 1:30 A.M., at which time heating comes on at maximum capacity ($R = 820,000$ Btu/hr) and continues at this rate until the air temperature reaches 70 F at 9 A.M., at which time the thermostat acts to reduce the supply of heat. All the energy that would have been supplied between 4:30 P.M. and 1:30 A.M. if operation were continuous, that is, $(468,000)(9) = 4,212,000$ Btu) is not saved because the output from 1:30 A.M. to 9 A.M. exceeds the value for continuous heating by

$$(820,000 - 468,000)7\frac{1}{2} = 2,490,000$$

The net reduction in daily heat requirement as a result of intermittent heating is therefore

$$4,212,000 - 2,490,000 = 1,722,000 \text{ Btu}$$

which is

$$\frac{1,722,000}{(468,000)(24)} = 15.3 \text{ per cent}$$

The saving can be determined from Fig. 12–5 as area *abcd* minus area *cefg*.

PROBLEMS

A storage room 10 ft by 10 ft by 10 ft (inside) is made with uniform walls, floor, and ceiling, and has the same exposure on all these surfaces. The construction is 8 in. thick, density is 100 lb/cu ft, specific heat is 0.18 Btu/(lb)(°F), and the over-all coefficient of heat transfer is 0.7 Btu/(hr)(sq ft)(°F). The inside and outside surfaces are unfinished.

12–1. The above room, empty, is at an initial inside temperature of 70 F when the outside air temperature is 20 F. The heating system is suddenly shut down. If the outside air temperature does not change, (a) use Figs. 12–1 and 12–3 to determine the number of hours before the inside air temperature will drop to 40 F; (b) determine the cooling time (to 40 F) by use of the analytical expressions.

12–2. If the above storage room were filled with 600 cu ft of a material having density of 140 lb/cu ft, specific heat of 0.22 Btu/(lb)(°F), and a very high thermal conductivity, (a) determine the time to cool from 70 F to 40 F (with outside air temperature constant at 20 F); (b) determine the cooling curve from an initial inside-air temperature of 70 F to a final air temperature of 30 F.

12–3. Calculate the size of the heating plant that would be needed if the inside air temperature is to be raised from 40 F to 70 F (outside air temperature constant at 20 F) in $3\frac{1}{2}$ hr for (a) the empty room of problem 12–1, (b) the filled room of problem 12–2.

12–4. Plot the heating curve for the conditions of problem 12–3, and by examination of heating and cooling curves, determine the required start-up time if heat is turned off at 5 P.M. and if the room is to be at 70 F by 8 A.M. for (a) the empty room, (b) the filled room.

12–5. Compare intermittent and continuous-heating operating costs for the conditions of problems 12–4(a) and (b).

Appendix

ABBREVIATED STEAM TABLES*

* With permission, reproduced from F. W. Hutchinson, *Thermodynamics of Heat-Power Systems* (Reading, Mass.: Addison-Wesley Publishing Co., Inc., 1957), as abridged from J. H. Keenan and F. G. Keyes, *Thermodynamic Properties of Steam* (New York: John Wiley & Sons, Inc., 1937).

TABLE A-I
Dry Saturated Steam: Temperature Table

Temp., °F	Abs. Press., (lb/in²)	Specific volume			Enthalpy			Entropy			Temp., °F
		Sat. liquid	Evap.	Sat. vapor	Sat. liquid	Evap.	Sat. vapor	Sat. liquid	Evap.	Sat. vapor	
t	p	v_f	v_{fg}	v_g	h_f	h_{fg}	h_g	s_f	s_{fg}	s_g	t
32	0.08854	0.01602	3306	3306	0.00	1075.8	1075.8	0.0000	2.1877	2.1877	32
35	0.09995	0.01602	2947	2947	3.02	1074.1	1077.1	0.0061	2.1709	2.1770	35
40	0.12170	0.01602	2444	2444	8.05	1071.3	1079.3	0.0162	2.1435	2.1597	40
45	0.14752	0.01602	2036.4	2036.4	13.06	1068.4	1081.5	0.0262	2.1167	2.1429	45
50	0.17811	0.01603	1703.2	1703.2	18.07	1065.6	1083.7	0.0361	2.0903	2.1264	50
60	0.2563	0.01604	1206.6	1206.7	28.06	1059.9	1088.0	0.0555	2.0393	2.0948	60
70	0.3631	0.01606	867.8	867.9	38.04	1054.3	1092.3	0.0745	1.9902	2.0647	70
80	0.5069	0.01608	633.1	633.1	48.02	1048.6	1096.6	0.0932	1.9428	2.0360	80
90	0.6982	0.01610	468.0	468.0	57.99	1042.9	1100.9	0.1115	1.8972	2.0087	90
100	0.9492	0.01613	350.3	350.4	67.97	1037.2	1105.2	0.1295	1.8531	1.9826	100
110	1.2748	0.01617	265.3	265.4	77.94	1031.6	1109.5	0.1471	1.8106	1.9577	110
120	1.6924	0.01620	203.25	203.27	87.92	1025.8	1113.7	0.1645	1.7694	1.9339	120
130	2.2225	0.01625	157.32	157.34	97.90	1020.0	1117.9	0.1816	1.7296	1.9112	130
140	2.8886	0.01629	122.99	123.01	107.89	1014.1	1122.0	0.1984	1.6910	1.8894	140
150	3.718	0.01634	97.06	97.07	117.89	1008.2	1126.1	0.2149	1.6537	1.8685	150
160	4.741	0.01639	77.27	77.29	127.89	1002.3	1130.2	0.2311	1.6174	1.8485	160
170	5.992	0.01645	62.04	62.06	137.90	996.3	1134.2	0.2472	1.5822	1.8293	170
180	7.510	0.01651	50.21	50.23	147.92	990.2	1138.1	0.2630	1.5480	1.8109	180
190	9.339	0.01657	40.94	40.96	157.95	984.1	1142.0	0.2785	1.5147	1.7932	190
200	11.526	0.01663	33.62	33.64	167.99	977.9	1145.9	0.2938	1.4824	1.7762	200
210	14.123	0.01670	27.80	27.82	178.05	971.6	1149.7	0.3090	1.4508	1.7598	210
212	14.696	0.01672	26.78	26.80	180.07	970.3	1150.4	0.3120	1.4446	1.7566	212
220	17.186	0.01677	23.13	23.15	188.13	965.2	1153.4	0.3239	1.4201	1.7440	220
230	20.780	0.01684	19.365	19.382	198.23	958.8	1157.0	0.3387	1.3901	1.7288	230
240	24.969	0.01692	16.306	16.323	208.34	952.2	1160.5	0.3531	1.3609	1.7140	240
250	29.825	0.01700	13.804	13.821	218.48	945.5	1164.0	0.3675	1.3323	1.6998	250
260	35.429	0.01709	11.746	11.763	228.64	938.7	1167.3	0.3817	1.3043	1.6860	260
270	41.858	0.01717	10.044	10.061	238.84	931.8	1170.6	0.3958	1.2769	1.6727	270
280	49.203	0.01726	8.628	8.645	249.06	924.7	1173.8	0.4096	1.2501	1.6597	280
290	57.556	0.01735	7.444	7.461	259.31	917.5	1176.8	0.4234	1.2238	1.6472	290

Temp											Temp
300	1.6350	1.1980	0.4369	1179.7	910.1	269.59	6.466	6.449	0.01745	67.013	300
310	1.6231	1.1727	0.4504	1182.5	902.6	279.92	5.626	5.609	0.01755	77.68	310
320	1.6115	1.1478	0.4637	1185.2	894.9	290.28	4.914	4.896	0.01765	89.66	320
330	1.6002	1.1233	0.4769	1187.7	887.0	300.68	4.307	4.289	0.01776	103.06	330
340	1.5891	1.0992	0.4900	1190.1	879.0	311.13	3.788	3.770	0.01787	118.01	340
350	1.5783	1.0754	0.5029	1192.3	870.7	321.63	3.342	3.324	0.01799	134.63	350
360	1.5677	1.0519	0.5158	1194.4	862.2	332.18	2.957	2.939	0.01811	153.04	360
370	1.5573	1.0287	0.5286	1196.3	853.5	342.79	2.625	2.606	0.01823	173.37	370
380	1.5471	1.0059	0.5413	1198.1	844.6	353.45	2.335	2.317	0.01836	195.77	380
390	1.5371	0.9832	0.5539	1199.6	835.4	364.17	2.0836	2.0651	0.01850	220.37	390
400	1.5272	0.9608	0.5664	1201.0	826.0	374.97	1.8633	1.8447	0.01864	247.31	400
410	1.5174	0.9386	0.5788	1202.1	816.3	385.83	1.6700	1.6512	0.01878	276.75	410
420	1.5078	0.9166	0.5912	1203.1	806.3	396.77	1.5000	1.4811	0.01894	308.83	420
430	1.4982	0.8947	0.6035	1203.8	796.0	407.79	1.3499	1.3308	0.01910	343.72	430
440	1.4887	0.8730	0.6158	1204.3	785.4	418.90	1.2171	1.1979	0.01926	381.59	440
450	1.4793	0.8513	0.6280	1204.6	774.5	430.1	1.0993	1.0799	0.0194	422.6	450
460	1.4700	0.8298	0.6402	1204.6	763.2	441.4	0.9944	0.9748	0.0196	466.9	460
470	1.4606	0.8083	0.6523	1204.3	751.5	452.8	0.9009	0.8811	0.0198	514.7	470
480	1.4513	0.7868	0.6645	1203.7	739.4	464.4	0.8172	0.7972	0.0200	566.1	480
490	1.4419	0.7653	0.6766	1202.8	726.8	476.0	0.7423	0.7221	0.0202	621.4	490
500	1.4325	0.7438	0.6887	1201.7	713.9	487.8	0.6749	0.6545	0.0204	680.8	500
520	1.4136	0.7006	0.7130	1198.2	686.4	511.9	0.5594	0.5385	0.0209	812.4	520
540	1.3942	0.6568	0.7374	1193.2	656.6	536.6	0.4649	0.4434	0.0215	962.5	540
560	1.3742	0.6121	0.7621	1186.4	624.2	562.2	0.3868	0.3647	0.0221	1133.1	560
580	1.3532	0.5659	0.7872	1177.3	588.4	588.9	0.3217	0.2989	0.0228	1325.8	580
600	1.3307	0.5176	0.8131	1165.5	548.5	617.0	0.2668	0.2432	0.0236	1542.9	600
620	1.3062	0.4664	0.8398	1150.3	503.6	646.7	0.2201	0.1955	0.0247	1786.6	620
640	1.2789	0.4110	0.8679	1130.5	452.0	678.6	0.1798	0.1538	0.0260	2059.7	640
660	1.2472	0.3485	0.8987	1104.4	390.2	714.2	0.1442	0.1165	0.0278	2365.4	660
680	1.2071	0.2719	0.9351	1067.2	309.9	757.3	0.1115	0.0810	0.0305	2708.1	680
700	1.1389	0.1484	0.9905	995.4	172.1	823.3	0.0761	0.0392	0.0369	3093.7	700
705.4	1.0580	0	1.0580	902.7	0	902.7	0.0503	0	0.0503	3206.2	705.4

TABLE A-2
Dry Saturated Steam: Pressure Table

Abs. press., (lb/in²) p	Temp., °F t	Specific Volume Sat. liquid vf	Sat. vapor vg	Enthalpy Sat. liquid hf	Evap. hfg	Sat. vapor hg	Entropy Sat. liquid sf	Evap. sfg	Sat. vapor sg	Internal energy Sat. liquid uf	Sat. vapor ug	Abs. press., (lb/in²) p
0.491	79.03	0.01608	652.3	47.05	1049.2	1096.3	0.0914	1.9473	2.0387	47.05	1037.0	0.491
0.736	91.72	0.01611	444.9	59.71	1042.0	1101.7	0.1147	1.8894	2.0041	59.71	1041.1	0.736
0.982	101.14	0.01614	339.2	69.10	1036.6	1105.7	0.1316	1.8481	1.9797	69.10	1044.0	0.982
1.227	108.71	0.01616	274.9	76.65	1032.3	1108.9	0.1449	1.8160	1.9609	76.65	1046.4	1.227
1.473	115.06	0.01618	231.6	82.99	1028.6	1111.6	0.1560	1.7896	1.9456	82.99	1048.5	1.473
1.964	125.43	0.01622	176.7	93.34	1022.7	1116.0	0.1738	1.7476	1.9214	93.33	1051.8	1.964
2.455	133.76	0.01626	143.25	101.66	1017.7	1119.4	0.1879	1.7150	1.9028	101.65	1054.3	2.455
5	162.24	0.01640	73.52	130.13	1001.0	1131.1	0.2347	1.6094	1.8441	130.12	1063.1	5
10	193.21	0.01659	38.42	161.17	982.1	1143.3	0.2835	1.5041	1.7876	161.14	1072.2	10
14.696	212.0	0.01672	26.80	180.07	970.3	1150.4	0.3120	1.4446	1.7566	180.02	1077.5	14.696
15	213.03	0.01672	26.29	181.11	969.7	1150.8	0.3135	1.4415	1.7549	181.06	1077.8	15
16	216.32	0.01674	24.75	184.42	967.6	1152.0	0.3184	1.4313	1.7497	184.37	1078.7	16
18	222.41	0.01679	22.17	190.56	963.6	1154.2	0.3275	1.4128	1.7403	190.50	1080.4	18
20	227.96	0.01683	20.089	196.16	960.1	1156.3	0.3356	1.3962	1.7319	196.10	1081.9	20
25	240.07	0.01692	16.303	208.42	952.1	1160.6	0.3533	1.3606	1.7139	208.34	1085.1	25
30	250.33	0.01701	13.746	218.82	945.3	1164.1	0.3680	1.3313	1.6993	218.73	1087.8	30
35	259.28	0.01708	11.898	227.91	939.2	1167.1	0.3807	1.3063	1.6870	227.80	1090.1	35
40	267.25	0.01715	10.498	236.03	933.7	1169.7	0.3919	1.2844	1.6763	235.90	1092.0	40
45	274.44	0.01721	9.401	243.36	928.6	1172.0	0.4019	1.2650	1.6669	243.22	1093.7	45
50	281.01	0.01727	8.515	250.09	924.0	1174.1	0.4110	1.2474	1.6585	249.93	1095.3	50
55	287.07	0.01732	7.787	256.30	919.6	1175.9	0.4193	1.2316	1.6509	256.12	1096.7	55
60	292.71	0.01738	7.175	262.09	915.5	1177.6	0.4270	1.2168	1.6438	261.90	1097.9	60
65	297.97	0.01743	6.655	267.50	911.6	1179.1	0.4342	1.2032	1.6374	267.29	1099.1	65
70	302.92	0.01748	6.206	272.61	907.9	1180.6	0.4409	1.1906	1.6315	272.38	1100.2	70
75	307.60	0.01753	5.816	277.43	904.5	1181.9	0.4472	1.1787	1.6259	277.19	1101.2	75
80	312.03	0.01757	5.472	282.02	901.1	1183.1	0.4531	1.1676	1.6207	281.76	1102.1	80
85	316.25	0.01761	5.168	286.39	897.8	1184.2	0.4587	1.1571	1.6158	286.11	1102.9	85
90	320.27	0.01766	4.896	290.56	894.7	1185.3	0.4641	1.1471	1.6112	290.27	1103.7	90
100	327.81	0.01774	4.432	298.40	888.8	1187.2	0.4740	1.1286	1.6026	298.08	1105.2	100
110	334.77	0.01782	4.049	305.66	883.2	1188.9	0.4832	1.1117	1.5948	305.30	1106.5	110

P												P
120	1107.6	312.05	1.5878	1.0962	0.4916	1190.4	877.9	312.44	3.728	0.01789	341.25	120
130	1108.6	318.38	1.5812	1.0817	0.4995	1191.7	872.9	318.81	3.455	0.01796	347.32	130
140	1109.6	324.35	1.5751	1.0682	0.5069	1193.0	868.2	324.82	3.220	0.01802	353.02	140
150	1110.5	330.01	1.5694	1.0556	0.5138	1194.1	863.6	330.51	3.015	0.01809	358.42	150
160	1111.2	335.39	1.5640	1.0436	0.5204	1195.1	859.2	335.93	2.834	0.01815	363.53	160
170	1111.9	340.52	1.5590	1.0324	0.5266	1196.0	854.9	341.09	2.675	0.01822	368.41	170
180	1112.5	345.42	1.5542	1.0217	0.5325	1196.9	850.8	346.03	2.532	0.01827	373.06	180
190	1113.1	350.15	1.5497	1.0116	0.5381	1197.6	846.8	350.79	2.404	0.01833	377.51	190
200	1113.7	354.68	1.5453	1.0018	0.5435	1198.4	843.0	355.36	2.288	0.01839	381.79	200
250	1115.8	375.14	1.5263	0.9588	0.5675	1201.1	825.1	376.00	1.8438	0.01865	400.95	250
300	1117.1	392.79	1.5104	0.9225	0.5879	1202.8	809.0	393.84	1.5433	0.01890	417.33	300
350	1118.0	408.45	1.4966	0.8910	0.6056	1203.9	794.2	409.69	1.3260	0.01913	431.72	350
400	1118.5	422.6	1.4844	0.8630	0.6214	1204.5	780.5	424.0	1.1613	0.0193	444.59	400
450	1118.7	435.5	1.4734	0.8378	0.6356	1204.6	767.4	437.2	1.0320	0.0195	456.28	450
500	1118.6	447.6	1.4634	0.8147	0.6487	1204.4	755.0	449.4	0.9278	0.0197	467.01	500
550	1118.2	458.8	1.4542	0.7934	0.6608	1203.9	743.1	460.8	0.8424	0.0199	476.94	550
600	1117.7	469.4	1.4454	0.7734	0.6720	1203.2	731.6	471.6	0.7698	0.0201	486.21	600
650	1117.1	479.4	1.4374	0.7548	0.6826	1202.3	720.5	481.8	0.7083	0.0203	494.90	650
700	1116.3	488.8	1.4296	0.7371	0.6925	1201.2	709.7	491.5	0.6554	0.0205	503.10	700
750	1115.4	598.0	1.4223	0.7204	0.7019	1200.0	699.2	500.8	0.6092	0.0207	510.86	750
800	1114.4	506.6	1.4153	0.7045	0.7108	1198.6	688.9	509.7	0.5687	0.0209	518.23	800
850	1113.3	515.0	1.4085	0.6891	0.7194	1197.1	678.8	518.3	0.5327	0.0210	525.26	850
900	1112.1	523.1	1.4020	0.6744	0.7275	1195.4	668.8	526.6	0.5006	0.0212	531.98	900
950	1110.8	530.9	1.3957	0.6602	0.7355	1193.7	659.1	534.6	0.4717	0.0214	538.43	950
1000	1109.4	538.4	1.3897	0.6467	0.7430	1191.8	649.4	542.4	0.4456	0.0216	544.61	1000
1100	1106.4	552.9	1.3780	0.6205	0.7575	1187.8	630.4	557.4	0.4001	0.0220	556.31	1100
1200	1103.0	566.7	1.3667	0.5956	0.7711	1183.4	611.7	571.7	0.3619	0.0223	567.22	1200
1300	1099.4	580.0	1.3559	0.5719	0.7840	1178.6	593.2	585.4	0.3293	0.0227	577.46	1300
1400	1095.4	592.7	1.3454	0.5491	0.7963	1173.4	574.7	598.7	0.3012	0.0231	587.10	1400
1500	1091.2	605.1	1.3351	0.5269	0.8082	1167.9	556.3	611.6	0.2765	0.0235	596.23	1500
2000	1065.6	662.2	1.2849	0.4230	0.8619	1135.1	463.4	671.7	0.1878	0.0257	635.82	2000
2500	1030.6	717.3	1.2322	0.3197	0.9126	1091.1	360.5	730.6	0.1307	0.0287	668.13	2500
3000	972.7	783.4	1.1615	0.1885	0.9731	1020.3	217.8	802.5	0.0858	0.0346	695.36	3000
3206.2	872.9	872.9	1.0580	0	1.0580	902.7	0	902.7	0.0503	0.0503	705.40	3206.2

TABLE A-3

Properties of Superheated Steam

Abs. press., (lb/in²) (Sat. temp.)		200	220	300	350	400	450	500	550	600	700	800	900	1000
							Temperature—Degrees Fahrenheit							
1 (101.74)	v	392.6	404.5	452.3	482.2	512.0	541.8	571.6	601.4	631.2	690.8	750.4	809.9	869.5
	h	1150.4	1159.5	1195.8	1218.7	1241.7	1264.9	1288.3	1312.0	1335.7	1383.8	1432.8	1482.7	1533.5
	s	2.0512	2.0647	2.1153	2.1444	2.1720	2.1983	2.2233	2.2468	2.2702	2.3137	2.3542	2.3923	2.4283
5 (162.24)	v	78.16	80.59	90.25	96.26	102.26	108.24	114.22	120.19	126.16	138.10	150.03	161.95	173.87
	h	1148.8	1158.1	1195.0	1218.1	1241.2	1264.5	1288.0	1311.7	1335.4	1383.6	1432.7	1482.6	1533.4
	s	1.8718	1.8857	1.9370	1.9664	1.9942	2.0205	2.0456	2.0692	2.0927	2.1361	2.1767	2.2148	2.2509
10 (193.21)	v	38.85	40.09	45.00	48.03	51.04	54.05	57.05	60.04	63.03	69.01	74.98	80.95	86.92
	h	1146.6	1156.2	1193.9	1217.2	1240.6	1264.0	1287.5	1311.3	1335.1	1383.4	1432.5	1482.4	1533.2
	s	1.7927	1.8071	1.8595	1.8892	1.9172	1.9436	1.9689	1.9924	2.0160	2.0596	2.1002	2.1383	2.1744
14.696 (212.00)	v		27.15	30.53	32.62	34.68	36.73	38.78	40.82	42.86	46.94	51.00	55.07	59.13
	h		1154.4	1192.8	1216.4	1239.9	1263.5	1287.1	1310.9	1334.8	1383.2	1432.3	1482.3	1533.1
	s		1.7624	1.8160	1.8460	1.8743	1.9008	1.9261	1.9498	1.9734	2.0170	2.0576	2.0958	2.1319
20 (227.96)	v			22.36	23.91	25.43	26.95	28.46	29.97	31.47	34.47	37.46	40.45	43.44
	h			1191.6	1215.6	1239.2	1262.9	1286.6	1310.5	1334.4	1382.9	1432.1	1482.1	1533.0
	s			1.7808	1.8112	1.8396	1.8664	1.8918	1.9160	1.9392	1.9829	2.0235	2.0618	2.0978
40 (267.25)	v			11.040	11.843	12.628	13.401	14.168	14.93	15.688	17.198	18.702	20.20	21.70
	h			1186.8	1211.9	1236.5	1260.7	1284.8	1308.9	1333.1	1381.9	1431.3	1481.4	1532.4
	s			1.6994	1.7314	1.7608	1.7881	1.8140	1.8384	1.8619	1.9058	1.9467	1.9850	2.0214
60 (292.71)	v			7.259	7.818	8.357	8.884	9.403	9.916	10.427	11.441	12.449	13.452	14.454
	h			1181.6	1208.2	1233.6	1258.5	1283.0	1307.4	1331.8	1380.9	1430.5	1480.8	1531.9
	s			1.6492	1.6830	1.7135	1.7416	1.7678	1.7926	1.8162	1.8605	1.9015	1.9400	1.9762
80 (312.03)	v				5.803	6.22	6.624	7.020	7.410	7.797	8.562	9.322	10.077	10.830
	h				1204.3	1230.7	1256.1	1281.1	1305.8	1330.5	1379.9	1429.7	1480.1	1531.3
	s				1.6475	1.6791	1.7078	1.7346	1.7598	1.7836	1.8281	1.8694	1.9079	1.9442
100 (327.81)	v				4.592	4.937	5.268	5.589	5.905	6.218	6.835	7.446	8.052	8.656
	h				1200.1	1227.6	1253.7	1279.1	1304.2	1329.1	1378.9	1428.9	1479.5	1530.8
	s				1.6188	1.6518	1.6813	1.7085	1.7339	1.7581	1.8029	1.8443	1.8829	1.9193
120 (341.25)	v				3.783	4.081	4.363	4.636	4.902	5.165	5.683	6.195	6.702	7.207
	h				1195.7	1224.4	1251.3	1277.2	1302.5	1327.7	1377.8	1428.1	1478.8	1530.2
	s				1.5944	1.6287	1.6591	1.6869	1.7127	1.7370	1.7822	1.8237	1.8625	1.8990
140 (353.02)	v					3.468	3.715	3.954	4.186	4.413	4.861	5.301	5.738	6.172
	h					1221.1	1248.7	1275.2	1300.9	1326.4	1376.8	1427.3	1478.2	1529.7
	s					1.6087	1.6515	1.6683	1.6945	1.7190	1.7645	1.8063	1.8451	1.8817

Abs. Press. (Sat. Temp.)														
160 (363.53)	v	....	....	....	....	....	3.008	3.230	3.443	3.648	3.849	4.244	4.631	5.015	5.396
	h	....	....	....	....	....	1217.6	1246.1	1273.1	1299.3	1325.0	1375.7	1426.4	1477.5	1529.1
	s	....	....	....	....	....	1.5908	1.6230	1.6519	1.6785	1.7033	1.7491	1.7911	1.8301	1.8667
180 (373.06)	v	....	....	....	....	....	2.649	2.852	3.044	3.229	3.411	3.764	4.110	4.452	4.792
	h	....	....	....	....	....	1214.0	1248.5	1271.0	1297.6	1323.5	1374.7	1425.6	1476.8	1528.6
	s	....	....	....	....	....	1.5745	1.6077	1.6373	1.6642	1.6894	1.7355	1.7776	1.8167	1.8534
200 381.79	v	....	....	....	....	....	2.361	2.549	2.726	2.895	3.060	3.380	3.693	4.002	4.309
	h	....	....	....	....	....	1210.3	1240.7	1268.9	1295.8	1322.1	1373.6	1424.8	1476.2	1528.0
	s	....	....	....	....	....	1.5594	1.5937	1.6240	1.6513	1.6767	1.7232	1.7655	1.8048	1.8415
220 (389.86)	v	....	....	....	....	....	2.125	2.301	2.465	2.621	2.772	3.066	3.352	3.634	3.913
	h	....	....	....	....	....	1206.5	1237.9	1266.7	1294.1	1320.7	1372.6	1424.0	1475.5	1527.5
	s	....	....	....	....	....	1.5453	1.5808	1.6117	1.6395	1.6652	1.7120	1.7545	1.7939	1.8308
240 (397.37)	v	....	....	....	....	....	1.9276	2.1120	2.247	2.393	2.533	2.804	3.068	3.327	3.584
	h	....	....	....	....	....	1202.5	1234.9	1264.5	1292.4	1319.2	1371.5	1423.2	1474.8	1526.9
	s	....	....	....	....	....	1.5319	1.5686	1.6003	1.6286	1.6546	1.7017	1.7444	1.7839	1.8209
260 (404.42)	v	....	....	....	....	....	....	1.9183	2.063	2.199	2.330	2.582	2.827	3.087	3.305
	h	....	....	....	....	....	....	1232.0	1262.3	1290.5	1317.7	1370.4	1422.3	1474.2	1526.3
	s	....	....	....	....	....	....	1.5573	1.5887	1.6184	1.6447	1.6922	1.7352	1.7748	1.8118
280 (411.05)	v	....	....	....	....	....	....	1.7674	1.9047	2.033	2.156	2.392	2.621	2.845	3.066
	h	....	....	....	....	....	....	1228.9	1260.0	1288.7	1316.2	1369.4	1421.5	1473.5	1525.8
	s	....	....	....	....	....	....	1.5464	1.5796	1.6087	1.6354	1.6834	1.7265	1.7662	1.8033
300 (417.33)	v	....	....	....	....	....	....	1.6364	1.7675	1.8891	2.005	2.227	2.442	2.652	2.859
	h	....	....	....	....	....	....	1225.8	1257.6	1286.8	1314.7	1368.3	1420.6	1472.8	1525.2
	s	....	....	....	....	....	....	1.5360	1.5701	1.5998	1.6268	1.6751	1.7184	1.7582	1.7954
350 (431.72)	v	....	....	....	....	....	....	1.3734	1.4923	1.6010	1.7036	1.8980	2.084	2.266	2.445
	h	....	....	....	....	....	....	1217.7	1251.5	1282.1	1310.9	1365.5	1418.5	1471.1	1523.8
	s	....	....	....	....	....	....	1.5119	1.5481	1.5792	1.6070	1.6563	1.7002	1.7403	1.7777
400 (444.59)	v	....	....	....	....	....	....	1.1744	1.2851	1.3843	1.4770	1.6508	1.8161	1.9767	2.134
	h	....	....	....	....	....	....	1208.8	1245.1	1277.2	1306.9	1362.7	1416.4	1469.4	1522.4
	s	....	....	....	....	....	....	1.4892	1.5281	1.5607	1.5894	1.6398	1.6842	1.7247	1.7623

TABLE A-3 (continued)

Abs. press. (lb/in²) (Sat. temp.)		Temperature—Degrees Fahrenheit													
		500	550	600	620	640	660	680	700	800	900	1000	1200	1400	1600
450 (456.28)	v	1.1231	1.2155	1.3005	1.3332	1.3652	1.3967	1.4278	1.4584	1.6074	1.7516	1.8928	2.170	2.443	2.714
	h	1238.4	1272.0	1302.8	1314.6	1326.2	1337.5	1348.8	1359.9	1414.3	1467.7	1521.0	1628.6	1738.7	1851.9
	s	1.5095	1.5437	1.5735	1.5845	1.5951	1.6054	1.6153	1.6250	1.6699	1.7108	1.7486	1.8177	1.8803	1.9381
500 (467.01)	v	0.9927	1.0800	1.1591	1.1893	1.2188	1.2478	1.2763	1.3044	1.4405	1.5715	1.6996	1.9504	2.197	2.442
	h	1231.3	1266.8	1298.6	1310.7	1322.6	1334.2	1345.7	1357.0	1412.1	1466.0	1519.6	1627.6	1737.9	1851.3
	s	1.4919	1.5280	1.5588	1.5701	1.5810	1.5915	1.6016	1.6115	1.6571	1.6982	1.7363	1.8056	1.8683	1.9262
550 (476.94)	v	0.8852	0.9686	1.0431	1.0714	1.0989	1.1259	1.1523	1.1783	1.3038	1.4241	1.5414	1.7706	1.9957	2.219
	h	1223.7	1261.2	1294.3	1306.8	1318.9	1330.8	1342.5	1354.0	1409.9	1464.3	1518.2	1626.6	1737.1	1850.6
	s	1.4751	1.5131	1.5451	1.5568	1.5680	1.5787	1.5890	1.5991	1.6452	1.6868	1.7250	1.7946	1.8575	1.9155
600 (486.21)	v	0.7947	0.8753	0.9463	0.9729	0.9988	1.0241	1.0489	1.0732	1.1899	1.3013	1.4096	1.6208	1.8279	2.033
	h	1215.7	1255.5	1289.9	1302.7	1315.2	1327.4	1339.3	1351.1	1407.7	1462.5	1516.7	1625.5	1736.3	1850.0
	s	1.4586	1.4990	1.5323	1.5443	1.5558	1.5667	1.5773	1.5875	1.6343	1.6762	1.7147	1.7846	1.8476	1.9056
700 (503.10)	v	......	0.7277	0.7934	0.8177	0.8411	0.8639	0.8860	0.9077	1.0108	1.1082	1.2024	1.3853	1.5641	1.7405
	h	......	1243.2	1280.6	1294.3	1307.5	1320.3	1332.8	1345.0	1403.2	1459.0	1513.9	1623.5	1734.8	1848.8
	s	......	1.4722	1.5084	1.5212	1.5333	1.5449	1.5559	1.5665	1.6147	1.6573	1.6963	1.7666	1.8299	1.8881
800 (518.23)	v	......	0.6154	0.6779	0.7006	0.7223	0.7433	0.7635	0.7833	0.8763	0.9633	1.0470	1.2088	1.3662	1.5214
	h	......	1229.8	1270.7	1285.4	1299.4	1312.9	1325.9	1338.6	1398.6	1455.4	1511.0	1621.4	1733.2	1847.5
	s	......	1.4467	1.4863	1.5000	1.5129	1.5250	1.5366	1.5476	1.5972	1.6407	1.6801	1.7510	1.8146	1.8729
900 (531.98)	v	......	0.5264	0.5873	0.6089	0.6294	0.6491	0.6680	0.6863	0.7716	0.8506	0.9262	1.0714	1.2124	1.3509
	h	......	1215.0	1260.1	1275.9	1290.9	1305.1	1318.8	1332.1	1393.9	1451.8	1508.1	1619.3	1731.6	1846.3
	s	......	1.4216	1.4653	1.4800	1.4938	1.5066	1.5187	1.5303	1.5814	1.6257	1.6656	1.7371	1.8009	1.8595
1000 (544.61)	v	......	0.4533	0.5140	0.5350	0.5546	0.5733	0.5912	0.6084	0.6878	0.7604	0.8294	0.9615	1.0893	1.2146
	h	......	1108.3	1248.8	1265.9	1281.9	1297.0	1311.4	1325.3	1389.2	1448.2	1505.1	1617.3	1730.0	1845.0
	s	......	1.3961	1.4460	1.4610	1.4757	1.4893	1.5021	1.5141	1.5670	1.6121	1.6525	1.7245	1.7886	1.8474
1100 (556.31)	v	......	......	0.4532	0.4738	0.4929	0.5110	0.5281	0.5445	0.6191	0.6866	0.7503	0.8716	0.9885	1.1031
	h	......	......	1236.7	1255.3	1272.4	1288.5	1303.7	1318.3	1384.3	1444.5	1502.2	1615.2	1728.4	1843.8
	s	......	......	1.4251	1.4425	1.4583	1.4728	1.4862	1.4989	1.5535	1.5995	1.6405	1.7130	1.7775	1.8363
1200 (567.22)	v	......	......	0.4016	0.4222	0.4410	0.4586	0.4752	0.4909	0.5617	0.6250	0.6843	0.7967	0.9046	1.0101
	h	......	......	1223.5	1243.9	1262.4	1279.6	1295.7	1311.0	1379.3	1440.7	1499.2	1613.1	1726.9	1842.5
	s	......	......	1.4052	1.4243	1.4413	1.4568	1.4710	1.4843	1.5409	1.5879	1.6293	1.7025	1.7672	1.8263
1400 (587.10)	v	......	......	0.3174	0.3390	0.3580	0.3753	0.3912	0.4062	0.4714	0.5281	0.5805	0.6789	0.7727	0.8640
	h	......	......	1193.0	1218.4	1240.4	1260.3	1278.5	1295.5	1369.1	1433.1	1493.2	1608.9	1723.7	1840.0
	s	......	......	1.3639	1.3877	1.4079	1.4258	1.4419	1.4567	1.5177	1.5666	1.6093	1.6836	1.7489	1.8083

Press. (Temp °F)		C1	C2	C3	C4	C5	C6	C7	C8	C9	C10	C11
1600 (604.90)	v	0.7545	0.6738	0.5906	0.5027	0.4553	0.4034	0.3417	0.3271	0.3112	0.2936	0.2733
	h	1837.5	1720.5	1604.6	1487.0	1425.3	1358.4	1278.7	1259.6	1238.7	1215.2	1187.8
	s	1.7926	1.7328	1.6669	1.5914	1.5476	1.4964	1.4303	1.4137	1.3952	1.3741	1.3489
1800 (621.03)	v	0.6693	0.5968	0.5218	0.4421	0.3986	0.3502	0.2907	0.2760	0.2597	0.2407	
	h	1835.0	1717.3	1600.4	1480.8	1417.4	1347.2	1260.3	1238.5	1214.0	1185.1	
	s	1.7786	1.7185	1.6520	1.5752	1.5301	1.4765	1.4044	1.3855	1.3638	1.3377	
2000 (635.82)	v	0.6011	0.5352	0.4668	0.3935	0.3532	0.3074	0.2489	0.2337	0.2161	0.1936	
	h	1832.5	1714.1	1596.1	1474.5	1409.2	1335.5	1240.0	1214.8	1184.9	1145.6	
	s	1.7660	1.7055	1.6384	1.5603	1.5139	1.4576	1.3783	1.3564	1.3300	1.2945	
2500 (668.13)	v	0.4784	0.4244	0.3678	0.3061	0.2710	0.2294	0.1686	0.1484			
	h	1826.2	1706.1	1585.3	1458.4	1387.8	1303.6	1176.8	1132.3			
	s	1.7389	1.6775	1.6088	1.5273	1.4772	1.4127	1.3073	1.2687			
3000 (695.36)	v	0.3966	0.3505	0.3018	0.2476	0.2159	0.1760	0.0984				
	h	1819.9	1698.0	1574.3	1441.8	1365.0	1267.2	1060.7				
	s	1.7163	1.6540	1.5837	1.4984	1.4439	1.3690	1.1966				
3206.2 (705.40)	v	0.3703	0.3267	0.2806	0.2288	0.1981	0.1583					
	h	1817.2	1694.6	1569.8	1434.7	1355.2	1250.5					
	s	1.7080	1.6452	1.5742	1.4874	1.4309	1.3508					
3500	v	0.3381	0.2977	0.2546	0.2058	0.1762	0.1364	0.0306				
	h	1813.6	1689.8	1563.3	1424.5	1340.7	1224.9	780.5				
	s	1.6968	1.6336	1.5615	1.4723	1.4127	1.3241	0.9515				
4000	v	0.2943	0.2581	0.2192	0.1743	0.1462	0.1052	0.0287				
	h	1807.2	1681.7	1552.1	1406.8	1314.4	1174.8	763.8				
	s	1.6795	1.6154	1.5417	1.4482	1.3827	1.2757	0.9347				
4500	v	0.2602	0.2273	0.1917	0.1500	0.1226	0.0798	0.0276				
	h	1800.9	1673.5	1540.8	1388.4	1286.5	1113.9	753.5				
	s	1.6640	1.5990	1.5235	1.4253	1.3529	1.2204	0.9235				
5000	v	0.2329	0.2027	0.1696	0.1303	0.1036	0.0593	0.0268				
	h	1794.5	1665.3	1529.5	1369.5	1256.5	1047.1	746.4				
	s	1.6499	1.5839	1.5066	1.4034	1.3231	1.1622	0.9152				
5500	v	0.2106	0.1825	0.1516	0.1143	0.0880	0.0463	0.0262				
	h	1788.1	1657.0	1518.2	1349.3	1224.1	985.0	741.3				
	s	1.6369	1.5699	1.4908	1.3821	1.2930	1.1093	0.9090				

BIBLIOGRAPHY

BIBLIOGRAPHY

1. *ASHRAE Guide.* New York: The American Society of Heating, Refrigerating and Air-Conditioning Engineers, 1960.
2. STROCK, CLIFFORD. *Handbook of Air Conditioning, Heating and Ventilating.* New York: The Industrial Press, 1959.
3. McADAMS, W. H. *Heat Transmission,* 3d ed. New York: McGraw-Hill Book Co., Inc., 1954.
4. ALLEN, J. R., J. H. WALKER, and J. W. JAMES. *Heating and Air Conditioning,* 6th ed. New York: McGraw-Hill Book Co., Inc., 1946.

INDEX